Military maps

for

Ian and Peter

Military maps

the one-inch series of

Great Britain and Ireland

Roger Hellyer

and

Richard Oliver

London
The Charles Close Society
2004

First published in 2004 by The Charles Close Society for the Study of Ordnance Survey Maps,
c/o The Map Library, British Library, 96 Euston Road, London NW1 2DB

Cartobibliography © Roger Hellyer, 2004
Index diagrams © Chris Higley, 2004
Historical essay © Richard Oliver, 2004

Quotations from unpublished Ordnance Survey documents are Crown copyright
Quotations from unpublished DGC documents are Crown copyright and are reproduced with the permission of the Controller of Her Majesty's Stationery Office

Maps and diagrams are reproduced with the authority of the Ordnance Survey under permit number NC/00/1340

A catalogue record for this book is available from the British Library

ISBN 1-870598-22-9

Typeset by Roger Hellyer

Printed and bound by CPI Bath Press

Contents

Divergence and convergence: the development of the military form of the Ordnance Survey one-inch map

Cartobibliography

Cassini Grid series

National Grid series

Appendices

Illustrations

Colour

Monochrome

Index diagrams

Acknowledgements and library sigla

The information offered in this book has been gathered from a great variety of sources, verbal and written, manuscript and printed, published and unpublished, and Richard and I would like to thank the many individuals, professionals and amateurs alike, who have responded so generously to our requests for information, advice and technical assistance: Brian Adams, David Archer, Christopher Board, Colin Bruce, Peter Chasseaud, Peter Clark, Peter Collier, John Cruickshank, Richard Dean, Brian Garvan, Alan Gordon, Yolande Hodson, Maria Mealey, Ian Mumford, Tim Nicholson, Bridget Oliver, Barry Phillips, Graeme Pitt and Andrew Teed. We have profited from their expertise and their personal experience, from their criticism and encouragement, their advice on where to seek additional information, and the many other ways in which they have assisted this project.

I would also like to thank the staff in the map libraries of the British Library, Royal Geographical Society (with the Institute of British Geographers) (Francis Herbert), Ordnance Survey's Historical Mapping Archive (Pete Clark), National Library of Scotland (Peter Milne and Chris Fleet), Imperial War Museum, Defence Geographic Centre (Nicholas Hutchings and Peter Jones), The National Archives, Library of Congress, Washington D.C.; also in universities and university geography departments in Aberdeen (Jackie Brown), Queen's Belfast (Doreen McShane), Birmingham (James Peart), Bristol, Cambridge (Anne Taylor), Trinity College, Dublin (Paul Ferguson), Exeter (Terry Bacon), Liverpool (Antonio da Cruz), London (Moira Courtman), Manchester (Chris Perkins), Newcastle upon Tyne (Ann Rooke), Oxford (Nick Millea and Linda Atkinson), Portsmouth (Robert Fletcher), Reading (Robert Parry) and Sheffield (Val Clinging), all of whom extended me every courtesy on my visits to inspect the map collections in their charge. There were in addition several members of the Charles Close Society and other individuals who generously allowed me access to their personal collections of maps, or wrote in response to my requests for information.

I would like particularly to thank Brian Garvan for the considerable time and trouble he has taken in assisting me with my investigations for this book, especially with regard to postwar mapping and the organisational chronology. Richard and I would like to thank Professor Roger Kain for making the photographic facilities in the School of Geography, Archaeology and Earth Resources at the University of Exeter available to us, and Mike Cottrell, who spent many hours proof reading the text, footnotes, and lists, and saved us from many errors and inconsistencies. Any that remain are the fault of the authors. And finally we would like to thank Chris Higley for the unstinting support he has given the authors in undertaking the design of the index diagrams and the book cover, the layout and compilation of the illustrations, and the preparation of the digital camera ready copy.

Library sigla

NB Part of the Superseded Collection of the Map Library of the Defence Geographic Centre (DGC) has been transferred to the British Library; the remainder is with DGC at Feltham. Further information is offered in footnote 260; textual references to the collection are in the form "DGC Superseded".

ALm: Aldershot, Military Museum; **BL**: British Library, with (**BL-d**) that part of DGC Superseded transferred there since 2001; **Cu**: Cambridge University Library, with (**Cu-m**) the Messenger collection; **DGC** (DGC Superseded): Superseded Collection, Defence Geographic Centre, Feltham; **Dtc**: Map Library, Trinity College, Dublin; **IWM**: Imperial War Museum, London; **Lk**: Liddell Hart Collection, King's College, London; **Lu**: London University Library; **NLS**: National Library of Scotland; **Ob**: Bodleian Library, Oxford; **OS**: Ordnance Survey's Historical Mapping Archive, Southampton; **PRO**: The National Archives (Public Record Office); **RAF**: Royal Air Force Museum, Hendon; **RGS**: Royal Geographical Society; **Wc**: Library of Congress, Washington D.C.. University geography department libraries: **Ag**: Aberdeen; **Bg**: Birmingham; **BSg**: Bristol; **DRg**: Durham; **EXg**: Exeter; **LDg**: Leeds; **LVg**: Liverpool; **Mg**: Manchester, with (**Mg-d**) the Dean collection; **NTg**: Newcastle upon Tyne; **Og**: Oxford (soon (2004) partly to be transferred to the Bodleian Library); **Pg**: Portsmouth; **Rg**: Reading; **Sg**: Sheffield. **PC**: private collection.

Military and other official abbreviations appearing in the cartobibliography

For abbreviations used on maps to identify civilian printers and military printing units, see appendix 4.

ACE	Army Certificate of Education
ADI (Maps)	Assistant Director of Intelligence, Maps, Air Ministry
AD Svy	Assistant Director of Survey
AF	Allied Forces
AM	Air Ministry
AMS	Army Map Service, United States Army
ARP	Air Raid Precautions
BAOR	British Army of the Rhine
BTNI	British Troops in Northern Ireland
CAA	Civil Aviation Authority
CCF	Combined Cadet Force
CR	Central Registry, Ordnance Survey
DGC	Defence Geographic Centre
D Geo Info	Directorate of Geographic Information
DGIA	Defence Geographic and Imagery Intelligence Agency
DGOS	Director General, Ordnance Survey
DMI	Directorate of Military Intelligence
DMO&I	Directorate of Military Operations and Intelligence
DMO&P	Directorate of Military Operations and Plans
D Mil Svy	Directorate of Military Survey
GHQ	General Headquarters
GSGS	Geographical Section, General Staff
GSGS Misc.	GSGS Miscellaneous allocation. Misc, (Misc), (Misc.) may also be found
HF	Home Forces
JARIC (UK)	Joint Air Reconnaissance Intelligence Centre (United Kingdom)
M	NATO Standard Series Designation prefix for the European Regional Area
MCE RE	Mapping and Charting Establishment, Royal Engineers
MI4	Directorate of Military Intelligence (later Military Operations and Intelligence), section 4 (GSGS)
MO4	Directorate of Military Operations, section 4 (TSGS, later GSGS)
MOD	Ministry of Defence
MRLG	Map Research and Library Group
NATO	North Atlantic Treaty Organisation
OR	GSGS Office Reference allocation. GSOR may also be found
OS	Ordnance Survey of England and Wales / Scotland / Great Britain, Southampton / Chessington
OSD&R	Ordnance Survey, Drawing and Reproduction, Revision and Specials Department
OSI	Ordnance Survey of Ireland, Dublin
OSNI	Ordnance Survey of Northern Ireland, Belfast
OTC	Officers' Training Corps
PTA	?Primary (or principal, or permanent, or practical) Training Area
RA	Royal Artillery
RAF	Royal Air Force
RE	Royal Engineers
RMAS	Royal Military Academy, Sandhurst
RUC	Royal Ulster Constabulary
SPC RE	Survey Production Centre, Royal Engineers
SPO	Survey production order
SSD	(AMS or NATO) Standard Series Designation
TEWT	Training exercise without troops
TM	Transverse Mercator
UTM	Universal Transverse Mercator
WD	War Department
WO	War Office
WOPD	War Office printing demand (sometimes just PD)

13/5
2/1.
21.
11

Divergence and convergence:

the development of the military form of the Ordnance Survey one-inch map

For much of its two-hundred-year history the Ordnance Survey (OS) one-inch and 1:50,000 map family has been produced in a single main form, intended for both civil and military use. However, between the 1920s and the 1980s separate printings to a modified specification were made for the military. Although production of a separate national military one-inch series only began in 1923, military influence over certain features of the one-inch went back much further, and thus it is useful to recapitulate the history of this scale.[1]

1. *1801-1923: One map for both military and civilians*

It is axiomatic that the Ordnance Survey 'began with the army' and that the one-inch (1:63,360) map which was the dominant topographic depiction of Britain and Ireland for much of the nineteenth and twentieth centuries had military origins. Whilst this may be true in a strictly organisational sense, in spirit the one-inch map was firmly civil in origin, and its adaptation for military purposes, culminating in the discrete military printings which are listed in this book, was a gradual process. The scale had been used by John Ogilby in his survey of main roads, published as *Britannia* in 1675, and in 1699 Joel Gascoyne published a one-inch map of Cornwall. It was the first of what was to be a long line of county maps at this scale, which by 1800 covered much of Britain, to various standards of geodetic accuracy and topographical completeness. The culmination of this phase and the first episode in the next was the publication, early in 1801, of a map of Kent, based on surveys by the Board of Ordnance,[2] but issued by William Faden (Hi.1).[3] What is sometimes described as 'the first Ordnance Survey map', but which might be argued to be the first published military map, was distinguished by neither its scale nor much of its detail, but by the unusually close attention it paid to relief.[4] Hachuring was expensive both to draw in the field and to engrave on copper: too expensive to be 'commercial', but of use for civil purposes, varying from fox-hunting to reconnaissance for civil engineering projects.[5] Having made some earlier fragmentary surveys of areas of particular military interest, following the outbreak of war with

---

[1] There is unfortunately no satisfactory modern narrative history of the OS one-inch map. The most accessible modern summary for England and Wales to 1919 is that in Yolande Hodson, *Popular maps*. London: Charles Close Society, 1999, 9 ff: other earlier accounts are cited in *ibid*, 17, n.33. The earlier period (to 1870) is covered in detail in the introductory essays by J.B. Harley and others in *The Old Series Ordnance Survey*. Lympne Castle: Harry Margary, 8 vols, 1975-92, and for Ireland in J.H. Andrews, *History in the Ordnance map*. Dublin: Ordnance Survey, 1974 (reissued Kerry: David Archer, 1993) and J.H. Andrews, *A paper landscape: the Ordnance Survey in nineteenth-century Ireland*. Oxford University Press, 1975 (reissued Dublin: Four Courts Press, 2002); see also Roger Hellyer, *Ordnance Survey small-scale maps indexes: 1801-1998*. Kerry: David Archer, 1999, and Richard Oliver, 'What's what with the New Series', *Sheetlines* 5 (1982), 3-8.

[2] Until 1855 the Board of Ordnance, with responsibility for the Royal Artillery and Royal Engineers, was a separate organisation from the War Office. The Ordnance Survey was the responsibility of the War Office from 1855 to 1870, of the Office of Works from 1870 to 1889, and of the Board of Agriculture (later Ministry of Agriculture) from 1889 to 1965.

[3] The 'Hi' numbers refer to the serial numbers in Roger Hellyer, *Ordnance Survey small-scale maps indexes: 1801-1998*. Kerry: David Archer, 1999.

[4] Faden's map of Kent was not the first to be based on Ordnance materials: maps of Jersey and of part of Sussex had been published in 1787 and 1795 respectively. The significance of the Kent map is that, though a commercial publisher was employed, the initiative seems to have come from the Board of Ordnance: see essay by J.B. Harley in *The Old Series Ordnance Survey*, I. Lympne Castle: Harry Margary, 1975, xxx-xxxii.

[5] For foxes see essay by J.B. Harley in *The Old Series Ordnance Survey*, V. Lympne Castle: Harry Margary, 1987, viii-ix; for engineering uses, see essay by J.B. Harley and R.R. Oliver in *The Old Series Ordnance Survey*, VIII. Lympne Castle: Harry Margary, 1991, xii, xvi.

France in 1793 the Board of Ordnance embarked on a national survey, which at first remained in manuscript. In 1805 there appeared the first maps to be wholly surveyed, engraved and published by the Ordnance: four sheets covering Essex. They were to be the first instalment of a national map of England and Wales, later known as the Old Series (Hi.2).

As a published map the Old Series was both civil and military in nature. It was based on surveys which were made for defensive purposes, but any sense of military urgency evaporated after the end of war with France in 1815, and by the 1820s the accent was very much on perfection, rather than speed. The adoption after 1840 by the Ordnance Survey of surveying at the six-inch (1:10,560) and larger scales, and subsequent investigation and discussion which culminated in the 'Battle of the Scales' in the 1850s, showed that the one-inch was a political necessity, but apparently far less of a military one. In 1840 the Duke of Wellington was quite prepared to countenance a change to the six-inch and leave any smaller-scale mapping to commercial enterprise, and the only published statement in the Battle of the Scales that the one-inch was a military necessity came from Colonel Henry James, who as head of the Ordnance Survey was hardly a disinterested observer.[6] No such support came from the War Office, which, as there was already Old Series cover of southern Britain, seemed content to let things take their course.[7]

Early in 1870, James, now knighted, observed that the completion of the military one-inch map of England at that time was the completion of the original task of the OS.[8] He wrote in the context of a possible transfer of the department from military to civil control. Although it had a military organisation, since 1840 most of the OS's work in Britain had been at the six-inch and larger scales. The justification for this was overwhelmingly civil, although it was undoubtedly convenient for the Ordnance and War Office to have at their command a large body of surveyors who were occasionally diverted to making surveys to assist with planning military works; these started with a survey of Devonport in 1848 and culminated in a whole series of surveys at 1:2500 in 1859-63 in connexion with the schemes dubbed 'Palmerston's follies'.

The first sign of reviving War Office interest in one-inch mapping came shortly afterwards. In 1870, Captain Charles Wilson, R.E., was sent to report on aspects of the Franco-Prussian war. He had previously had experience on the Ordnance Survey, and would return to it in 1886 as its Director General. Amongst his observations were that, though the French had excellent maps of the areas beyond their frontiers, the 1:80,000 of their own territory (similar in appearance and functions to the Old Series) was seriously out of date and had hampered operations.[9] The War Office duly made representations to the Treasury that the one-inch of southern England (just where an invasion was most likely) was seriously out of date. Whilst the French experience no doubt counted for something (presumably some of the defective mapping was of Alsace-Lorraine, which was lost to Prussia), more might be attributed to the circumstance of the OS no longer being a charge on War Office funds. It was also surely not a coincidence that when the Treasury consulted Sir Henry James, he was able to supply them with a specimen of a completely re-engraved map, based on the 1:2500 resurvey of southern Britain which had been authorised in 1863. Given the slow speed of engraving, it seems as though James was merely waiting his chance for what he had been aiming at all along. In 1861 he had told the Commons Select Committee investigating the proposed resurvey that it could be used to revise the Old Series, but in the event the rather limited

---

[6] Wellington to Chancellor of the Exchequer, 5 October 1840, in National Archives, Public Record Office (PRO) T1/4060; evidence by James, in *Report from the Select Committee on Ordnance Survey of Scotland*. British Parliamentary Papers (House of Commons Series) [hereafter BPP (HC)] 1856 (198), XIV, 361, evidence, q.477.
[7] It may be indicative of the WO's southern-oriented attitude that when there was a French war scare in 1848, it ordered four sets of one-inch maps for England and Wales south of Birmingham, but only two sets of the country to the north. (The writer regrets that he has mislaid the source for this.) At this time the one-inch only covered up to the southern half of Lancashire and the southern third of Yorkshire.
[8] Memorandum by James, 14 January 1870, in PRO T1/7021B/22049.
[9] Report by Wilson, n.d., in PRO WO 33/22.

revision to which the Old Series had hitherto been subject was further curtailed, to the addition of new railways.[10] One may suspect that James put Wilson up to it.

How far the military used mapping in actual operations and manoeuvres, as opposed to indoor planning, at this time has been little studied, and it may be that the materials for a detailed study simply do not exist.[11] In the light of later developments, not least the publication of a one-inch sheet of Salisbury Plain for the autumn manoeuvres in 1872, it may hypothesised that there was a growth of military interest in the use of maps in the last third of the nineteenth century. The creation of the new state of Germany in 1871 brought a new power onto the European scene, although it was probably not until the enactment of the Naval Law of 1899 that it seemed possible that that it would supplant France as the most likely enemy. The development of the Empire proceeded apace: Disraeli's proclamation of Queen Victoria as Empress of India in 1877 seemed to add a new dimension to British activity overseas. Adding these to a growing population and economy made for a potential increase of interest in maps generally and military maps in particular.

Whether or not the concept really belonged to the civil-orientated OS rather than to the military-orientated War Office, in July 1872 the Treasury duly authorised the making of a new one-inch map of southern Britain (Hi.3).[12] It was based on the 1:2500 resurvey which had been authorised in 1863 and became known as the New Series. It was laid out nominally in 360 sheets, 18 inches west-east by 12 inches south-north (45.7 by 30.5 cm), though in practice some sheets were combined, and in northern England it adopted and renumbered those sheets of the Old Series which were based on post-1840 large-scale surveys. The first published New Series sheet, 285, issued early in 1874, covered Aldershot, which was appropriate for a series of avowedly military inspiration. The new map was to be published, like the northern English sheets, in two forms: in 'outline' with contours, and 'with hills', in the style of the standard Old Series sheets. It made slow progress: by 1884 only 49 of a nominal 287 sheets had been published in outline (covering London, Hampshire, Kent, Surrey and Sussex), and only one – once again, sheet 285 – 'with hills'. The second hill sheet appeared in 1886. Considerable effort was still being devoted to completing the one-inch of Scotland which seems to have been as much a political as any other necessity (Hi.13).[13] It had been begun in 1856, and was laid out nominally in 131 sheets, 24 inches west-east by 18 inches south-north (61.0 by 45.7 cm). In 1871-2 James had referred to the possibility of supplying hachures by photo-zincography rather than by engraving, and a few sheets were issued in this style, including a manoeuvre map of Aldershot *circa* 1877 and sheet 271 some years later. A half-tone technique was tried for a manoeuvre map of the Berkshire Downs in 1890. On all these maps the hill features were printed in brown, as they had been on a six-inch survey of hills to the south and west of London, produced in 1861-8 for the War Office; grey was also tried.[14] The real significance of these maps is that they are part of the gradual emergence of a distinct military one-inch. Another sign was the preparation of a few sheets in 'War Department only' editions, showing fortifications, contours and spot-heights in strategically important areas, which were omitted from the ordinary editions placed on sale. These special editions were discontinued after 1907, when their discrete content was added to the standard sales edition.[15]

---

[10] Evidence by James, *Report from the Select Committee on the Cadastral Survey.* BPP (HC) 1861 (475), XIV, 93, evidence, qq 86, 207-16; cartobibliographies in *The Old Series Ordnance Survey*, III-VIII. Lympne Castle: Harry Margary, 1981-92.

[11] The only substantial contribution to date is Tim Nicholson, 'The Ordnance Survey and smaller scale military maps of Britain 1854-1914', *Cartographic Journal* 25 (1988), 109-27.

[12] The papers are in PRO T1/7200B/11660.

[13] This is explored in Richard Oliver, *The Ordnance Survey in Great Britain, 1835-1870* (unpublished University of Sussex D.Phil. thesis, 1986).

[14] There is a set of the six-inch hill surveys in the British Library Map Library, at Maps 144.e.12.

[15] Circular, 18 July 1908, citing War Office decision A/2508/1907, in 'Southampton Circulars', Book 2, (Ordnance Survey Office, Dublin, now in National Archives of Ireland, Dublin; photocopy in Ordnance Survey library, Southampton): this decision only applied to the one-inch and smaller scales and separate 'War Department purposes only' editions continued to be produced for the larger scales. Though there is no doubt that these special editions of one-inch sheets were produced, we have not so far located any specimens. (There does not appear to be anything in PRO class WO 78, which is otherwise an invaluable source for nineteenth century military

The outline-with-contours form of the New Series was completed in 1896, and the hachured 'hills' style in 1902-3; the Scottish map was completed in outline in 1887 and with hills in 1895. By that time the design of the map had been modified, largely if not wholly in response to military influence. Apart from anything else, a third form was now being offered: coloured.[16]

Although there had been tentative experiments with printing the New Series in other than monochrome, including a version of sheets 255 and 274 with contours in red and water in blue in 1887 (Hi.3.7), by the early 1890s there were demands for something more elaborate. Also, the mapping of Britain at 1:2500 was now approaching completion and there was the question of revision to be considered. By this time Charles Wilson was Director General of the Ordnance Survey (DGOS), a Major-General, a national hero, and presumably influential at the War Office. Early in 1892 two committees were appointed: one, a Departmental Committee under the chairmanship of Sir John Dorington, M.P., was appointed by the Board of Agriculture, which had had ministerial responsibility for the OS since 1889; the other was appointed by the War Office, under the chairmanship of the Quartermaster-General, Lieut-General Sir T.D. Baker, with Wilson and the Director of Military Intelligence, Major-General E.F. Chapman, as its other members.

The Baker Committee got in first in taking evidence and reporting, and it would have been fresh in Wilson's mind when giving his evidence to the Dorington Committee a few weeks later. So far as the one-inch map was concerned, the Dorington Committee's most important recommendation was that it should be revised once every fifteen years.[17] Such a revision was put in hand early in 1893, and it was completed in 1898; the fieldwork was undertaken by a specially formed section of eighty Royal Engineers.[18] The 'revised New Series', as it is sometimes known, was published in 1895-9 (Hi.4); Scotland was republished in 1896-8 (Hi.14), and Ireland, first published in outline in 1855-62 (Hi.22), was revised in 1898-1901 and republished 1899-1902 (Hi.23).

The Baker Committee and its witnesses were more concerned with map content and style: it made recommendations concerning road, railway and church depiction, and the inclusion of information on post and telegraph facilities, and the more distinct depiction of information already shown, such as bridges and wetlands. All these were faithfully reflected in the revised maps which began to appear in March 1895.[19] Also collected by the revisers, but not published, were data on bridge construction, water supply and uncultivated ground unsuited to camping.[20] More troublesome were questions of scale and style. Several of the Baker Committee's witnesses suggested a distinct military map, to cover at least south-east England, which seems to have been the overwhelming focus of military interest, at a scale of somewhere between 1.5 and 4 inches to one mile (1:42,240 to 1:15,840). As the New Series one-inch was so far advanced (completing Scotland in outline in 1887 had had a marked effect), the Committee recommended retaining that, with the modifications of content and emphasis already mentioned. As for style, there was no doubt

---

cartography.) There are references to military editions of OS maps in Intelligence Department, Quartermaster General's Office, *Notes on Government Surveys*. London: HMSO, 1882.

[16] The inception and development of the coloured one-inch is discussed fully in Tim Nicholson, *The birth of the modern Ordnance Survey small-scale map*. London: Charles Close Society, 2002, and its continuation in Roger Hellyer and Richard Oliver, *A guide to the Ordnance Survey one-inch Third Edition maps, in colour*. London: Charles Close Society, 2004.

[17] *Report of the Departmental Committee appointed by the Board of Agriculture to inquire into the present condition of the Ordnance Survey*. BPP (HC) 1893-94 [C. 6895], LXXII, 305, report, x. [Chairman Sir J. E. Dorington].

[18] Board of Agriculture minute, December 1893, in PRO OS 1/2/5.

[19] For the specification changes to the New Series, see Richard Oliver, 'Design and content changes on one-inch mapping of Britain, 1870-1914', *Sheetlines* 62 (2001), 6-23, and Richard Oliver, 'The one-inch revision instructions of 1896', *Sheetlines* 66 (2003), 11-25.

[20] See sections 14, 21 and 23: printed in Richard Oliver, 'The one-inch revision instructions of 1896', *Sheetlines* 66 (2003), 11-25.

that there was considerable military demand for a coloured map: this must have been stimulated far more by continental, notably French, practice than by anything on offer in Britain at that time.[21]

      Experiment with colour was authorised in 1894, after pressure on the Treasury from General Sir Redvers Buller (his reputation as yet untarnished by the Boer War), who wrote that 'The want of such a map is …more than an inconvenience, it is an evil…'.[22] Coloured one-inch manoeuvre maps were printed by the OS in 1895-6, and publication of a colour-printed version of the revised one-inch began in September 1897 (Hi.5). There were five printings: outline in black, hachures in brown, water in blue, contours in red, and roads infilled in various shades of sienna: the Baker Committee's suggestions of railways and altitudes in colour were never realised, and coloured woodland only began to appear in 1901. Up to the introduction of helio-zincography to the one-inch in the 1920s the design of the coloured version of the map was largely dictated by the basic record for this scale being engraving on copper. The ornamental borders with graduations for latitude and longitude of the parent engraved sheets were replaced by plain borders with alpha-numeric referencing letters and figures. The south-east of England was covered first, and then, with either the War Office or OS evidently persuaded of the worthiness of the concept, cover was extended to the rest of England and Wales, with publication completed in March 1904.[23] Although the map was on sale to the public from the start, it does not at first appear to have been a great sales success, and its instigation and justification were wholly military.[24] By the time that the coloured map of England and Wales was complete, publication of a similar map of Ireland had begun in 1902 (it was completed in 1906) (Hi.24), and that of a coloured map of Scotland started in March 1905 (Hi.16): it was probably delayed in order that it could be based on the further revision of Great Britain which had begun in 1901 and which produced the 'Third Edition'.

      By that time the War Office had decided that it needed another scale: the half-inch (1:126,720). It had used maps at this scale or broadly similar in the South African War of 1899-1902. They were amongst the worst maps ever issued to British troops, but they convinced the War Office of the value of this scale, and it decided that half-inch maps of Britain were needed. (Apart from anything else, one-inch cover was much more expensive and took much longer to print.[25]) Of this period H.StJ.L. Winterbotham wrote in 1936:

> '…the Boer War had, as everyone knows, a chastening and sharpening effect on the British Army. We learnt to earmark the largest ant heap in sight for our next step forward, to regard every fold in the ground with deep suspicion, and to look on a good map as at once unexpected and heaven sent. In the period which followed that war the officer studied ground and maps as never before nor since.'[26]

      In 1900-01 John Bartholomew's half-inch mapping of Great Britain was well advanced, and the War Office commissioned from that firm six special sheets, covering London and the south-east (four sheets), Aldershot, and Salisbury Plain. Bartholomew described the parent map as 'Reduced Ordnance Survey', which was wholly justified, but the use of their name upset the OS, and a complicated situation ensued which was resolved by Bartholomew omitting 'Ordnance' from

[21] *Report of Committee on a military map of the United Kingdom*. London: War Office, 1892 (War Office number A.237). [Chairman Sir T.D. Baker]. This report was apparently confidential (see Board of Agriculture to Treasury, 4 February 1902, in file 13984/02 in PRO T1/9850B), which would explain why few copies appear to be extant: there is one in PRO WO 33/52, and another in the Royal Geographical Society, London, reference Z.72/4 [we are indebted to Yolande Hodson and Ian Mumford for this information].

[22] Tim Nicholson, *The birth of the modern Ordnance Survey small-scale map*. London: Charles Close Society, 2002, 16, citing file 10077 in PRO T1/8834C.

[23] Sir John Farquharson, 'Twelve years' work of the Ordnance Survey, 1887 to 1899', *Geographical Journal* 15 (1900), 565-98, 587.

[24] The relative lack of sales can be inferred from the print-run information in Tim Nicholson, *The birth of the modern Ordnance Survey small-scale map*. London: Charles Close Society, 2002.

[25] War Office to Treasury, 22 September 1900, papers in group 16078/00 in file 19069/01, in PRO T1/9744.

[26] H.StJ.L. Winterbotham, *A key to maps*. London & Glasgow: Blackie, 1936, 82.

their series title and the OS being authorised to produce a half-inch map.[27] From the print-run information now in the public domain, it seems fair to say that in the 1900s the standard topographical map of Britain was, so far as civil users were concerned, not the OS one-inch but the Bartholomew half-inch.[28] By 1909 the average run for a coloured OS one-inch sheet was 750 copies and for a half-inch 2000 copies but this may have applied to sales rather than printings; by 1914 these had risen to 1000 and 2500 respectively, and the main customer for the half-inch was the War Office. It was 'the principal military map of Great Britain'.[29]

The detailed story of the half-inch remains to be told, but it had only covered about three-quarters of England and Wales when in April 1905 the War Office expressed dissatisfaction with the standard sheet sizes of 18 by 12 inches (45.7 by 30.5 cm) of both the half-inch (Hi.35) and the one-inch: it suggested 24 by 16 inches (61.0 by 40.7 cm).[30] The OS had already produced some rather larger one-inch coloured sheets of England and Wales, and the standard size of the one-inch of Scotland had always been 24 by 18 inches (61.0 by 45.7 cm): possibly the inception of the coloured version of the Scottish mapping prompted the War Office suggestion, although as it was accompanied also by a request for a hypsometrically-tinted half-inch, one may suspect that the real reason was the recent appointment of Major Charles Close as head of the Topographical Section, General Staff.[31] The OS adopted a standard sheet size of 27 by 18 inches (68.6 by 45.7 cm) for the half-inch and coloured one-inch. The 'large sheet series' half-inch of England and Wales (Hi.36) was completed in March 1908 in its hill-shaded form and a year later in its layered form, but the large-sheet one-inch was only completed in December 1913 (Hi.8): waiting for the one-inch revision of 1901-12 to be completed was evidently more important than wholesale conversion. It nicely points up the greater attention being given to the latest military map, the half-inch.

In 1909, in a report on mapping for the Australian government, Close noted that 'In the United Kingdom, the scale for general issue is ½ inch to 1 mile… with a very small issue of 1 inch maps…', and that the standard military scales elsewhere were 1:80,000 in France, 1:100,000 in Germany and Italy, 1:125,000 in Orange River Colony, and 1:126,000 in Russia; in Canada no decision had yet been made whether to standardise on one-inch or half-inch.[32]

Although all the innovations can be traced to military desires, one style of mapping sufficed for both civil and military needs. A number of special sheets were prepared at War Office behest, for use in annual manoeuvres, but they were freely on sale to the public (manoeuvres at this time were something of a spectator sport): they were just Ordnance Survey maps. One can see in the half-inch and one-inch Large Sheet Series an epitome of the period 1900-1914: of a movement for 'national efficiency', which on the one hand reflected a desire for social improvement exemplified by Fabian Socialism, and on the other by military expansion and refinement, which was partly the outcome of the South African War, exemplified by the formation of the Territorial Army in 1907 (much more efficient-sounding than its predecessor, the 'Volunteers'), and influenced by external events such as the Anglo-French *entente cordiale* of 1904, the Anglo-Russian *entente* of 1907, and the Agadir incident of July 1911. There was a feeling that war was a question of When rather than

[27] File 19069/01 in PRO T1/9744 and file 13984/02 in PRO T1/9850B.

[28] See Tim Nicholson, *The birth of the modern Ordnance Survey small-scale map.* London: Charles Close Society, 2002, Roger Hellyer and Richard Oliver, *A guide to the Ordnance Survey one-inch Third Edition maps, in colour.* London: Charles Close Society, 2004, 9, and Eugene Burden, 'Early issues of Bartholomew's Reduced Ordnance Survey of England & Wales Scale 2 Miles to an Inch', *Sheetlines* 56 (1999), 22-26.

[29] Memoranda by Col Hedley in PRO OS 1/270; *Report of the Departmental Committee on the sale of small-scale Ordnance Survey maps,* [1914], report, 30 (comment by Col C.F. Close), minutes of evidence, qq 691, 713 (from Col Brooker). [Chairman Sir S. Olivier. Copy PRO OS 1/6/5].

[30] War Office to Board of Agriculture & Fisheries, 17 April 1905 (where the reference seems at that point to be to the half-inch rather than to the one-inch), in file 14847/06 in PRO T1/10667A.

[31] See War Office to Board of Agriculture & Fisheries, 5 February 1906, and Elliott to Murray, 6 March 1906, in file 14847/07 in PRO T1/10667A, and see C.F. Close, 'The ideal topographical map', *Geographical Journal* 25 (1905), 633-647.

[32] Report by Close, 29 March 1909, in Australian Archives, Brighton, Victoria, 133/2 item 143/10/29, quoted in John D. Lines, *Australia on paper: the story of Australian mapping.* Box Hill, Victoria: Fortune publications, 1992, 41-3.

If: '… the remark "England and Germany are bound to fight" renders war a little more likely each time that it is made, and is therefore made the more readily by the gutter press of either nation.'[33] The conjunction of social progress and militarism is perfectly epitomised in two of the three members of a committee considering the sale of OS small-scale maps which sat in June and July 1914: Sir Sydney Olivier, a senior civil servant who is better known to posterity as a Fabian socialist, in company with the Webbs and George Bernard Shaw, and Colonel Charles Close, a soldier-intellectual who had become Director General of the Ordnance Survey in 1911.

Close's apparent involvement with restyling the half-inch map from 1905 onwards has already been noted. He had decided views on map design and content, and when he came to the OS he determined to improve on the style of the coloured one-inch which, except for the addition of green for woods, was substantially that of 1897: 'a fairly good map for the date', as Close described it in 1914, but now inadequate. He intended to republish the one-inch in a new style with a more elaborate road classification (devised by a War Office committee),[34] and more elaborate relief depiction, by a combination of layers, shading and hachuring. This would involve eleven printings instead of the six of the current design. There would be a complementary outline version with water in blue and contours in red or brown.[35] Similar innovation on the half-inch would be constrained by the needs of the War Office, which would use the road classification, but seems to have been less inclined to accept innovation in relief depiction, preferring straightforward layering.[36]

In 1913-14 these ideas were tried out on several experimental sheets, of which that of Killarney was the first and most celebrated.[37] The timing of these experiments was such that, by the time that the last Scottish and English coloured Third Editions were published, in December 1913, they were obsolescent both in style and content. In 1912 work had begun on what was described as a 'third national revision' of the one-inch New Series; apart from general updating, it provided the data for the new road classification.

In or before June 1914 a sheet covering South Devon was printed, probably in a limited run for consultation purposes, and a little later, possibly in July or August, two sheets which together covered the Aldershot Command were printed in greater quantities, embodying the new road classification and relief depiction, but did not go on sale (Hi.10.12.1). At the same time Close was developing the idea of a much simpler style, which might be used on cheap 'district' maps, on which relief would be shown only by contours.[38] Such a style was not wholly innovative: in 1901 the OS had produced for the War Office sixteen six-inch 'War Game' maps of part of the Thames valley: outline and water were in black, road infills sienna, wood infills green, and contours red.[39] A modification of this style was used on topographical maps published by GSGS under Close's direction, for example the 1:125,000 series of the Orange Free State, and the initially confidential 1:25,344 map of East Anglia, apparently prepared in 1911-14 for counter-invasion purposes.[40] A similar style was also used on the one-inch and half-inch mapping of Canada, which began to appear at this time, the early sheets of which were printed by the OS, and were used as an illustration in the official military map-reading manual.[41] It also started to appear on half-inch

---

[33] E.M. Forster, *Howards End* (1910), chapter VII.

[34] To date no copy of this committee's report has been traced.

[35] See Instructions of 6 March 1913, original in PRO OS 1/4/3, and printed in Yolande Hodson, *Popular maps*. London: Charles Close Society, 1999, 220-3.

[36] Memorandum by Close, 25 June 1914, in *Report of the Departmental Committee on the sale of small-scale Ordnance Survey maps*, [1914], 30-1. [Chairman Sir S. Olivier. Copy PRO OS 1/6/5].

[37] This subject is more fully discussed in Roger Hellyer and Richard Oliver, *A guide to the Ordnance Survey one-inch Third Edition maps, in colour*. London: Charles Close Society, 2004, 18-21, 143.

[38] Yolande Hodson, *Popular maps*. London: Charles Close Society, 1999, 25-6, 29-30.

[39] There is a set of these maps in the British Library Map Library, Maps 145.e.5.

[40] The East Anglia map was later designated GSGS 3036: there is a set in the British Library Map Library, Maps MOD GSGS 3036. See also Roger Hellyer and Richard Oliver, *A guide to the Ordnance Survey 1:25,000 First Series*. London: Charles Close Society, 2003, 3-5. For the 1:125,000 see Elri Liebenberg, 'Mapping British South Africa: the case of G.S.G.S. 2230', *Imago Mundi* 49 (1997), 129-42.

[41] *Manual of map reading and field sketching*. London: HMSO, 1912, plate 9: roads were not infilled.

manoeuvre maps. Hitherto these had been printed either with hill-shading or with layering: now less elaborate styles were tried, including outline, water and contours, plus manoeuvre overprint (*Army Exercise Map, 1913*), outline, water, contours, woods, roads and manoeuvre overprint (*Army Manoeuvre Map, 1914*), and outline, water, contours and roads (*Chatham Manoeuvre Map, 1914*).[42] In 1914, probably after the outbreak of war, the two Aldershot sheets were printed in an alternative six-colour version showing relief only by contours. At about the same time the half-inch was issued in a three-colour 'training map' version, black outline with blue water and brown contours (Hi.36.B.4, 37.B.3, 39.A.3). All the stocks of the relief style Aldershot sheets seem to have been used by the military, rather than placed on sale.[43] Surviving stocks of the non-relief version were put on sale after the war. The Aldershot sheets represented the culmination of two lines of development: of a highly coloured elaboration of the nineteenth century hachured map, relying heavily on artistic skill; and of a much less elaborately coloured, but more 'scientific' non-relief map.

2. *The emergence of a separate military version of the one-inch*

In 1914-15, at the same time as the half-inch map was being printed in 'training map' form, the OS began producing a series of 1:20,000 artillery training maps: nearly all of these were photo-reduced from the six-inch rather than newly drawn, and all had coloured contours. They were not placed on sale, and though presumably considerable numbers were printed, very few have survived.[44] Both these series were emphatically military, whereas military needs for the one-inch, at any rate in Britain, were largely supplied by issuing the Third Edition (Large Sheet Series), albeit now with 'covers' printed directly onto the backing linen rather than hinged. As before the war, maps from the same printing served for both civil and military purposes; only the final 'packaging' differed, and numerous examples exist of sales copies which have had 'military' covers concealed by civil covers.

One exception was represented by the two styles of the two Aldershot sheets already mentioned: another was represented by sheets with overprinted reference systems.[45] The alphanumeric referencing system used on the standard one-inch and half-inch enabled location within a two-inch square, which was useful for place-names, but useless for 'pinpoint' references to features such as road junctions or corners of woods, say. From 1910 squaring lines at two-inch (5.08 cm) intervals were drawn across the face of all half-inch maps, but the only one-inch maps to carry these were the Oxford and Cambridge district sheets (Hi.8.9), both of which seem to have been produced with a view to use by the Officers' Training Corps (OTC), and a pair of district sheets of north and south London (Hi.8.9); there was no squaring across the face of the 1914 South Devon or Aldershot sheets. In 1912 a one-inch manoeuvre map of Kilworth in Ireland was overprinted with a squaring system which permitted slightly more refined referencing, and at about the same time one-inch large sheet 135 was overprinted in red with a set of fine squares at 400-yard (365.8 metres: about 0.23-inch (0.90 cm) on the map face) intervals, with every fifth line accentuated.[46] In 1914-15 a much more elaborate squaring system was devised by Close for artillery use on the Western Front, but its use in Britain was largely confined to the 1:20,000 training maps of GSGS 2748.[47] A few one-inch maps are known to have been provided with squaring, but they were apparently exceptional.[48]

---

[42] The examples seen by the writer were all in a private collection.

[43] For the South Devon and Aldershot sheets see Yolande Hodson, *Popular maps*. London: Charles Close Society, 1999, 23-6.

[44] There is a set in the British Library Map Library, Maps 150.d.14.

[45] For grids and reference systems see Richard Oliver, 'The evolution of the Ordnance Survey National Grid', *Sheetlines* 43 (1995), 25-46, but this article is not perfect.

[46] Copy in private collection.

[47] For a listing see Peter Chasseaud, 'The development of artillery squares and artillery training maps of the U.K. 1914-1918', Part I, *Sheetlines* 10 (1984), 2-8, Part II, *Sheetlines* 11 (1984), 12-14.

[48] So far, this squaring has been noted on 'non-relief' printings of *Aldershot (North)* and *Aldershot (South)*, a printing of England Third Edition (Large Sheet Series) 107, three printings of England Third Edition (Large Sheet

Various reference systems were used by the Allied armies on the Western Front, and this proved increasingly inconvenient, particularly with the arrival of American troops. At a conference in June 1918 a new system was adopted, based on a French Lambert Grid system using numerical co-ordinates, but with the addition of letters to satisfy the British and the Americans.[49] This, which later became known, at any rate in the United Kingdom, as the British System (BS) of the War Office False Origin (WOFFO) grid, was to have come into use on 1 January 1919, but was overtaken by the Armistice seven weeks earlier. This grid, as used in Britain, had its real origin at Dunnose on the Isle of Wight, and the false one (hence "WOFFO") 500,000 metres west and 100,000 metres south of this point – this in order to ensure that all grid references would have positive values. Unlike the squaring system of 1914-15 it was not dependent on a parent sheet number, but had the disadvantage that, were a single letter to be used, references repeated every 50 kilometres. However, as the system was devised for tactical artillery use on 1:20,000 and larger scale maps, rather than as a 'theatre grid' for smaller-scale ones, this evidently did not present itself as a disadvantage. With the addition of a second letter, references would only repeat every 250 km, and with the addition of a third letter they would only repeat every 1250 km. The only known use of this three-letter version was used by the Royal Air Force on 1:253,440 aviation mapping in the late 1920s.[50]

In 1918 the first sheets of a one-inch 'Popular Edition' were printed: they went on sale in June 1919 (Hi.10). The style was that of the 'non-relief' Aldershot sheets of 1914, with the addition of two-inch squaring on the map face. What seem to be the earliest sheets printed, 119 and 120, were in five colours, outline (black), water and water tint (blue), woods (green), first class roads (red) and contours and second class roads (orange), but almost immediately this was modified so that second class roads were in yellow and contours were in reddish-brown, and on coastal sheets the water tint was printed from a separate plate: elsewhere it was provided by ruling. Though in 1919 the map was approved by the War Office, at the same time military training seems to have used a large stock of half-inch maps accumulated during the war and various 1:20,000 training maps.[51] In 1918 work began on a redrawn version of GSGS 2748, on sheet lines related the new metric Dunnose grid: it was contoured at 5 metre intervals. Some forty sheets were issued in one of two provisional formats during 1918 and 1919; the first sheets in the "final" format seem to have been printed at the turn of 1920-21.[52] GSGS 2748 was a very clear map, being similar to the training version of the half-inch, with the addition of red grid figures. A tactical map evidently did not need the elaborate road classification of the one-inch Popular Edition, or the diluted version used on the 1:25,344 map of the Eastern Counties (now known as series GSGS 3036). The sheets of GSGS 2748 covered an area 15 by 10 km on the ground; the sheets were numbered into 25 divisions of notional parent sheets covering 75 by 50 km. This suggests that the sheet numbering was designed so as to accommodate a 1:100,000 series, which would be the natural metric equivalent in the half-inch, with the same 1:5 scale ratio of the half-inch (1:126,720) and GSGS 3036 (1:25,344). Though there is no evidence whatever of any work being undertaken on a

---

Series) 115, one of England Third Edition (Large Sheet Series) 124 and a copy of Scotland Third Edition 22 (all in private collections): see Roger Hellyer and Richard Oliver, *A guide to the Ordnance Survey one-inch Third Edition maps, in colour.* London: Charles Close Society, 2004, 32, 143. An Identification Trace for this series, which could supply squaring for copies without overprint, was issued in 1915 as GSGS 2766: we are indebted to Ian Mumford for this information.

[49] Peter Chasseaud, *Artillery's astrologers.* Lewis: Mapbooks, 1999, 438-440; for the American contribution see notes (undated, but evidently 1932-3, and unsigned, but evidently, on stylistic grounds, by Winterbotham) in file, 'The history of the formation and work of M.I.4', in Royal Engineer Corps Library.

[50] Roger Hellyer, 'Some notes on the origin of the Modified British System of the War Office Cassini Grid', *Sheetlines* 55 (1999), 3-11, esp. 10-11.

[51] For the Popular Edition see Yolande Hodson, *Popular maps.* London: Charles Close Society, 1999, esp. 27-9, 32-3, 76-7, 185; for post-war military map-use see notes (n.d., presumably by Winterbotham), in file 'The history of the formation and work of M.I.4', in Royal Engineer Corps Library.

[52] Information from Ian Mumford, citing the War Office 'Proof and transfer day book'. There is a set of these maps in the British Library Map Library, Maps MOD GSGS 2748.

1:100,000, the sheet numbering system does confirm the policy of using the half-inch or a similar scale rather than the one-inch or 1:50,000.

In 1920 the Popular Edition began to be offered in an 'outline' edition, at first with contours in red-brown and all else in black, but soon with water in blue as well: whatever the theoretical resemblances to the half-inch training map and GSGS 2748, this was purely a civil map. This was to be emphasised by an abrupt change in War Office map policy.

In 1921 a half-inch map of *Salisbury Plain* (Hi.35.3) was printed with the new metric grid at 1 km intervals.[53] The gauge of line was perhaps not as fine as it might have been, but, nonetheless:

> 'The result was that the grid square was so small that the map was practically buried in squares, and something had to be done about it. Curiously enough the Army instead of scrapping this new fangled foreign grid, decided to scrap its training map... and adopt the 1-inch.'[54]

This sheet was the only known example of the type and seems to have precipitated the end of the military half-inch. The only further significant use of the scale was during World War II. A civil map of *Greater London*, published with hill-shading in 1935, was issued in 1940 with relief shown only by contours and black grid at 10 km intervals (GSGS 4159; Hi.35.M.1): it may have covered a convenient area on a conveniently sized piece of paper for administrative purposes. In 1941 very incomplete 1:100,000 cover of Britain was produced (GSGS 4167; Hi.41) by photo-enlarging the half-inch, adding the grid at 1 km intervals, and printing it in the same style as the Second War Revision of GSGS 3907, discussed later. Some sheets carried a note that the map was for training purposes, and the series seems to have been produced so as to familiarise troops with this scale, which was extensively used for Allied invasion mapping of north-west Europe produced later in the war.[55]

In 1920 Close announced that the one-inch Popular Edition had been approved by the War Office as a military map.[56] 'Approved' and 'adopted' are not quite the same thing, and it is unclear whether, at this time, the War Office actually made much use of the Popular. If it did, it was presumably on the same basis as the Third Edition, of a common stock being used for both civil and military issues: but the statement noted above that there were large stocks after the war of half-inch and 1:20,000 make this unlikely. The only exceptions so far noted are some one-inch Popular mapping adapted for Officers' Training Corps and Staff College entrance examinations; on one example the wood infill is omitted, but hachures appear. The 1921 edition of the official military map-reading manual added the description 'Military Edition' to the samples of what look like ordinary OS one-inch and half-inch maps, and this prompted the comment by Colonel [?] H.StJ.L. Winterbotham (whom we shall encounter again):

> 'It is curious to note that the words 'Military Edition' appear above the samples of Ordnance Survey maps. There is no special Ordnance Survey 'Military Edition' and the samples refer to the ordinary series on sale to the public.'[57]

---

[53] A copy of the Salisbury Plain sheet, from the Ministry of Defence Military Survey map library, was briefly exhibited at the Charles Close Society study meeting on the half-inch in 1984. The writer recollects that it was hill-shaded.

[54] Comments by MacLeod on p.49 of H.StJ.L. Winterbotham, 'The use of the new grid on Ordnance Survey maps', *Geographical Journal* 82 (1933), 42-54.

[55] See Roger Hellyer, *Ordnance Survey small-scale maps indexes: 1801-1998*. Kerry: David Archer, 1999, section 41 for an index and list of sheets issued, to which should be added sheets L3E and a Second Edition of O6E, both recorded since the book was published. Ian Mumford tells us that a map with a centimetre grid was requested by the School of Artillery.

[56] Yolande Hodson, *Popular maps*. London: Charles Close Society, 1999, 76-7, citing OS annual report, 1919-20.

[57] Ian Mumford, 'Ordnance Survey Military Editions (non-existence of...)', *Sheetlines* 27 (1990), 23, citing review by H.StJ.L. Winterbotham in *Royal Engineers Journal* XXXV, no.3 (March 1922), 168-9, of *Manual of map reading and field sketching*. London: HMSO, 1921; the specimens are at plates IV, V and VI.

There are two explanations as to why the half-inch was abandoned and the one-inch was reinstated as the standard military scale. The one which this writer finds more convincing is that given by MacLeod in 1933 and quoted above, that the half-inch was unsuited to a kilometre grid. The alternative explanation was given by Winterbotham, in 1932, in notes for a history of GSGS which never got beyond rough draft form:

'Throughout the more civilised world the scale of ordinary national topographical series was raised in theory to 1/50,000, and many sheets were appearing. Such sheets were easy to procure and to copy. It seemed time to introduce the general use of the one-inch in Great Britain.'[58]

Although there was certainly interest in the 1:50,000 at this time, and it had been adopted by several European countries such as France and Switzerland which had previously favoured a standard scale in the range 1:75,000-1:100,000, this was hardly a new development, and it suggests *post hoc* rationalisation: Winterbotham was an entertaining writer, but a lot of what he wrote has an air of evenings with liqueurs and cigars, and students are advised to exercise their critical faculties. However, Britain had the advantage that there was an up-to-date one-inch civil map either ready or in prospect, and this probably assisted the decision: in the shorter term, too, a one-inch might be a substitute for a 1:20,000.

These two explanations might be reconciled to an extent by suggesting that there were doubts in some military circles about the preference for the half-inch over the one-inch, particularly as a greatly superior OS quarter-inch map was being published at this time. These doubts could have been reinforced by the increasing use of the 1:50,000 in Europe. Experience with the grid on the *Salisbury Plain* sheet may have decided the point. Whatever the 'correct' explanation, the point is one of some importance, as in the long term the civil map evolved into a gridded form: in this respect the advent of the British System-gridded one-inch is as much a prototype of later twentieth-century mapping as are the two non-relief Aldershot sheets of 1914.

3. *The military one-inch with the British System grid*

The first one-inch sheet to have been printed with the metric grid may have been 115, for which the plate was prepared in January 1923 (Iii.10.M.1).[59] According to Captain (later Major-General) R.L. Brown, writing in 1933, the one-inch was officially adopted in place of the half-inch for training in November 1923, but that may have been after sufficient sheets had been printed for immediate purposes.[60] No complete set of the military version of the Popular Edition from this period is known, but enough copies have been located to suggest that the first priority, in 1923-4, was for areas of particular military interest: thus sheet 99, which included the naval base at Pembroke Dock, appeared with a plate dated December 1923, not long after the parent civil map was issued, and slightly ahead of sheet 116, covering the Medway, dated January 1924. Thereafter, printing of the military version closely followed first publication of the civil version, and at the same time the backlog of printing for areas of lesser military interest was cleared, this being completed perhaps early in 1927 with a group of sheets in Lincolnshire and the east midlands.

---

[58] Notes (n.d., presumably by Winterbotham) in file 'The history of the formation and work of M.I.4', in Royal Engineer Corps Library.

[59] This assumes that the '1.23' code means that the plates for the sheet were prepared in January 1923, following OS date-coding practice on civil mapping from 1904 to 1922: see Roger Hellyer and Richard Oliver, *A guide to the Ordnance Survey one-inch Third Edition maps, in colour.* London: Charles Close Society, 2004, 33-4. (We are also indebted to Peter Clark and Ian Mumford for guidance on this point.) However, the plates may not necessarily have been printed *from* until a later date. It is also worth noting that the earliest sheets produced retain civil month-year codes which we believe to indicate reprint dates: thus the first military printing of England 123 has '12.21. W.O.3.23.', whereas the 1925 reprint has 'W.O.3.23. Reprint 2,250/25.'

[60] Brown to Winterbotham, 14 August 1933, in file 'The history of the formation and work of M.I.4', in Royal Engineer Corps Library.

As on the *Salisbury Plain* half-inch of 1921, the grid was printed in purple: this may have been chosen so that it would stand out distinctly from the other colours. The purple plate included the grid lines at 1 km intervals, with heavier lines every 10 km, full values in metres in the border, which were invariably printed in such a way that they cut into the legend and other marginalia, and a diagram showing cover by the relevant 1:20,000 sheets of GSGS 2748. (As only about 100 sheets of nearly 1900 of GSGS 2748 needed to cover Britain had been issued by the time that the series was abandoned in 1930, these diagrams would seem to express no more than optimistic hopes.) A small change, effected from some time between February and August 1924, was the substitution of large open letters for 10 km squares in place of small hatched ones.[61] At least some of the earlier grid plates were amended later in the 1920s, by substituting the open letters.[62] From 1926 a dated diagram for differences between true, magnetic and grid north was added to the grid plate, usually appearing in the right hand margin. The precise method of producing the grid plates for this series, and the other military one-inch series of the inter-war period discussed here, is not known. However, it may be germane that in 1940 grid plates for the Irish series, GSGS 3917, were being produced by the Vandyke method. In this the drawing was made in ink on paper, and laid over a sensitised printing plate; the combination of paper and plate were then exposed to strong sunlight or artificial light, so that the image was copied onto the printing plate.[63] Although this gridded one-inch mapping was produced exclusively for military use, it did not carry a GSGS series number; as the allocation of a GSGS number was a matter for the War Office, it remains for elucidation as to why this should be so, though it may be noted that the gridded half-inch map of *Salisbury Plain* also lacked a GSGS number, as did the early (1914) sheets of GSGS 3036.

As well as the regular numbered sheets there were several special sheets. The pair of Aldershot sheets were formally published as Popular Editions in 1919, now with two-inch squaring across their faces. In 1920 a special sheet of *Salisbury Plain* was published (Hi.10.12). Both of these were standard OS publications, sold to the public in covers, and *Salisbury Plain* appeared at a time when the OS was publishing a number of special one-inch sheets, but the main motive in publishing them at all was probably military. They may thus be viewed as joint civil-military mapping, continuing the practice followed ever since the inception of the coloured one-inch in the 1890s. In 1923 most of the area covered by the two-sheet Aldershot mapping was republished on a single sheet *Map of the Aldershot Command*; there was both a civil version, available folded in covers and perhaps a modest seller, and a military version with the grid, which was reprinted at least seventeen times (Hi.10.M.2). In 1924 a gridded version of the one-inch Tourist Map of the *New Forest* was printed (Hi.10.13), in Popular Edition colours rather than with the more elaborate relief treatment of the original, as was a special sheet of *Blandford* (Hi.10.M.2). The *Blandford* sheet had border and marginalia as for a civil Popular, and its sheet lines were laid out on the Delamere meridian used for the New Series and its derivatives, but it was not available in a civil version. It thus seemingly marks a new departure: one-inch mapping quite definitely only for the military.

The trend towards mapping intended only for the military was reinforced by the set of three sheets, covering Salisbury Plain and adjacent areas, issued for the annual manoeuvres in 1925, which was laid out on sheet lines related to the metric Dunnose grid. It was cartographically of interest not for the manoeuvre overprint showing such things as out-of-bounds areas and gallops, which had appeared on pre-war manoeuvre maps, and which were available for sale, but that only one road infill colour – yellow – was used. It thus marked the beginnings of the retreat from the highly elaborate system devised in 1912. In December 1925 a *Catterick area* special sheet was produced (Hi.10.M.3): like *Blandford* it had standard road colours, civil border and marginalia, but like the manoeuvre map set, it was laid out on Dunnose grid rather than Delamere engraved sheet lines. And, like *Blandford*, it wasn't for sale. More special sheets on grid sheet lines followed.

---

[61] The break is not a clean one: the '12.25' printing of England sheet 112 still has shaded figures.

[62] This certainly happened on England sheets 112 and 117.

[63] For a more detailed description of vandyking see *Methods and processes used by the Ordnance Survey for map reproduction by photo-lithography*. [Printed at Ordnance Survey, 1928], 5-7.

Two curious exceptions to the general adoption of gridded mapping may be noted. One was the overprinting in 1925 of civil Popular Edition sheets 116 and 132 to show War Department lands (Hi.10.2.3); the other was the reprinting in 1927 of the Third Edition *War Department Land on Salisbury Plain* sheet, complete with hachures and, most unusually for a post-1914 Third Edition printing, some revision, including aerodromes and golf courses (Hi.7.3.2).[64]

One possible military influence on the sheet lines of the civil map may be noted at this point. The original intention, shown on map-back-cover indexes into the mid 1920s, was that sheet 34 should be a landscape-shaped sheet, which would have overlapped two-thirds of its area onto sheet 33. Some time before the sheet was published, in the third quarter of 1924, the sheet lines were changed, so that it was published as a portrait-shaped sheet, with a much reduced overlap onto sheet 33, and with the addition of an overlap south on sheets 39 and 40. It is possible that the change was made in order to provide single-sheet cover of the mouth of the Humber, which had been heavily fortified during the war, and for which a garrison was maintained subsequently.[65]

Publication of the Popular Edition for Scotland began late in 1924 (Hi.18.A.1), and the first known military printings were of sheets 90, 91 and 92, all from plates dated February 1925 (Hi.18.M.1).[66] This Scottish mapping differed from that of England and Wales in that it was produced by heliozincography rather than by engraving and litho transfer. The outline, water and contours were drawn at the two-inch scale and photographed; 'offsets' from these were used to draw road, water and wood infills. The mapping also differed from its predecessor by being laid out on the Cassini projection using the Delamere meridian, so that it formed a neat continuation of the mapping of England and Wales: two cross-border sheets (86/3 and 89/5) bore dual numbers, and two Scottish sheets, 75 and 81, wholly duplicated the cover of England sheet 1. Also, there was a minimum overlap of one inch between all sheets. The desire to produce a uniform map of the whole of Britain meant that the general style of the Scotland Popular followed that of its southern counterpart, which in turn had been largely dictated by the dependence on engraving. However, the writing and linework were noticeably bolder, and solid black was used for all building infill, in place of the hatching for larger blocks used hitherto on all mapping derived from engraving. All sheets were printed in principle in seven colours, with a separate water tint plate being used on inland as well as coastal sheets, but some highland and island sheets omitted either the first class roads or the woods plate, or both, as these were redundant.

The adoption of heliozincography also helped the production of the Popular Edition in alternative civil and military editions. In theory topographic detail was common to the two versions, but the civil version carried two-inch squaring on the black plate, which was necessarily omitted from the military printings, which of course carried the grid instead. For the mapping of England and Wales (except possibly the post-1923 northern sheets) the squaring, with its letters and numbers in the border, was added to the stone after transfer from copper: it therefore had to be deleted before the stone or any derivative therefrom, such as a duplicate zinc plate, could be used for military printings. On some civil Popular sheets, especially those with extensive areas of foreshore stipple, one can sometimes see on later printings where the squaring has been deleted and then redrawn, not always in exactly the same place.[67] A variation on this was to duplicate the stone onto a zinc plate, and then to delete the squaring from the zinc plate; another method (it is not known if it was actually used for any Popular Edition sheets), would have been not to draw the

---

[64] Third Edition revision is discussed further in Roger Hellyer and Richard Oliver, *A guide to the Ordnance Survey one-inch Third Edition maps, in colour*. London: Charles Close Society, 2004, 25-8.

[65] Richard Oliver, 'Fourth Edition [*sic*] one-inch map of England and Wales: sheet 34', *Sheetlines* 2 (1981), [7]; Jeffrey E. Dorman, *Guardians of the Humber*. Hull: Humberside Leisure Services, 1990.

[66] For the Popular of Scotland see Richard Oliver, *A guide to the Ordnance Survey one-inch Popular Edition of Scotland*. London: Charles Close Society, 2000: this is a much less detailed study than is Hodson's *Popular maps*.

[67] See for example, sheet 40, civil printing 1035, at 7B, 7C, 8B, 8C. The removal of squaring for a military printing is particularly apparent in the north-west part on the 3500/39 military printing of sheet 57. The possibility that, from 1924 onwards, duplicate plates for military printings were made before the addition of squaring for civil printings is hinted at by the civil outline edition of sheet 34, which bears the code 'W.O. 8.24': this could have been added to the stone (possibly in error) to identify the W.O. printing, or duplicate plates, and not have been removed when the squaring was added.

squaring on the stone at all, but rather to draw it onto duplicate zinc plates. For heliozincographed mapping such as the Popular of Scotland, the procedure was much simpler: the outline negative was used to produce two zinc plates, on one of which squaring could be drawn for civil printing, and the other of which, unsquared, could be used for the military printings.[68]

By 1932 it was exceptional to print directly from stone; instead, a duplicate reverse plate was made for rotary offset printing. A new helio plate could be made from a negative in 'an hour or less', and helio plates were preferred to duplicate plates by the printers.[69]

The practice until 1930 seems to have been for the date of the preparation by the OS of the plate(s) for military printings to be indicated by a month-year code.[70] It seems reasonable to suppose that the preparation of the plates was followed fairly soon by printing a quantity for stock. On the earliest sheets, only the month-year code is present: reprints are indicated by 'Reprint' followed by a quantity-year code, thus 1000/26 for 1000 copies printed in 1926. During 1926 the practice was adopted on first printings of following the month-year plate-preparation code by a quantity-year code: it may not be coincidence that, whereas since late 1922 civil OS small-scale reprints had been indicated by quantity-year codes, in 1926 quantity-year codes started to appear on first printings as well. The month-year code was sometimes removed from reprints, and this may sometimes be indicative of a new black plate being prepared.[71] However, sometimes the month-year code appears, but the quantity is omitted.[72]

Surviving copies are most often encountered printed on linen-backed paper; printings on ordinary paper are uncommon, apart from those prepared for use in examinations, and it may be that all the stock of the surprisingly small run of 300 copies of England sheet 132, *Portsmouth & Southampton*, printed some time in 1926, was on paper for some special purpose. A printing of England sheet 112 with a '12.25' code is on waterproof paper; Place's version of this material was used from about 1928 to 1936 for a considerable number of military one-inch printings in both Britain and Ireland, but the policy for its use on particular printings is not known. It was used for civil printings from 1929 to 1935, and its use for military printings in 1935-6 may have been purely to use up stocks before reverting to linen-backed paper.[73]

The adoption of heliozincography had been decided on by 1921, and indeed the original intention was to use it for the Popular in northern England as well as in Scotland, although in the event engraving was retained for these sheets.[74] However, experience with the early military printings of the Popular strengthened the case for heliozincographic production of the one-inch even before the first Scotland Popular was printed. The copper plates for the Popular Edition had been made up essentially by cutting and joining duplicates of the New Series copper plates. The practical result was that the fitting together was more cosmetic than rigorous, and led to problems of fitting the grid in sympathy with detail; it was not enough simply to calculate the co-ordinates of the sheet corners on the Dunnose grid and then draw grid lines across the map at equal intervals.[75] This problem was not expected to arise with heliozincography. The Popular Edition covering northern England was, except for the cross-border sheets, completed as an engraved map, but before the last sheets had been completed, never mind printed with the military grid, a trial heliozincographed section of Aldershot was produced, broadly following Scotland Popular style,

[68] The application of squaring on the Popular Edition of England and Wales is further discussed in Yolande Hodson, *Popular maps*. London: Charles Close Society, 1999, 74-78.

[69] Notes by OP, July 1932, 5A in PRO OS 1/52.

[70] England sheet 23 has a '7/30' code (and no quantity-year code), which may provide a terminal date.

[71] See England sheet 112.

[72] See the '3.28' state of sheet 117, which carries road revision to July 1926.

[73] Tim Nicholson, 'Ordnance Survey maps on Place's waterproof paper: some notes', *Sheetlines* 14 (1985), 10-13.

[74] E.M. Jack, 'Report on engraving…', [March 1923], in PRO OS 1/9/5, which refers to an intention to abandon engraving at the Preston-Hull line. If interpreted literally this would have meant sheets 29-34 being produced from a hybrid of engraved a heliozincographed material: perhaps sheets north of the row 29-34 were meant.

[75] Yolande Hodson, *Popular maps*. London: Charles Close Society, 1999, 76-7.

though with some experiments with woodland depiction.[76] From the start, therefore, the metric grid was being applied in England and Wales to an obsolescent map.

The Scottish map was also obsolescent in one respect at least, long before it was completed, in 1932. As in England and Wales it was on the Cassini projection, as indeed was all OS mapping at larger scales. The Cassini enjoyed the advantage that it was easily calculated and constructed, but the disadvantage that it distorted angles. All map projections distort something, and angular distortion perhaps did not matter much in the nineteenth century, when the enemy was a visible target. ('Don't shoot till you see the whites of their eyes.') However, it was found to be a distinct disadvantage when 'map shooting' at invisible targets came into general use during World War I. It is unclear, though, whether this disadvantage was fully appreciated in 1918 when the Cassini British System grid was adopted. One feels that it ought to have been, as Sir Charles Close was something of an expert on map projections.

It was certainly appreciated by 1928, when work started on a replacement for the Popular Edition.[77] The Fifth Edition (Hi.11) was laid out on the Transverse Mercator (TM) or Gauss Conformal projection, which had the advantage for military purposes over the Cassini that it did not distort angles. It thus differed from the Popular in construction. It also differed cartographically, with the use of a new alphabet derived from that used on Trajan's Column in Rome, which was intended to avoid hairlines and thus be more suitable for heliozincography than the imitation engraved style used hitherto, and in content, including a much simpler road classification. Perhaps the most radical difference was in the reference system, which was based on full co-ordinates in yards (in practice rounded to 50 or 100 yards at the one-inch scale), and thus differed radically from anything being used on military mapping. According to MacLeod, who succeeded Winterbotham as head of GSGS in 1930 on the latter's appointment as DGOS, the yard system was adopted on the advice of a Commandant of the School of Artillery who was 'an individual notorious for the emptiness of his head'.[78] MacLeod was pro-metric; Winterbotham was anti-metric, and the unfortunate Commandant would perhaps have found MacLeod harder to convince. Nonetheless, in 1933 an experiment was made with getting ordinary soldiers to use the yard grid with its full co-ordinates, and it was reported to be within the capabilities even of drummer-boys, but that seems to have been the last that was heard of its military possibilities.[79]

Still, while Winterbotham had his Transverse Mercator yard grid at the OS, MacLeod had the metric grid at GSGS and therefore a strong measure of control over how the army would actually refer to its positions. Indeed, he took over at a time when the metric grid was undergoing change. As was noted above, a problem with the British Grid as introduced in 1919 and used on the 1:20,000 and military printings of the Popular was that references repeated every 50 kilometres. The shortcomings of the British System grid were exposed in the course of manoeuvres around Winchester in 1927, when orders had to be framed using one-inch maps because no gridded smaller-scale maps were available, and shortly afterwards when the Shanghai Defence Force embarked, equipped only with quarter-inch maps. In 1928 a modified version of the grid was tried out during manoeuvres in Yorkshire, in which a reference of six figures, only repeated once every 100 km, and with the addition of a letter only once every 500 km. The experiment, carried out using 1:20,000, one-inch and quarter-inch mapping, was successful, and thus the Modified British System (MBS) grid came about.[80] At about the same time as the Yorkshire experiment, the civil one-inch tourist map of London was printed in a contours-only military version, with marginal

---

[76] A set of these from a private collection were exhibited at the Charles Close Society OS bi-centenary exhibition at the Royal Geographical Society in 1991.

[77] For the Fifth Edition see Richard Oliver, *A guide to the Ordnance Survey one-inch Fifth Edition*. London: Charles Close Society, 2000: as with the companion studies of the Scotland Popular and New Popular, it is by no means as exhaustive of its subject as is Hodson's *Popular maps*.

[78] MacLeod to Craster, 10 December 1934, item 46A in PRO OS 1/84B.

[79] Reported in PRO OS 1/111.

[80] Roger Hellyer, 'Some notes on the origin of the Modified British System of the War Office Cassini Grid', *Sheetlines* 55 (1999), 3-11: this cites the reports on the 1927 and 1928 manoeuvres in PRO WO 279/59 and WO 279/64 respectively.

figures anticipating the Modified British System style. However, progress with Modified British System mapping was initially slow, and it would seem that in 1929 the only mapping available to illustrate the system in the official manual of map-reading were a 1:250,000 of part of China near Hong Kong, reflecting recent operations, and a 1:25,000 of Singapore.[81] The last known newly-prepared Scotland Populars with the British System grid are dated 1930; it is open to question whether mainland sheets 9-20 were ever printed in this style, and very improbable that the Outer Hebrides, Orkney and Shetland were. The last known reprinting of a British System-gridded one-inch was in 1932, of England Popular sheet 32, but the system was still being explained and illustrated (by a specimen with the earlier style of hatched grid-letters) in the official military map-reading manual current during and after World War II.[82]

Replacement of the British System-gridded Populars with Modified British System sheets took place in 1931-33 (Hi.10.M.5, 18.M.2). This was not unduly hurried: after the First World War and until 1933 there was the 'ten year rule', the policy in which it was assumed by politicians and military planners that Britain would not be involved in a major war for at least ten years, and could accordingly plan ahead with a corresponding lack of urgency. The conversion to Modified British System mapping was effected by 'belts'.[83] One can be inferred as covering quarter-inch Third Edition (later GSGS 3950) sheets 10, 11 and 12 (Hi.54): all the constituent one-inch sheets (GSGS 3907) bear 1931 publication dates, and (as far as we know) 1931 print-dates. As there is a scatter of sheets with 1931 publication and printing dates at the south end of quarter-inch sheets 7, 8, and 9, it is possible that these sheets and those in quarter-inch sheets 4, 5 and 6 represent two more 'belts'. There seems to be another one in northern England and north Wales of one-inch sheets 1-34, 41-43, 49-51 and 59-60, which corresponds to the area covered by quarter-inch sheets 1-4, in which a few sheets, though bearing 1932 publication dates, were apparently only printed in 1933.[84] The most obvious 'belt' which can be inferred is in Scotland, all the sheets for which (GSGS 3908) were apparently printed in 1933, but in practice they may have been produced in more than one phase.

4. *Essays in colour: GSGS 3907 and 3908, 1931-1940*

The new mapping was distinguished from the old in more respects than in simply carrying the Modified British System grid. Except for first printings of a few sheets in southern England, the mapping now carried GSGS numbers, 3907 for England and Wales and 3908 for Scotland.[85] (The two cross-border dual-numbered sheets carried both GSGS numbers.) Whereas the British System sheets had needed one more printing than their civil counterparts, for the grid in purple, GSGS 3907 and 3908, as first printed, actually needed one less printing. This was achieved by omitting infill for woodland, and using a single road infill colour. This last had already been tried on the 1925 manoeuvre mapping; that it was not adopted generally at that time may have been because it was less trouble to use whatever plates happened to be available for the civil map, rather than make new plates. In this respect GSGS 3907 and 3908 were more ambitious, though the simplification of the road classification was being approximately paralleled on the nascent civil Fifth Edition at the same time: in 1934 Winterbotham observed:

'A fellow now upon a road is faced with a whole variety of widths, but mainly of a surface which to the map makers of fifteen years ago would have been of the first class… Military

[81] The War Office, *Manual of map reading, photo reading, and field sketching.* London: HMSO, 1929, plates IX and X.

[82] The War Office, *Notes on map reading 1929 (reprinted with amendments (Nos 1 to 4) 1939).* London: HMSO, 1940: see especially plate IX, opp. 47. The British System was still in use in Staff College examination papers in March 1932, but was replaced by the MBS in the autumn papers.

[83] Boulnois to MacLeod, 24 June 1938, item 26A in PRO OS 1/111.

[84] Sheets known with 1931 publication or printing dates: 88-90, 92-98, 100, 103, 105-108, 110-146; sheets with apparently the first printing in 1933: 28, 33, 41.

[85] These are 106, 107, 115 and 132: that they covered much of the London area and Portsmouth may be suggestive.

requirements are no longer important in England because there is practically no road in the country over which a lorry could not go with the most profound ease'.[86]

In practice, sometimes printing was from the two civil road plates, rather than a specially-made plate for military use.[87]

The need for elaborate road classification was no doubt greatly lessened by the progress of road tarring at this time, with an accompanying much greater uniformity of surface.[88] One printing of sheet 144 went further, and omitted road infill altogether, so that, except for the water-tint plate, the colour-scheme was nearly the same – outline, water, contours, grid – as for the Modified British System-gridded 1:25,000, series GSGS 3906, which replaced the 1:20,000, GSGS 2748, at this time. Unfortunately, only one copy of this interesting printing of sheet 144 is known at present, and its margins have been cropped, so it is impossible to say whether this was a very early sheet which was felt to take the reduction in colour too far, or a later experiment.[89]

Wood infill was also omitted on late (1931-2) printings of the British System mapping. All sheets of GSGS 3907 and 3908 were initially printed without wood infill, but this was evidently as unsatisfactory as unfilled roads and by 1934 wood infill was being included on all reprints (except on some Scottish sheets where there was no woodland anyway). Although in theory symbols on the black plate ought to be a functional substitute for coloured infill, in practice this depends on how bold the tree symbols are. They were certainly bold on GSGS 2748 and GSGS 3906: they strike this writer as adequately bold on the Scotland Popular, but they were often worn and perhaps too discreet on the copper-derived Popular in England and Wales. However, several training maps were printed without road and wood infills later in the 1930s as part of GSGS 3907.[90] In contrast, the *Colchester* and *East Kent* special sheets produced in 1934 and 1935 respectively, though on metric grid sheet lines, in other respects were in the same style, including marginalia, as the standard civil-parented sheets of GSGS 3907.

On many sheets of GSGS 3908 the adjoining sheet diagram (usually much larger than on GSGS 3907) on the black plate was moved from the left of the bottom margin to the lower right-hand margin, to make way for the grid-instruction box (something which had not had to be considered when the Scotland Popular marginalia was evolved in the 1920s), but on some sheets the adjoining sheet diagram was left *in situ* and the grid-instruction box was placed in the lower-right margin. The problem arose on GSGS 3908 because on all except the earliest sheets the legend was split into two, perhaps for aesthetic effect when single flat sheets were displayed as a whole, as on a wall. An alternative arrangement was to put the military combined sheet line and grid-letter diagram in the bottom right margin, but this may have been regarded as undesirable because of the separation of this from the grid-instruction box. On some coastal sheets the grid-instruction box and sheet line and grid-letter diagram were placed in the sea area.

As on the British System-gridded mapping, the grid was in purple, but its presentation was much tidier. Grid figures were confined to the border, and the grid instructions were accompanied by a diagram covering 400 square kilometres and showing not only the grid letters but also a comprehensive selection of sheets. The letters which had appeared on the face of the map for the British System disappeared, and figures were provided instead. These were initially at 5 km

[86] H.S.L.W. [i.e. Winterbotham], 'Sidelights: being notes on Ordnance Survey matters…' [sometimes referred to as Winterbotham's 'handover notes'], unpublished manuscript in Ordnance Survey Library, Southampton, 122.

[87] Examples, numbering at least fifty separate printings, dating from between 1931 and 1939 have been noted in the private collections of the writers: unfortunately, this was only noticed when the research for this book was at an advanced stage, and it has not been possible to search comprehensively for it.

[88] For the development of road tarring see H. Percy Boulnois, *Modern roads.* London: Edward Arnold, 1919, and Rees Jeffries, *The King's Highway.* London: Batchworth Press, 1949: we are indebted to Yolande Hodson for drawing our attention to these. Jeffries notes (p.143) that by 1934-5 115,000 of 174,000 miles of road were still to be surfaced with tar.

[89] Of course, a prosaic explanation might be that it was a sheet from which the road infill was accidentally omitted: such things are not unknown (occasional examples are known for the Seventh Series), but it seems a 'tame' explanation. The one copy known is in the RGS.

[90] *Bordon, Farnborough, Lark Hill and West Down, Netheravon, Okehampton, Tilshead.* See section 2, supplements 4 and 5 below.

intervals, but this seems to have been found unsatisfactory after a few years as, probably in 1934, grid figures at 1 km intervals, to the east and north of the 10 km lines, were adopted.[91] Some of the sheets already printed in 1931-3 were later changed to this style, but it was evidently not of too great importance, as quite a number of sheets were still being printed with the earlier style as late as 1943. From 1939 the dated magnetic, true and grid north diagram in the right-hand margin was replaced by an undated diagram showing the difference between sheet-north, true north and grid north.

The inception of the Fifth Edition has already been noted. Publication began in 1931, as a 'Relief Edition' which was a close imitation of the 'Killarney' style, but only needed seven printings: a 'non-relief' version, initially in five colours but later in six, was issued from 1935 onwards and in 1937 the Relief Edition was abandoned. The original intention seems to have been to start in the south-west and work eastwards and northwards, but very soon GSGS requested that the Aldershot Command area be revised, and so a 'second front' was opened there. A pair of Aldershot district sheets were published in civil Relief Edition style in 1932 (Hi.11.7), but a single-sheet 'non-relief' version for the military only appeared in 1934 (Hi.11.M.3), as part of GSGS 3907 and in the standard colour-scheme then used. Unlike the Popular Edition-derived predecessor, it was co-extensive with the two district sheets. Although Fifth Edition publication proceeded, albeit at a much slower rate than first envisaged, little use of it was made for military mapping: it is epitomised by a printing of 200 copies of a non-relief Modified British System-gridded version of the *Dartmoor* special sheet in 1937 (Hi.11.M.4). Perhaps there wasn't enough Fifth Edition cover to justify a large-scale conversion programme; and there was the argument in 1939 that an up-to-date map might actually be undesirable for training, because it would encourage over-reliance on the map.[92] In 1938 GSGS 3907 sheet 107, *N.E. London,* was remade using Fifth Edition material (Hi.10.M.5), and Fifth Edition material was used in 1938-9 for *Aldershot Command* and *Thames Valley* manoeuvre maps. Sheet 107 was perhaps treated as a special case because of rapid building development since the Popular had been revised nearly 25 years earlier, though on those grounds one would have thought the other three sheets covering parts of London would have been equally deserving of renewal. But perhaps the reproduction materials for sheet 107 were in a particularly worn state.

In the mid-1930s, the base material for GSGS 3907 was a mixture of technically seriously obsolescent lithographic stones and zinc plates. The OS was disinclined to put much effort into revising these, but the slow progress of the Fifth Edition meant that in northern England the Popular would not be replaced for some time. Accordingly, as an interim measure, a considerable number of Popular Edition sheets which were not expected to be replaced in the near future (including apparently sheets 1-42, 47 and 48) were converted to heliozincographic production by making negatives.[93] These were obtained by photographing pulls on paper from either stone or copper; a pull from stone was preferred, as it would incorporate post-publication revision, but sometimes the stones were so deteriorated that a pull from copper had to be used instead, and the cumulative revision redrawn.[94] As well as being used to produce zinc plates, the resulting negatives could also be used to produce positive 'security prints' on enamelled zinc, which could be re-photographed in the event of the loss of the original negative. The uncertain international situation in 1938 led to such security prints being made of most of the OS's small-scale negatives. By the late 1930s, negatives might either be on glass, or on film, referred to in internal OS documents as 'Kodalines' after the brand-name of film originally used.[95]

This refurbishing seems mainly to have affected the outline, as the Popular's contours and water were apparently on negatives from the start. The standard procedure for road and wood infills

---

[91] Of two special sheets issued in 1934, *Colchester* has the earlier style and *Aldershot* has the later.

[92] WO (Anderson) to OS and MacLeod to DMI, 14 and 19 November 1939, 22A and 23A in PRO OS 1/219.

[93] See index at 6A in PRO OS 1/219: this is slightly at odds with the list in *ibid* at 30A of August 1940.

[94] Yolande Hodson, *Popular maps.* London: Charles Close Society, 1999, 52-3.

[95] W.A. Seymour (ed.), *A history of the Ordnance Survey.* Folkestone: Dawson, 1980, 281. The earliest reference to Kodalines that we know of is in an unpublished OS research report, dateable to about July 1938 (copy in private collection).

on heliozincographed sheets up to 1940 seems to have been to draw them direct onto zinc plates, which were liable to wear and would therefore have to be redrawn periodically. The road plates would also need either extensive revision or else complete redrawing from 1934-5 onwards, when the OS modified the road classification on the Popular so as to use red for Ministry of Transport 'A' roads and eliminated the 'indifferent' (broken yellow) classification, although this amended classification was only adopted on those sheets not expected to be replaced fairly shortly by the Fifth Edition.

In practice, right up to 1940, GSGS 3907 was printed from a variety of material, of which some dated from the original production of the series in 1931-3, and others used the most up-to-date Popular material available. What seems an extreme example is represented by sheet 106, which included north-west London, and which in 1940 was still being printed from a base with a 1928 civil print-code: a conspicuous omission is the Metropolitan Railway branch to Stanmore, opened in 1932, and added soon afterwards to the civil Popular Edition, to say nothing of extensive post-1914 building development between Uxbridge and Harrow. (It also includes several military aerodromes, some of which had subsequently been built on, but all of which ought to have been removed under the security rules introduced a few months before the outbreak of war.) In 1939 sheet 119 was still being printed using a black plate with a '6.25' code, followed by a string of quantity-year codes. Some Popular sheets had a long interval between initial publication and first reprint, and the base used for GSGS 3907 might be out-of-date on more that topographic grounds. A striking example is provided by sheet 34, *Mouth of the Humber*, which was still being printed in 1939 on the basis of the initial civil printing fifteen years earlier. Not only did it omit new building around Grimsby and Cleethorpes which had been added to sheets 39 and 40 in 1935, using recent 1:2500 revision, but it showed all the fortifications built during World War I and the Admiralty oil depot at Killingholme; under a new security policy adopted by 1928, all of these should have been deleted. In many cases the state of the plate used for GSGS 3907 was one which was not used for any civil printing. An example is sheet 66, which was apparently never reprinted for civil purposes following its first publication in 1921. However, GSGS 3907 printings carry a 'Minor corrections 1928' note and have post-1923 railway names. Sometimes the use of plates is not straightforward. The 1939 printing of sheet 39 used an up-to-date outline plate, which included additions from recent large-scale revision around Grimsby, including a landward shift in low water mark, and the Scunthorpe by-pass, opened in 1933. However, the road plate is evidently that prepared in 1932, so that the by-pass lacks infill and the pecked yellow for 'indifferent' roads is retained. This difficulty was evidently noticed at proof stage, as the infill in the legend was redrawn to accommodate the pecked infill, though the result is a virtual nonsense in terms of both the earlier and the later Popular road classification systems. The water plate is also an old one, so that there is a misfit between the new low water mark and the water tint.

Though the regular sheets of GSGS 3907 continued to be printed in the style adopted in 1934, the opportunity was taken with manoeuvre mapping to try different colour schemes, all of which needed fewer printings than the standard one. The 1937 manoeuvre map, which covered a large part of East Anglia on two sheets, had roads in orange and contours in reddish-brown, grid lines on the black plate and grid figures on the blue plate, which carried both water outline and water tint. The 1939 printings of standard GSGS sheets for the Yorkshire manoeuvres (designated GSGS 3907Z) and the 1939 manoeuvre version of the Aldershot sheet took this one stage further, by combining roads and contours on the same plate. The *Aldershot Command Manoeuvre Area* map of 1938 and the *Thames Valley* map of 1939, also for manoeuvres, had a similar colour-scheme, except that the contours and roads were printed in a deep reddish-brown, giving a quite different look from the standard GSGS 3907 colours. These sheets were also exceptional in that, unlike other special sheets which carried combined grid-letter and adjoining sheet diagrams which showed the relationship to the Popular sheet lines, the adjoining sheet diagrams showed the relationship to the Fifth Edition, which was very incomplete, with a correspondingly curious appearance.

In contrast to the experiments in colour on the manoeuvre maps, a small number of GSGS 3907 sheets, usually printed for officer examination purposes, in effect used the pre-1931 colour scheme used for British System-gridded sheets, with green woods and two road infill colours. It is unknown why this was done.[96]

Another group of 'special' sheets covered various training areas and centres and were produced from at least as early as 1926. Early sheets, such as *Castle Howard*, seem to have followed the standard colour-scheme of the British System-gridded one-inch. After 1931 the usual colour scheme was outline, water and contours plus training-area overprint, on Cassini grid sheet lines.[97] The *Bordon* and *Farnborough* sheets of 1934 (Hi.11.M.5) seem to have been made up from civil material for the two civil Aldershot sheets, and retained yard grid lines on the map face, though the sheet lines were mostly related to the Cassini grid. There was also a series of 'pocket maps', produced from 1932 onwards, in the standard GSGS 3907 colours.[98] Both series were characterised by a lack of standardisation of size.

There were moves after 1935 away from using separate water tint plates for coastal sheets in the civil Popular Edition of England and Wales, but these do not seem to be reflected on the numbered sheets of GSGS 3907. On the Fifth Edition and on some other contemporary small-scale mapping the water tint plate was replaced by a stipple on the main water plate. This was presumably added to the water plate by litho-drawing. In the late 1930s an alternative method of applying stipple was devised, which seems to have been applied to the original drawing, or a duplicate on enamel, and which could thus be photographed and be on the water negative. This gave a 'heavier' appearance: it was extensively used from 1940 onwards. GSGS 3908 seems to have been unaffected by any experiments, and so far no peculiarities of the sort described above have been noticed on any sheets; perhaps this was the outcome of having heliozincographed base materials, but perhaps also it was a consequence of lesser importance attached to the mapping of Scotland.

It is unclear whether the initiative for these experiments in colour came from the War Office or from the OS, but they all reduced the number of printings, and this developed what had been done with the first printings of GSGS 3907 and 3908 in the early 1930s. A reduction in the number of printings had two advantages: it reduced the cost of printing (though the extra cost of more elaborate plate-making had to be offset against this), and it enabled a given number of copies to be printed in less time. This latter would be especially valuable in wartime, when stock might be needed in a hurry. One may suspect that the colour-reduction initiative came from MacLeod, who succeeded Winterbotham as DGOS in January 1935 and who seems to have had very definite ideas on map design, though, as he never produced anything resembling *Killarney*, and indeed abandoned the relief style of the Fifth Edition, his contribution in this regard has perhaps been underrated. After all, MacLeod was in charge at GSGS when the original colour scheme for GSGS 3907 and 3908 was adopted, and by the late 1930s he was overseeing a policy at the OS of reducing the number of colours for the standard one-inch to five, corresponding to that on the earliest Popular sheets of 1918. As an example of his attitude, in 1936, at an early stage in the design of a civil 1:25,000, he was presented with a sheet of GSGS 3906 hand-coloured to mimic contemporary Popular and non-relief one-inches: he liked the look of it, but seems to have wanted a three-colour design, with no road or wood infills.[99] At about the same time the number of colours of the non-relief Fifth Edition were increased from five to six, by having contours and first class roads printed from separate plates, but this appears to have been as a result of criticism from users, notably the Automobile Association.[100] In 1938 experiments were carried out on the Popular to combine contours and second-class roads; the result was the adoption of a five-colour scheme for

---

[96] Examples are noted in section 2, supplement 8 below (all GSGS 3907 or equivalent): 7 (1933), 28 (in 1931/2, still with British System grid), 98 (1932), 109 (1938).

[97] *Aldershot and District*, *Barden Moor*, *Bordon*, *Builth Wells*, *Castle Howard training area*, *East Kent*, *Farnborough*, *Lark Hill and West Down*, *Netheravon*, *Okehampton*, *Redesdale*, *Tilshead*, *Trawsfynydd*. See section 2, supplements 4 and 5 below.

[98] *Christchurch*, *Dover*, *Lympne*, *Shorncliffe*, *Swanage*. See section 2, supplement 6 below.

[99] Minute 1, 12 August 1936, in PRO OS 1/355.

[100] OSC 72, submission by AA, 13 February 1936, in Evidence to Davidson Committee [unpublished: in Ordnance Survey Library, Southampton, G.5186].

the Popular and for the projected New Popular Edition, but the Fifth Edition and Popular of Scotland were to be left as they were.[101] MacLeod was also responsible for the removal of tree symbols from the Fifth Edition, so that green alone indicated woodland.[102] Cartography was being brought into the age of streamlining.[103]

Whilst the Fifth Edition lagged behind the schedule originally envisaged, it did not suffer from post-1918 economies in national expenditure generally, and OS budgets in particular, anything like as much as did the large scales. It was the increasing outdatedness of the latter which prompted the appointment early in 1935 of a departmental committee on the Ordnance Survey, under the chairmanship of John (later Viscount) Davidson. Although the seeds of the appointment of the Committee were sown in Winterbotham's time, its recommendations very much reflected MacLeod's ideas. The most important of the Committee's terms of reference was the need to consider large-scale revision, and that was soon disposed of, at any rate in a way which would meet the most urgent needs, in an interim report issued in 1936. The final report appeared over two years later. It recommended that all the mapping of Great Britain should be recast on a metric grid on the Transverse Mercator projection. In fact, the grid was the Transverse Mercator yard grid, renumbered in metres. MacLeod wanted to go further, and adopt full metrication for the OS, but this was one change too many for the Davidson Committee. Also too much for the Committee was the idea of printing small-scale civil mapping only in gridded editions: they recommended dual format, gridded and non-gridded, publication.[104]

It is perhaps ironic that GSGS 3907 and 3908 first appeared when MacLeod was head of GSGS, as in many ways they marked the most extreme stage in the divergence between the civil and military forms of the one inch, a contrast emphasised by the appearance of the Fifth (Relief) Edition at the same time. MacLeod's appointment as DGOS led to a gradual convergence once again. One symptom of this trend was his advocacy of a national 1:25,000 (GSGS 3906 only covered limited areas of particular military interest), which the Davidson Committee recommended should be tried experimentally. Another was the use in the Committee's final report of an extract from the *Aldershot Command* sheet of GSGS 3907 as a specimen of a one-inch with a 1 km grid, albeit with a unique colour scheme of solid black grid, woods with tree symbols, and roads in red and yellow. Thirdly were the experiments in reducing the number of printings on both the civil and military one-inch maps.

5. *A dual civil-military map? The New Popular Edition and after, 1938-40*[105]

These trends came together in what by the turn of 1938-9 was being referred to as the New Popular Edition (Hi.19), but which earlier in the year had been called the Metric Fifth Edition. In 1935 the original sheet-line system for the Fifth Edition, which was based largely on a butt-jointed concept, had been varied by the introduction of more irregular 'large' sheets (Hi.12), with the result that by 1938 the Fifth Edition combined a high standard of cartography with an unbecomingly ramshackle layout. The recommendation of a metric grid provided an opportunity for a fresh start, and a new set of sheet lines was drawn up, covering the whole of Great Britain in a single sequence for the first time, laid out on the metric grid, and based on standard sheets of 40 km west-east by 45 km south-north. It is perhaps once again due to MacLeod's winkling-out of inefficiencies that the original concept of an additional 1 km on two sides to provide a minimum overlap was dropped,

---

[101] OP (GC) to EO, 26 January 1938, minute 8, and specimen of sheet 109 at 8A, in PRO OS 1/52.

[102] Actually, the decision to remove tree symbols was first decided on at a late stage in the production of the half-inch *Greater London* map in 1935 (see PRO OS 1/149), and then was evidently quickly seen to be effective and adopted in September 1935 for the Fifth Edition (the date is given on Plate IIA in The War Office, *Notes on map reading 1929 (reprinted with amendments (Nos 1 to 4) 1939)*. London: HMSO, 1940).

[103] For MacLeod and military mapping see Yolande Hodson, 'MacLeod, MI4 and the Directorate of Military Survey 1919-1943', *Cartographic Journal* 38 (2001), 155-172.

[104] *Final report of the Departmental Committee on the Ordnance Survey*. London: HMSO, 1938, 4 (paragraph 9) [Chairman Viscount Davidson].

[105] For the New Popular Edition see Richard Oliver, *A guide to the Ordnance Survey one-inch New Popular Edition*. London: Charles Close Society, 2000.

although not before an experimental sheet, *New Forest*, published in the heavy disguise of a relief-style yard-gridded 'tourist' sheet, had been prepared in the original slightly larger size, to provide evidence for posterity (Hi.12.5).[106] It was intended to use existing Fifth Edition material and to continue in the same basic style, but printing would be in the five-colour style recently adopted for the Popular Edition. MacLeod and his OS officers were not keen on printing the small-scale maps in both gridded and non-gridded editions; past experience with the relief and non-relief versions of the Fifth Edition and hill-shaded and layered versions of the half-inch suggested that the public's preference was for one style rather than the other. Accordingly, by early 1939 MacLeod was experimenting with showing the grid by rouletted lines, in the hope that this would avoid the need for dual-format civil publication, which, if insisted on, would have meant either overprinting, or preparation of duplicate outline plates.[107]

Having remodelled the imperial-oriented Fifth Edition as the metric-oriented New Popular Edition, MacLeod tried to persuade the War Office to adopt it. The episode was ultimately unproductive, but interesting in view of the possibility of a joint civil-military gridded map. The difficulty was he and the War Office had markedly different views on the function of the OS. The War Office view seems to have been a parochial one: that the OS was there to provide survey training, drawing and printing facilities. It certainly does not seem to have regarded the functions of the DGOS as including the proffering of unsolicited advice and suggestions, notwithstanding that the DGOS held higher rank than the head of GSGS, and, having also previously served in GSGS, was bound to be a more experienced officer. It is against this background that MacLeod tried to argue the case for the importance of artillery survey generally and 1:25,000 mapping in particular.[108] Matters were not improved by personalities. MacLeod had to negotiate with Colonel Percy Boulnois, the head of GSGS from 1935 to 1941, who had been appointed as MacLeod's successor and on his recommendation, having previously served at the OS. (Presumably MacLeod's scope for recommendation was circumscribed by the availability of officers of suitable rank.) Not much is known about Boulnois: his portrait suggests a stolid, perhaps pompous, definitely overweight man, whom by September 1939 MacLeod had come to dislike and perceive as 'idle, ignorant and inept'.[109]

The possibility of replacing the Cassini-gridded mapping by Transverse Mercator metric-gridded mapping seems to have been discussed first in the summer of 1938, between the completion of Viscount Davidson's *Final report* and its publication. In May, the cost of new grid plates, apparently for the existing military versions of the small scales, were being investigated by the OS. In June Boulnois, presumably primed informally, wrote to MacLeod that discussion was desirable. There were 273,170 gridded one-inch sheets in stock: 'We cannot "scrap" all these at once and a "belt" programme similar to the one you adopted when the army changed over to the British Modified system would seem indicated'.[110] (273,000 maps seems impressive at first, but works out at an average of not much more than 1000 copies of each one-inch sheet, if allowance for rather larger stocks of training areas such as Aldershot and Salisbury Plain are taken into account.) MacLeod replied that the Davidson Committee's recommendations had not yet been officially adopted, and until then they could only plan and prepare. Boulnois responded by

---

[106] This is discussed in Richard Oliver, 'The sheet lines and overlaps of the one-inch Fifth and New Popular Editions', *Sheetlines* 44 (1995), 22-44; for a dissenting view, see Rob Wheeler, 'Sheetlines and overlaps of the one-inch Fifth and New Popular Editions', *Sheetlines* 45 (1996), 42-3. For the metric-gridded version of *New Forest* of 1945 see Roger Hellyer, 'Some notes on the civilian use of Ordnance Survey small scale mapping during the Second World War, *Sheetlines* 48 (1997), 45-57, esp. 55-7.

[107] 'Discussion on the Final Report of the Departmental Committee on the Ordnance Survey', *Geographical Journal* 99 (1939), 314-32, esp. 316.

[108] Yolande Hodson, 'MacLeod, MI4 and the Directorate of Military Survey 1919-1943', *Cartographic Journal* 38 (2001), 155-172, 158-9.

[109] Yolande Hodson, 'MacLeod, MI4 and the Directorate of Military Survey 1919-1943', *Cartographic Journal* 38 (2001), 155-172, 162-4, quotation from 162: this draws extensively on PRO files OS 1/1159, OS 1/1160 and OS 1/1161, where MacLeod's side of his relations with Boulnois and the War Office may be studied at great length.

[110] EO to OP, 21 May 1938, and Boulnois to MacLeod, 24 June 1938, 22 and 26A in PRO OS 1/111.

suggesting that there be a definite date for a complete changeover, and that he was willing to adopt a scrapping policy provided that it did not all have to be done in one year.[111] The beginnings of a conversion programme, which would involve 1:25,000 and quarter-inch as well as one-inch mapping, were discussed by various OS officers in April 1939, with one noting that a common series and grid would enable printing for the War Office to be much simplified, 'and in many cases urgent demands could be supplied from stock'.[112]

On 3 May 1939 MacLeod wrote to GSGS with a firm proposal. He argued that 'economy and facility of supply' would be greatly assisted if the War Office would adopt 'the new Ordnance Survey sheets' as soon as possible. He enclosed a proof of New Popular sheet 160, *London N.W.*, and suggested March 1942 for the first changeover for GSGS 3906 and 3907 sheets to Transverse Mercator metric gridded form. This was based on the expectation that 54 of the projected 190 sheets of the New Popular Edition would be ready by March 1942, roughly coincident with quarter-inch sheets 8 to 12, and Eastern and Southern Commands. The War Office seems to have accepted these proposals but did not reply formally: meanwhile, in the summer of 1939 the OS proceeded with preparations for the conversion of the War Office 1:25,000, GSGS 3906, to Transverse Mercator gridded form.[113]

However, the War Office does seem to have indicated that the form of the New Popular Edition exemplified by the proof of sheet 169 sent to them in June 1939 was unacceptable: the rouletted grid was too faint, there were no grid figures on the map face, and there was no 'grid reference box'. Accordingly, early in October MacLeod sent to the Directorate of Military Intelligence (DMI) a new version of the same sheet. It had a continuous-line grid, intended to be accentuated every 10 kilometres, grid figures in the contour colour (presumably browny-orange?), which was preferable to blue for technical reasons, and a 'grid box' which differed from the military standard but which was intended for civil and military use. The intention was that the outline, water and woods plates would be common to the civil and military printings; it would be easy to print the roads in one colour when the civil and military versions were being printed together. For sheets such as that of Aldershot, four-colour printing would be possible, by having roads, contours and grid on a separate negative. He hoped for 'a very early decision'.[114]

By early November all Fifth Edition sheets had been taken up for conversion to New Popular, and MacLeod wrote again to the Directorate of Military Intelligence, asking for a review of his changeover proposals of 3 May:

'It is thought that if there is no objection to starting the change over to the new grid system at the first convenient opportunity, the best time for it would be when the existing stocks of 1-inch maps recently printed for training purposes are nearing exhaustion.'

The area covered by quarter-inch sheets 8-12 would be a suitable block for the first stage of the change:

'By concentrating all available drawing resources on the sheets in this area, they can be got ready to print in the new style by the end of 1940, and if existing stocks of training maps can be made to last until about this date, it is thought that the best time to change over to the new grid would be during the months October, November and December 1940. The extension of the new grid to the rest of England would have to be done in two further stages requiring approximately one year each.'

---

[111] MacLeod to Boulnois, 27 June 1938, and Boulnois to MacLeod, 14 July 1938, 27A and 29A in PRO OS 1/111.

[112] Minutes 1-3, 5A (5-27 April 1939); quotation is from OP to ODR, 27 April 1939, item 5A in PRO OS 1/111.

[113] MacLeod to DMO&I, 3 May 1939, 6A in PRO OS 1/219; the second paragraph of MacLeod to DMI, 7 November 1939, 18A in *ibid*, suggests that the WO had replied verbally. For preparations for the 1:25,000 conversion, see minutes and papers 10 to 14A, 4 July – 17 August 1939.

[114] MacLeod to DMI, 2 October 1939, 15A in PRO OS 1/219.

But if the existing grid could not be changed until the end of the war, then it would be necessary to prepare new editions of the existing Fifth Edition sheets, which would carry the Cassini grid, and refurbish some of the Popular Edition material, which could not be replaced by redrawn (i.e. New Popular) material in less than two years.[115]

The War Office response was that it would not consider having two separate grid systems in England, though it would be prepared to have separate grids for England and Scotland. Training requirements now overrode Command boundaries, and any issues would have to be replaced immediately with fresh stocks: it was not possible to assume that stocks could be run down during 1940 on the assumption that new stock would be available in 1941. '…the fact that a sheet is out of date need not be taken into account since, from the point of view of training for war, complete up-to-dateness in a map is considered to be more of a disadvantage than otherwise'. However, the War Office would be prepared to accept the latest OS suggestion, of new sheet lines with the new grid on the black plate, but overprinted with the Cassini grid in purple, which would avoid for the present preparing a special brown plate for War Office printings.[116]

MacLeod responded that retaining the Cassini grid would mean work for the OS possibly equal to that of introducing the new Transverse Mercator grid, but 'of no permanent value'. If the OS was not diverted to other work, such as drawing new grid plates, it expected by late 1940 to have completed enough of the New Popular to leave a gap between it and the area for which the Popular was on negatives of a size which could be covered by New Popular drawing in a further year. The alternative was to prepare new plates for the Popular from the original copperplates, and there were limits to the advantages of a map being out of date: 'while it may be agreed that the occasional omission of minor features does no harm, in preventing too great a reliance on the map, … the omission of some major feature like a new main road, would give an even more misleading impression.'[117] By this time the detail plates for about ninety one-inch sheets were completely worn out, though new grid plates had been prepared recently. Though the War Office was apparently now willing to accept an overprinted version of the New Popular, by 27 November MacLeod thought it better to retain the Popular sheet lines, and put it to Boulnois for consideration how far New Popular material might be used where 'old' Popular material was too worn. By this time he had abandoned the idea of a 'Combined Civil and Military Edition' in favour of a civil map with fine pecked grid lines. The War Office response did not take things further, and by 9 December MacLeod felt the matter was not worth pursuing further until the OS had a more definite proposal, depending on how far Popular Edition plates could be used.[118] There matters rested for the next six months, but the decision by August 1940 to use New Popular material for the whole of GSGS 3907 sheets 68-146, discussed below, indicates that MacLeod went ahead with doing everything possible to accelerate production of the New Popular.

The difficulty was that MacLeod was proactive whereas Boulnois was reactive. In the ordinary course of things he might have expected to succeed MacLeod as DGOS when the latter was due for retirement later in 1939, but the outbreak of war resulted in both men staying in post. By the winter of 1939-40 the DGOS was promoting the idea that, to secure maximum efficiency in military map production, a single organisation should be responsible for the OS, GSGS and colonial survey; MacLeod offered to stand down to give the new organisation a fair chance, but he made no headway.[119]

---

[115] MacLeod to DMI, 7 November 1939, 18A in PRO OS 1/219.

[116] Anderson for DMI to DGOS, 14 November 1939: see also minutes between ODR and DG, 11 and 14 November 1939: items 22A, 20 and 21 in PRO OS 1/219.

[117] MacLeod to DMI, 19 November 1939, 23A in PRO OS 1/219.

[118] MacLeod to Boulnois, 27 November 1939, Anderson, GSGS, to DGOS, 4 December 1939, MacLeod to ODR, 9 December 1939: 24A, 26A, 29 in PRO OS 1/219.

[119] Yolande Hodson, 'MacLeod, MI4 and the Directorate of Military Survey 1919-1943', *Cartographic Journal* 38 (2001), 155-172, 164-6.

6. *War Revision and Second War Revision*

Following the 'Munich Crisis' of September 1938 war had seemed more rather than less likely, and late in 1938 a programme was started of building up stocks for training. The quantities to be printed of GSGS 3907 and 3908 were increased fivefold in mid-1939, 'when the enhanced demands of the expanding military forces was foreseen'; a limited measure of conscription had been introduced in May 1939. This programme was apparently nearing completion by November 1939, but 'a large repeat printing order' would be necessary immediately.[120] There was further extensive printing in the summer of 1940. Most of this printing seems to have been undertaken by the OS and War Office, but since 1939 there had been some use of commercial firms, and by the summer of 1940 the OS had completely taken over several civil works, such as Forman's of Nottingham.[121]

The opportunity to get rid of the stones and plates and replace them with heliozincographed materials came at what on the face of it seems the worst possible time for any change, in the immediate aftermath of the Dunkirk evacuation at the end of May 1940, and the consequent acute threat of invasion. MacLeod felt confident enough of his position to take the initiative to produce an improvised 1:25,000 of the rest of Britain, and then of Ireland as well, which he believed would be needed for defence if the invasion did take place. This completion of GSGS 3906 was accomplished by adding the Cassini grid to the latest available six-inch mapping, thereby ensuring the best chance of sympathy of grid and detail in the circumstances of extremely hasty production. In 1938-9 the OS had produced a 'Special Emergency Edition' of the six-inch for Air Raid Precaution (ARP) purposes, which was made to one-inch standards of completeness and provided up-to-date cover for new roads and buildings for practically every town with a population of about 2000 or more. Most of this extraordinary work of completing GSGS 3906 appears to have been accomplished in about two months.[122]

By early August 1940 there were considerable stocks of one-inch maps, but:

'Some complaints are being received about the War Office one-inch (Popular Edition, gridded) map being out of date. Some Units have been able to obtain copies of the fifth (civil) edition map, which is more up-to-date, and consider that the whole series should be replaced at once.'[123]

The immediate reaction to the threat of invasion, and the possibility of having to counter it with the assistance of seriously out-of-date and technically decrepit one-inch maps, was the production of 'War Revision 1940', which heading appeared top right (Hi.10.M.8, 11.M.2, 18.M.3). It was admitted to be a stopgap, and it was not always possible to add the revision before printing. 'Reserves of maps, and dispersal of plates, had to be built up quickly and at some inevitable sacrifice.'[124] This embodied, usually in a roughly-drawn manner, data from the ARP revision; on GSGS 3907 new areas of building were shown in a very generalised way, with bold hatching relieved only by a few roads, although sometimes, for example around Coventry on sheet 72 (see figure 22), new industrial buildings are shown solid black. (On GSGS 3908 the new buildings were shown in black, with more minor roads: the effect was much less incongruous, but then much of the work seems to have been undertaken after the autumn of 1940, when the immediate threat of invasion had lessened.) On a few sheets, notably GSGS 3907 sheets 8, 66 and 76, new areas of afforestation were shown by green without tree symbols: some of this may have been derived from revision intended for the New Popular rather than the ARP six-inch. By the time that War Revision 1940 was printed, almost all the GSGS 3907 and 3908 water plates had had stipple added to them,

---

[120] Anderson to OS, 14 Nov 1939, 22A in PRO OS 1/219.

[121] See appendix 4.

[122] Yolande Hodson, 'MacLeod, MI4 and the Directorate of Military Survey 1919-1943', *Cartographic Journal* 38 (2001), 155-172, 162-3. The most complete set of the ARP six-inch map of which we are aware is to be found in the ex-MOD collection in National Library of Wales; another collection is in the RGS.

[123] Circular by Hotine, 10 August 1940 (ref. HF/7272/CV), in PRO WO 402/91.

[124] Circular by Hotine, 10 August 1940 (ref. HF/7272/CV), in PRO WO 402/91.

so that the separate tint plate could be dispensed with. GSGS 3907 sheet 100 was exceptional in retaining a water tint plate when printed as War Revision 1940; GSGS 3908 sheets 30, 31 and 44 and GSGS 3907 sheet 117 were also exceptional in being printed with the water plate but without either stipple or tint. Other oddities encountered on single printings, not all readily explained, include the printing of adjoining sheet diagrams in brown on GSGS 3908 sheets 57 and 80, and the scale-bars in blue on GSGS 3907 sheet 77. Sometimes alterations were made to the purple grid plate: for example, on GSGS 3907 sheet 18, the older style of north diagram was replaced by the newer. The quality of the finished maps varies from nearly up to pre-war standards for some Popular Editions, particularly in Scotland, to very coarse, sometimes with uneven road infills: for example, on some copies of the 30,000/40M printing of sheet 56 these are wholly lacking in the north-east part of the sheet. It is unclear whether this was due to deteriorating plates, or duplicate plates, or running the presses at maximum speed; but given the haste with which the stock was needed, it is surprising that so many sheets were of such comparatively good quality.

It is also unclear as to what the War Revision 1940 revision was drawn on: whether onto the stones, or onto zinc duplicates, which could then be duplicated further to provide new plates.[125] It was important to have duplicate sets of plates, so that printing could be carried out well away from Southampton, which, as a port, would be an obvious high priority target for the enemy. By 8 July 1940 there were incomplete sets of duplicate plates for GSGS 3907 at Edinburgh, Bristol and Nottingham: the Nottingham and Edinburgh sets were certainly all 'uncorrected', whereas those at Bristol were apparently 'corrected', i.e. presumably War Revision 1940, and duplicates were being made for Nottingham and Edinburgh. There were also a few GSGS 3908 duplicates at Bristol and Edinburgh.[126] The Scottish duplicate plates proved difficult, as the duplication was made using transfer paper, which distorted unevenly, so that different sets of plates were of slightly different dimensions, and could not be used interchangeably.[127]

In the south-west of England, the existing GSGS 3907 material was wholly replaced by Fifth Edition material, a process facilitated by the lie of the eleven sheets concerned (118, 119, 127, 128, 136-138, 143-146) in relation to the Popular Edition (Hi.11.M.1). These sheets were provided with Cassini grid plates and printed, apparently without further revision. At first they usually retained both 'Fifth (RELIEF) Edition' and the yard grid on the face of the map, though with the values deleted from the margins, but omitted a War Revision 1940 statement. They were treated functionally as War Revisions from the start, and later all had this heading added. (Although most of us are inclined to treat 'War Revision 1940' as an edition heading, there is an argument for suggesting that it was information hitherto usually provided discreetly in footnotes which now appeared more prominently: the headings in the style of 'Revision of 19xx' which appeared on contemporary large-scale mapping suggest a parallel.) The retention of 'Fifth (RELIEF) Edition' seems anachronistic for 1940 and is difficult to reconcile with the presence of the yard grid: on the one hand, the Relief Edition heading may have been retained on the parent negatives, but, as far as is known, the grid was added to the printing plates, and the indications are that the plates used for War Revision 1940 were reasonably up to date, rather than old Relief Edition ones which had been disinterred. The yard grid and Relief Edition headings were soon deleted, and 'War Revision 1940' added (Hi.11.M.2). It was anticipated that differences between Popular and Fifth sheet lines might lead to difficulties when converting from sheets of the former already issued, and Assistant Directors of Survey were authorised in such cases to issue more military Fifth Editions than had been requisitioned by units.[128] GSGS 3908 sheet 91 was also produced from civil material, initially retaining two-inch squaring.[129]

---

[125] 'Report of the work of Home Forces Survey Service during the year 1941' (copy in PRO WO 252/1412) refers (p.15) to 'rapid revision on plates', although as this work was actually undertaken by the OS we do not think this reference precludes the work being done on the stones.

[126] Circular by Director of Survey Home Forces, 8 July 1940 (ref. CV/2/2), in PRO WO 402/91.

[127] 'Report of the work of Home Forces Survey Service during the year 1941' (in PRO WO 252/1412), p.15.

[128] Circular by Director of Survey Home Forces, 8 July 1940 (ref. CV/2/2), in PRO WO 402/91.

[129] This is the 10,000/41 B printing listed in the cartobibliography below.

The opportunity was sometimes taken on War Revision 1940, particularly in Scotland, to tidy up the marginalia, including the removal of civil adjoining sheet diagrams and sometimes publication notes. Some cosmetic changes are surprising, for example the correction of misalignment of the GSGS publication note between the March and May 1941 printings of GSGS 3908 sheet 45.

Having put War Revision 1940 in hand to meet the immediate situation, MacLeod and the OS then turned to a somewhat longer-term solution. This was Second War Revision 1940 (Hi.10.M.11, 10.M.12, 18.M.4). The 'second' referred to the revision, not the war, and the title may not have come into use until some months after instructions for it were issued on 16 August 1940, which were couched in terms of converting the whole of GSGS 3907 to negatives, and to four-colour printing.[130] The four colours were those of the 1938-9 *Aldershot* and *Thames Valley* manoeuvre maps except that roads and contours were to be in orange. The reduction in printings would save machine time compared with the six colours of a standard War Revision 1940 sheet. The apparently semi-experimental pre-war manoeuvre-map style had developed into the routine operational map, although another interpretation might be that the five-colour style proposed for the civil New Popular Edition had been adapted by adding the red plate's contents to the orange plate. Popular Edition material was to be used for sheets 1 to 67, Fifth Edition for the remainder.

The work of producing negatives was divided into three concurrent programmes. In the first, 39 sheets were to be produced from the New Popular drawings, some of which were certainly as yet incomplete. These were to be brought up to date 'from all available sources of information', and then photographed. From the resulting negatives prints would be made onto enamel: that for the outline would have the grid added, that for the water would have grid figures added, that for contours would have the road infills added, and a ferroprussiate blue print would provide a drawing-key for the wood infills.[131] In the second programme, covering 29 sheets, prints on enamel foil from Fifth Edition and New Popular outline negatives were to be made, cut and fitted within the margins of the 'old Popular' sheets being superseded, and revision and the grid added; the grid was to be controlled by the intersections of latitude and longitude appearing on the parent material. This would then be photographed, and a ferroprussiate blue from the resulting negative would be used to control the fitting, by 'shining up', of Kodaline prints of the outline and water. These would then be photographed, with grid figures and road and wood infills supplied as for those sheets in the first programme.[132] In the third programme, which continued that in hand at the outbreak of war, twenty sheets were to be converted from stones to negatives, with the enamels to be brought up to date before photography.[133] For those sheets already converted to negatives, the detail was to be brought up to date either (preferably) on the existing negatives or on positive prints from the negatives, and the negatives for the other colours were to be produced as for the other sheets. As many men as possible were to be concentrated on these three programmes, which seem to have marked a significant change for the British heliozincographed one-inch, in that instead of outline, water and contours being on negatives, which were 'permanent' and everything else being on zinc plates, which were liable to deterioration, in future everything would be on negatives, thereby avoiding the problem of wear, and facilitating the production of duplicate sets of plates, as well as

---

[130] 'Conversion of 1″ (G.S.G.S. 3907)', 16 August 1940: copies at 19A in PRO OS 1/52 and 30A in PRO OS 1/219.

[131] Sheets to be produced thus: 68-70, 72-75, 78, 80-87, 89-92, 94, 97-101, 116, 117, 126, 134, 135; sheets 71, 76, 77, 79, 88, 93, 102, 109 (already on Popular Edition negatives) to be undertaken as soon as the previous group were complete: see 'Conversion of 1″ (G.S.G.S. 3907)', 16 August 1940: copies at 19A in PRO OS 1/52 and 30A in PRO OS 1/219.

[132] Sheets to be produced thus: 95, 96, 103-108, 110-115, 120-125, 129-133, 139-142: sheets 107 and 122 were only to be converted after the others had been completed. Sheet 107 was already based on Fifth Edition material, with extensive War Revision additions; ground revision for sheet 122 was still awaited on 1 March 1942: see Circular by Director of Survey Home Forces, GHQ Home Forces (ref. HF/7260/CV), in PRO WO 402/92.

[133] Sheets 31, 43-46, 48, 49-51, 52, 54-56, 58-60, 63-66; to be converted in the order 58, 66, 48, 56, 65, 55, 64, 46, 54, 63, 31, 45, 44, 52, 43, 51, 60, 50, 59, 49: see 'Conversion of 1″ (G.S.G.S. 3907)', 16 August 1940: copies at 19A in PRO OS 1/52 and 30A in PRO OS 1/219.

'security enamels'. The actual order in which the sheets would appear was in theory determined by the state of existing GSGS 3907 material.[134]

The Second War Revision mapping was to be to 'peace time standards' in style;[135] thus new roads and buildings would be drawn in the same detailed way as on pre-war civil mapping, and new woodland would, where necessary, have tree symbols. Revision for the New Popular Edition had been abandoned at the time of Dunkirk, and much of the new drawing would have been 'provisional' in content, though presumably not in style. Though the War Office had apparently not responded to his offer to accelerate New Popular production, nonetheless MacLeod did just that, which would involve a considerable effort to complete the redrawing south of a line from Towyn to Great Yarmouth. One-inch field revision had been abandoned at the end of May 1940, and the redrawn mapping of parts of Wales and the west midlands would be based on the revision for the 'old' Popular Edition, twenty or more years before.[136]

The conversion procedure first seems to have been used on sheet 114, presumably as a pilot, where Fifth Edition material was fitted inside a Popular Edition border and marginalia: this was apparently first printed in mid-August 1940, initially with purple rather than black grid.[137] Sheet 114 was later converted to standard Second War Revision marginalia. At about the same time as this 'special Popular', as it was first called in documentation, of 114 was being produced, so was a Fifth Edition style version of sheet 132, designated 'Military Edition 1940 Second War Revision': this may have been a first attempt at a standard heading on a printing not intended for distribution, and indeed there seems to have been at least one subsequent War Revision printing of this sheet.[138]

It is improbable that consideration was ever given to converting the eleven sheets in the south-west to Second War Revision form, as their revision was already fairly up to date, and the instructions of August 1940 relate purely to GSGS 3907. Work on preparing War Revision continued into 1941; the War Revision version of GSGS 3908 was completed in September 1941 with the printing of sheet 28, and the last War Revision version of GSGS 3907 to appear was 63, *Leicester*, in August 1941. Nine GSGS 3907 sheets were apparently not produced as War Revision at all, but went straight from unrevised to Second War Revision, and three others were printed but probably few if any were issued before conversion to Second War Revision; most of the copies seem to have been withdrawn for salvage (or 'recycling' as it would be called nowadays).[139] Late in 1940 the standard colour-scheme of War Revision was changed, so that henceforth roads were usually a striking scarlet and contours were orange, though some sheets of GSGS 3907 appeared in 1941-2 with contours and roads in orange, although apparently printed in slightly different shades from separate plates, and some sheets, particularly in GSGS 3908, printed by outside firms early in 1941 retained yellowy or sienna roads and brown contours. Some non-standard colour-schemes are sometimes encountered, both on War Revision 1940 and on sheets without War Revision, such as the heading only of the grid letter and sheet line diagram of GSGS 3907 sheet 48 being in blue, though the diagram itself is in standard purple. From July 1940 the usual practice was to add a month to the quantity/year print codes, although some printings without this were made into 1941. This practice may have been adopted to distinguish more clearly between different printings at a

---

[134] Circular by Hotine, 10 August 1940 (ref. HF/7272/CV), in PRO WO 402/91.

[135] Circular by Director of Survey Home Forces, GHQ Home Forces, 3 November 1940 (ref. HF/7272/28/CV), in PRO WO 402/92.

[136] See 27J in PRO OS 1/196.

[137] Circulars by Hotine, 10 August 1940 (ref. HF/7272/CV), and 21 August 1940 (ref. HF/7272/1/CV), in PRO WO 402/91. See also figure 19.

[138] The 'Military Edition' printing seems to be from the same materials as the 'production' version: it has 1940 publication and OS authorship dates, and a 1941 magnetic variation date: it is printed on oversize paper of rather heavier quality than usual for GSGS printings on paper in 1940-1. Both have grid squares of erratic size in the sea around 150150. There were several anomalies in headings to quarter-inch maps as well at this time. See figure 23.

[139] Sheets probably or certainly not prepared: 6, 21, 45, 48, 57, 106, 108, 114, 115. Sheets printed, but possibly not generally distributed: 74, 116, 117.

time when many sheets were being printed more than once a year, and possibly at several different sites.[140]

Apart from sheet 132, the first Second War Revision 1940 sheet to appear with that heading was 114 in late October 1940, with 22 following early in November.[141] This sheet showed very little change as compared with its predecessors, and later printings have a note to this effect. Sheet 22 may have been produced because the existing material was in particular need of replacement, or because, as there was so little work to do, it could serve as a sample for the new style. The intention was to produce Second War Revision first for those areas, notably the south and east coasts, which were likely to be the seat of an invasion, and their hinterlands. Priority was to be given both to those sheets in most urgent need of revision, and those for which the existing plates were most in need of replacement. As noted above, in November 1940 the style was expected to be of 'peace-time standard', and sheets were expected to appear at the rate of two or three a week, which implies a year or more to convert the whole of GSGS 3907 to the new style.[142]

Although the predecessors of the sheets using the Popular Edition had been provided with a separate purple plate, there would have been registration problems in fitting the existing grid plates to the new enamels, and so it would have been more satisfactory to redraw the grid. Whilst it would have been possible to copy the grid from a War Revision or earlier sheet by ensuring similar sympathy with detail, this would not have been possible for sheets based on Fifth or New Popular material. The rigorous method would have been to plot the grid with reference to trigonometrical points, but in practice the grid was laid across the sheets without such control. MacLeod wrote 'Whatever was done was done in a hurry, and no attempt was made to distort the grid so as to make it fit exactly to the trig. points', but he didn't think this mattered as 'the sheets have no pretensions to precise accuracy'.[143] Presumably the incidence of the sheet corners were calculated and the grid was added by making equal divisions between them. Such a grid would not necessarily be in sympathy with trig. points, but this was evidently not a major drawback.

Just after the first Second War Revision sheets had been printed there came a serious setback. On 30 November and 1 December 1940 two nights of bombing seriously damaged a large part of the OS headquarters at London Road, Southampton. The offices where the Second War Revision was being prepared were in effect wholly destroyed, together with nearly all the original drawings and negatives for the Fifth Edition and New Popular Edition. These included a large quantity of the latter for the west midlands and southern Wales which were evidently not yet advanced enough to have been photographed and preserved on security enamels. Also lost were the enamels for a number of Second War Revisions which had been started. The extent of the destruction was such that it was difficult at first to specify exactly what had been lost.[144] The outcome of the bombing was probably unsatisfactory for both sides: the OS lost its drawings and negatives, but the printing presses and plates at London Road were apparently unscathed, and what would presumably have been the primary object of the raids, to disrupt map supply, was not achieved.

Work resumed on Second War Revision, but it was no longer possible to think in terms of replacement at the rate of two or three per week. By the spring of 1942 the area north of a line from the Bristol Channel through Nottingham to the Wash was regarded as 'generally less urgent because these areas are not so "hot" operationally. In some areas, however, 2 W.R. is being published for sheets on which there was a good deal of revision for the W.R. edition.'[145] After the autumn of 1942 the rate of output noticeably reduced, as the revision of many of the remaining sheets was much less urgent, and between January 1943 and January 1944 only eight appeared; the last sheet to be converted, 93, was dated August 1944. By that time 119 sheets of GSGS 3907 had been issued in Second War Revision. Three more seem to have reached, or been ready for, colour-

---

[140] See appendix 4.

[141] Circular from GHQ Home Forces, 3 November 1940 (ref. HF/7272/28/CV), in PRO WO 402/91.

[142] Circular from GHQ Home Forces, 3 November 1940 (ref. HF/7272/28/CV), in PRO WO 402/91.

[143] MacLeod to Hinks, 6 November 1941, 43A in PRO OS 1/111.

[144] See lists in PRO OS 1/196.

[145] Memorandum (undated: evidently March or April 1942), in PRO WO 402/92.

proof stage; eleven more were printed only in outline and water form for civil use, of which more later.[146] Strips on the north and west of sheet 93, the east of sheet 96 and the north of sheet 103 were supplied from Popular mapping; on 93 and 103 this can be explained by the destruction of Fifth or New Popular Edition material, but this does not explain sheet 96.

Two sheets were issued with amended sheet lines. Sheet 117A was a successor to *East Kent Special Sheet*, which had first been issued in 1935, and covered a rather larger area (42 by 42 km), on grid sheet lines. Sheet 1A had no predecessor, and was unusual for a post-1925 military one-inch in that it was on Delamere New Series sheet lines. Strictly speaking, both sheet 1 and sheet 1A were unnecessary for complete cover, but 1A had the advantage that Berwick upon Tweed could be shown close to the centre of the sheet. Apart from the eleven sheets in the south-west, all the sheets which were not printed or apparently even prepared as Second War Revision were in the midlands and Wales. Sheet 122 also incorporated some *ad hoc* post-1940 revision, but was exceptional in this, though elsewhere one can find occasional examples of temporary wartime railway station closures.[147] As a result of the loss of field documents in the bombing, eight Second War Revision sheets using mostly unpublished New Popular material – 73-75 and 83-87 – omitted infills for tarred roads under 14 feet wide. GSGS 3908 does not appear originally to have been within the scope of the Second War Revision programme, but in 1942 sheets 45 and 92 were revised and republished as Second War Revision at the request of the Director of Surveys, Home Forces.[148]

At first there were not always enough stocks of Second War Revision to enable earlier stocks to be withdrawn and sent for salvage, and War Revision and unrevised Popular continued to be listed as current editions for some sheets.[149] Also, for some sheets the differences were so slight that there was no point scrapping existing stocks. Stocks were dispersed around the country at various depots, and stock replacement was therefore not the straightforward job that it would have been had all stocks been held by the OS at Southampton. Sometimes superseded mapping was sent for salvage, but sometimes it was issued for training, and it should not be assumed that copies of War Revision or earlier mapping bearing annotations are evidence of use before Second War Revision was printed. This particularly applies to copies known or likely to have come from Cadet Corps, Air Training Corps, and the like.[150] (In theory 'training copies' were rubber-stamped to this effect but these seem to be even less common than regimental, corps or unit stamps on pre-war issues.) The standard first print-run for a Second War Revision seems to have been 45,000 copies in April 1941; by late 1941 it was 70,000 copies. Reprints could be anything from 10,000 to 50,000 copies: 30,000 may be taken as an average. These were much larger than anything pre-war, and it is perhaps unsurprising that, even within a single printing, the colours should vary: the orange in particular can vary from relatively pale to almost dun-brown. There are similar variations between successive printings of sheets, and between different sheets, particularly where the printing was undertaken by outside firms; the 'orange' on the December 1943 printing by the Haycock Press of

---

[146] Sheets 29, 41, 42, 52, 61, 62, 81, 82, 92, 100 and 109 are only known in outline-and-water printings: the lists of current editions of GSGS 3907 (see appendix 1 below) indicate that sheets 24, 44 and 51 were 'ready' for printing in 2WR, but were not taken further, and sheet 109 was apparently colour-proved in November 1943.

[147] 'Conversion of 1″ (G.S.G.S. 3907)', 16 August 1940: copies at 19A in PRO OS 1/52 and 30A in PRO OS 1/219. There are several station closures on sheet 2, at U 516701 (Scremerston), U 542662 (Goswick), U 646515 (Lucker) and U 720381 (Little Mill): these were all closed to passengers on 5 May 1941 and reopened on 7 October 1946: see C.R. Clinker, *Clinker's register of closed passenger stations and goods depots in England, Scotland and Wales 1830-1977.* Weston-super-Mare: Avon-AngliA, 1988 and M.E. Quick, *Railway passenger stations in England, Scotland and Wales: a chronology.* Richmond, Surrey: Railway & Canal Historical Society, 2002.

[148] See unpublished OS annual report for 1942-3 in PRO OS 1/141.

[149] The currency of the various editions at various times is listed in appendix 1 below: this derives from circulars of 3 November 1940, 6 February, 14 May, 8 July and 31 October 1941, 28 February, 25 March, 11 May, 10 July and 31 July 1942, 4 January, 20 February and 31 May 1944: copies in PRO WO 402/91 (1940- July 1941), WO 402/92 (October 1941 – 1942) and in GSGS 3907 series file, at present with DGC (1944). For publication of new editions in 1942-5 see reports in PRO WO 402/94.

[150] The writer particularly has in mind a large quantity of GSGS 3906 and 3907 formerly at De Aston School, Market Rasen, which he persuaded the then head of geography, the late W.F.V. Harries, to dispose of in 1972.

sheet 57 is almost brown. It should be borne in mind that an invasion was regarded as a distinct possibility until well into 1942, but thereafter the focus of attention moved to counter-attack and invasion of Europe, and military map production went in the same direction. Perhaps the surprising thing is not that the Second War Revision programme was never completed, but that it was not curtailed sooner, though it may well have been treated latterly as a 'stock job', to be taken up and left off according to the flow of more urgent work on overseas mapping. (It may be no coincidence that the cessation of Second War Revision production roughly coincides with the start of work on the civil 1:25,000 series.)

Whilst the basic design of Second War Revision remained unchanged, there were two significant modifications: to marginalia and to colours. The first was theoretically effective from September 1941, and applied to both GSGS 3907 and 3908, though the first sheet embodying it, GSGS 3908 sheet 55, was apparently only printed on 13 October.[151] The margins were considerably reduced in width, legend panels and grid instructions were omitted, a heading 'Popular Edition Style' or 'Fifth Edition Style' appeared in the top margin as appropriate on GSGS 3907 sheets, and the magnetic variation diagram in the margin was replaced by a large black arrow on the map face. The object was to save paper.

> 'The General Staff argued that a trained soldier did not need grid reference boxes, conventional signs etc. in Great Britain, and by reducing the information given on the map to the absolute minimum, by compressing the remaining essential information at the foot of the map, by placing the Magnetic North Point on the face of the map, and by reducing the size of lettering for the heading, it was possible to make a saving of upwards of 25% of paper on each sheet.'

Because of the problems with the duplicate plates for GSGS 3908, prepared in 1940, it was decided to prepare completely fresh sets of plates for this series, and these were all in the new 'narrow margin' style.[152]

The last 'wide margin' sheet to be printed was GSGS 3907 sheet 45, in February 1942. Only four GSGS 3907 War Revision sheets based on Popular Edition material – 37, 90, 93, 112 – were printed in 'narrow margin' style; the eleven War Revisions on Fifth Edition sheet lines and all those in GSGS 3908 were all printed at least once in the narrow-margin style. The adoption of the new style may have been facilitated by the adoption by the OS around 1938 of plastic film for negatives, and it may have been easier to 'strip in' the new marginalia than it would have been with glass. A supply of conventional sign cards was made available, primarily for training purposes, to replace the deleted legends, but very few of these seem to survive.[153]

The adoption of the new marginal style was the opportunity for further non-topographic change on GSGS 3908, in that, though a few sheets had already been converted to the later style of grid figures on the map face, at 1 km intervals, the change of marginalia seems to have been the occasion of remaking the grid plates as well. Sometimes errors would creep in: for example there are instances of incorrect or incorrectly located grid values in the 'relation of grid letters and sheet numbers' diagram.[154]

The 'narrow margin' style was adopted to save paper, though it also enabled slightly smaller plates to be used, therefore increasing the range of machines on which the mapping could be printed. Before the style was adopted the OS also experimented with paper-saving by printing a pair of sheets back-to-back, but the disadvantages were felt to outweigh the advantages.[155] One can

---

[151] Date from record copy in OS job file: see cartobibliography below.

[152] 'Report of the work of Home Forces Survey Service during the year 1941' (in PRO WO 252/1412), p.15.

[153] See Circular by Director of Survey Home Forces, GHQ Home Forces, 2 December 1941 (ref. HF/7278/74/CV), in PRO WO 402/92. See also figure 12.

[154] One such is on GSGS 3907 sheet 72, 27,050/1/43 BJ printing, where the 300 km easting incorrectly passes through sheets 81 to 83 instead of 71 to 73.

[155] 'Report of the work of Home Forces Survey Service during the year 1941' (in PRO WO 252/1412), p.15. The sheets in question were England and Wales 116 and 126: see note to 126 in the cartobibliography below.

occasionally encounter 'narrow margin' sheets printed on decidedly oversize paper – a group printed by Nos 14 and 16 Map Reproduction Sections in the winter of 1943-4 particularly come to mind – but these seem to apply to copies printed away from the OS. Other problems were more significant. The first narrow-margin printing of GSGS 3907 sheet 83 had incorrect sheet numbers in the adjoining sheet diagram and had to be corrected by overprinting; sheet 125 had an erroneous railway station name.[156] Magnetic data was incorrect on a few sheets, but as this information was only used by Royal Engineers and Royal Artillery, notification was limited.[157] On the first printings of GSGS 3907 sheets 4, 11 and 14 a 'Fifth Edition Style' heading was provided in error, and a rubber stamp circulated round map depots to enable 'Popular Edition Style' to be stamped in its place.[158] It must have been a tedious operation.

Supplying duplicate plates to commercial firms was not wholly satisfactory, as the plates sometimes became oxidised in transit, due to the packing getting damp. An alternative was to supply the civil firms with miniature glass negatives, from which, duly enlarged to the proper size, the firms could make their own plates. This also had the advantage in saving considerable bulk in transit.[159]

The adoption of the new margin style also coincided with the cessation of printing GSGS 3907 and 3908 on linen-backed paper. By mid-1941 it was apparent that no further supplies of linen-backed paper were to be made, and it was necessary to conserve all remaining stocks for tank and RAF maps.[160] Although a mounted map is obviously more durable, the quality of paper in use by 1941 was far better than it had been in, say 1901 or 1921, and an additional advantage was that superseded stock which was not mounted could be reused almost immediately by overprinting 'CANCELLED' boldly in red, usually with zigzags, and printing another map on the other side. (The Germans do not appear to have used linen-backed paper for their invasion maps of western Europe. From their point of view it was perhaps a false economy: when several map depots in north-western Europe were 'liberated' by the advancing Allied armies around August 1944, a large stock of mapping was available for immediate re-use by and on the 'other side'.)

The other significant change was to the colour used for the contours and roads plates, and was decided on late in 1943, though the orange was still in use in April 1944. This colour was liable to disappear when viewed using torches with orange filters, as was standard practice in the Royal Air Force. After experiments on GSGS 3907 sheet 50 with Griblet Brown, Blue Grey, and Third Layer Violet, 'Air Force number 17 brown' (a colour which has been described as variously very dark red or chestnut or even magenta) was adopted.[161] There was no intention of replacing existing stocks, but the new colour was used for a batch of Second War Revision sheets printed in June and August 1944, which seem to have been the last wartime printings of GSGS 3907 and 3908, and included the last new Second War Revision, 93, to be printed. The colour was still in use in 1946-7, when the first sheets of GSGS 4620 were printed, as described later, but orange was reverted to for the last printings of Second War Revision, in 1948. As in 1919 with the half-inch and 1:20,000, in 1945-6 there were still considerable quantities of GSGS 3907 and 3908 which would suffice to meet needs for some time to come. Air Force brown was tried on one of the proofs of the pilot sheet for the civil 1:25,000 in 1944, but in the event orange or orange-brown was used, and it is noticeable that the basic four-colour-with-orange scheme of the Second War Revision has since been extensively used on other series: the 1:25,000 Second Series and various military training derivatives of the one-inch and 1:50,000 in Great Britain, several topographic series in

---

[156] See Circular by Director of Survey Home Forces, GHQ Home Forces, 16 March 1942 (ref. HF/7201/CV-52), in PRO WO 402/92: but we have not found a corrected version of the sheet.

[157] Circular by Director of Survey Home Forces, GHQ Home Forces, 11 April 1942 (ref. HF/7201/CV), in PRO WO 402/92: the sheets with incorrect data were the 'reduced margins' GSGS 3907 War Revision sheets 93 and 112, and Second War Revision sheets 21, 26, 46, 47, 60, 103, 113, 121, 123 and 126.

[158] Circulars by Director of Survey Home Forces, GHQ Home Forces, 24 April 1942 and 2 June 1942 (ref. HF/7260/CV), in PRO WO 402/92.

[159] 'Report of the work of Home Forces Survey Service during the year 1941' (in PRO WO 252/1412), p.16.

[160] 'Report of the work of Home Forces Survey Service during the year 1941' (in PRO WO 252/1412), p.15.

[161] Willis to DSA, 6 Dec 1943; OS to Survey 2; GHQ Home Forces to D Survey, 19 February 1944; Directorate of Military Survey to DGOS, 23 February 1944: in GSGS 3907 series file, at present with DGC.

Europe (e.g. 1:25,000 series in France and Germany and, with substitutions for the orange, two 1:100,000 series in Denmark), and the extensive military mapping of seemingly almost everywhere by the former Soviet Union.[162] How far these colour schemes were in conscious imitation of British practice, and how far they were the result of separate development, would be an interesting subject of study.

Other possible changes did not get beyond the suggestion stage: some users seemed to find the conjunction of, for example, 'Fifth Edition style' and 'Second War Revision' confusing, the magnetic variation diagram was noted as at variance with that in the official map-reading manual, and the 'black arrow' was thought liable to confusion with railways: green was suggested as an alternative, but was noted as a weak colour.[163]

As has so often been the way with Ordnance Survey mapping of Scotland, GSGS 3908 underwent much less drastic change than did GSGS 3907: from the autumn of 1941 all sheets were printed in the 'black arrow' style, but still in six colours, with purple grid, red roads and orange contours. In 1941-2 the standard print run was 10,000 or 15,000 copies: for some sheets this was sufficient to last until 1950. A considerable number of Scottish sheets were printed in Edinburgh by Bartholomew or Johnston: this was not for reasons of sentimentality, but in continuation of the policy established at the time of Dunkirk of dispersing printing around the country in order that, were southern England to be invaded or otherwise incapacitated, map supply could continue.

In 1947 six GSGS 3907 sheets were overprinted with layers for use by the Staff College (Hi.10.M.12.3).[164] The shades of brown used were striking, but rather deep, and on four of the sheets on higher ground completely obscured the orange for contours and road infills. On sheets 104 and 122, which used 'Air Force brown' printings, the result was much more successful.

7. The 'Sales copies'

As recounted above, for a time in 1939 MacLeod hoped that the New Popular Edition could be flexible enough to be usable by the military with minimal adaptation. Though he failed to persuade Boulnois and the War Office that they needed the New Popular Edition, work on it was pushed ahead. In order to assimilate OS and War Office practice, in the autumn of 1939 the treatment of the grid on the new mapping was redesigned. Full co-ordinates at 5 km intervals in the margin were replaced by double figures at 1 km intervals as for the Modified British System, and the lower marginalia was rearranged so as to make room for a grid-instruction box and national diagram of grid letters; this was accomplished most ingeniously without any increase in the size of the map when trimmed ready for folding. The omission of grid instructions from the original design seems curious, but perhaps has its origin in the Davidson Committee's recommendation that the small-scale maps be published in both gridded and non-gridded versions: the prototype for the New Popular, the *New Forest* sheet of 1938, was gridded (albeit still with the yard grid), and had instructions for its use printed inside the cover of folded copies.

Work on the New Popular Edition was seriously disrupted by the destruction of 30 November – 1 December 1940, but a few sheets had already been printed, and more were ready, whenever there was a slackening of war work. The bombing had destroyed most of the OS's stock of civil mapping at all scales, but the plates survived. The large-scale mapping being either monochrome or (perhaps half the six-inch mapping) two-colour, was replaced over the next two years, much of the work being undertaken by civil firms. The small-scale mapping was more of a problem. Although the available New Popular material only provided patchy cover, MacLeod wanted to issue what there was. The problem was the Transverse Mercator metric grid: whereas in 1939 the War Office had not liked the pressure to adopt it, whatever might happen in civvy street,

---

[162] The Soviet mapping made extensive use of separate road, contour and other plates printed in similar shades of orange or brown, with the result that often ten or eleven printings were called for, but the general resemblance to the orange-dominated schemes of the Second War Revision and 1:25,000 Second Series is unmistakable.

[163] Hudson to Director of Survey Home Forces and reply, 9 and 11 April 1942, in GSGS 3907 series file, at present with DGC.

[164] WOPD 1255/R of 14 November 1947: completed 16 December 1947: sheets 104, 105, 112, 113, 122, 123. See figure 11 for an extract of sheet 122.

now it did not want it to be brought into use at all, for fear that New Populars would get into the hands of Home Guards and others who had to work closely with the army, and whose misguided use of Transverse Mercator grid references could produce a result which was at worse 'definitely dangerous'.[165] From this point of view MacLeod's reworking of the New Popular's grid to bring it into line with the War Office Modified British System in principle seems a miscalculation, in the short-term anyway. Perhaps he should have retained the full co-ordinates and marginalia with no instructions, as Fifth Edition mapping of this type continued to be available, whenever stocks survived; the full co-ordinate method of working was not very user-friendly compared with the Modified British System. MacLeod persisted, had five New Populars printed with the grid figures omitted, and produced two versions of a proof of sheet 159 with the grid figures blacked out and the grid-instruction box defaced. This last was acceptable to the War Office, but the patchy cover by New Populars, together with the six sheets printed with grid figures which were particularly objectionable to the War Office, seems to have decided the matter in favour of issuing the military one-inch instead.[166] The New Popular Edition eventually went on sale on 31 August 1945, with the grid figures added to the five sheets printed without them, and with the grid modified so as to identify 100 km squares by number rather than by letter, which involved pasting a large amendment sticker on the eleven sheets printed in 1940-41 with the Modified British System grid.

In 1941-3 a few full-colour small-scale printing jobs initiated before December 1940 were completed, including the only five-colour printing of a Fifth Edition sheet (127) in approximately the colours intended for the New Popular Edition.[167] That these jobs were completed may have been a consequence of their proceeding so slowly that it was not realised in the higher reaches of the OS that they were continuing at all; equally, they may have been allowed to continue as and when there was press capacity, particularly once it became apparent that there was no point in printing further New Populars which the War Office refused to allow to be sold. As a short-term expedient to meet civil demands (mostly official, one suspects), the OS printed outline-and-water versions of the one-inch and the smaller scales (Hi.10.3, 11.4, 12.4, 18.A.3, 36.B.7, 37.B.5, 56.A.3, 60.A.3).[168] These were always in runs of 1000, and always printed by the OS (usually at Southampton), and the junction between Fifth Edition and Popular Edition cover was so arranged as to minimise overlap between the two and minimise the total number of maps to be printed. By restricting the printings to two colours the whole operation was completed in about a year. To print 140 two-colour sheets covering England and Wales would mean 280,000 cylinder revolutions: the same number of cylinder revolutions would only yield about fifteen sheets of standard Popular or Fifth Edition mapping each in six colours and a typical 'pre-war' run of 3000 copies. Immediate restoration of coloured civil mapping was just not practicable, and even if there had been a little more capacity, it might still have been questionable in view of its obsolescence.

The provenance of the one-inch outline-and-water printing plates varied. At least some of the Fifth Edition sheets were obtained by rephotographing security enamels made some time before the outbreak of war: thus Fifth Edition sheet 131 in its February 1942 printing derives from the original coloured printing of this sheet in 1938, which shows military aerodromes deleted from the 1939 reprint.[169] The Popular Edition sheets are more complicated. The earlier sheets of England and Wales, printed up to about December 1941, seem to have been derived from either security enamels or from printing plates for the civil edition, and do not embody post-1939 revision. However, they may be in a state which corresponds neither to any civil nor any military printing; such a sheet is sheet 33. Sheets issued after December 1941 carried the War Revision additions of

[165] Copy, Hudson to MO1, 39B in PRO OS 1/219.

[166] See minutes and papers 43A-58, 29 December 1941 – 3 November 1942, in PRO OS 1/219.

[167] These are listed in Roger Hellyer, 'Some notes on the civilian use of Ordnance Survey small scale mapping during the Second World War', *Sheetlines* 48 (1997), 45-57.

[168] These are discussed further in Roger Hellyer, 'Some notes on the civilian use of Ordnance Survey small scale mapping during the Second World War', *Sheetlines* 48 (1997), 45-57, and Roger Hellyer, 'Some notes on one-inch mapping produced for civilian use during the Second World War', *Sheetlines* 59 (2000), 17-38.

[169] Military aerodromes are shown at 1,016,000-1,255,000 and 1,036,500-1,268,500 on the 5038 and 1000/2/42 LR civil printings, but are omitted from the 5039 civil printing.

mid-1940 onwards (readily identifiable by the hatching of newly built-up areas), and presumably were printed from either duplicate plates, or War Revision plates rendered redundant by the production of Second War Revision sheets. At about the same time civil publication dates, and often the whole publication note, were deleted from both the remaining War Revisions with 'wide' margins and from the civil outline-and-water printings.

The outline-and-water mapping of Scotland was different again: all but two sheets (28 and 47) apparently derived direct from War Revision 1940, were in the 'narrow' style of margin, and retained the heading and GSGS publication notes. Though War Revision 1940 might have been made for the War Office, the OS evidently saw no reason why it should not use it for its own purposes. Any residual security objection must have been countered with each new air raid.

Although the outline-and-water printings met immediate needs, and anything more elaborate was impracticable, it is evident that the OS still wanted to make a better map available for civil use. MacLeod therefore suggested to the War Office that GSGS 3907 and 3908 be put on sale. This seems to have been agreed in principle in the late summer of 1942, but it was another six months or so before any were issued, and even then publication of Britain was only completed in the summer of 1944. The practical effect was that, even though everyone concerned recognised that it was a temporary makeshift, one map served for both military and civil purposes, in principle anyway.

In practice, the OS was anxious that the WOFFO Cassini grid should not be used more than necessary for civil purposes, as it was intended to be replaced by the Transverse Mercator metric grid after the war.[170] It was impracticable to do anything about the grid on Second War Revision, but its being on a separate plate on War Revision meant that it could readily be omitted. Thus around the turn of 1942-3 a number of War Revision sheets were printed in the normal way for military use, and as a run-on with the grid omitted for civil sale. The civil runs were often in odd quantities, such as 350 or 1450 or 1650, and a quantity-code such as '31,650' on a gridded sheet is a sure indicator that there was a civil run-on with the grid omitted.[171] Three short-run GSGS 3907 printings, all of 2000 copies in October 1943, of sheets 49, 106 and 111, seem to have been made purely so as to provide sales stock.

By the summer of 1943 stocks of some of the civil outline-and-water printings made in 1941-2 were evidently running low, and from September 1943 outline-and-water printings of some GSGS 3907 War Revision and Second War Revision sheets were made, usually in runs of 600 copies.[172] On the War Revision sheets the grid was of course omitted. Eleven Second War Revision sheets issued in outline are not known to have been issued in four-colour form.[173]

'Sales copies' were identified by either an overprint or a sticker, bottom right: this was 'calculated to prevent the soldiery offering their free issue for sale to the public'.[174] The stock placed on sale varied. At least some copies of Scotland 21 were of a 1939 printing, but this seems to be unique. Although for most sheets where Second War Revision had been printed this was made available, sometimes War Revision was sold instead. GSGS 3907 68 was made available successively in both War Revision and Second War Revision forms. The continuing use of older stock seems to have reflected its retention as 'valid' where change effected on Second War Revision was minimal, but it also enable the mapping to be offered mounted rather than paper flat.

---

[170] MacLeod to DMO&P, 16 October 1941, 35A in PRO OS 1/219; *A description of Ordnance Survey medium scale maps.* Chessington: Ordnance Survey, 1949, 17; cf DGOS to GSGS, 9 September 1942, 52A in PRO OS 1/219.

[171] Sheets printed with the grid plate omitted: GSGS 3907: 41, 44, 52, 61, 81, 82, 90, 92, 93, 100, 109, 143, 144, 146 (total 14); GSGS 3908: 1, 7, 8, 12-14, 17, 18, 25, 28-30, 33, 34, 37, 38, 44, 48-53, 55, 61, 62, 67, 68, 70-76, 78-81, 85, 87 (total 41). See also appendix 3.

[172] War Revision 1940: 118, 119, 138, 145 (total 4). Second War Revision 1940: 4, 7, 11, 19, 20, 25, 26, 29-31, 35-37, 41-43, 45, 49, 52, 54, 60-62, 71, 72, 80-85, 91-95, 97, 100, 102, 103, 105-107, 109-113, 115, 116, 120, 125 (total 52). See also appendix 3.

[173] Sheets 29, 41, 42, 52, 61, 62, 81, 82, 92, 100 and 109: 109 was certainly proved in four-colour form, and it is possible that some or all of the others were too. See also appendix 3.

[174] MacLeod to Clough, 19 February 1943: 64A in PRO OS 1/219.

As part of a stock-reduction policy, in April 1945 some 400,000 sheets were sent to the OS for overprinting as 'sales copies'.[175]

Sales copies of GSGS 3907 and 3908 are sometimes encountered in covers or 'packaging' supplied by retailers, varying from sectioning by Sifton Praed to a cursory rubber-stamp on the outside by the Youth Hostels Association. Two GSGS 3907 sheets are known to have been issued by the OS in covers: War Revision sheet 42 and Second War Revision sheet 36.[176] It is not known when or why this was done. A sales copy of Second War Revision sheet 66 is known in a 'narrow margin' printing mounted on cloth; this exception to the then usual practice suggests that the map was mounted for sale.[177]

With one definite exception, the sales copies of GSGS 3907 and 3908 were presumably withdrawn from sale as each sheet was replaced by post-war civil mapping, as discussed shortly. The exception was GSGS 3907 sheet 17, *Isle of Man*, which was only replaced by a civil equivalent in 1957. This sheet underwent a civil reprint with the Cassini grid in the late 1940s, and was republished with the Transverse Mercator grid in 1950 (Hi.10.M.14). The Standard Series Designation (SSD) M721 was originally allocated to the series by the United States Army Map Service (AMS), but never appeared on any printed sheets, and was subsequently reallocated to series GSGS 4136, discussed later.[178] M724 was allocated to GSGS 3908 and subsequently reallocated to GSGS 4639, discussed below.

8. *The New Popular Edition and GSGS 4620 and 4639*

The destruction of so much material in 1940 meant that completing the New Popular Edition (Hi.19) as originally intended would be a prolonged affair. In 1944-5 it was proposed to produce 64 sheets – 127-190 – of the New Popular in Fifth Edition style, and the remainder of England and Wales in 'provisional' form, using Popular Edition material with what was now called the National Grid superimposed. The intention was that the 'provisional' sheets would be replaced by redrawn sheets in Fifth Edition style at the earliest opportunity. In 1943 MacLeod had been succeeded as DGOS by Major General Geoffrey Cheetham, and Cheetham seems to have been quite fanatical in his determination to issue Transverse Mercator metric gridded mapping for Britain as soon as possible: 'these damned gridded maps, on which Cheetham & Co are barmy', as an OS Archaeology Officer called them. (He moved elsewhere shortly afterwards.)[179]

In the event, this programme proved to be too ambitious, and only fifty New Populars were published in Fifth Edition style. In principle, sheets for which there was partial Fifth-style cover were completed thus, but as there was only a small part of sheet 154 available, it was published using Popular Edition material, so that Cardiff and its environs were rather less up-to-date in the New Popular than they had been in Second War Revision. Sheet 154 and the other Popular-derived sheets were produced by photographing the original copper plates, sticking positive prints on enamelled aluminium foil down inside standard borders and margins on enamelled aluminium or zinc, and adding the grid and all available revision, which meant all revision since the original engraving between 1914 and 1925.

Precise details are lacking, but parallels with other series suggest that the grid would have been plotted on the base enamels at 10 km intervals, and similarly on the aluminium foils. The foils would then have been fitted to the base by, if necessary, 'shining up', i.e. making small cuts and joins so as to overcome distortions due to projection differences and slight changes of shape to the copper plates whilst in store. The result would have been in sympathy along the 10 km lines, but

---

[175] Survey Directorate, GHQ Home Forces, report for April 1945: copy in PRO WO 402/94.

[176] One copy of each is known in private collections.

[177] Copy in private collection.

[178] Information from lists of AMS series numbers on open access in the map room of US National Archives & Records Administration, College Park, Maryland. The allocation of these numbers presumably postdated the USA's entry into the war in December 1941.

[179] Roger Hellyer, 'The archaeological and historical maps of the Ordnance Survey', *Cartographic Journal* 26 (1989), 111-133, 120, quotation from Grimes to Crawford, 27 February 1946, in Crawford MSS, Bodleian Library, Oxford, 68 f.163.

discrepancies in gridding of up to 50 metres between the New Popular Edition and its successor suggest that the 1 km lines were drawn arbitrarily, giving a cosmetic rather than a rigorous result. It would suffice for giving locational references to 100 metres, but it would not be a permanent solution. The two surviving 'job files' for the New Popular Edition suggest that the usual procedure was first to fit to the 10 km grid lines, and then to draw the revision. The assembly would then be photographed, to produce an 'ungridded' negative. The 1 km grid lines would then be added, and the assembly photographed again, to produce a 'gridded' negative.[180]

For Scotland, things were more straightforward. The security enamels for the Popular Edition were revised and the grid added (Hi.18.C).[181] Publication of England and Wales was completed in December 1947 and of Scotland in April 1948. Cover of the Isle of Man continued to be provided by Second War Revision sheet 17, although back cover indexes for both the New Popular Edition and the gridded Scotland Popular suggested that it was published as New Popular sheet 87.

For both England and Wales and Scotland the colour schemes were modified, so that contours were printed separately in brown, and water tint was on a separate plate. This was perhaps an aesthetic improvement, but it may also have reflected the difficulties with orange on GSGS 3907 which had led to the adoption of the effective but assertive Air Force brown. In addition, on the 'provisional' sheets of England and Wales parish boundaries were shown in grey; these had been omitted from the Popular Edition, and drawing them (not very accurately) in continuous lines in grey was presumably quicker than using the usual convention of black dots. After all, the maps were 'provisional'. As a result Fifth Edition style and Scottish sheets needed seven printings, and the others eight. This apparent relative extravagance was offset by the OS having equipped extensively with two-colour presses during the war, so the increase in printings required was more modest in terms of workload than it might at first seem.[182] The maps were printed in much larger quantities than had been the practice before the war; this seems to have reflected increased demand for the maps, and may have been conditioned by the loss of pre-war printing statistics, and a relatively low marginal run-on cost for long runs. The luxuriance of the colour might perhaps have offset one problem, that generally the quality of the black plate was not up to the best pre-war standards. Some of the 'provisional' sheets derived from the Popular, such as 105, were extremely good, but some of those based on Fifth material which had had to be reconstituted from various security enamels, were much less so.

The New Popular Edition therefore resembled one of the schemes put forward by MacLeod in the autumn 1939, of reusing Popular material on New Popular sheet lines as a short-term expedient. With the end of the war there was no longer a security justification for suppressing the Transverse Mercator metric National Grid and, after all, it had been adopted not least because of its advantages for artillery purposes. However, it is apparent that the military did not wish to convert to the grid piecemeal, and an additional reason for delaying the change was the 'road revision' of 21 New Popular sheets in south-east England which began in 1946. This involved rather more than changes to roads, and included reconstituting some of the New Popular sheets made in 1939-41, to improve the quality of the black plate in particular.[183]

The military version of the New Popular Edition was designated GSGS 4620 and the gridded Scotland Popular was GSGS 4639 (Hi.18.M.6). The first GSGS 4620 sheets, of *Aldershot* and *Salisbury Plain*, were printed in 1946 (Hi.19.M.1). Both were evidently makeshifts, and,

[180] Richard Oliver, *A guide to the Ordnance Survey one-inch New Popular Edition.* London: Charles Close Society, 2000, 21-3; this in turn draws on job files for New Popular Edition sheets 160 and 190 now in the Charles Close Society Archives (Ordnance Survey deposit) in Cambridge University Library, and Geoffrey Cheetham, 'New medium-scale and small-scale maps of the Ordnance Survey', *Geographical Journal* 107 (1946), 211-24.

[181] Richard Oliver, *A guide to the Ordnance Survey one-inch Popular Edition of Scotland.* London: Charles Close Society, 2000, 12-13, drawing on Geoffrey Cheetham, 'New medium-scale and small-scale maps of the Ordnance Survey', *Geographical Journal* 107 (1946), 211-24.

[182] Report on production for 1:25,000 2nd Series, appendix A (item 26B in PRO OS 1/1192) gives ages of OS printing machines at February 1958.

[183] Richard Oliver, *A guide to the Ordnance Survey one-inch New Popular Edition.* London: Charles Close Society, 2000, 16, 20-21.

together with an adaptation for training purposes of the *New Forest* tourist sheet of 1938, are the closest approach to MacLeod's suggestion for Cassini-gridded mapping on New Popular sheet lines. They derived from New Popular material, but their colour scheme (including Air Force number 17 Brown) and marginalia (without legends) closely resembled the latest style of GSGS 3907. It seems to have been fortuitous that New Popular Edition sheets 169 and 167 conveniently covered these two areas, if a small extension necessary on *Salisbury Plain* be excepted.

In October 1947, printing began of GSGS 4620 in its standard form, carrying the 'National Grid (Military System)' (Hi.19.M.3). All 115 sheets were formally ordered on 25 October, although the printing of 15,000 copies of sheet 187 had been completed on 15 October.[184] GSGS 4620 and 4639 added a purple overprint plate to the colour scheme used for the civil map, thereby entailing eight or nine printings, but ensuring that, for the first time since the advent of the Modified British System map in 1931, the same basic design was used for both civil and military versions. The grid figures on the overprint plate were noticeably larger than they had been hitherto on GSGS mapping of Britain. The overprint also carried a note of the GSGS edition in the top margin (initially it was just 'War Office Edition'), cancelled the price note and the diagram of 100 km grid squares and their identifying numbers, substituted letters agreeable to the Modified British System, and added 'MILITARY SYSTEM' to the grid explanation in the footnotes. Trying to register the purple to the 1 km grid printed on the black plate could be troublesome (this may have been a consequence of 'shining up'), and many GSGS 4620 printings used black plates made from the 'ungridded' negatives. Cover of the Isle of Man was provided by a purple overprint which included changing the sheet number to 87. The actual order of printing seems to have been determined partly by the programme for reprinting the corresponding sheets of the civil map, so that where possible a sheet was printed simultaneously in civil and military versions.

The use of single letters for the 100 km grid squares on civil mapping, adopted in 1939 in a vain attempt to win over the War Office, had been abandoned by December 1944, in favour of numerical designations. This was in order to facilitate cross-reference between the gridded small-scale maps and the new mapping at 1:25,000 and larger scales which would depend on the grid for their numbering, and was undertaken after wide consultation. Brigadier Hotine of GSGS advocated using the military system, but Cheetham decided against this, on the grounds that national cover would mean the use of two letters rather than one, thus losing the advantage of greater concision, and the letters would be arbitrary as compared with references derived from full co-ordinates. On the other hand, suggestions from MacLeod, A.R. Hinks and Professor Frank Debenham ('three authorities independently') for what was in fact the system used in the Davidson Committee report, of abbreviated full co-ordinates, were also rejected, one reason being that it would mean totally different numbering for military and civil purposes, whereas the proposed system was nearly the same as the military system.[185]

The Catterick training map, first produced in 1925, was replaced in September 1948 by a sheet on National Grid sheet lines and in standard New Popular colours. This was printed in two versions, one for short-term use as GSGS 3907 with the obsolescent Cassini grid and the other as GSGS 4620 with the Transverse Mercator grid. In general, post-war manoeuvre, exercise and training maps were provided either by overprinting GSGS 4620 and 4639, or else by GSGS (Misc.) series sheets. These last were usually printed in modest quantities. Printed in larger quantities was GSGS 4620A, a layered version produced for the Staff College, of which there were thirteen sheets in south-central England (Hi.19.M.4). They were usually prepared by overprinting ordinary GSGS 4620 stock, but the final printings in 1959-62 were made specially; those of sheets 144, 157 and 169 in December 1962 were also the last official printings of the New Popular.

Printing of GSGS 4620 was completed in December 1949 and of GSGS 4639 in March 1950, and GSGS 3907 and 3908 each seem to have been superseded *en bloc* immediately afterwards. Some surplus civil New Popular sheets in south-east England, replaced by the republished 'roads revised' versions in 1947-9, were overprinted as GSGS 4620, with a note on the

---

[184] Ministry of Defence, 'Old Nick's cards'.
[185] Memorandum by Cheetham, 27 December 1944, 96A in PRO OS 1/111.

purple plate that they were for training purposes only. Sometimes the purple grid fitted the original black one very imperfectly. Most of the sheets covering Wales were printed during 1949 by the Survey Production Centre, RE (SPC), and are instantly recognisable by the lighter purple used for the grid plate. It is unclear why the work was transferred from the OS, whether because of OS capacity problems, or for some other reason. GSGS 4620 and 4639 were usually printed on 72 gsm Wet Strength paper, whereas civil small-scale coloured mapping was printed on 92 gsm Chart paper.[186] In 1951 a special sheet covering London was produced, covering an area 64 by 58 km (39.77 by 36.04 miles; map area 101.1 by 91.6 cm), designated GSGS 4692 (Hi.19.M.5): it was printed by the Hydrographic Department, possibly because neither Ordnance Survey nor Military Survey had a press large enough.[187]

At this point, history repeated itself: in mid-1949 GSGS 4620 and 4639 were still incomplete but they were obsolescent, in two respects. One of these was predictable: in 1947 the OS had decided that, rather than replace the 'provisional' New Popular (and, by implication, gridded Scotland Popular) with redrawn sheets in Fifth Edition style, a completely new start would be made: the Seventh Edition. A pilot sheet for the series was completed and circulated for comment in August 1949 and, after considerable modification to the design, the first published sheets went on sale, as the Seventh Series, in September 1952.

The other was perhaps less predictable: it concerned a difficulty which surely ought to have been recognised and considered earlier. On 7 June 1949 Brigadier J.C.T. Willis, of the Directorate of Military Survey, wrote to the OS that he was 'disturbed by the differences... as between Civil and Military practice', in the use of figures and letters. When civilians and the military worked alongside each other, 'different systems of grid reference will be in use by each. This will lead to confusion in peace, and possibly to calamity in war.' The military system could not be changed, 'tied as we are to the system in use in the United States and all Western Union Powers'. He asked for the OS's views on changing, or on producing a special edition for civil defence use, similar to the War Office edition.[188] Cheetham's successor, Major-General R.Ll. Brown, who had just taken office, wrote that he had raised the question some time before, but that it had been thought that the OS system had gone too far to be changed. 'It may have been thought then that the "short reference" being identical in both systems would meet the defence problem, but this is clearly not so.'[189] There would seem to have been a strange lack of communication between some departments somewhere: it is inconceivable that the Directorate of Military Survey (D Mil Svy), as GSGS had become, would not have been sent proofs of GSGS 4620 and 4639 as they were prepared, and objections ought surely to have been raised in 1947 rather than 1950. It is possible that the difficulty lay not in communications between Military Survey and OS – after all, there were regular interchanges of officers between the two – but within the War Office, and it may not be coincidence that the difficulty only arose after large quantities of GSGS 4620 had arrived, ready for issue. The fact remains that D Mil Svy did protest, and a new method of designating 100 km squares was adopted which retained the Modified British System principle of using letters rather than numbers: two letters were used, and appeared in marginal diagrams and explanations printed inside the covers of folded civil issues, but single letters were used on the map face.[190]

---

[186] DD Fin. to DMP, 21 January 1954, 20A in PRO OS 1/939.

[187] The largest OS presses at this time seem to have been Quad Crown size, allowing a maximum printed area of 43 by 32 inches; this was sufficient for a standard 1:625,000 sheet or a 1:63,360 tourist sheet covering a maximum area of 62 km by 49 km.

[188] Willis to DGOS, 7 June 1949, 142A in PRO OS 1/111.

[189] DG to DDG, 16 June 1949, minute 146 in PRO OS 1/111.

[190] The discussion is fully documented in PRO OS 1/111, minutes 145 onwards. Though an immediate reading of these might be taken to suggest that the system adopted was effectively enforced by the Americans, the history of the Modified British System suggests that it was British influence which was at the heart of the standard system adopted by the Western Powers. Unfortunately this file does not seem to have been studied as carefully as it might have been, and the date for the WO objection is misquoted in Richard Oliver, *A guide to the Ordnance Survey one-inch New Popular Edition*. London: Charles Close Society, 2000, 8-10, and Richard Oliver, 'The evolution of the Ordnance Survey National Grid', *Sheetlines* 43 (1995), 25-46.

The change in practice, effected on all OS gridded mapping as it was reprinted or republished from about the spring of 1951 onwards, was paralleled by the republication of GSGS 4620 in a 'Second Edition'. The first sheet (177) was printed in May 1951; by January 1953 85 sheets had been republished on New Popular bases. The only justification for the operation would appear to be the refashioning of the grid, but as the changing had been by the OS rather than the War Office, it is not easy to see even that as being applicable. Further production of second editions of GSGS 4620 on New Popular bases effectively ceased in 1953; publication of new editions continued when Seventh Series bases were substituted, and new editions were prepared of a few New Populars in the later 1950s.[191]

It is noticeable that no GSGS 4639 sheets were issued in a second edition (though the reprinting of sheets 74 and 80 in 1953 have many of the characteristics of a Second Edition in GSGS 4620) and, indeed, very few were reprinted. From the early 1950s onwards surplus civil stocks of the New Popular and Scotland Popular, superseded by the Seventh Series, were overprinted for military use. They are often readily identifiable both by the imperfect register of the purple plate with the black, by the heavier weight paper used for civilian issues, and by odd quantities in the print-runs, e.g. 2800 or 13,100.

Around 1951, apparently as a by-product of various NATO agreements on map standardisation, the use of 'series' and 'edition' was rationalised. The practical effect was that each *series* (e.g. GSGS 4620) would be subdivided into *sheets* (e.g. sheet 176) which would be subdivided into *editions* (e.g. 2nd Edition). From 1951 'refer to' boxes appeared on new printings, embodying the new system. As a result of this the nascent one-inch Seventh Edition became the Seventh Series. A further development took place in 1957, when NATO Standard Series Designations (SSDs) were introduced; in fact, they were a development of the AMS SSDs, which predated the formation of NATO in 1949. GSGS 4620 became M722; GSGS 4639 was allocated M724, but became obsolete before any sheet was printed with this. GSGS and GSGS (Misc.) series numbers were retained for training maps and others which were not NATO standard series. The allocation of GSGS edition numbers did not keep in step with OS edition changes, as alterations made by the OS on reprints were often not regarded by D Mil Svy as justifying a new GSGS edition with, potentially, wholesale replacement of existing stocks.

9. *The Seventh Series and M722*[192]

Whereas the War Office had apparently often been in no great hurry in the past to obtain its version of the latest generation of the one-inch, printing of the military edition of the Seventh Series (Hi.20.M.1) began in May 1952, some four months before the first civil sheets went on sale, though some two months after the first had been printed. This activity can be related directly to the programme of republishing GSGS 4620 in Second Editions. Once again, the Seventh Series (Hi.20) had elements of early obsolescence about it which were, paradoxically, partly the result of the great care which had been taken in its design. The first 38 sheets to be produced had hand-written lettering reminiscent of the Scotland Popular. Experiments in 1950-1 resulted in the adoption of photo-typesetting and a daring but effective combination of Times Roman and Gill Sans, but the first sheet in the new style only appeared in January 1954. Though intended as a fresh start for the one-inch map, the Seventh Series always lacked overall uniformity.

The pilot sheet of 1949 had been in eight colours; the definitive style evolved in 1951 used ten. In 1938-9 MacLeod had devised an effective five-colour scheme for the New Popular. One of the extra colours in the definitive Seventh Series scheme was brown for B-roads, which was an innovation, but the others were in the nature of clarification rather than suppliers of additional

---

[191] Sheets published in Second Edition-GSGS: 71, 82, 84, 86, 88, 90-93, 95-119, 122-126, 130-137, 143, 144, 147-149, 155-187, 189-190; in 'Edition-3 GSGS': 167, 179, 187; in 'Edition 4-GSGS': 187. Sheets 137 and 149 were printed in Second Edition in September 1953, and sheets 163 and 164 in 1957-8: in 1954-5 sheets 64, 75, 85, 146, 150 and 188 were printed in 1954-5 as 'Edition 1-GSGS' with modified grid.
[192] For a more detailed account of the Seventh Series see Richard Oliver, *A guide to the Ordnance Survey one-inch Seventh Series*. London: Charles Close Society, 2004. The job files for the civil printings are preserved complete in the Charles Close Society Archives (Ordnance Survey deposit) in Cambridge University Library.

information. There were two brown printings, for contours and B-roads, two blue printings, solid for outline and names and a tint for infill, and three grey printings, for the grid, building infill and tree symbols. The end result was unquestionably excellent, but with only one or two more printings Close had produced the Killarney style, and with three less Winterbotham had managed the Fifth Relief. It may be questioned whether such a style would have been adopted had not the OS been so well-equipped with two-colour presses. The first military printings were more economical, being in eight colours: the grid was on the black plate, vegetation symbols were omitted, and grid figures were on the dark blue water plate.

The expansiveness of the ten-colour scheme did not go unremarked, and in 1952 experiments were made with printing the Seventh Series in six colours: the B-roads and contours were combined in a single brown printing, the water tint was replaced by screened blue added to the water-outline plate, the grid was in black on the outline plate, and the tree symbols and building infills were in screened black. (There were also two seven-colour printings, one with grey grid, second class roads screened on the red plate, and one with grey grid and contours and second class roads combined.)[193] The result was a perfectly legible map, but the available screens were still very coarse, and the result compared unfavourably in delicacy with the ten-colour design, at any rate for civil use. At the same time the War Office asked for six-colour experiments, and the result rejected for civil use was more than acceptable for military printings. With the omission of the tree symbols, which were not regarded by the military as essential, and the transfer of the grid figures to the red plate, the six-colour scheme was adopted for military printings from October 1952 onwards, starting with sheet 139. By this time the OS had a three-colour machine, so a six-colour map could be printed in only two passes.[194] As a result only five sheets (141, 142, 151, 152, 154), were printed in the eight-colour scheme. Once again the civil and military versions of the one-inch exhibited notable differences in style.

Reduction of the number of printings for the civil Seventh Series was investigated again early in 1961. In 1959-60, demand for the one-inch had been such that OS presses had been under considerable pressure, and some printing was farmed out to the Hydrographic Department and, for one sheet, to a civil firm. Some civilian printing, notably of the new half-inch Second Series, was simply deferred. Much of the capacity problem could have been readily solved if the Seventh Series, which accounted for about two-thirds of OS colour printing, could be printed in fewer than ten colours. Although in 1958 the OS had made a striking job of the *North York Moors* tourist sheet in twelve colours, which included layers and hill-shading, subsequent tourist and other layered mapping was less lavish: for example, the half-inch Second Series was layered, but only needed nine printings. An obvious economy was to print the grid in black, either solid (as on the half-inch) or rouletted (as on one-inch tourist maps), and to screen the building infill, and this was done. By 1960 much finer screens were available than had been a decade earlier, and a six-colour Seventh Series, comparable with the ten-colour one, was a likely proposition. In February 1961 Seventh Series sheet 187 was experimentally printed in six colours, following the scheme tried in 1952, except that the grid was rouletted and the screening on the black and blue plates was much finer.[195] The result was a success, and the War Office thought it 'most interesting', but, as in 1939, asked for a solid rather than a rouletted grid.[196] M722 (as GSGS 4620 had become in 1958) sheet 184 was printed in April using the proposed colour-scheme to test whether the finer stipples would stand up to a long run.[197] As the War Office still needed grid figures on the map face, and as it was usual to print black and red together on the first two passes, to facilitate joint civil-military printing the OS investigated, using sheet 163, the possibility of printing the grid in green, brown, blue or yellow;

---

[193] Solid red for first-class roads and screened or broken red for second-class roads was used by Bartholomew on some printings of their half-inch map in the late 1940s.
[194] See PRO OS 1/939: the experimental printings are at 30A.
[195] Sheet 187 was printed before 10 February 1961: example at 94A in PRO OS 1/939.
[196] Directorate of Military Survey to DGOS, 20 February 1961, 97A in PRO OS 1/939.
[197] OS to DMS, 14 March, and DMS to OS, 23 March 1961, 101A and 102A in PRO OS 1/939.

the experiments merely proved the impracticability of all these.[198] At about the same time, in July 1961, M722 sheet 169 was printed in what would prove to be the definitive six-colour scheme, similar to the experimental printing of sheet 187 except that the grid was solid rather than rouletted, and, being a military sheet, the grid numbers were on the red plate. The first six-colour civil sheet to be printed was 118, in November 1961. Some Seventh Series sheets continued to be reprinted from existing plates in ten colours into 1964, and in August 1962 M722 sheet 53 was printed in ten colours; it is not known why, but it might have been less trouble to reuse serviceable plates than make up a new set. Also, a number of M722 sheets were printed in the old six-colour scheme during 1962, again presumably because serviceable plates were available.

The initial publication of the civil version of the Seventh Series was completed in July 1961. By that time full revision had begun, and several sheets had already been republished. So far, the military version had only patchily replaced New Popular mapping, and the adoption of the new six-colour scheme for both civil and military mapping meant that only 121 of the 190 sheets were printed in the military six-colour style.[199] Whereas up to January 1953 there had been a vigorous programme of printing Second Editions of GSGS 4620, regardless of the stock position of individual sheets, thereafter printing only appears to have been undertaken when stock levels were low enough to justify this. As a result, sheets were only republished using Seventh Series material when stock replenishment was called for. Thus GSGS 4620 sheet 115, which was printed in a Second Edition on a New Popular base in June 1952 and in a Third Edition on a Seventh Series base in January 1953, is very much an exception.

The need for stock based on Seventh Series material was lessened for many sheets by the practice, already noted, of overprinting surplus civil stocks. (An alternative explanation is that there was a deliberate policy of overstocking the civil map in order to provide a reserve which could be overprinted in an emergency, but there is no documentary evidence which might support this. If such a policy really had been in operation one might expect the spatial distribution and actual quantities of overprinted civil stock to provide more compelling evidence.) Whilst these overprintings were sometimes of modest residual stocks superseded by the Seventh Series, others seem to have been the result of over-optimistic ordering of first printings. Thus in January 1952, 5,500 copies of the nominal 20,000 printed in December 1946 of sheet 105 were converted to GSGS 4620 by overprinting. Three months later 13,100 copies of two civil printings of sheet 153 were overprinted. In at least one instance overprinting of what seemed to be surplus civil stock may have been premature, as after 14,000 copies of sheet 146 had been overprinted in January 1952, another civil printing was made in 1953, which seems to have sold modestly, and itself provided more surplus stock for overprinting in September 1955. Sometimes – e.g. on sheets 99 and 113 – the overprinted stock retained the designation War Office Edition, though the Second Edition had been printed some time before; the policy seems to have been to have retain War Office Edition for those sheets using the earlier form of National Grid.[200] Few if any overprintings for GSGS 4620 were made after 1957, partly because most of the new Seventh Series publication in 1956-9 was in Scotland (some Scotland Populars were overprinted for GSGS 4639 in 1957-60, but compared with GSGS 4620 they were comparatively few), and partly because the remaining New Populars were in southern England where they sold well anyway, with the last civil reprinting as late as the turn of 1960-61. If some civil New Populars were evidently printed in excessive quantities, so too probably were some GSGS 4620, largely as a consequence of the production of Second Editions in 1951-3. In July 1952 9000 copies of sheet 131 were overprinted as War Office Edition and 11,000 more were newly printed as Second Edition. There were a few instances – e.g. sheets 90, 93 and 153 – where sheets of two civil printings were overprinted in one operation, and instances where a large surplus civil stock was overprinted either almost simultaneously with or actually after the

---

[198] DMP to DDSS, 8 May 1961, minute 103, and specimens of 163 with blue, brown and green grids (116D-F) in PRO OS 1/939.

[199] Sheets 6, 7, 9-17, 19-22, 24-31, 33, 35, 36, 39, 41-48, 64, 70-75, 77-83, 86, 90-94, 98-103, 107-113, 115-131, 135-145, 148-160, 164-168, 170, 173, 175, 176,178, 183, 190.

[200] Sheet 114 seems to be an exception to this. Copies of sheets 146, printing 1307, and 153, printing 1250, seem to be amongst the least common of New Populars to be met with.

printing of a replacement using the Seventh Series, e.g. sheets 84 and 92 in 1955-6. (It may be to the point that some copies of overprinted sheets were stamped as for CCF (Combined Cadet Force) or ATC (Air Training Corps) use only.) There were also some instances, e.g. sheet 126 in June 1955, where there was a new large military printing of GSGS 4620 retaining the New Popular base close to or even after the publication of the equivalent Seventh Series civil sheet. In at least two instances the Seventh Series replacement was printed as soon as the civil map was ready, these being sheet 160 in February 1960 and sheet 105 in December 1961. Sheet 105 was the first Seventh Series sheet to be printed simultaneously for both civil and military stock, but the latter was printed in two batches, 3000 copies simultaneously with the civil version in December 1961 and 17,000 more as a separate run in February 1962, suggesting that stock was needed in a hurry to replenish that based on the New Popular which had been printed in January 1953. Only one instance is known of a ten-colour civil Seventh Series sheet being overprinted in M722, and that was the A/* sheet 172 in December 1961. As printed, this showed the new M.20 passing over the A.249 when it should have passed under; the civil stock was replaced by A/*/, which corrected the error, and the remaining stock of A/* was overprinted as M722, with a marginal note drawing attention to the error. One printing of sheet 158 was used for the only printing of GSGS 4620A to use a Seventh series base.

As a result of large stocks produced of Second Editions in 1951-3 and overprinting civil stock, some of the last GSGS 4620 sheets based on the New Popular to be replaced by M722 based on the Seventh were some of the most surprising, considering the likelihood of change on the ground: 96 *Leeds and Bradford* in August 1962 and 95 *Blackburn* and 147 *Bedford and Luton* in January 1963. The last two were the last New Populars to be superseded. The replacement of GSGS 4639 was completed in February 1963 with the printing of the four M722 sheets covering Shetland. However, at this time the military were also using the 1:25,000 (originally GSGS 4627, later M821), and as this incorporated revision made from 1947 onwards for the Seventh Series, this mapping was often more up to date than was GSGS 4620.

In 1960 the London special sheet, GSGS 4692, was replaced by another on different sheet lines, covering 61 by 58 km, and designated M725 (Hi.20.M.4). Like its predecessor, it was printed by the Hydrographic Department. In 1967 the OS produced a civil special one-inch sheet covering Greater London (Hi.20.11), which had become a local government unit in 1965: this covered an area 64 by 55 km, and was the largest sheet published by the OS. Presumably it had acquired a larger press since 1960. This map was used as a base for two further editions of M725.

10. *The six-colour Seventh Series: towards a common-specification map*

In 1960 the War Office reviewed its map policy, with a view to ensuring that up-to-date mapping was available at the one-inch and 1:25,000 scales, and this meant keeping M722 printings broadly in step with the civil map.[201] The adoption of a common six-colour scheme (the grid figures apart) for the military and civil versions would have facilitated this, though it is unclear whether this was realised in 1960-61 when the experiment with sheet 187 was put in hand. The practical outcome was that it was now possible to make 'solo' and 'joint' printings of the Seventh Series, with only either a substitution of red plates or a red overprint necessary for M722. There is some evidence from the 'job files' for the civil sheets that completely separate sets of plates were made; this would have been essential when stock was printed either by SPC or, as with a number of sheets in 1966, by the British Army of the Rhine (BAOR). There are frequent references to M722 printings in the 'job files' for the civil map and in internal Military Survey documents, but from the administrative point of view a complete record was apparently not regarded as particularly important. It is possible that some apparently solo military printings were in fact overprinting of surplus civil stock. One instance where this definitely took place concerned sheet 167, the B edition of which, as printed in April 1971, showed certain public rights of way across the live firing ranges around Imber; the stock was hastily withdrawn from sale, and overprinted for M722. There are occasional examples of military printings preceding the civil equivalent: a notable instance is sheet 108,

---

[201] Directorate of Military Survey to OS and reply, 1 June and 12 July 1960, 4A and 8A in PRO OS 1/776.

printed in M722 in July 1965, with the public rights of way information omitted, this being included when the civil version was published in December.

The M722 version of the mapping as printed up to the mid-1960s retained the large grid figures on the map face inherited from GSGS 4620, and a few sheets had additional quirks on the red plate applied in error, such as National Grid geodetic information notionally applicable to the Universal Transverse Mercator (UTM) Grid, which had been adopted as a NATO standard in 1953, though over fifty years later it has not got beyond a few training maps in Britain. In February 1966 much smaller grid figures on the map face were introduced, and M722 thereby moved still closer to the civil map.

However, though closer, the military and civil versions remained distinct in 1969, when the OS announced a metrication programme, and they were no closer in 1971 when work began on a 1:50,000 series, laid out in 204 sheets, each covering an area 40 kilometres square. In fact, once again, the Seventh Series had been implicitly obsolescent almost as soon as it was completed. In 1962, as a consequence of the United Kingdom's application to join what was then called the European Economic Community, with the expected necessity of adopting metric units, the OS investigated metrication, though without immediate results. In 1963 D Mil Svy both enlarged the military editions of six Seventh Series sheets (166-168, 178-180) to 1:50,000 (GSGS (Misc.) 1999) and reduced them to 1:100,000 (GSGS (Misc.) 2000) (Hi.20.M.1),[202] and the 1:50,000 enlargements were used by the OS in 1966-7 to construct mock-ups of possible 1:50,000 sheets. In 1967-8 the OS considered publishing a 1:50,000 tourist sheet of Oxford, partly because there might be a market, and partly so as to test public reaction to the scale. In the event this project did not go ahead, as there was felt to be little potential sales justification.[203] By 1969 the OS was drawing a small 1:50,000 specimen section, but it also toyed at this time with 1:62,500, 1:66,667, 1:75,000 and 1:100,000 as alternatives to the one-inch (Hi.20.8).[204]

11. *The 1:50,000, series M726, and the end of separate publication*[205]

A problem with the Seventh Series reproduction material was that the copying of negatives and positives inherent in the revision process led to a gradual loss of quality, and by about 1970 it was apparent that some of the Seventh Series sheets would have to be redrawn sooner rather than later. There was therefore a good long-term justification for replacing the one-inch, based on glass and pen-drawing, with a 1:50,000 based on plastic materials and scribing. However, the time needed to draw the new map meant that, in order to minimise the time taken to change over from the one-inch to the 1:50,000, it would be necessary initially to produce most of the sheets of the latter by photo-enlarging one-inch material and reassembling it on the new sheet lines: all rather reminiscent of the conversion of the Fifth Edition to the New Popular Edition. The 1:50,000 was published in two blocks, sheets 102-204 on 7 March 1974 and sheets 1-101 on 20 February 1976 (Hi.21). Three

[202] David Forrest, 'GSGS Misc Series 1999 and 2000', *Sheetlines* 52 (1998), 17-20. These sheets are listed in section 8, supplement 2.

[203] For the early work on developing the 1:50,000, in 1966-70, see PRO OS 1/1368.

[204] There is a copy of the redrawn 1:50,000 section in the CCS Archives (OS deposit): for a description and a monochrome extract see Bill Henwood, 'The Luton experiment', *Sheetlines* 63 (2002), 8-10.

[205] OS Office Notice 175/71: copy in CCS Archives (OS deposit). As yet there is no good study of the 1:50,000 and, unless there is a change of access to official information, a thorough study of it will, as with the Seventh Series, have to wait until the map itself is long obsolete. There are overlapping accounts of its early development in G.A. Hardy, 'The Ordnance Survey 1:50,000 map series', *Geographical Journal* 140 (1974), 275-83, and J.G. Price, 'A review of the design and production factors for the Ordnance Survey 1:50,000 map series', *Cartographic Journal* 12 (1975), 22-9; for later history see Richard Oliver, 'Twenty years of the Ordnance Survey 1:50,000 map', *Sheetlines* 39 (1994), 6-19, which includes a summary list of editions. In recent years there have been several articles in *Sheetlines* commenting on aspects of the map (*e.g.* David Kimber, 'Landranger sheet 139 *Birmingham and Wolverhampton*', *Sheetlines* 52 (1998), 14-17), but these are no substitute for a comprehensive historical overview. The CCS Archives (OS deposit) includes most of the job files for the First Series, and a copy of 'Report on the development of the 1:50,000 series', which includes material excluded from the Hardy and Price articles. The Public Record Office probably contains a growing number of OS policy files, but these will be closed under the 'thirty year rule'.

sheets of the first block and forty-eight of the second were published from the start as 'Second Series', wholly redrawn, except sometimes for the contours, which were relabelled imperial contours. Most of these sheets were printed simultaneously in a civil edition and as a military edition, M726 (Hi.21.A.6, 21.B.11), and sheets 100-190 of M722 were declared obsolete in July 1974.[206] The last M722 printing was sheet 60, in a run of 1000 copies, in September 1975; the last civil Seventh Series printing was 1026 copies of sheet 49 on 27 November 1975. Like M722 in its later years, M726 was very similar to its civil counterpart. The 1:50,000 First Series, as the enlarged sheets were termed, followed the colour scheme of the Second Series, which included the grid in blue, and M726 had blue grid figures on the map face. The 1:50,000 was initially a six-colour-series, but late in 1977 it started to be printed in four process colours.

In the spring of 1978, a review committee to investigate the OS was appointed under the chairmanship of Sir David Serpell, and it is clear from passages in the evidence presented to the Serpell Committee, that a decision in principle, to merge the civil and military versions of the 1:50,000, had recently been taken, with a view to production economies. The evidence also discloses that at this time the military were paying part of the field revision and drawing costs for the 1:50,000 Second Series.[207] However, it was only in the summer of 1980 that a number of 1:50,000 sheets were put on sale with elements of the dual civil-military specification, to test public reaction.[208] As well as grid figures on the map face, which were reduced in numbers in areas of close detail, these included the use of pure magenta for roads and contours instead of synthetic red and brown. The grid figures on the map face were a decided improvement for that minority of the public which uses the grid, and a similar innovation was made on the 1:25,000 Second Series shortly afterwards. Public reaction was presumably not such as to discourage carrying the scheme forward, and dual civil-military production began as standard late in 1981, though complete merger of civil and military printing was only achieved in 1987. The Second Series was completed in 1988 as an analogue scribed map, but from 1994 it was produced from raster scans, which had the effect of arresting deterioration of the reproduction materials, and enabling some of the advantages of digital production.

It might be supposed that the story has come full circle: but not quite. In about 1976 GSGS 5215, a version of M726 overprinted in purple with power lines and other overhead obstructions, began to appear, as did other special purpose overprints.[209] GSGS 5215 continues to be produced by overprinting ordinary dual civil-military stock, and provides, like GSGS 3907, 3908, 4620 and 4639, complete cover of Britain, distinct from the civil map. The marriage of civil and military on the 1:50,000 seems to be as much of convenience and economy as anything else: the military would prefer the UTM grid, and graticule sheet lines, amongst other things, and a few sheets overprinted with the UTM grid have been printed for training purposes. The 1:50,000 in its present form is certainly not ideal for military purposes: 'the... sheet size is generally considered too big for Army operational purposes and... the OS spheroid, grid and datum have all been judged inappropriate in the modern era of global positioning'.[210] Against this, the military appear to exercise some influence over 1:50,000 design: at the British Cartographic Society Symposium in 2001 someone speaking in defence of the OS said that 1:50,000 design was constrained by what was acceptable to the military, to which someone else in the audience replied that with 'modern technology' it ought to be possible to produce a separate military version. One reason why this has not yet come about may be the production method for the 1:50,000, which has stopped short of a vector database which might generate a separate military 1:50,000. However, it is expected that

[206] Information from Product Information Branch card index held by DGC.

[207] Ordnance Survey Review Committee, 1979 (especially evidence, volume VI, RC 301): unpublished: copy in British Library, Map Library, Maps 207.e.1.

[208] Careful attention to dates will show that those who might wish to see the joint civil-military 1:50,000 as a symbol of the rightward, more militaristic policies of the Conservative government which took office in May 1979 will have to be a little more ingenious.

[209] Roger Hellyer, *Ordnance Survey small-scale maps indexes: 1801-1998*. Kerry: David Archer, 1999, 68.

[210] Ron Blake, 'Landranger study day in Derby, 4 July 1998', *Sheetlines* 52 (1998), 3-4.

production of the 1:50,000 direct from the 'Landline' large-scale database will begin in 2004, and this may have the effect of reopening the question of the joint civil-military policy.

12. *Interlude: a question of copyright*

At this point it is convenient to consider the question of how far the maps which are the subject both of this essay and of this book are 'Ordnance Survey' and how far they are 'War Office' (and its divisions and successors). An answer of sorts is provided by correspondence in January 1931 between Winterbotham (DGOS) and MacLeod (then head of GSGS). The question seems to have arisen because of the inclusion of GSGS series mapping in HMSO publications. MacLeod was quite definite on the point: 'The gridded 1-inch in conformity with principles said to have been laid down by yourself when sitting in this chair, is *our* publication though the O.S. are the actual printers.'[211] Winterbotham noted that the map consisted of (a) the OS 1-inch, 'surveyed, drawn, plotted & printed by OS', and (b) 'A grid overprinted, which – though for W.O. use – is calculated, drawn & printed by *O.S.*', and replied rather more fully to MacLeod:

'With regard to the gridded 1-inch, it is true that I regarded it as a War Office map for certain purposes but not for all. For example I was quite definite that I did not want the map sold in the normal way through Ordnance Survey agents. We in the War Office, do you see, paid for the printing and for the overprinting of a particular grid, but of course I never put forward any claim to being technically responsible for the survey, or for its drawing, or for its reproduction.

'... as it at present stands the grid may be said to number amongst its ancestors the pre-war system of squaring the French Lambert grid, the allied agreement in Paris (1917) and the subsequent efforts of myself and Learmont the Gunner, to evolve something a little more modern. In this mixed parentage it is doubtful whether the Ordnance Survey strain is less or greater than that of the Geographical Section, but if it come back to personality I think both you and I may claim, shall we say, an equal interest. Outsiders, however, might justifiably say that we have never had any patent about this, and that all sorts of grids used by Tom, Dick and Harry, are very similar. I do not think, then, that the War Office should, and I am sure they do not mean to claim anything particularly inviolable about the British Modified pattern. Whereas the Ordnance Survey can maintain that the competition for its cutting lines, the actual draughtsmanship, its rights upon the matter, and its subsequent printing, were all matters in which our draughtsmen were involved. If the discussion were one between you and me I would not waste a moment upon it because I should not care a bit who had the honour or glory, but if the discussion is between the Stationery Office and the Ordnance Survey on the matter of copyright then I dig my toes in and say, our workmanship, or right to produce.'[212]

MacLeod was unconvinced: 'It seems to me that, for copyright, the Gridded 1" should be regarded as a W.O. publication only printed by you on War Office instructions.'[213] The matter does not seem to have been pursued further by the two men, at any rate on official record, but in October Colonel G.S.C. Cooke wrote to the War Office that the important point was that whereas the War Office had paid for the 1:20,000 and 1:25,000 series (GSGS 2748 and GSGS 3906), the survey they were based on was paid for by the OS, and therefore should not be sold without OS sanction, as they would be in competition.

13. *Ireland: the treaty ports and GSGS 3917*

Although the publication of a coloured one-inch of Ireland in 1902-6 (Hi.24) suggests a measure of assimilation of British and Irish practice, the two began to diverge almost immediately. An Irish

---

[211] MacLeod to Winterbotham, 13 January 1931, item 2A in PRO OS 1/540.
[212] n.d. note by Winterbotham and Winterbotham to MacLeod, 21 January 1931, item 3A in PRO OS 1/540.
[213] MacLeod to Winterbotham, 29 January 1931, item 4A in PRO OS 1/540.

one-inch Large Sheet Series was proposed in 1906, and investigated again in 1909 and 1913, at the time that *Killarney* was published, but all that came of it was the publication, around 1918, of three sheets coloured in 'Killarney' style: 16/17, *Belfast,* 80, *Cork,* and a *Dublin* district sheet (Hi.26).[214] A Third Edition (Hi.25) was published in outline between 1909 and 1917, based on field revision of 1908-14, but this only covered less than two-thirds of Ireland when it was abandoned, and only very limited use of it was made as a basis for coloured mapping. The remainder, including *Dublin*, was covered only by the one-inch, revised between 1898 and 1901 (Hi.23). During World War I a 'provisional edition' for military purposes only of the Irish small-sheet series (SSS) was produced, with outline in black and contours in red (Hi.25.5). Only a few sheets of this series are known (there is no 'archive set' anywhere), and it is unclear whether it covered the whole of Ireland. The contouring of Ireland seems to have been completed by 1914, but on many one-inch sheets they were only engraved somewhat later. In 1911, publication of a half-inch map of Ireland had begun (Hi.39): it was completed in 1918, and may have helped reduce the need for a one-inch. The significant thing about the 'provisional edition' is that, although the sheets bear prices, the series appears to have been created specifically as a separate military series; as such, it has no parallel in the contemporary one-inch in England, and only a qualified one in the half-inch training maps.

The Treaty of 6 December 1921 divided Ireland into the Free State, of twenty-six counties which henceforth was outside the United Kingdom, though until 1949 still a Dominion within the British Commonwealth, and Northern Ireland, of six northern counties, part of the United Kingdom but with its own parliament. The United Kingdom retained three 'treaty ports', at Lough Swilly (Lenan Head and Dunree Head), Bear (or Bere) Island in Bantry Bay, and at Queenstown (soon to revert to its pre-1849 name of Cobh). Despite the grandiose description of these as 'naval bases', they were really just sheltered anchorages, although Queenstown had proved useful as a base for anti-submarine operations in the war.[215] Like many other defence establishments, they seemed to have been garrisoned and maintained in a minimal way after 1921.

Separate Ordnance Survey departments were set up for both Northern Ireland (effective on 1 January 1922) and the Free State (effective on 1 April 1922). The Free State demanded and got all the documents, plates, equipment and other articles to which it was entitled, but some of the material for Northern Ireland, including the reproduction materials for the small-scale mapping, remained at Southampton.[216] Whilst documentary proof is lacking, it may be strongly suspected, in the light of subsequent events, that the OS duplicated all the small-scale material before handing it over to the Free State, and also, such larger-scale material as might be useful, such as six-inch mapping of the treaty-port areas.[217]

If the finer details of the British System-gridded military edition of the one-inch Popular in Great Britain in the 1920s are still not ideally clear, and many sheets have yet to be located, they are nonetheless a straightforward subject as compared with their counterparts in Ireland. In 1924-5, the OS produced on behalf of GSGS a quarter-inch map of *North East Ireland*, known only from its republication as GSGS 3942 in 1933 (Hi.73.M.1), and one-inch sheets of *Londonderry* (possibly for civil use), *Bantry Bay*, and *Cork*. No copies of these survive, and they are known only from the republished versions of 1932-3, to be discussed shortly. The *Cork* sheet, which included 'Queenstown', was the outline and contour plate (but not water) of the large sheet 80, dated 1918. The *Londonderry* sheet, with a map area of 28 by 19 inches (71.1 by 48.3 cm), was laid out on sheet lines parallel to those of the Irish SSS; its eastern sheet line corresponded to the eastern sheet line of SSS 6, 12 and 18. The *Bantry Bay* sheet was a mixture of SSS sheet lines on the east, but grid sheet lines on the other sides. As the Lough Swilly naval base lay outside the *Londonderry*

---

[214] J.H. Andrews, *A paper landscape: the Ordnance Survey in nineteenth-century Ireland.* Oxford University Press, 1975, 294, citing OS of Ireland files OSL 10559, 12186 and 15253.

[215] Joseph T. Carroll, *Ireland in the war years.* Newton Abbot: David & Charles, 1975, 25.

[216] J.H. Andrews, *A paper landscape: the Ordnance Survey in nineteenth-century Ireland.* Oxford University Press, 1975, 295-6. For materials at Southampton see papers in PRO OS 1/648.

[217] Indicative of this is series GSGS 3936, being Donegal sheets 9 and 16, and Cork parts sheets 115/128, 116/129, printed with 'secret' overprint at the War Office, September 1932: copy in British Library Map Library, Maps MOD.

sheet it is possible that a one-inch sheet for this was produced for this area as well; if the procedure was the same as later, then material for sheet 1/5 of the coloured SSS would have been used.

The layout of the sheet lines of all of these suggests the bare minimum of effort, particularly for *Cork*, which reused existing material. *Bantry Bay* suggests the clear influence of the policy, adopted by 1925, of laying out future one-inch military sheets on grid sheet lines, but it was evidently less trouble to retain the SSS sheet lines on the east of the map. *Londonderry* bears a note 'Ordnance Survey 1924', and the nearest parallel in Britain may be *Blandford*, i.e. a map produced exclusively for military use, but still on 'civil' sheet lines. (Another possibility is that *Londonderry* was originally prepared for some civil purpose, and only adapted for military use later.) If the republished versions of these sheets of 1932-3 are a guide, then both *Cork* and *Bantry Bay* would have been black with grid in purple, but it is unclear whether the 1924 version of *Londonderry* was in this style as well.[218]

It is possible that there was also a British System-gridded version of the 1918 *Belfast* sheet, as the republished version of this sheet of 1932 bears a military magnetic variation diagram dated 1927, of a type which on GSGS 3907 and 3908 is a reliable indicator of a printing at about the time that the diagram is dated.[219] Should such a printing ever be found it would, of course, answer the question of what colour-scheme was used.

The adoption of the Modified British System grid and the creation of GSGS 3907 and 3908 in Great Britain had their parallels in Ireland. Two Irish series were created: GSGS 3917 for Northern Ireland (Hi.27), and GSGS 3943 for the two 'treaty port' sheets in the south (Hi.25.M.2, 26.M.2). The latter, though only printed in 1934, may conveniently be dealt with first. Both sheets were printed in black, with the Modified British System grid added in purple. Neither is known to have been reprinted, and from April 1938 there was perhaps little justification in maintaining them, as the three 'treaty ports' were relinquished to the Free State, in the hope that this move would help reconcile southern opinion to continued partition in the north. (It didn't.) By this time 'the shore installations were regarded as primitive and totally inadequate for a modern fleet', and whereas in 1921 there was a school of British military thought that one day France might once more be an enemy, and therefore the treaty ports would be well situated, by 1938 it was obvious that the coming enemy was Germany, the ports seemed irrelevant, and the service chiefs were quite content to relinquish them.[220]

GSGS 3917 is, in relation to its few sheets, remarkably complicated: 'a rag-bag of a map series'.[221] Its constituent sheets fall into two groups, five issued in 1932 and sixteen more issued in 1934. The five 1932 sheets were *Armagh*, *Belfast*, *County Down S.E.*, *Londonderry* and *Lough Swilly*. *Belfast* was the most straightforward, being a derivative from the 1918 'large' sheet 16/17, though these numbers were now omitted. *Londonderry* was a reissue of the presumed 1924 sheet already mentioned. *Armagh* was SSS 47, and *Lough Swilly* was SSS 1/5, but extended north to include Inishtrahull in its correct position; both lacked outer frames. *County Down S.E.* was possibly the most singular: the north sheet line was the south sheet line of *Belfast*, the east sheet line was the east sheet line of SSS 49 and 61, the south sheet line was the south sheet line of SSS 60 and 61, but the west sheet line was related to the grid, falling on easting 319, and, as if to demonstrate that at the time full coverage of Northern Ireland was not policy, some 11,200 metres short of *Armagh*. 3000 copies were printed of *Belfast* and 2000 of *County Down S.E.*, which were comparatively large by the standards of GSGS 3907 and 3908: it is possible that the large run of *County Down S.E.* was because of a training or manoeuvre requirement. Both *Belfast* and *County Down S.E.* bear 1931 publication dates, and they may have been decided on before the other three.

---

[218] *Bantry Bay* and *Cork* are noted as gridded on an annotated index in the Charles Close Society Archives (Ordnance Survey deposit) in Cambridge University Library.

[219] There was a 500/27 printing of the civil version, but the military version, if indeed printed then, would presumably have carried a military-style month-year code, bottom left.

[220] Joseph T. Carroll, *Ireland in the war years*. Newton Abbot: David & Charles, 1975, 25 (quotation); Max Beloff, *Dream of Commonwealth 1921-42*. London: Macmillan, 1989, 251-2.

[221] Roger Hellyer, 'Sheet lines: some notes on GSGS 3917 and other one-inch large sheet maps of Ireland', *Sheetlines* 43 (1995), 4-24, 12.

The precise dates when these sheets were printed is unknown, but a copy of *Belfast* carries a receipt date of 26 October 1932, so it was obviously printed and available for issue by then.[222] All five carried a combined grid-letter and sheet-layout diagram which showed only these five sheets, and all five were printed on Place's waterproof paper.

Common to all five were the grid in purple, contours in red-brown, water in blue, and roads in yellow. So far, the colours resembled those of the early (1931-3) issues of GSGS 3907 and 3908. However, whereas *Belfast* used the separate water-tint plate of the parent sheet, the others retained water-lining: it is to be suspected that their water plates were derived from those of the coloured SSS. On *Belfast* the contours appeared on both the black plate, dotted, and on the contour plate, solid; on the other sheets they were only shown in colour. They were reputedly taken from the Provisional one-inch produced during World War I.[223] The road infills superficially resembled those of GSGS 3907 and 3908, but in fact their use was radically different: though it was not made clear in the legend, comparison of these five sheets with the quarter-inch road map issued by the Ordnance Survey of Northern Ireland shows that solid yellow was used for 'A' roads and broken yellow was for 'B' roads. Not until 1935 would Ministry of Transport classifications determine road infills on the one-inch of Great Britain, and even then they only appeared on civil printings. It was another 'first' for Ireland.

The other sixteen sheets were printed in black with the grid in purple. As the index on page 83 shows, nine were pairs of SSS sheets; all but two of the others were formed of SSS sheet lines on the 'inside', and grid sheet lines on the 'outside'. *Cushendall* had a small overlap onto *Belfast*: its south sheet line fell on northing 391. All resemble *Armagh* and *Lough Swilly*, in that the frames and latitude and longitude values have been deleted, though the marginal directions of main roads have been retained. All carry combined grid-letter and sheet-index diagrams which show both these sheets and the five previously published. This strongly suggests that these sixteen sheets were an afterthought, but it was evidently a fairly quick afterthought, as a proof copy of sheet 8 is dated 30 November 1932. The others were all printed in 1934, and thereby completed the military one-inch of the United Kingdom. Also known are copies of sheets 7 and 19, which carry the Modified British System grid, but have had some of their margins cropped: it is thus unclear how they relate to the development of GSGS 3917 as a whole. They retain their borders with the graticule, the grid figures in the border are at 10 km intervals, and the grid figures on the map face are at 5 km intervals. The writers have two completely contrasting explanations for this and, in default of further evidence, leave the reader to decide which explanation is more convincing. One possibility is that the first scheme, in 1932, was to complete GSGS 3917 using individual SSS sheets, and 7 and 19 were gridded and proved in this form, but that then the combined sheet scheme was decided on. If this explanation were correct, then the timescale for deciding, first to extend GSGS 3917, then to draw and prove sheets 7 and 19, and then to decide on the combined sheet scheme instead, was evidently a pretty quick one, in view of the proving of sheet 8 late in 1932 without the graticule border. The alternative explanation is that these two sheets are a relic of the extension and republication of GSGS 3917 in 1940, discussed further below. To confuse matters further, sheets 1/5 and 45/57 both omit the engraved imprint and instead have 'Ordnance Survey 1924' as on the *Londonderry* sheet; this date may have been carried over from the imprint on a group of one-inch outline sheets of Northern Ireland reprinted at Southampton in 1924. The new sheets made both *Armagh* and *Londonderry* redundant for complete cover of Northern Ireland, though the index on these sixteen sheets indicates that these two were retained in the series.

The only GSGS 3917 sheet known to have been reprinted is *Belfast*, in a run of 1500 copies in 1939. The red contour plate was omitted, leaving the black plate to carry this information, the road infill was decidedly orangey, and there was still no green plate. Nothing quite resembling the resulting colour-scheme is known to have been printed in GSGS 3907 or 3908.

In 1935 the Ordnance Survey of Northern Ireland began publishing a one-inch 'Popular Edition': the printing, and probably the preparation, was carried out by the Ordnance Survey of

---

[222] Copy in private collection.
[223] Susan Hall, 'A history of series GSGS 4136 Ireland 1:63,360 1940-1943', unpublished paper in DGC, 1.

Great Britain at Southampton. Six sheets were printed between 1935 and 1940 (Hi.30), and six more were published between 1948 and 1950 (Hi.31). Sheet 7 was a revised issue, from rather worn material, of the Belfast 'large' sheet of 1918, and the sheet lines of the others were fitted round it, as a result of which almost all the sheets were of different sizes to each other. No military edition was ever prepared, and it is not known whether there was any scheme in the later 1930s to use the completed Popular Edition to replace GSGS 3917. The title 'Popular Edition', though justified in the event by the much greater sales of these sheets as compared with their SSS predecessors, was a curious one, as the sheets were layered, in shades of brown and buff. The inspiration may have been a combination of the 1918 Belfast sheet and the Fifth (Relief) Edition in England, without the additional expense of hachuring.

The invasion of the Low Countries and the fall of France in May 1940 exposed both parts of Ireland to the very real risk of invasion, not so much as a target in its own right, but as a back-door route to the United Kingdom. Throughout the war, whatever the theory might be because of its membership of the Commonwealth, the Irish Free State was officially studiously neutral. In practice its sympathies were with Britain, and quite early in the war it was giving covert aid such as turning a blind eye to RAF planes taking a short cut by overflying Donegal on the way to and from patrols over the Atlantic. This did not satisfy Churchill, whose sympathies were fundamentally unionist and imperialist, and who thought that the war effort was being seriously impeded through lack of access to the erstwhile treaty ports. There was a vague possibility in the earlier years of the war that he might go against his advisers and order an invasion of the Free State in order to seize the ports.[224]

In practice, British operations in the twenty-six counties were much more likely as a counter to a German landing. Although the threat of invasion only became imminent from May 1940, by mid-April it had been decided to extend military one-inch cover to the whole of Ireland, in outline-and-purple-grid style. Initially this was to be GSGS 3943; later it was redesignated GSGS 3917. This seems to have been effected in two stages. The first was to photograph pulls of the outline, to produce negatives for making helio plates. The second was to draw grid overlays; these would appear to have been drawn on tracing paper, and then used to produce printing plates by vandyking. The evidence is that all sheets were prepared, and several were proved in mid-1940.[225]

14. *Ireland: GSGS 4136*

At this point there seems to have been a change of policy, perhaps aided by the fact that, whatever might be done in the way of drawing, pressure on the presses for mapping of Britain meant that actually printing GSGS 3917 would be a lesser priority. The change of policy was certainly far more radical than any for military map series of Britain during World War II; GSGS 3917 was to be wholly abandoned, and replaced by a new series, GSGS 4136 (Hi.28), laid out on Irish grid sheet lines, in 76 sheets, numbered 301 to 376.[226] This was to obviate confusion with other Irish one-inch series, as was the heading '(Large Sheet Series)'. The standard area of cover was 50 km west-east by 30 km south-north (a map area of 31.07 by 18.64 inches, 78.95 by 47.37 cm), although there were a few portrait-shaped sheets. An anomaly which was never corrected was that a small piece of the coast of County Wicklow which fell outside sheets 350 and 355 was not covered in this series.[227]

---

[224] For more on all this, see Joseph T. Carroll, *Ireland in the war years*. Newton Abbot: David & Charles, 1975.

[225] The proof for this was in OS and WO job files which have now been disposed of. A surviving file for sheet 92 shows that the black outline was ordered by 16 April: it was photographed by 16 June, and a tracing of the grid for vandyking was ready by 21 June. The finished sheet was proved by 24 June.

[226] The main sources for GSGS 4136 are Susan Hall, 'A history of series GSGS 4136 Ireland 1:63,360 1940-1943', unpublished paper in DGC, and the GSGS 4136 series file: we are indebted to Brian Garvan for access to these.

[227] This might be attributed to the haste of war, but exactly the same happened to a small portion of the Berwickshire coast which fell between and initially was omitted from 1:50,000 sheets 67 and 75, issued in 1976. Could the second Wilson government be blamed?

GSGS 4136 was produced in three editions between 1940 and 1942: as with other Irish military series, no complete sets of either the first edition or of the second edition are known, but the evidence is that all sheets were published in all three editions. As most of the sheets covered an official non-belligerent, and would only be needed in quantity were Britain to be forced to mount a counter-invasion, presumably most of the stock was never issued, and instead went for salvage: in November 1941 it was noted that 'until active operations begin the consumption is very small'.[228] All three editions had outline and grid in black, with grid figures in red. The GSGS number was allocated on 3 July 1940; the first five sheets of the first edition were printed in July, all 76 sheets were ready by 10 August, and eighteen sheets seem to have been reprinted.[229] The work on the extension of GSGS 3917 probably did not go to waste: having negatives would have facilitated taking prints to cut and join on the new sheet lines.

The first edition was in black and red only. It can be identified by the lack of any publication or edition note. 'Because of the black colour, the density of detail and the poor quality of the reproduction, the maps were very hard to read.'[230] In fact, some town and village names were replaced with typesetting, to aid legibility, and there were notes of conversions from feet to metres and vice-versa, a refinement denied to users, military and civil, of one-inch maps of Great Britain then and for many years after. The legend was a redrawn version of that of the parent engraved maps, including the distinctive 'pond-insect' style of lightship and distinctive trigonometrical point with height in bold figures. Revision of the map face was minimal, but on sheet 314 at Belfast and Lisburn the one-inch Popular cover of the built-up area, derived from a revision of 1936, was substituted for the engraved cover: this was at the expense of losing water information, with the result that the 'Blackstaff Riv' was left without anything to refer to.[231]

'By December 1940 Road Revision was in hand for all sheets.'[232] The second edition was printed in 1941. Publication or authorship notes are still usually omitted, but 'Second Edition' appears, usually in red, but sometimes in black, in the top margin. A third, green, printing was added for woods, and road infills and overprinting of the border between the North and the Free State were added to the red plate; an all-Ireland grid-letter diagram was also added. 'It is undoubtedly a great improvement on the First Edition, and general comment has been very favourable.' To make the relief more legible, the easternmost 51 sheets were also produced with orange-brown layers (Hi.28.2.2), prepared and overprinted by the survey unit (515 (Corps) Field Survey Company) attached to the army in Northern Ireland. The plates were made from duplicate rulings supplied by the OS; the printing, on double-demy mobile presses, was completed in February 1942, with a standard run of 1000 copies. This was adopted as much less trouble than producing separate water or contour plates. To save time, these were issued initially without the green wood plate; later this was added, either in second or third edition form, to all sheets. 'The improvement has been universally approved, particularly by the Gunners.'[233] At least ten sheets were issued with road revision, which used a revised system, based on suitability for military convoy traffic.[234] Copies of both the first and second editions were printed on linen-backed paper.

The Third Edition, first printed between February and May 1942, was the most elaborate, and, in the trouble taken to incorporate all available revision, to a reasonable standard of drawing, suggests a parallel with the Second War Revision version of GSGS 3907. Production of the Third

---

[228] Lt Col Shewell to GSGS, 16 November 1941 (ref. CV/S/4/85) (in the context of the layered version, discussed below), in GSGS 4136 series file, at present with DGC. It is possible that some first edition sheets were converted to Second Edition by overprinting roads and woods (on the analogy of GSGS 3906, where some Second Editions are first editions with contours overprinted in brown, and 'Second' on the overprint plate), but so far there is no proof of this. It may, however, be significant that 'Second Edition' was usually on the red plate, i.e. might be symptomatic of overprinting in some cases.

[229] Job sheet in GSGS 4136 series file, at present with DGC.

[230] Susan Hall, 'A history of series GSGS 4136 Ireland 1:63,360 1940-1943', unpublished paper in DGC, 2.

[231] As so few first editions have been found, it is possible that further revision was added to other sheets at this stage which has escaped our notice.

[232] Susan Hall, 'A history of series GSGS 4136 Ireland 1:63,360 1940-1943', unpublished paper in DGC, 2.

[233] Lt Col Shewell to GSGS, 16 November 1941 (ref. CV/S/4/85), in GSGS 4136 series file, at present with DGC.

[234] Sheets 309, 313, 317, 320, 321, 325, 326, 327 to 10 July 1941; sheets 312, 364 to 1 November 1941.

Edition seems to have been primarily due to a requirement to increase stocks. Although maintenance of the series was the responsibility of the Assistant Director of Survey, British Troops in Northern Ireland, the volume of work was beyond the capacity of 515 (Corps) Field Survey Company's print trailers; the scope for printing by civil firms was limited, as for security reasons they could only handle sheets of Northern Ireland. For this reason, the work was undertaken by the OS. To facilitate overprinting with layers by 515 (Corps) Field Survey Company, most of the stock was not to be trimmed after printing.[235] Revision for the first six sheets was ready by 24 December 1941, as were a complete set of one-inch maps covering the Free State.[236] All sheets now used the military convoy road classification, and had a simplified legend: this omitted the symbols for contours, boundaries, navigation features, trig. heights and postal facilities, which continued to appear on the maps themselves, but retained the windpump symbol, which would not have appeared at all on the large minority of sheets based on the one-inch revision of 1898-1901, and which in practice appeared rarely on those sheets derived from Third Edition material. The grid-letter diagram was modified to regional cover, and an adjoining-sheet diagram was added to the black plate. The magnetic variation diagrams were altered to show variations at sheet edges, in accordance with a recent GSGS ruling. The rearrangement of marginalia was prompted by a slight reduction in the maximum size of printed area, to 33 by 22 inches (83.9 by 55.9 cm), because of the size of most of the paper available in Northern Ireland.[237]

A blue water plate was added (overprinted on black), and contours were shown in orange, at 100 feet to 1000 feet, and above that at 125 feet intervals; this was a consequence of the contour intervals of the engraved sheets, which were used as a guide for this interpolation.[238] The easternmost 51 sheets were also printed with layering, and all sheets were also issued with a bog overprint (Hi.28.3.3). Some printings omit a 'Third Edition' statement in the lower margin, but are readily identifiable by the presence of the water and contour plates. A characteristic of all sheets was a note that road classification was as at 1 January 1942, though in practice this date seems to have been conventional rather than absolute.[239] Unlike most European GSGS series with similar notes, there was no qualification as to lack of reliability for want of reconnaissance. Nor was there any need: through the offices of the British Military Mission in Dublin, a complete set of the most up-to-date half-inch and one-inch mapping of the Free State was obtained, and manuscript sheets of the Irish Geological Survey were sent to Belfast to supply data for the bog overprints.[240] In Northern Ireland there was both further revision and further 'patching' of Popular in place of engraved cover of towns: thus on sheet 314, Popular cover of Newtownards was used, south of Belfast new building development was added which would not appear on the Popular Edition until 1953, and the water detail was made good: thus Blackstaff Riv. once again referred to a watercourse.

Three sets of reproduction materials seem to have been produced: one for OS, one for Belfast, and one for a security store.[241] By the early 1960s the reproduction materials for the series were held by the Directorate of Military Survey, and some were apparently converted from glass to film base.[242]

[235] Lt Col Shewell to GSGS, 16 November 1941 (ref. CV/S/4/85), in GSGS 4136 series file, at present with DGC. For progress on overprinting see 515 Corps monthly reports in 1942-3 in PRO WO 402/95.

[236] Faded letter, 24 December 1941, in GSGS 4136 series file, at present with DGC. The six sheets were 331-333 and 337-339.

[237] Lt Col Shewell to GSGS, 24 December 1941 (ref. CV/S/4/99), in GSGS 4136 series file, at present with DGC.

[238] Susan Hall, 'A history of series GSGS 4136 Ireland 1:63,360 1940-1943', unpublished paper in DGC, 2.

[239] Shewell to [OS], 17 February 1942, in GSGS 4136 series file, at present with DGC.

[240] Ward to GSGS, 28 May 1943, in GSGS 4136 series file, at present with DGC; see also report for January 1943 by AD Survey, BTNI, in PRO WO 402/95, at which time Northern Ireland and five Free State counties were completed, and five more were in hand.

[241] Ian Mumford's comments on Susan Hall, 'A history of series GSGS 4136 Ireland 1:63,360 1940-1943', unpublished paper in DGC.

[242] MOD record cards: via Ian Mumford.

At about the same time as the Third Edition of GSGS 4136 was being printed, Ireland received a very small supply of arms from Britain.[243] As far as is known it did not receive any supplies of maps, nor is any request for them known. In 1940 Ireland had produced its own cartographic response to the threat of invasion: a combined-sheet version of the one-inch, in 55 sheets (Hi.29). Once again, it seems to survive only in fragments. As with a contemporary 'emergency' half-inch series, it covered the 'six counties' as well as the Free State: perhaps someone hoped that Churchill's wish for the Irish to enter the war as allies would overcome his distaste for the necessary price of ending partition. The most interesting thing about this mapping was that it employed a yard grid: had British and Irish troops embarked on joint operations, it would presumably have been necessary to address this difference.[244]

In contrast to all the one-inch military series of Britain, which were in principle only issued in one standard military form, though individual sheets might be overprinted for special purposes (GSGS 4620A being the main exception), GSGS 4136 was distinguished by the number of alternative standard formats. Apart from the overprints with bogs and layers already mentioned, there was also a training areas overprint (Hi.28.3.4), covering Northern Ireland only, where by 1943 large numbers of American troops were stationed; this version seems to have been produced mainly for their use. The overprint was made by TASC, NI, and went through two editions, both in 1943.[245] Although by this time it was apparent that the risk of Nazi invasion was diminishing and that it was increasingly likely that there would be an Allied invasion of Europe instead, nonetheless large stocks of GSGS 4136 were held in readiness:

> 'The huge stocks of German military maps of Ireland found by the allies in Brussels in 1944 and the manuals on how to treat the natives (their 'lack of hygiene' was noted) were paralleled by the lorry loads of maps which the British army in Northern Ireland had ready for the day it might be called on to cross the border either to help the Irish resist a German invasion or to take the ports by force…' [246]

GSGS 4136 continued to be a current series after the war, despite the completion in 1950 of the Popular Edition of Northern Ireland, which in general was better printed and probably more up to date: sheets 7, 10 and 11 certainly were, after they were revised and republished in 1953-8. The probable reasons are that, first, GSGS 4136 covered the whole of Ireland, which might prove useful in the event of a future war, and, second, that it was laid out on the Cassini grid which the Popular Edition was not: indeed, the latter started with alpha-numeric squaring in the borders, and progressed via grid figures in the border only from about 1948 through a 10 km grid on the map face on sheet 7 in 1953 to a full-blown 1 km grid in 1956. Was it felt a pity to spoil the look of the map with horrid little black squares? If so, one can sympathise. Meanwhile GSGS 4136 continued to be reprinted as need arose. 'Refer to' boxes were added in the margins from 1952, but otherwise they were unrevised; SSD M721 was reallocated to this series, but never appeared on any sheet.[247] The last printings were of sheets 313 and 314 (both including Belfast) in 1962, which, being firmly in the 'six counties' are understandable, but no explanation is known for the printing between 1953 and 1959 of sixteen sheets which lay wholly within what since 1949 had been the Republic of

[243] Joseph T. Carroll, *Ireland in the war years*. Newton Abbot: David & Charles, 1975, 115.

[244] See Roger Hellyer, 'Some further notes on military mapping in Ireland', *Sheetlines* 46 (1996), 29-32 and Roger Hellyer, *Ordnance Survey small-scale maps indexes: 1801-1998*. Kerry: David Archer, 1999, 88-9.

[245] Susan Hall, 'A history of series GSGS 4136 Ireland 1:63,360 1940-1943', unpublished paper in DGC, 3. Sheets 304, 305, 307-309, 311-314, 317-321 and 325-7 were overprinted .

[246] Joseph T. Carroll, *Ireland in the war years*. Newton Abbot: David & Charles, 1975, 173-4. Operational issues of 'maps of Eire' to troops in Northern Ireland were recalled on 5 March 1943 'in view of revision of attitude regarding prospects of invasion': report on closing down of Survey Directorate Northern Ireland, 13 May 1943, in PRO WO 402/95.

[247] Information from lists of AMS series numbers on open access in the map room of US National Archives & Records Administration, College Park, Maryland.

Ireland, and no longer even a residual member of the British Commonwealth.[248] The bog overprints were declared redundant on 16 October 1963.[249] Eleven of the standard sheets covering the six counties were declared obsolete in November 1966, following the production of M723.[250] In April 1968 there were instructions to reduce the stocks of the unlayered map to 500 copies each of the remaining 65 sheets, with the excess to be offered to Ireland.[251] The rest of the series seems to have been made obsolete some time in the late 1970s; there was extensive distribution of superseded stock to university and other libraries, where no doubt the lack at that time of any more up-to-date cover of the Republic of Ireland at around this scale made them useful acquisitions.[252] Some reproduction material was still extant in 1980 and, when it was finally disposed of in the mid-1990s, some specimens of this were sent to Ireland.[253]

15. *M723, Northern Ireland, and after*

GSGS 4136 was eventually replaced for Northern Ireland in 1965 by series M723 (Hi.32.M.1), which was a military version of the Ordnance Survey of Northern Ireland's one-inch Third Series (Hi.32). The civil version was published between 1960 and 1964, based on revision of 1953-62. It was a direct development of the Popular Edition, being based on the old engraved material, and with layers and the grid at 1 km intervals, but it was evidently produced by rephotographing the Popular material, and lacked the crispness of its predecessor. The standard sheet size covered an area of 60 km west-east by 40 km south-north (a map area of 37.28 by 24.86 inches, 94.74 by 63.16 cm); sheet 1 was an exception, covering 60 by 24 km. There were no overlaps. M723 added a purple overprint, changed to red in 1980. All nine sheets were initially printed in May 1965 in a run of 10,000 copies; following the outbreak of 'the troubles' in 1969, reprints were frequent. The list below gives only the basic printings: from 1968 to 1975 the quantity code was omitted.

M723 was declared obsolete in 1985, following the completion of 1:50,000 cover of Northern Ireland (Hi.34.A.1), and was replaced by M728 (Hi.34.A.5).[254] The 1:50,000 was published in its civil form in 1978-85 as part of an all-Ireland series, so that the eighteen sheets bore discontinuous numbers between 4 and 29. Whereas in Britain the production of military versions of redrawn mapping had usually appeared either simultaneously with, or after, the civil counterpart, in Northern Ireland the reverse was the case. M728 was initially issued in 1981, with some sheets supplied by photo-enlargements, without layers, of one-inch Third Series material. Other sheets were initially issued in redrawn style, but without layers, and with a single colour for contours and roads. When the Ordnance Survey of Ireland began publishing its sheets in 1988 the styles adopted – first contours only, and then a layered map – were markedly different from those of the Northern Ireland map, both in style and some content, and in their production method: they were wholly digital. 1:50,000 cover of Ireland was completed in 1999: in 1999-2002 Ordnance Survey of Northern Ireland republished its eighteen sheets in digital form, with some redesign. M728 continues; the 1:50,000 sheets of the Republic have grid figures on their faces, and appear to be designed as a dual civil-military series.

Richard Oliver

---

[248] Sheets reprinted in 1952-4: 301-316, 318-321, 324-327; sheets reprinted in 1959: 322, 323, 328, 329, 333, 339, 345, 350, 351, 355.

[249] Product Information Branch series card index held by DGC.

[250] Sheets 305, 308, 309, 311-314, 318-321: see Product Information Branch series card index held by DGC.

[251] Product Information Branch series card index held by DGC.

[252] For example, the holdings of the geography department map library at the University of Exeter, at the time of writing.

[253] Susan Hall, 'A history of series GSGS 4136 Ireland 1:63,360 1940-1943', unpublished paper in DGC, 4; information from Ian Mumford.

[254] Product Information Branch series card index held by DGC.

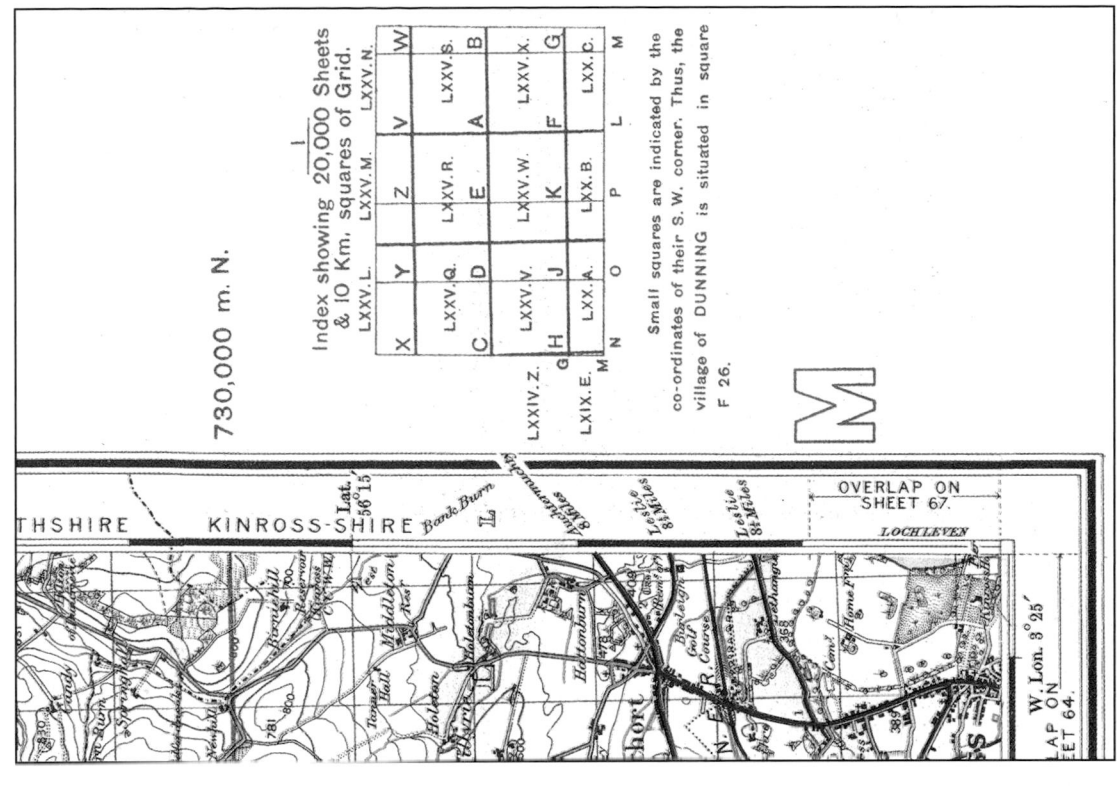

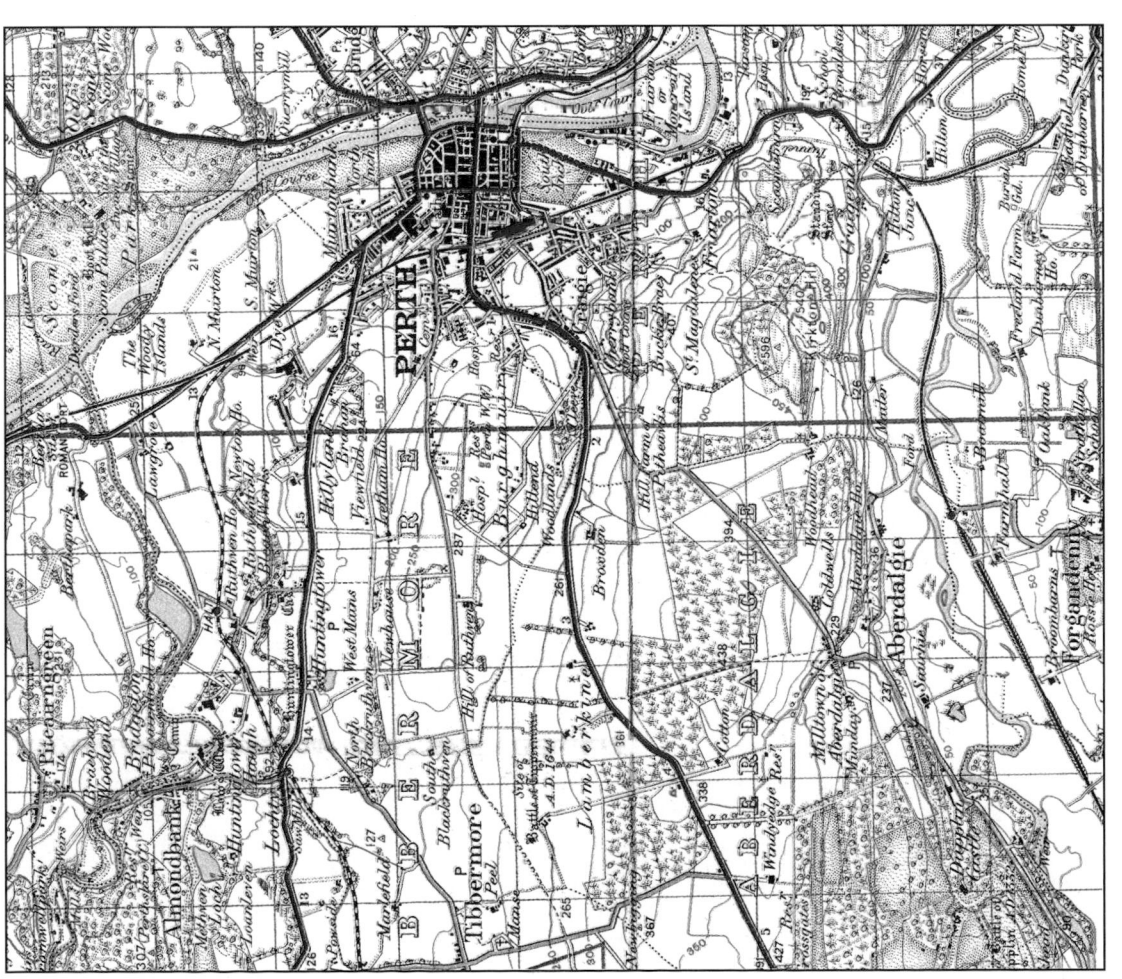

Figure 1 Two extracts from Scotland sheet 63, printing 200/31: this is one of a number of sheets printed in 1931-3 which omitted the green (woods) plate. In the right margin is a diagram showing component sheets of the 1:20,000 series, GSGS 2748: in practice none of the sheets in this area were ever produced.

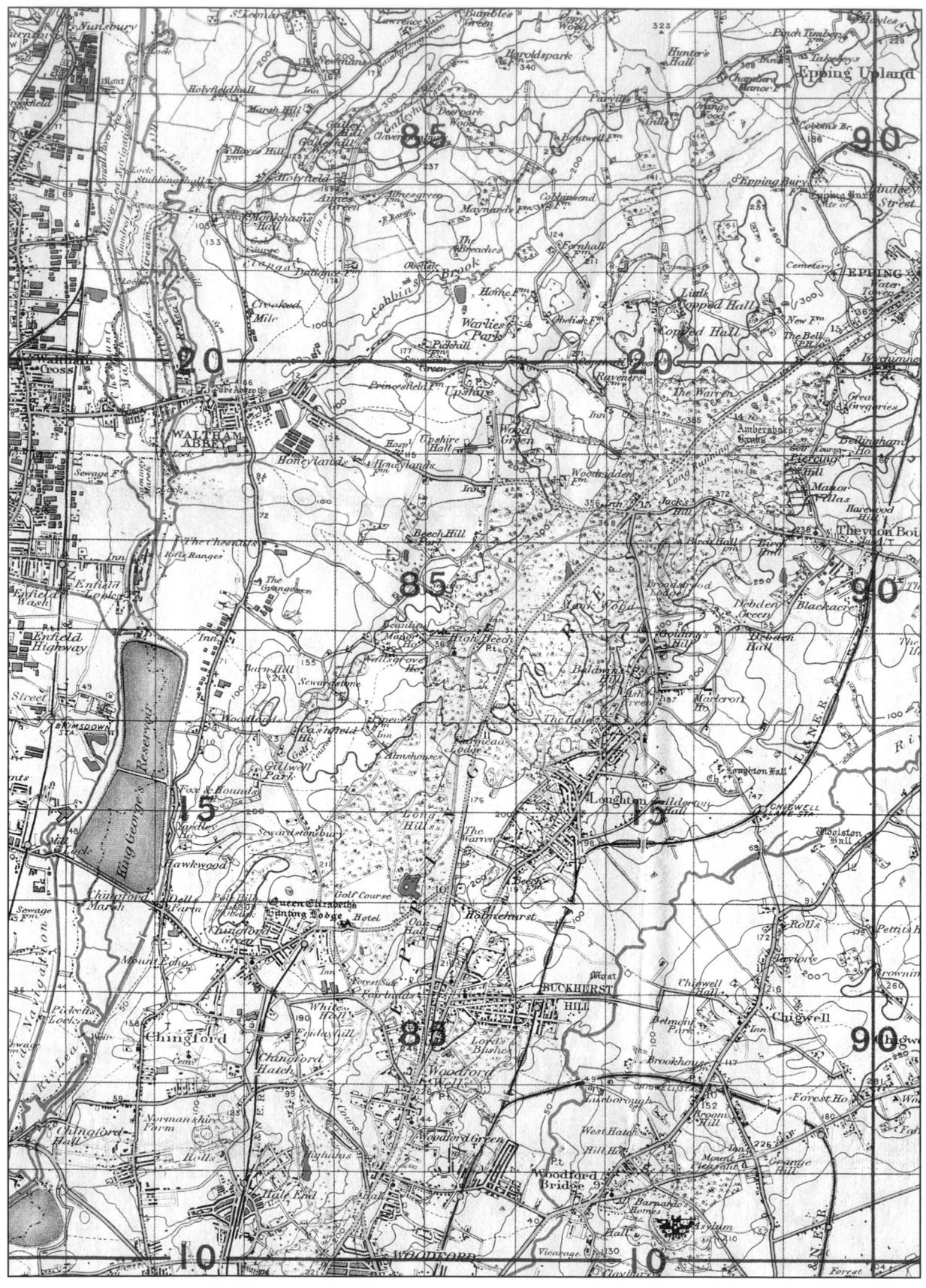

Figure 2 Part of GSGS 3907 sheet 107, printing WO 4550/31: this is one of the early MBS sheets which omits the GSGS number. It is in the standard colour style for the first printings of GSGS 3907 and 3908, omitting wood infill. Grid figures on the map face are in the original standard style for the Modified British System, at 5 km intervals.

Figure 3 Part of GSGS 3907 sheet 107, printing 5000/7/40 F: this was the only numbered sheet of this series to be remade using Fifth Edition material before the outbreak of war in 1939, though its construction remained on Popular Edition sheet lines. Apart from this, the colour scheme is the standard one for this series in the late 1930s.

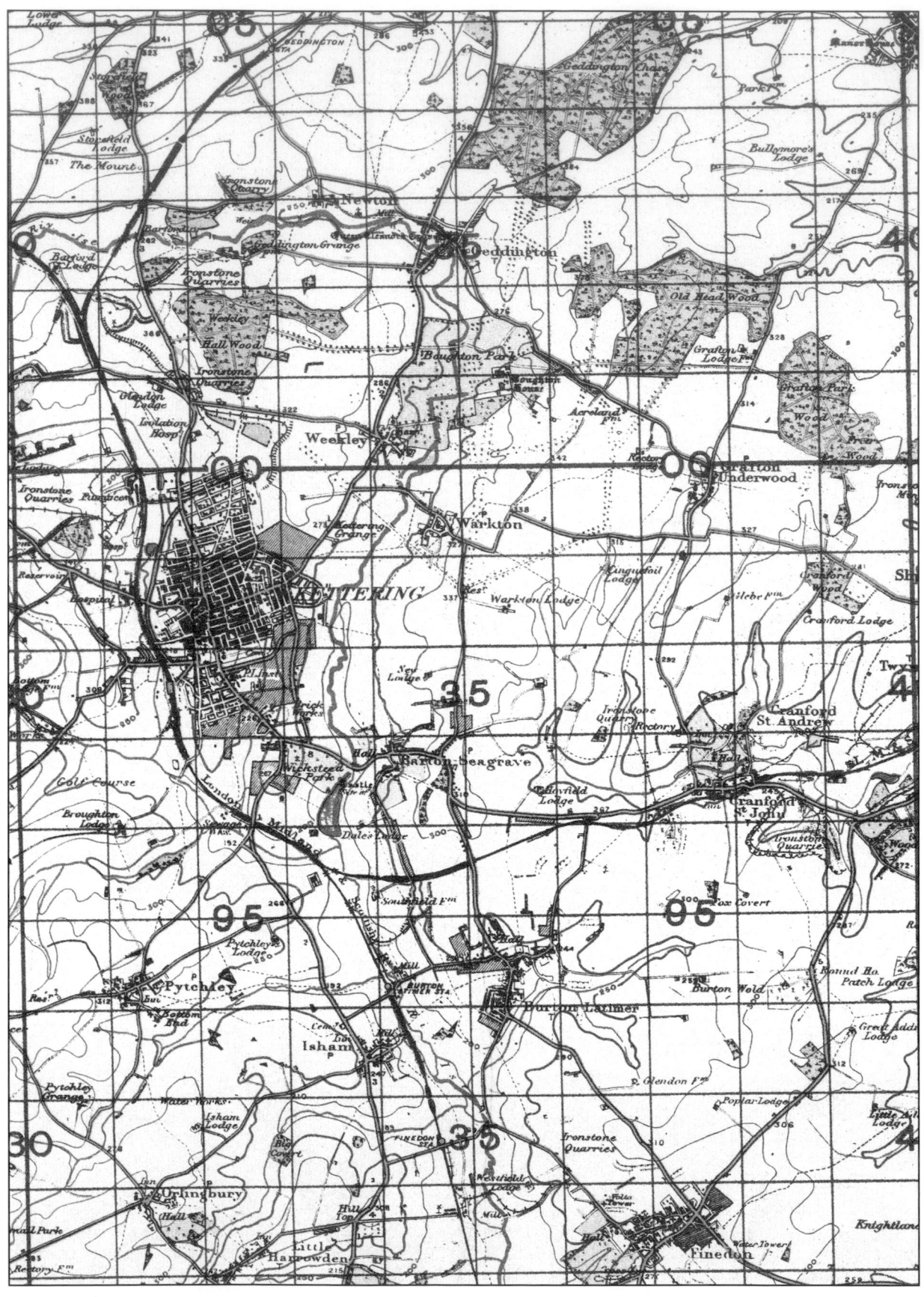

Figure 4 GSGS 3907 sheet 74, War Revision 1940, without print code: an extract from the only known copy, in the Library of Congress, Washington D.C. The general print-quality is not crisp and register of colours is not perfect. Note the areas of new building around Kettering shown by swathes of hatching, derived from ARP revision for the six-inch map. *Reproduced by courtesy of the Library of Congress.*

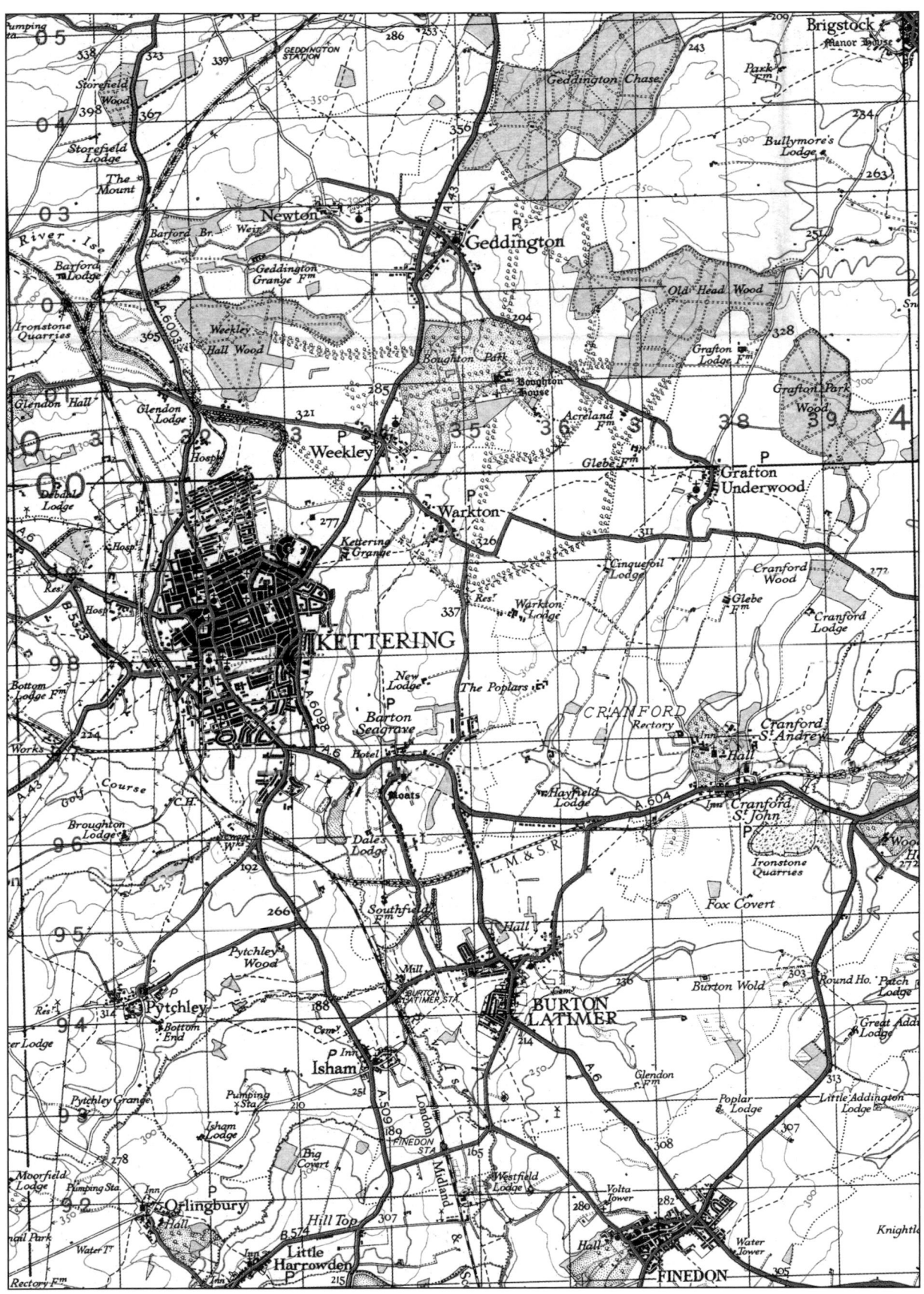

Figure 5 GSGS 3907 sheet 74, Second War Revision 1940, printing 10,000/2/43 LR. This was prepared in 1941 from unpublished New Popular Edition material. The swathes of hatching employed as an emergency measure on War Revision are converted on Second War Revision to detailed mapping of buildings and roads. Because of the destruction of revision material in 1940, there is no infill for tarred roads under 14 feet in width.

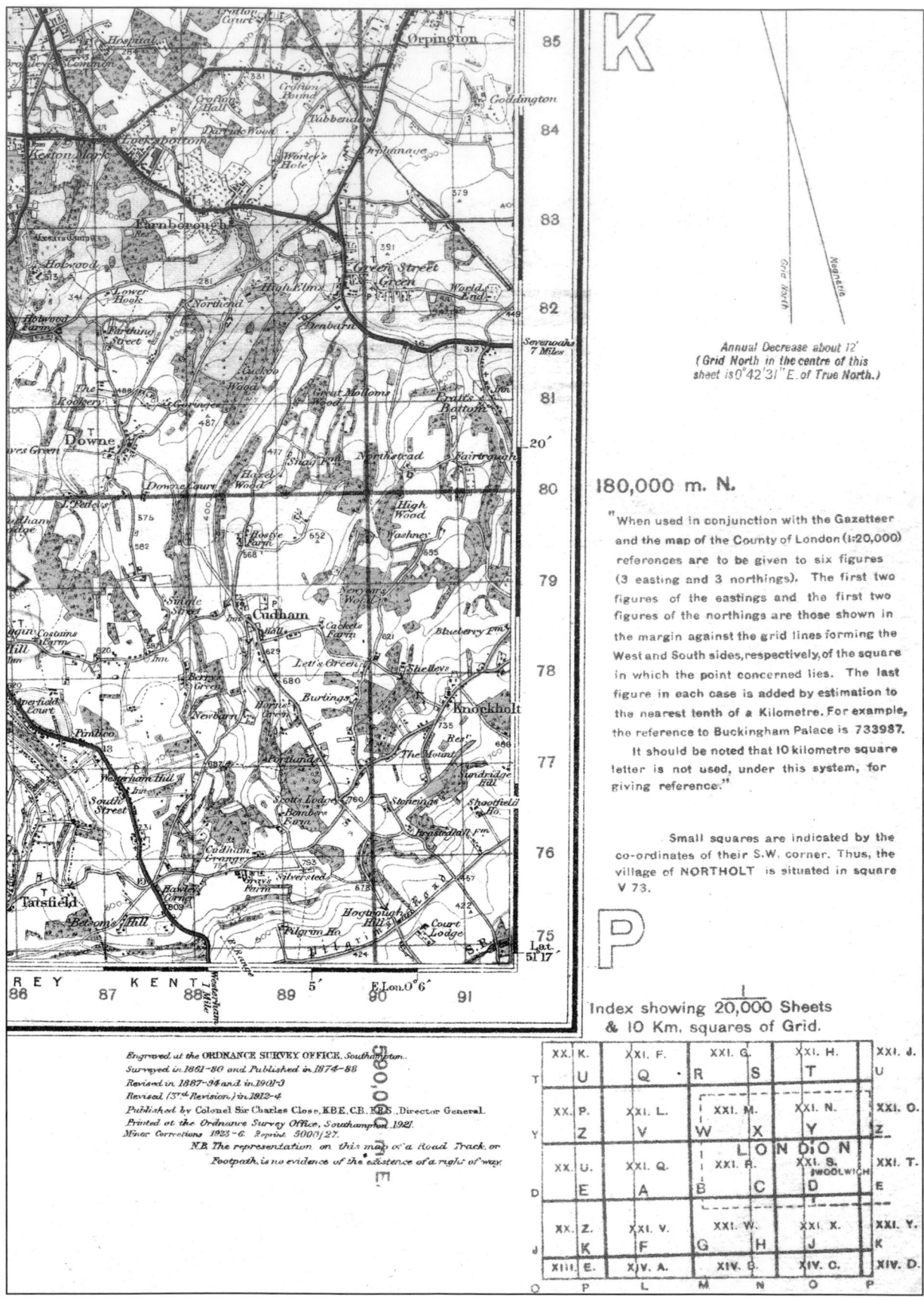

Figure 6 The south-east part of *London*, printing WO 500/28, printed with an experimental grid, which would become the Modified British System. Otherwise, the colour scheme is the standard one for military printings of the one-inch Popular Edition of 1923-30, with grid in purple and woods in green. However, the civilian parent *London* sheet was printed with hachures and layers.

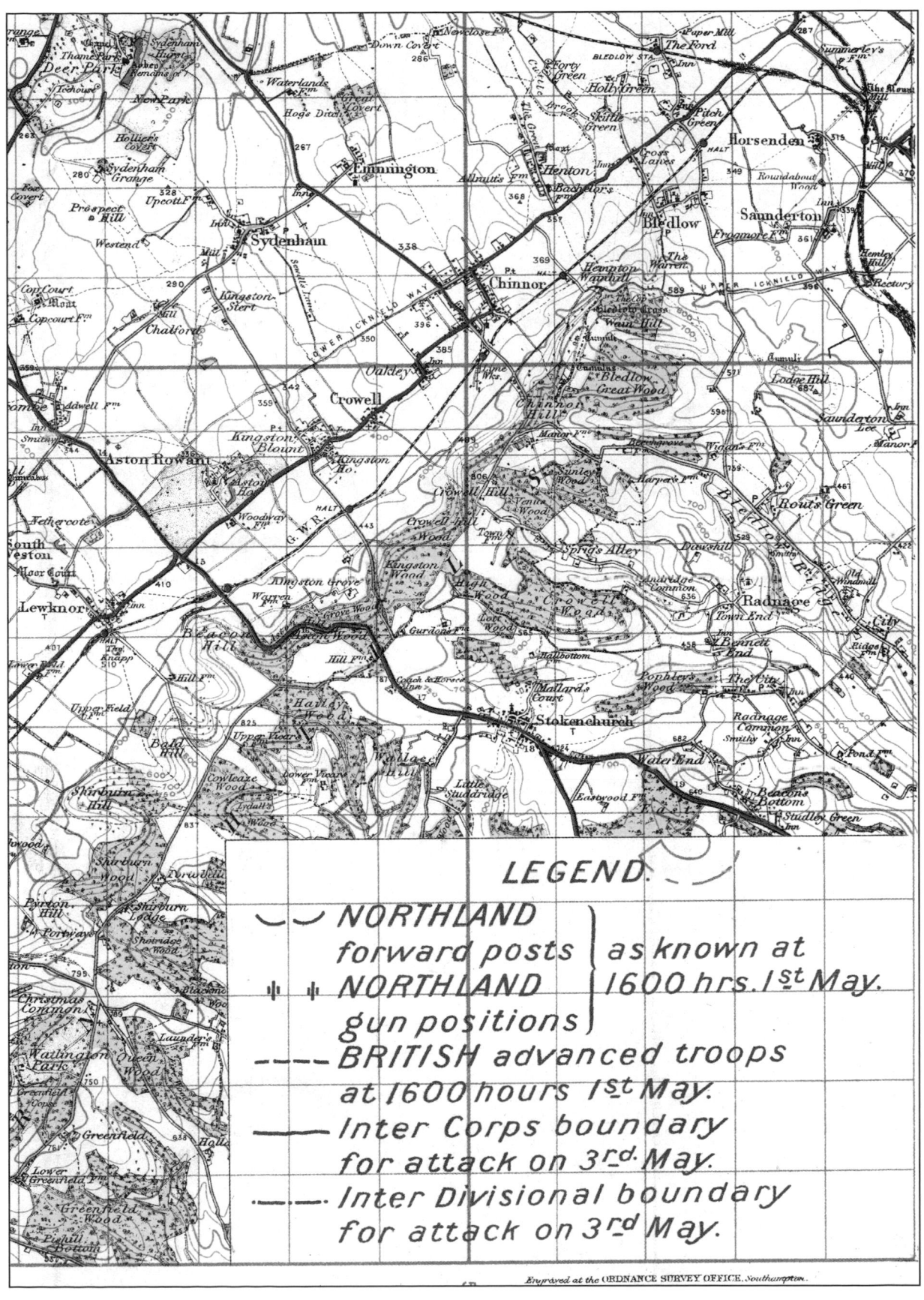

Figure 7 Part of a map made for a War Office exercise which was held near Oxford between 30 April and 3 May 1928. This extract shows the legend of military symbols added to standard one-inch military mapping. Exercise maps of this type were produced for War Office use at least once every year between 1925 and the outbreak of the Second World War.

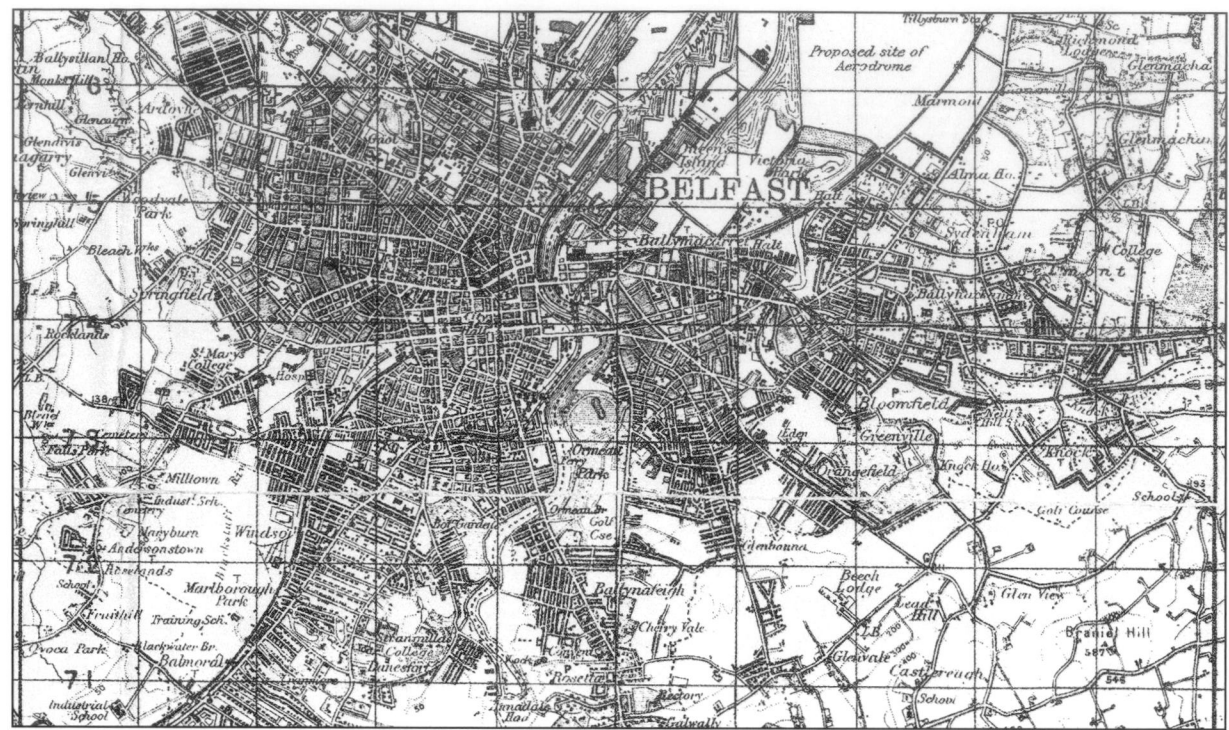

Figure 8a Part of GSGS 4136 sheet 314, first edition, without print code: the grid figures are in red, and the joins of the component engraved 'small' sheets are clearly visible. The discontinuities of the grid lines indicates that the grid was laid down onto the 'small' sheets before they were cut and reassembled on 'large' sheet lines, in order to obtain the best sympathy between grid and detail. However, the built-up part of Belfast has been transferred from the Popular Edition mapping published in 1937.

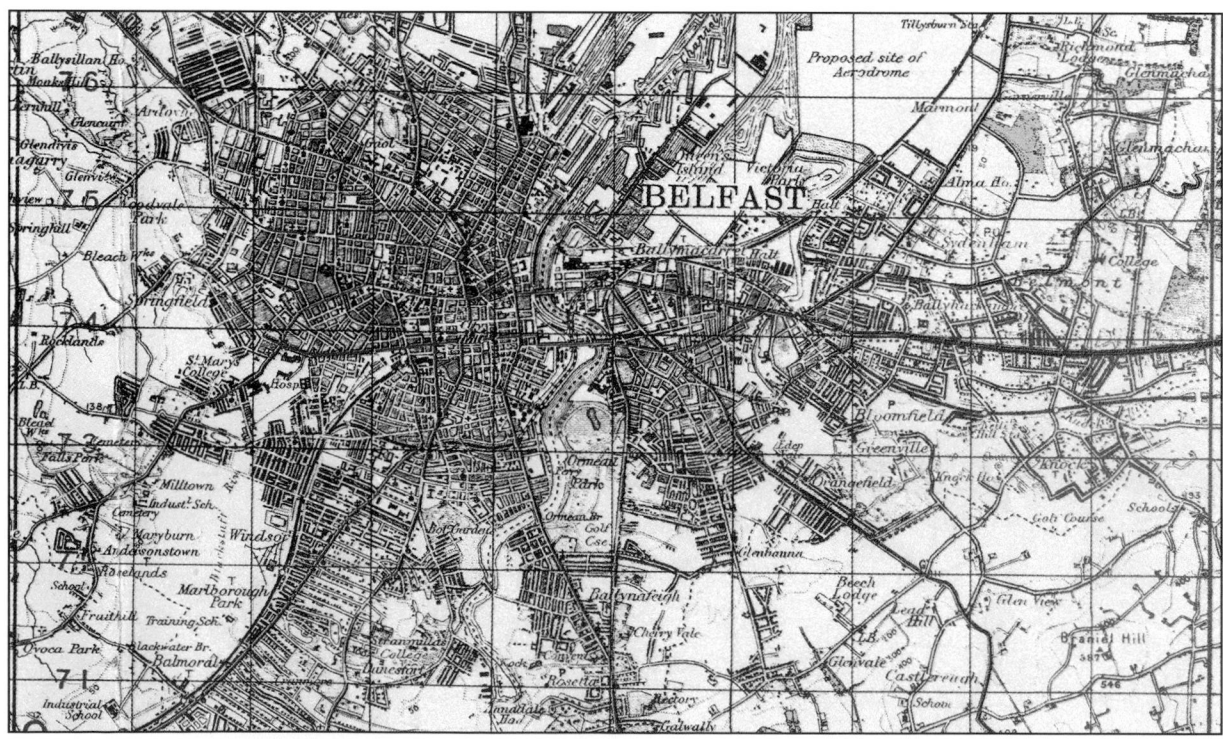

Figure 8b Part of GSGS 4136 sheet 314, Second Edition, without print code: red road infill and a green woods plate have been added. This is the first known printing of the second edition; the sheet was quickly reprinted in a version incorporating the new military four class road classification.

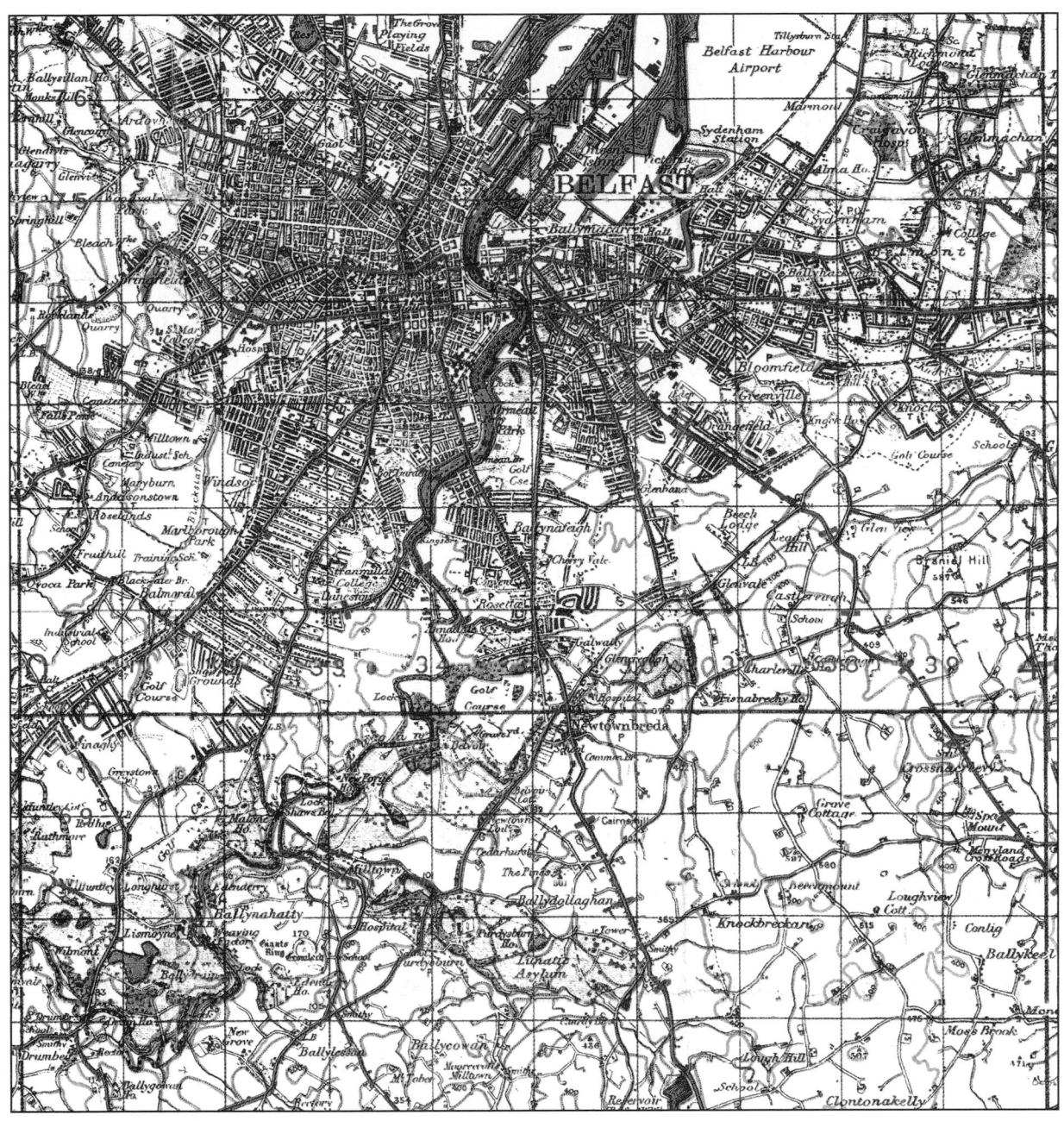

Figure 9 Part of GSGS 4136 sheet 314, Third Edition, printing 31,516/5/42/M: the map is now in five colours, with contours overprinted in orange, and water overprinted in blue. Revision of new building has been added; this would not appear on the civil Popular Edition until 1953.

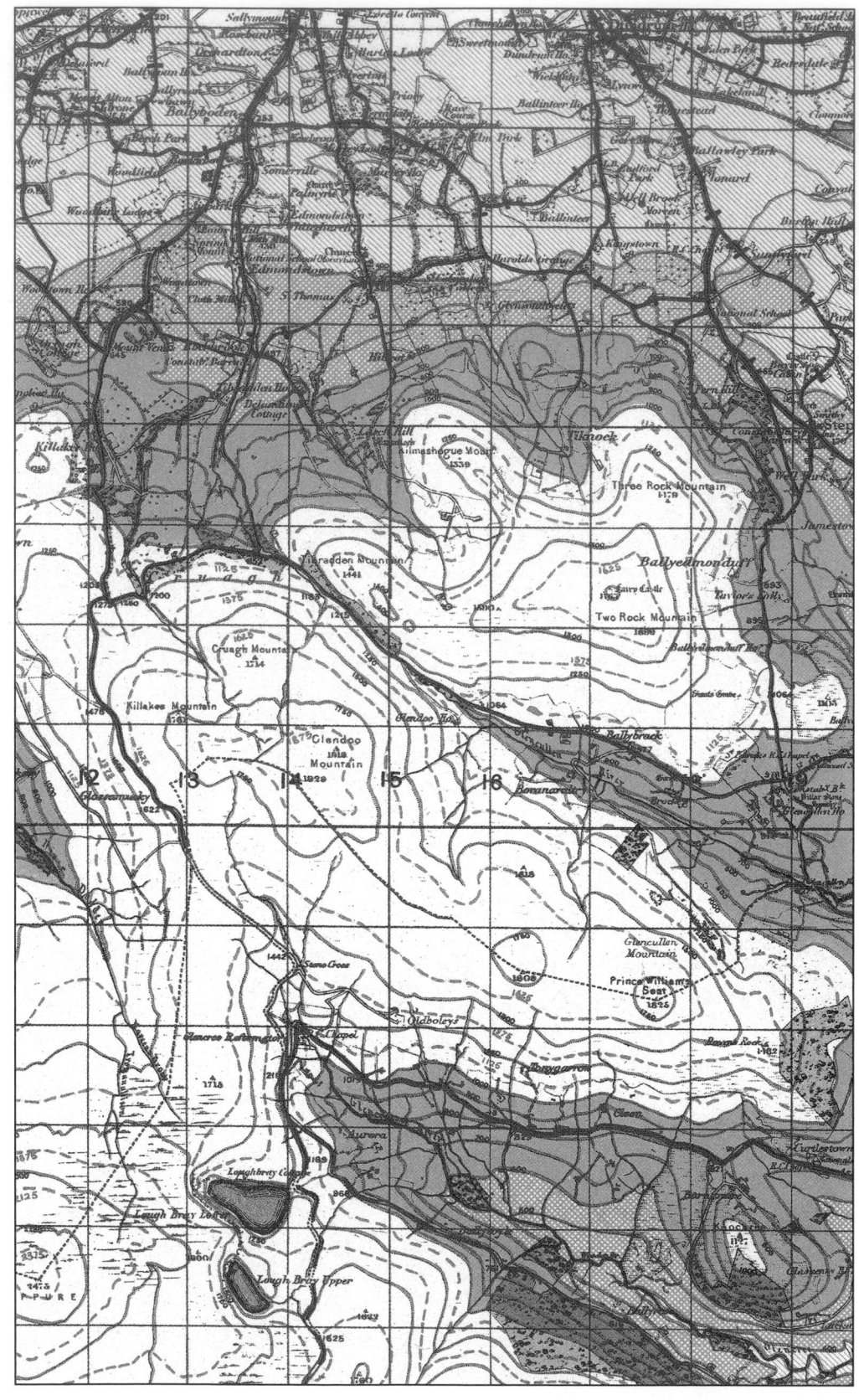

Figure 10 Part of GSGS 4136 sheet 345, printing 14,500/2/42 C, overprinted with layers: these are not used for ground under 200 feet (on north edge of this extract) or over 1000 feet, making for a curious effect. Note also the interpolated contours added at 125 feet intervals over the 1000 feet level, which are shown as pecked lines.

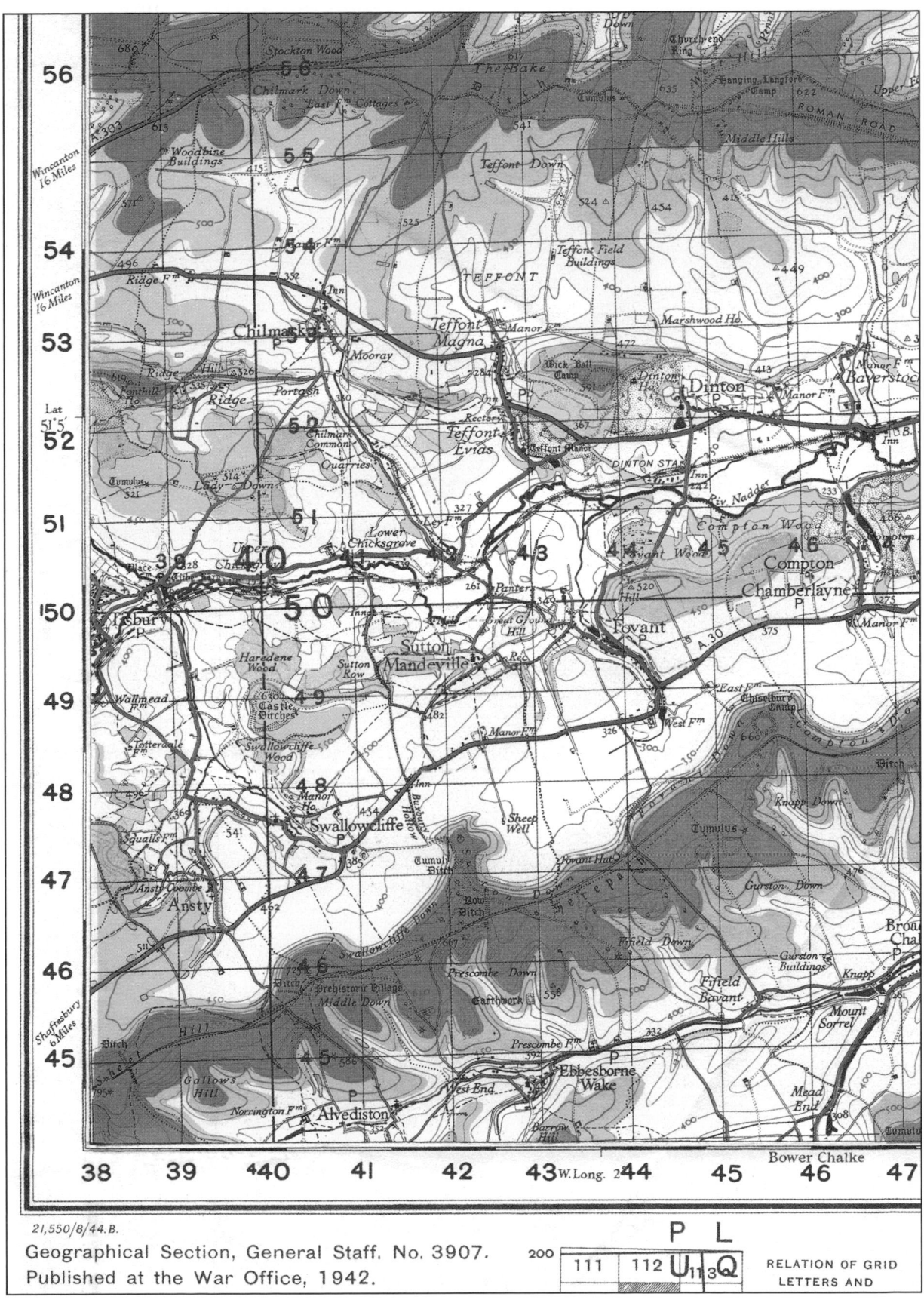

Figure 11 Part of GSGS 3907, sheet 122, printing 21,550/8/44 B, overprinted in 1947 with layers for the training of officers in the Staff College. Only six such Second War Revision sheets were made. The base map has the roads and contours plate printed in Air Force brown.

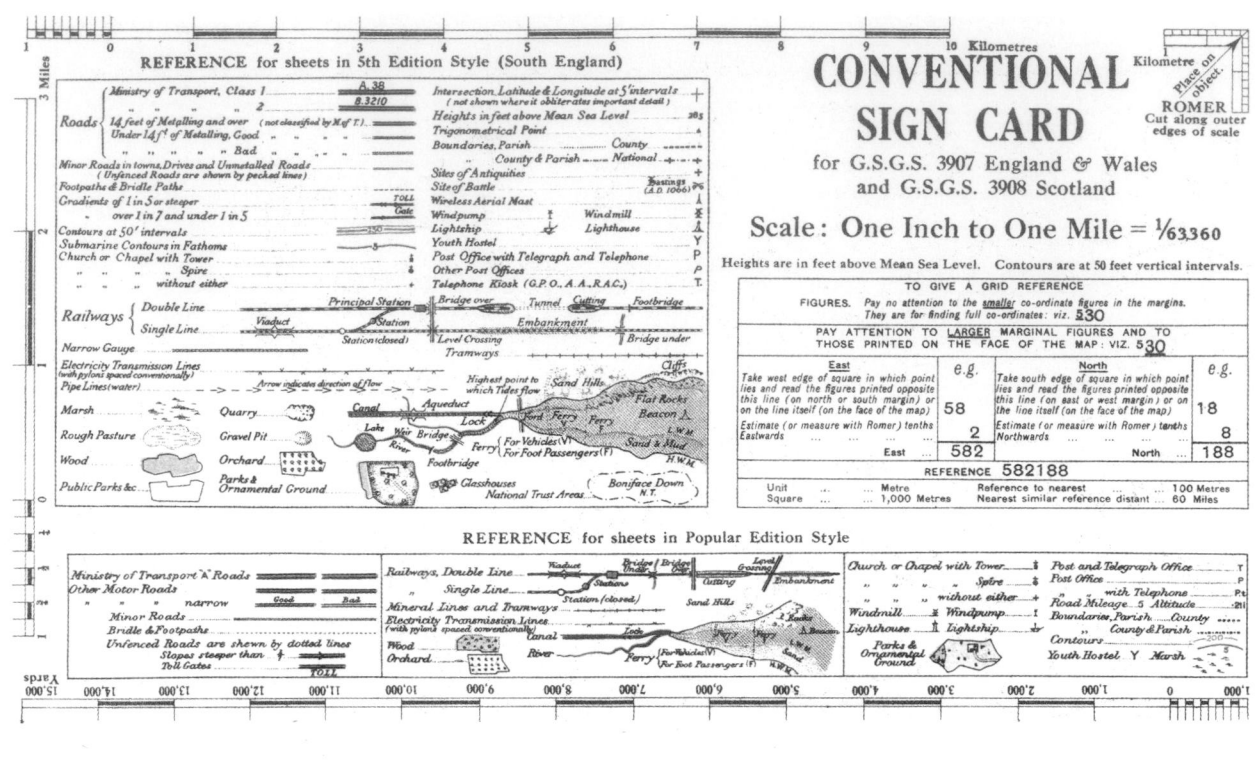

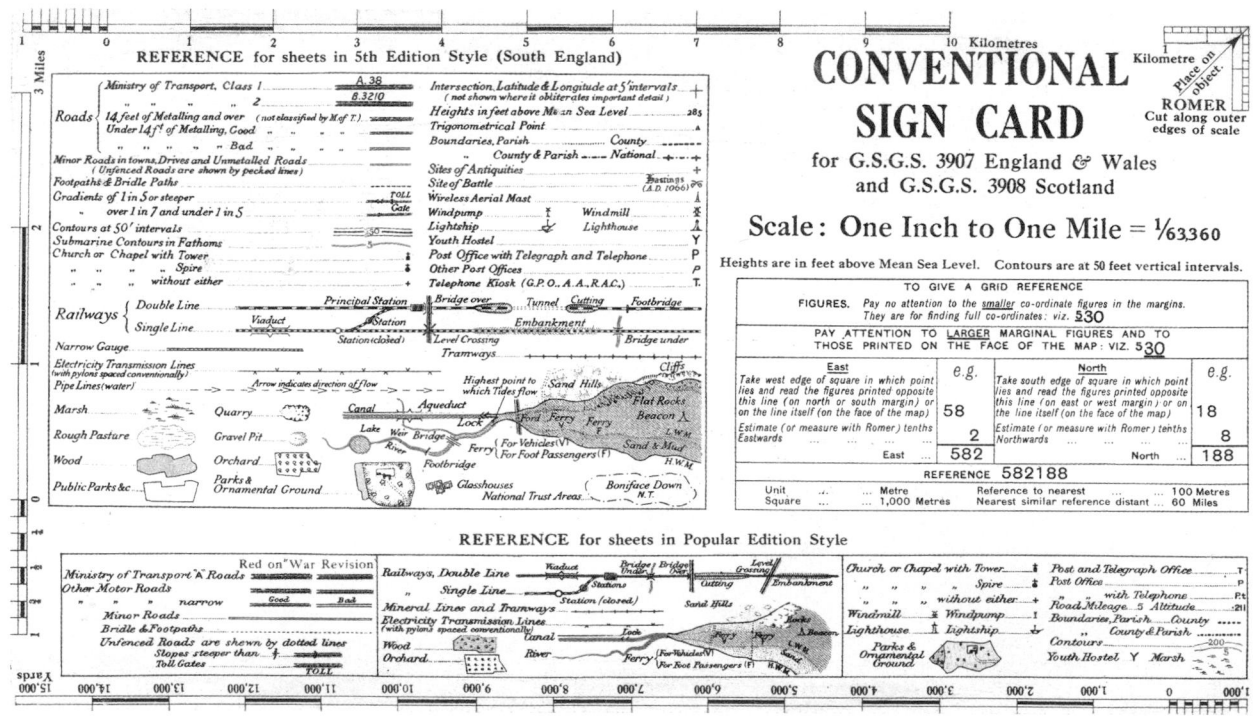

Figure 12 Conventional sign cards for GSGS 3907 and 3908, produced following the introduction of printing maps with narrow margins in the autumn of 1941. Missing from these margins were the legends showing characteristic symbols; thus these cards were made available to troops as necessary. The upper example was printed on paper in 1942, and has a sheet index on the same face, with samples of Popular Edition and Fifth Edition style mapping on the reverse; the lower example was printed on card in 1943, with an index on the back showing the sheet lines of the one-inch series GSGS 3907 and 3908 in blue, and the quarter-inch series GSGS 3957 and 3958 in red. Reduced to 70%.

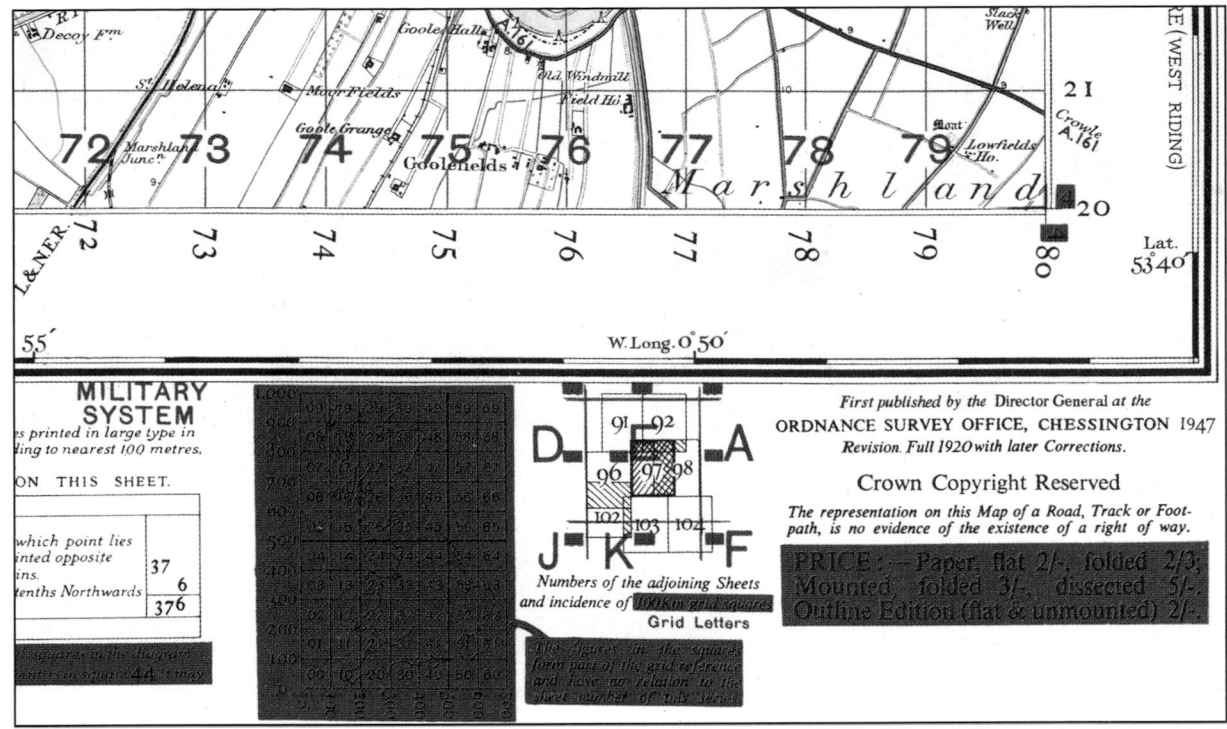

Figure 13a The south-east part of GSGS 4620 sheet 97, War Office Edition, printing 13,000/10/48, with heavy purple overprint to cancel the price note and adapt the grid for military use. The National Grid is in the style adopted in *circa* 1944-5, with numerical values for the 100 km squares: observe the eastings in the margin printed sideways.

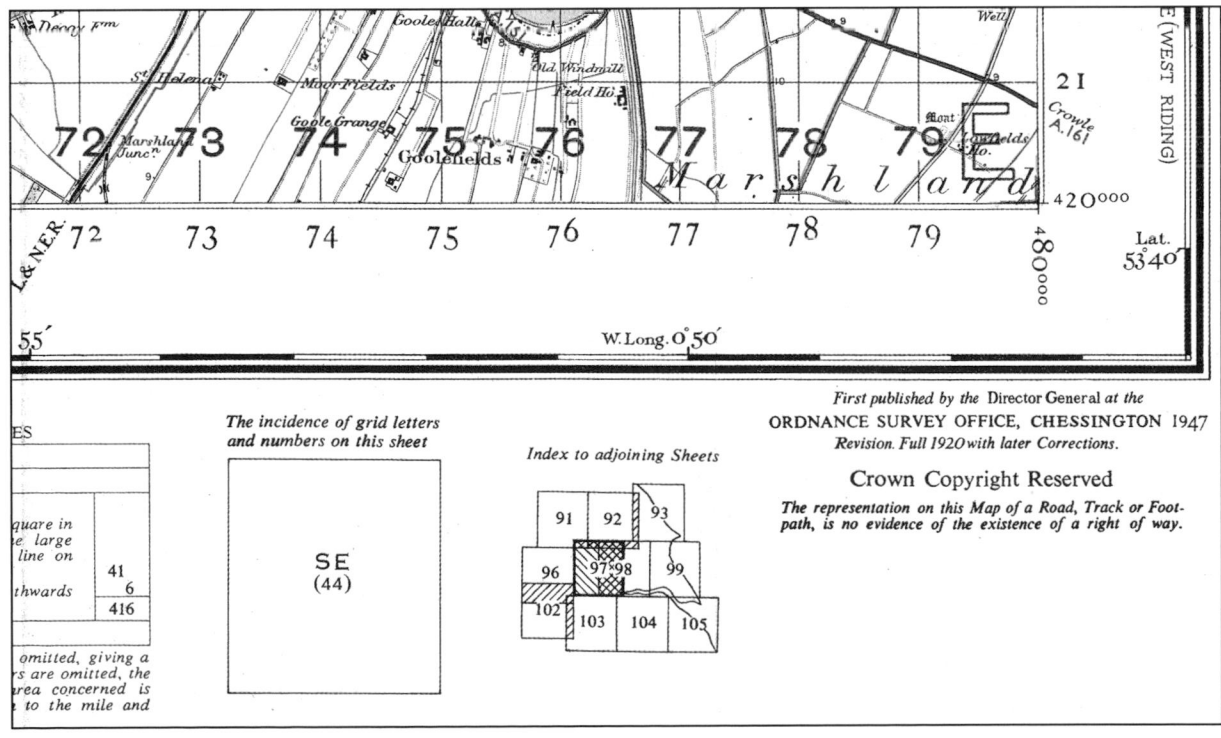

Figure 13b The south-east part of GSGS 4620 sheet 97, Second Edition, printing 20,000/12/54 OS, with the later style of grid in use once the Ordnance Survey followed military practice of letter references for the 100 km National Grid squares. Observe the eastings printed upright, and the considerable economies in purple ink.

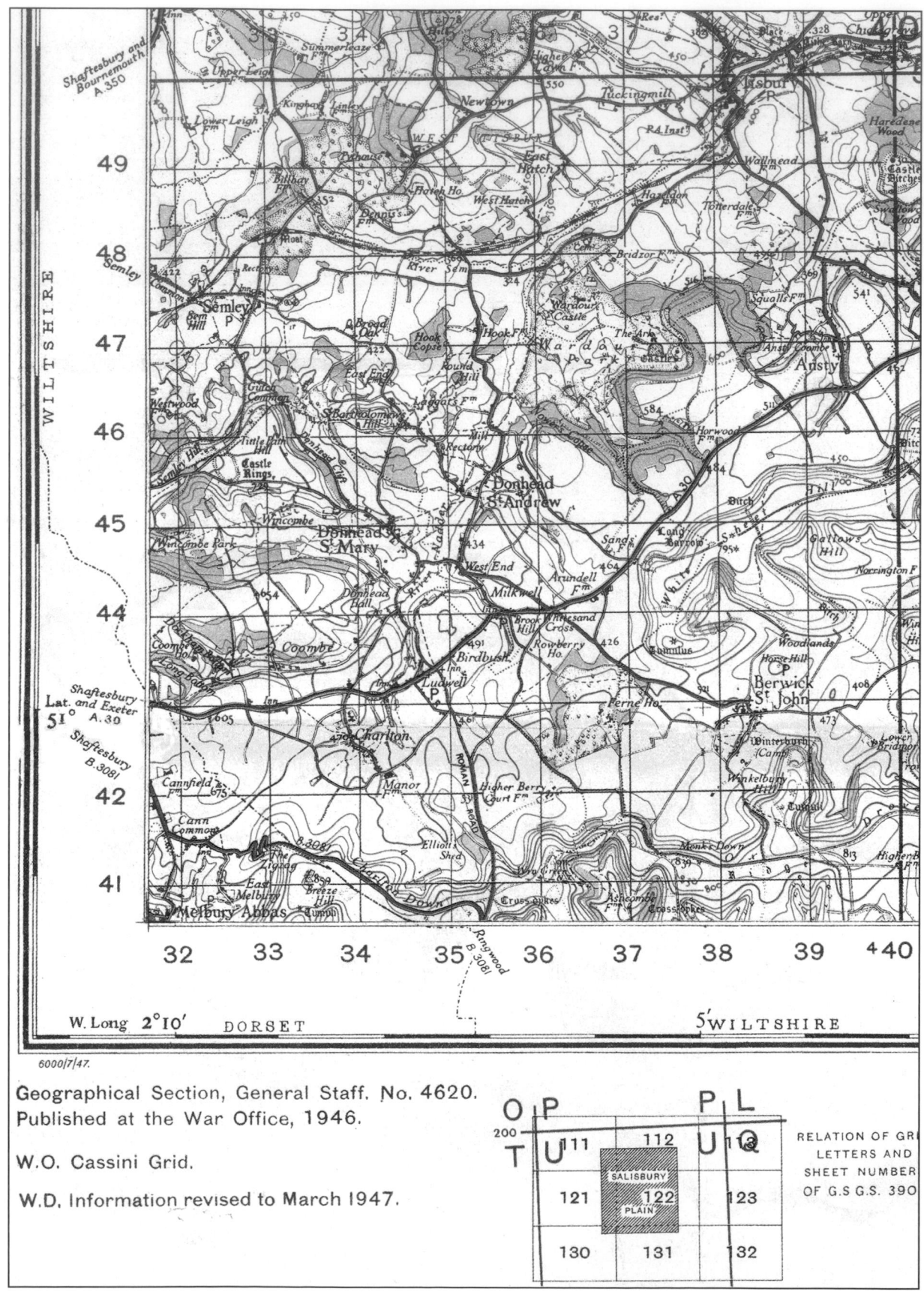

Figure 14 GSGS 4620 *Salisbury Plain*, 1946, printing 6000/7/47. Maps of the Salisbury Plain and Aldershot areas remained in constant demand in the immediate postwar years before the National Grid was adopted by the War Office. This resulted, as here, in the temporary association of the War Office Cassini Grid with New Popular Edition mapping. Roads and contours are in Air Force brown.

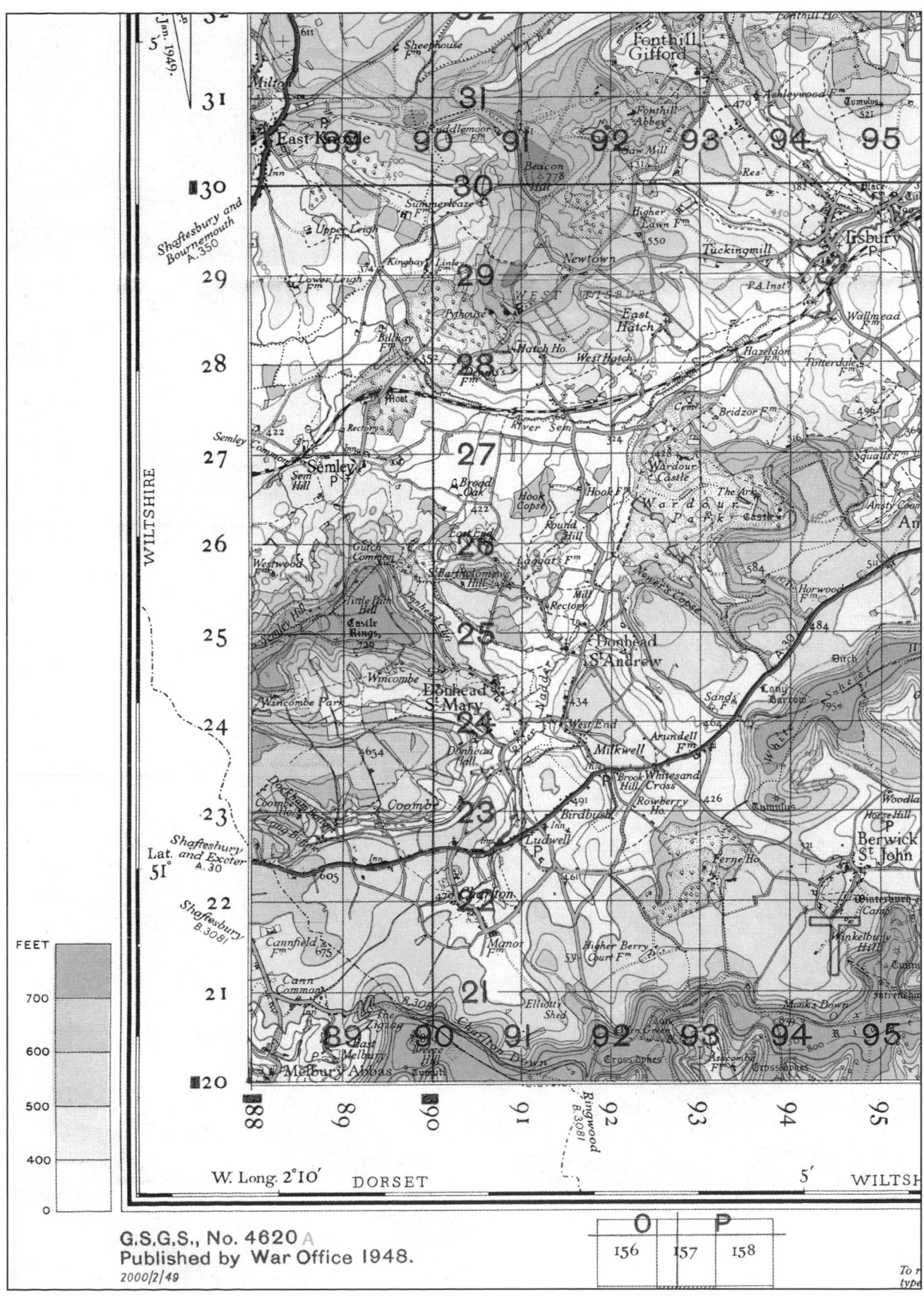

Figure 15 The south-west part of GSGS 4620A sheet 167, 1948, printing 2000/2/49, overprinted with layers for the training of officers in the Staff College. Thirteen New Popular Edition sheets covering central southern England were overprinted for this purpose. Four of them were reprinted for the last time as late as 1962.

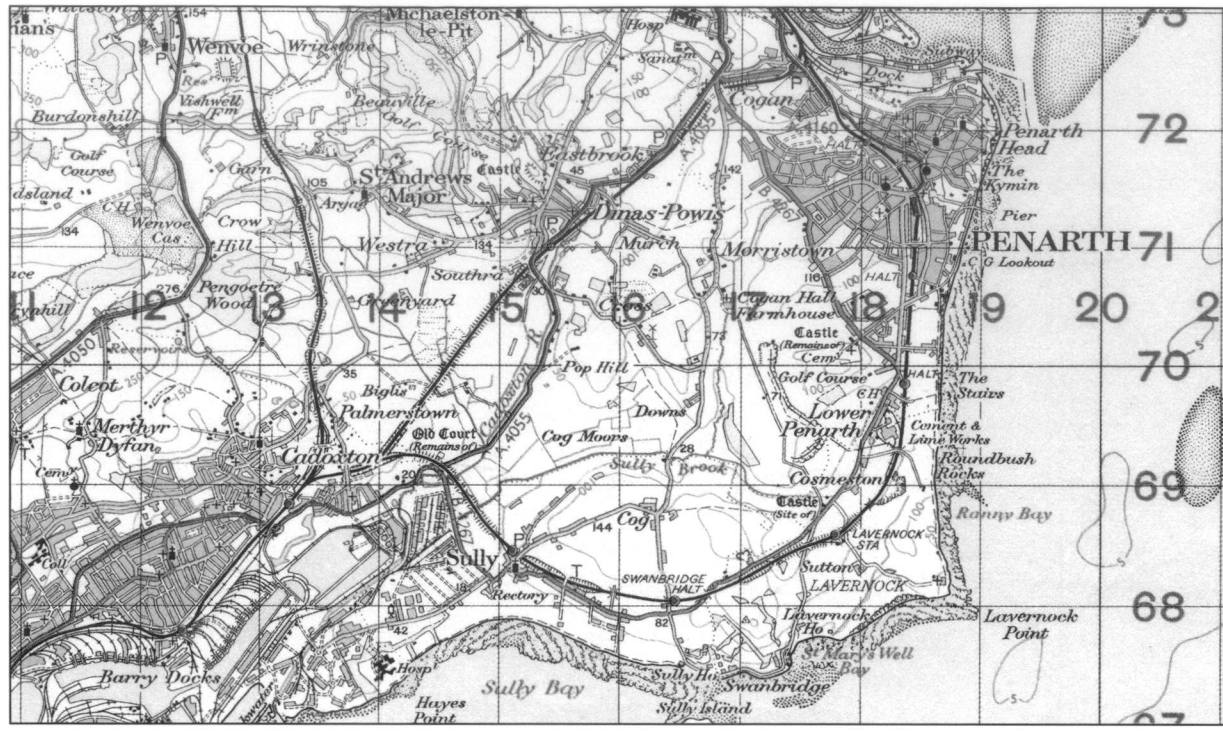

Figure 16a GSGS 4620 sheet 154, printing 20,000/6/52. This was one of six sheets printed in the original colour-scheme for GSGS 4620 printings using Seventh Series material, with building infill in grey, water infill in pale blue and grid figures in blue. Tree symbols are omitted.

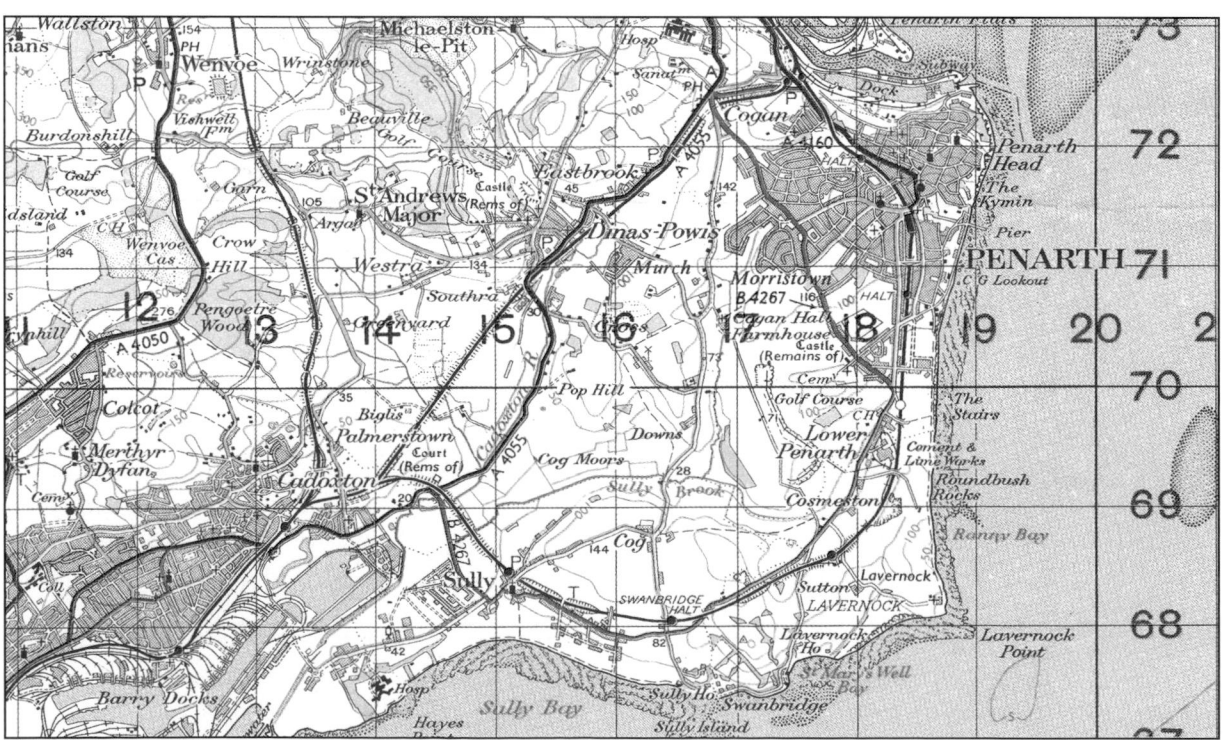

Figure 16b M722 sheet 154, printing 20,000/4/61/6118/OS. This is in the standard six-colour style adopted in 1953 for mapping using the Seventh Series: building infill is screened black, water infill is screened blue, and grid figures are in red. As with the earlier eight-colour style, tree symbols are omitted.

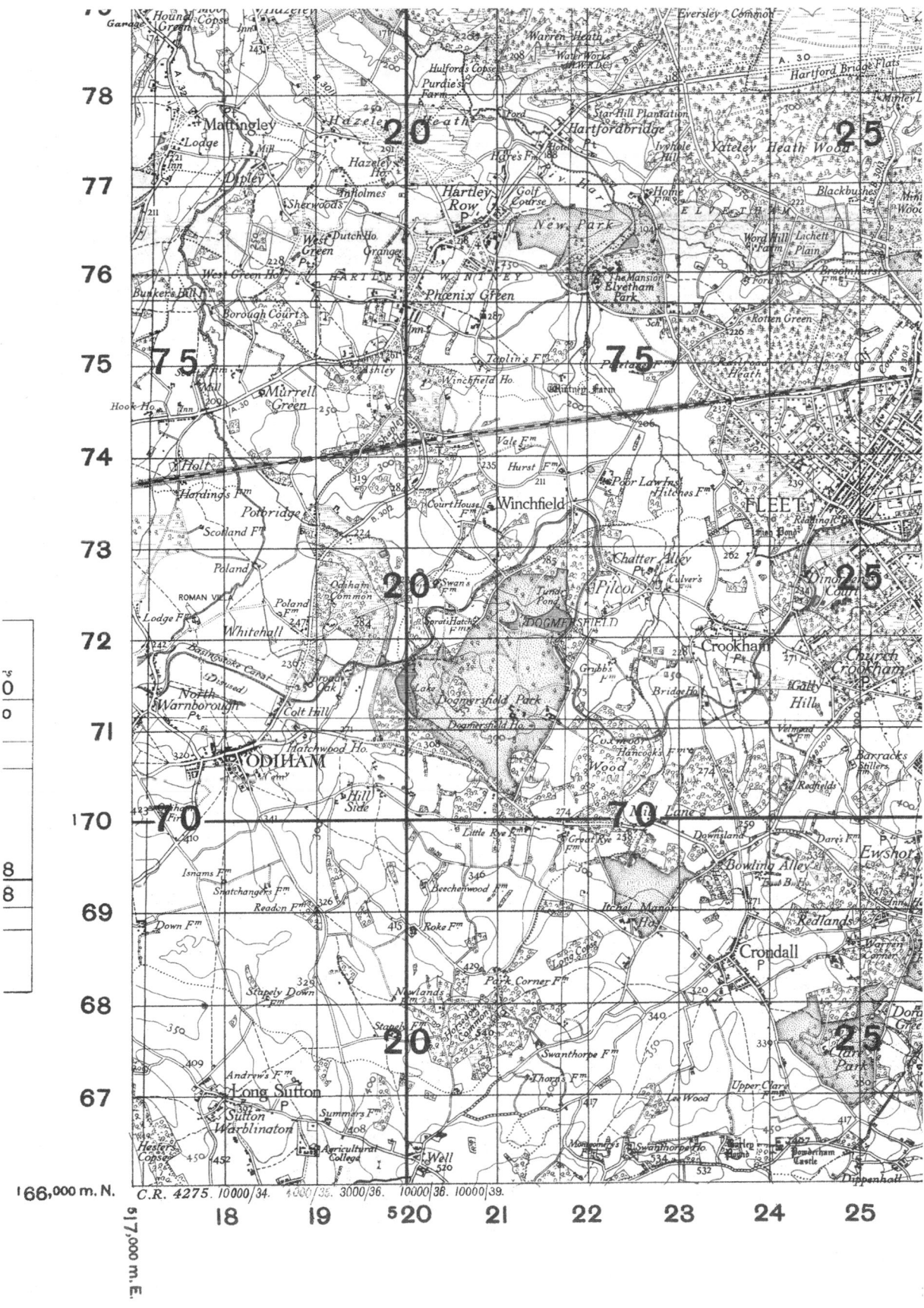

Figure 17 *Farnborough*, printing 10,000/39. This covered a small area of the Aldershot Command district and was first printed in 1934, using Fifth Edition mapping, and retaining the lines of the yard grid. There was a similar map, *Bordon*, covering the area south of this one. The military grid is in purple; there are no road or wood infills.

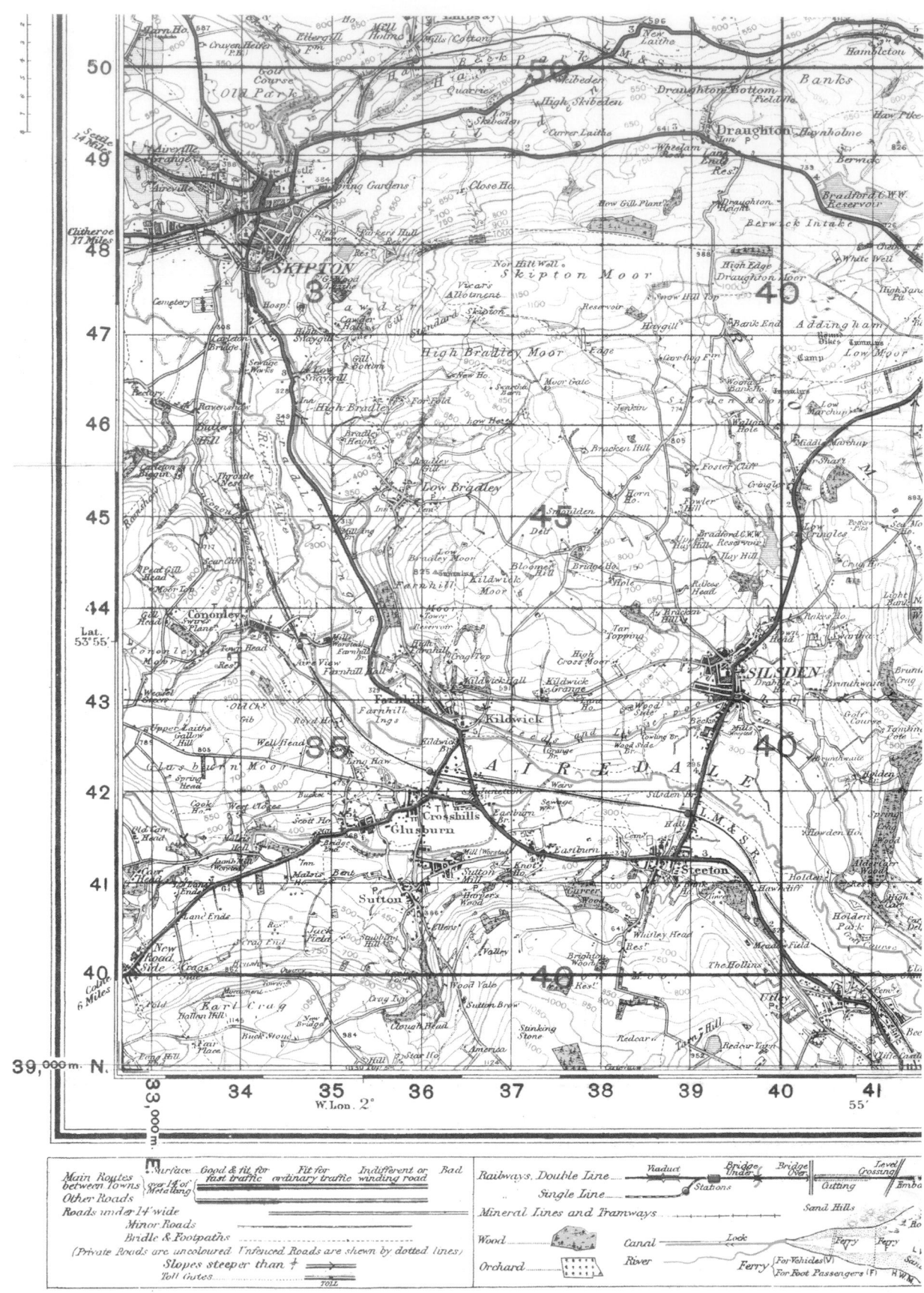

Figure 18 The south-west part of England and Wales Popular Edition sheet 26, printed in 1928: this has what would be designated the Modified British System grid in the 'definitive' style as regards marginal figures, but with the grid printed in black. The grid is laid out parallel and perpendicular to the sheet lines of the Popular Edition on the Delamere origin, but with a false origin near Atherton.

72

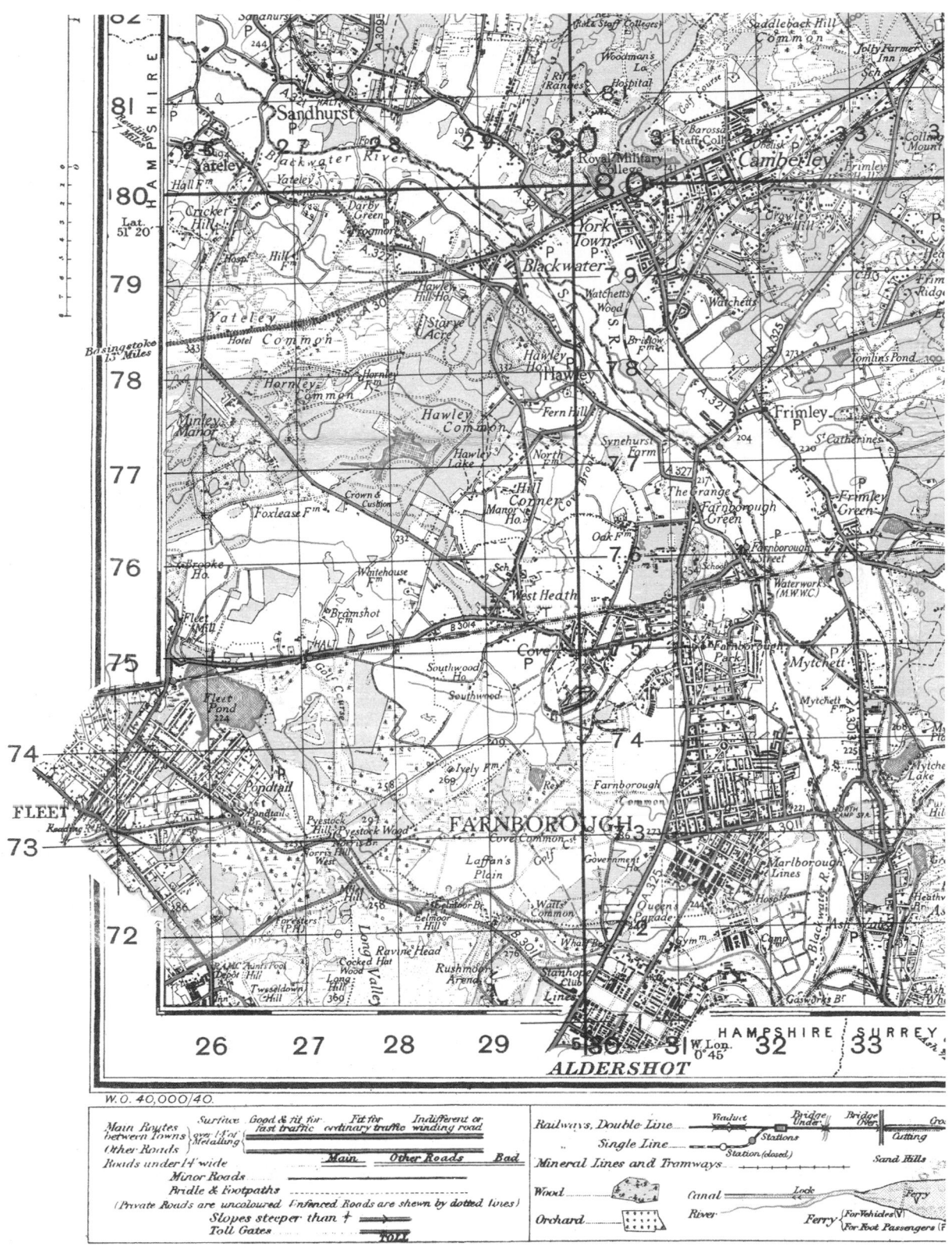

Geographical Section, General Staff. No. 3907.
Published at the War Office, 1940.

Figure 19 The south-west part of GSGS 3907 sheet 114, printing WO 40,000/40, printed in August 1940 with Fifth Edition mapping fitted into a Popular Edition frame. This was in effect the first of the Second War Revision sheets, but was designated 'Special Popular' in contemporary documents. It was to be printed in the Second War Revision four-colour scheme, but in the event was printed in five, with purple grid, and roads combined with contours. It remained valid until the stock ran out in February 1942.

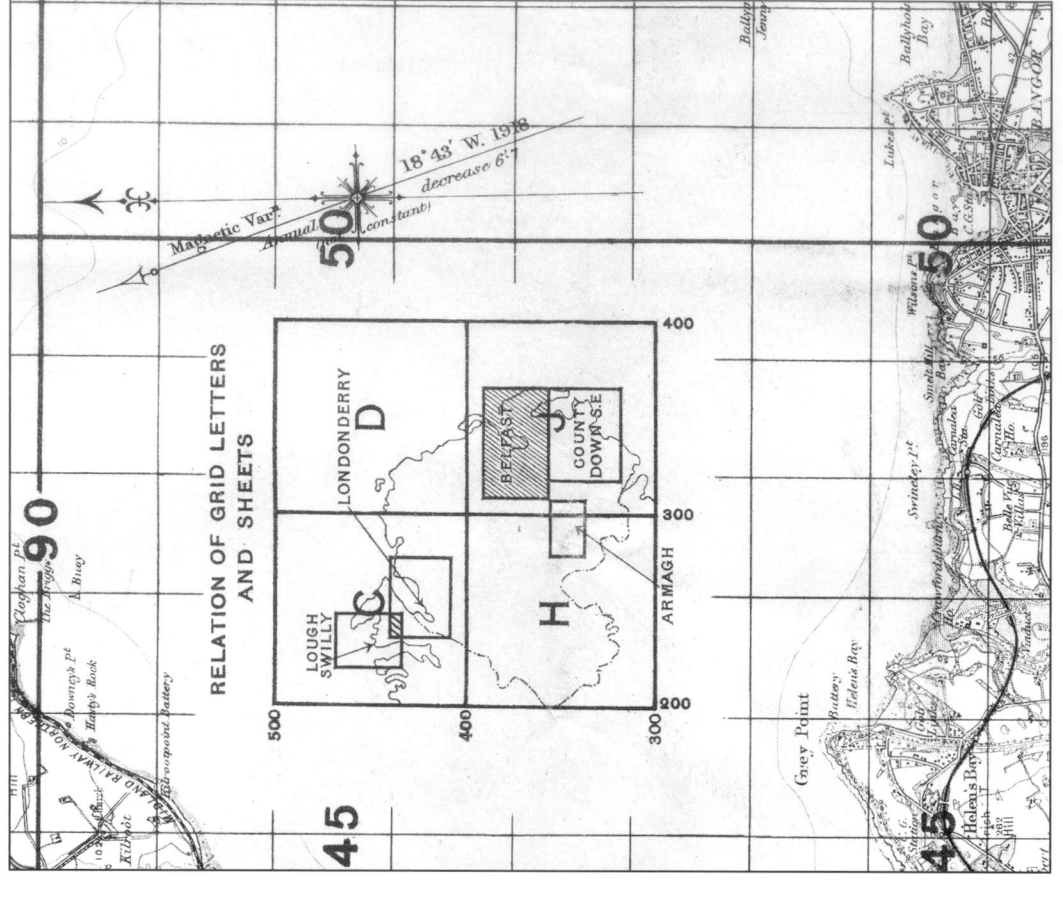

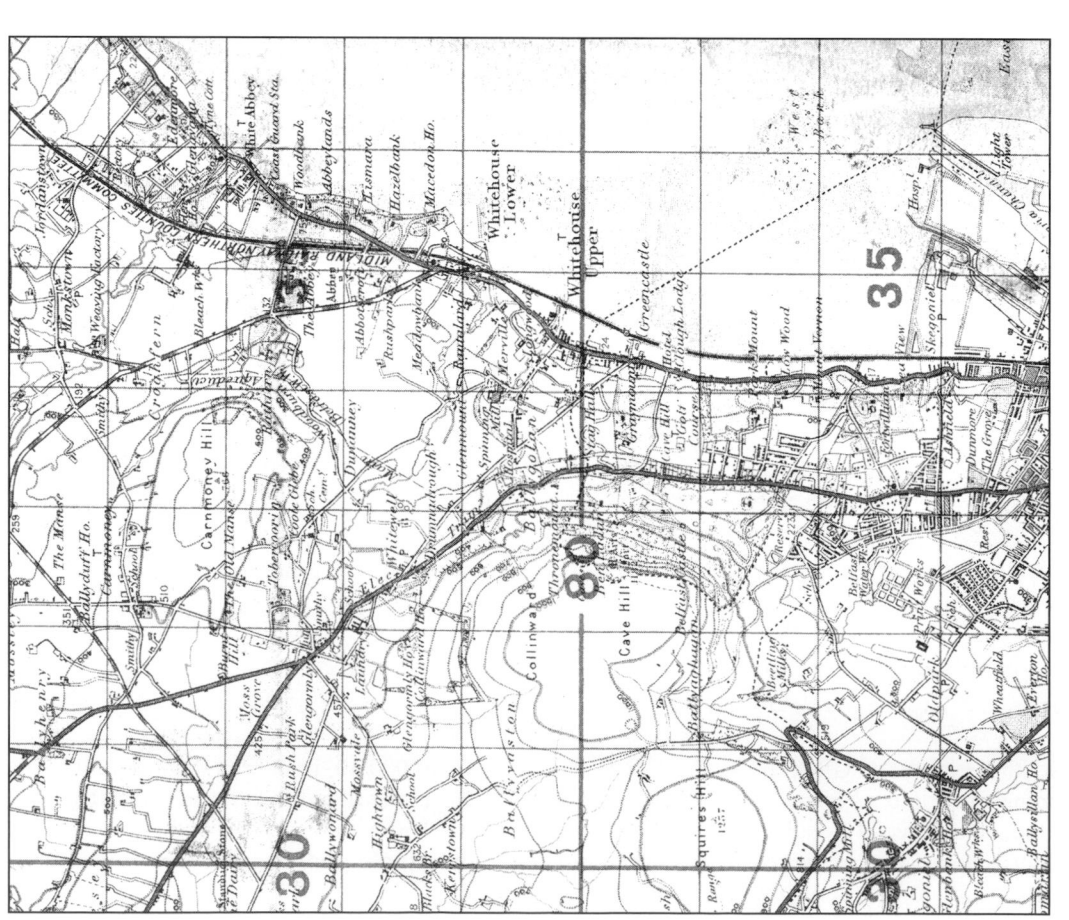

Figure 20 Two extracts from GSGS 3917 *Belfast*, printing WO 3000/32, showing the treatment of road infills and the sheet diagram. This copy is printed on Place's waterproof paper, and was stamped by the unit to which it was issued on 26 October 1932. The base mapping dates from 1918, but new contour and road plates were prepared. The road plates are of particular interest, in that colouring is by official classification: 'A' roads are solid yellow-sienna, 'B' roads are pecked yellow-sienna, though there is nothing on the map to advise users of this.

74

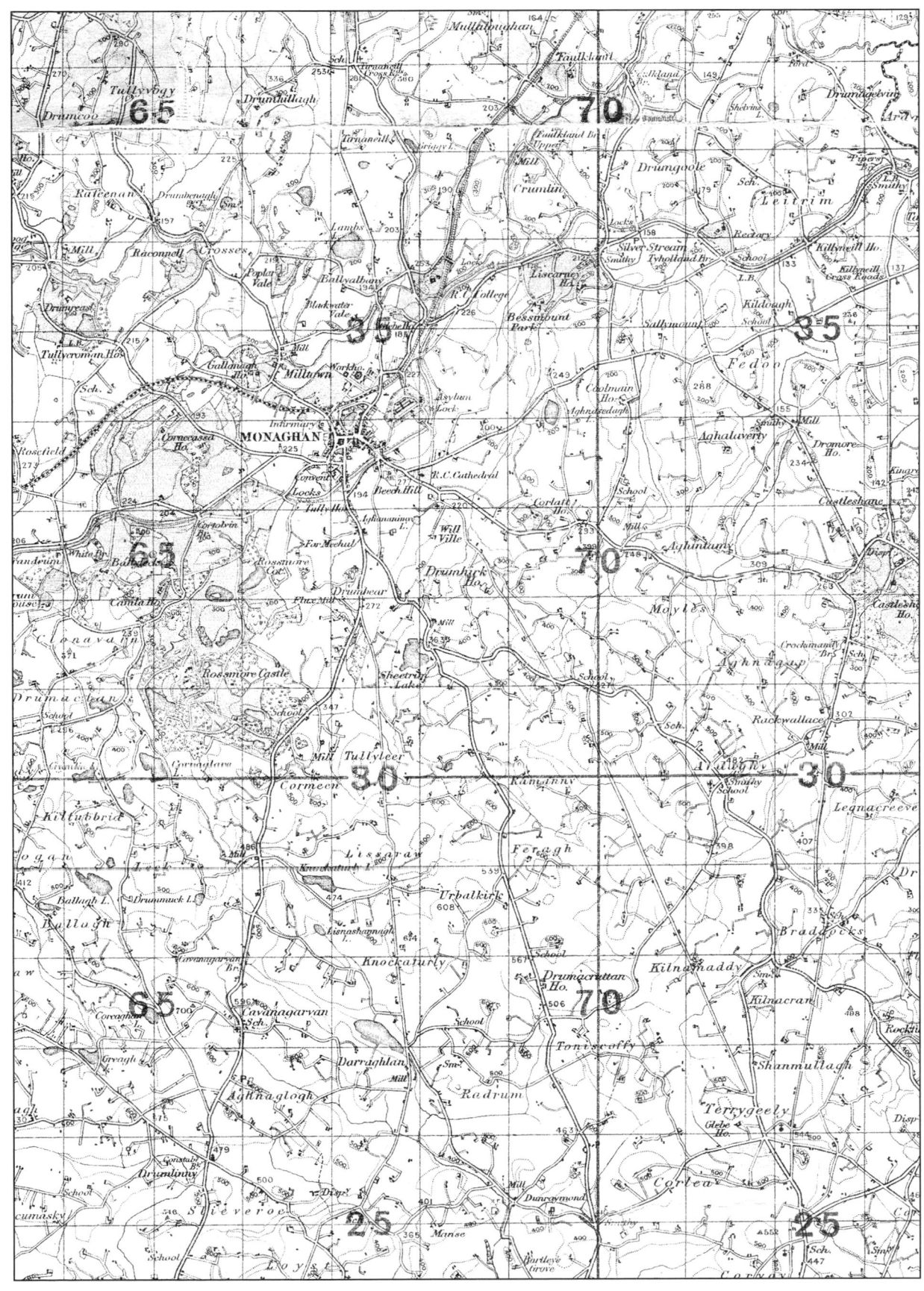

Figure 21 An extract from GSGS 3917 *Monaghan,* printing 500/34: the monochrome mapping is derived directly from the engraved one-inch, with the War Office Irish Grid overprinted in purple

75

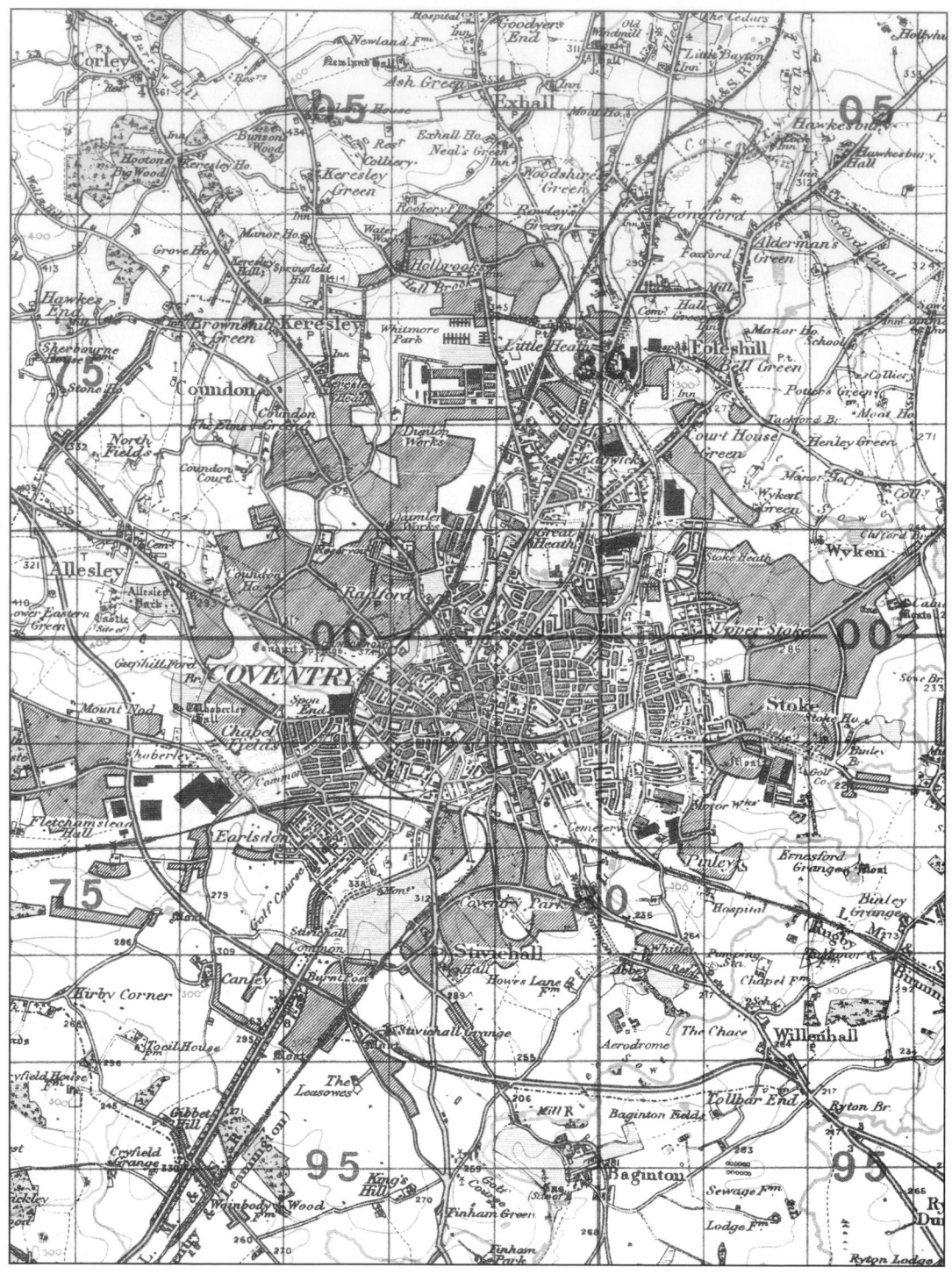

Figure 22 GSGS 3907 sheet 72, War Revision, without print code. This illustrates both the serious outdatedness of the Popular Edition by the late 1930s for areas such as Coventry which were growing rapidly, and the subtle distinction in the depiction of revision made for ARP purposes of industrial from other building: the former is solid black, the latter is hatched.

MILITARY EDITION (1940)

SECOND WAR REVISION SHEET 132

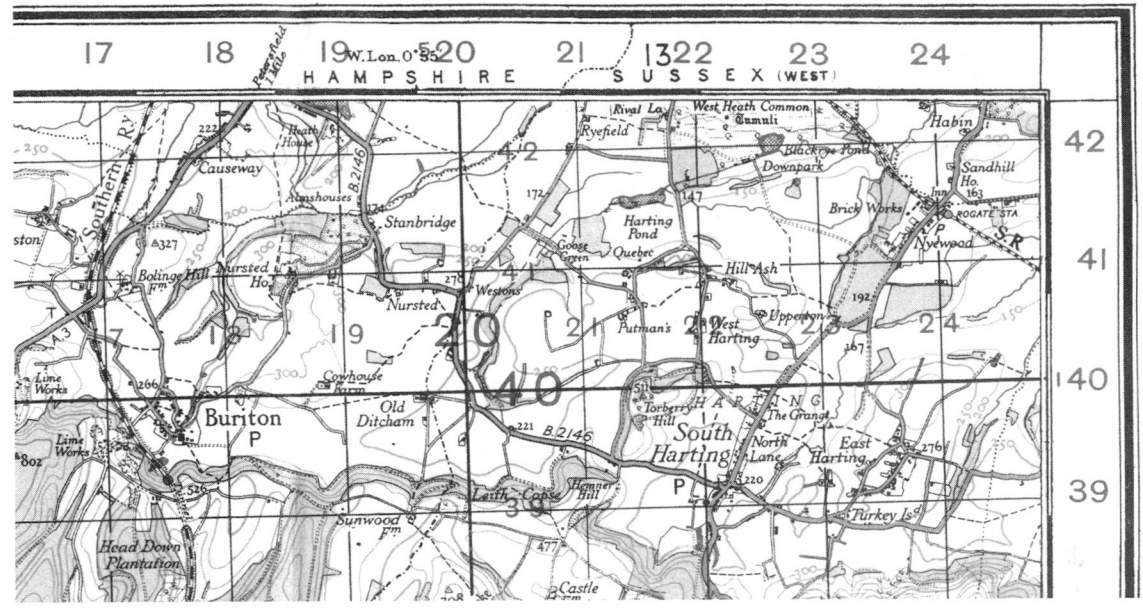

SECOND WAR REVISION 1940 SHEET 132

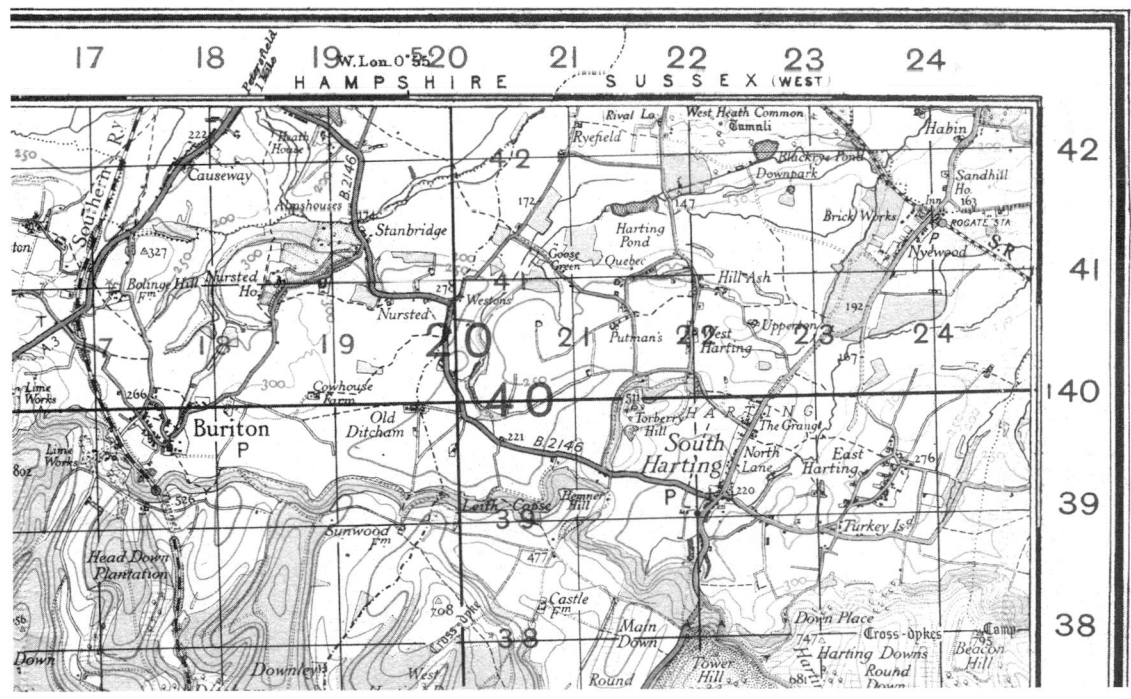

Figure 23 GSGS 3907 sheet 132, Second War Revision. At the top is a prototype printing without print code, with what was presumably the heading for Second War Revision as originally intended; underneath the map as issued, printing WO 50,000/5/41, where 'military edition' was thought superfluous.

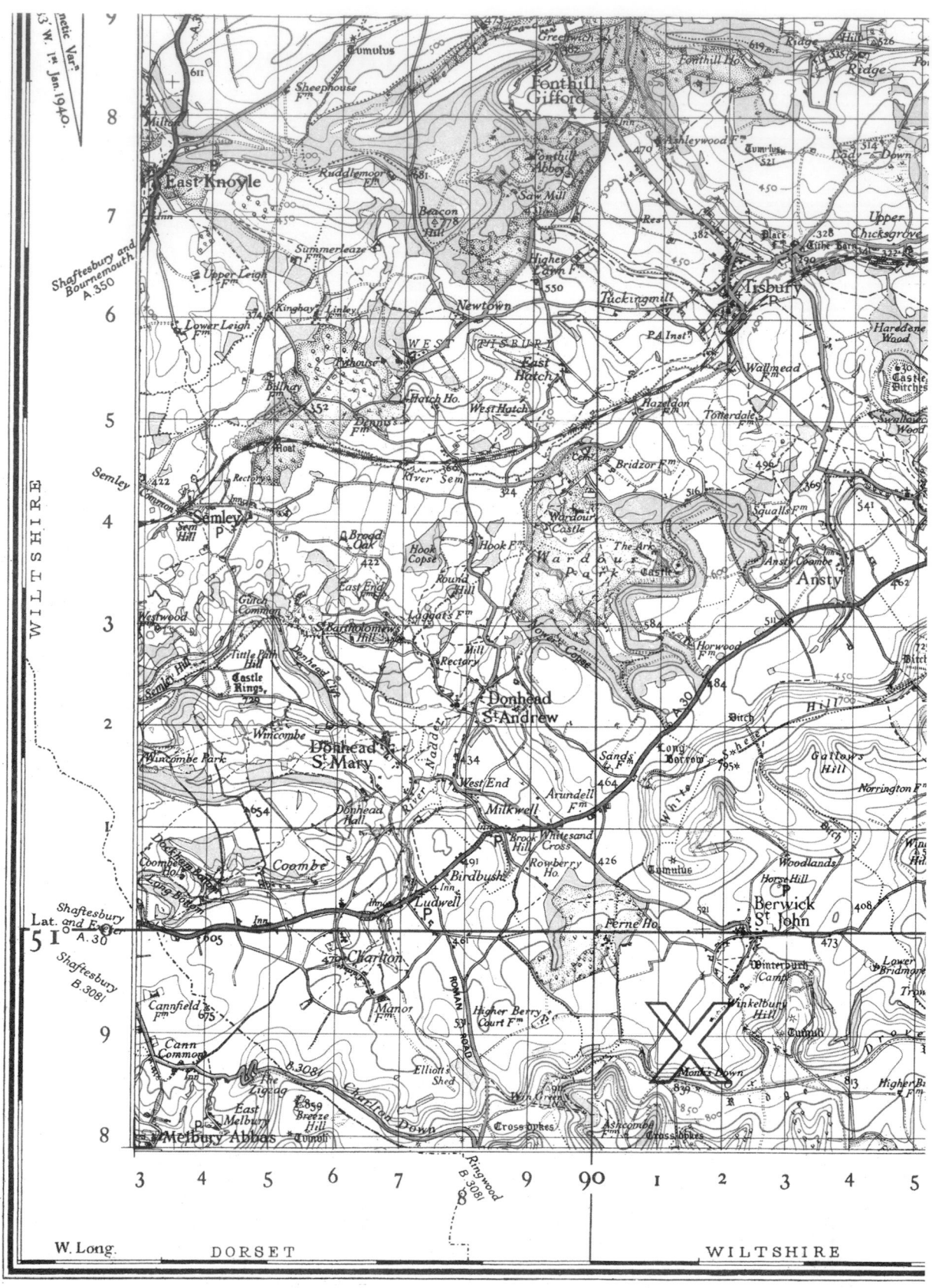

Figure 24 The south-west part of an experimental printing for artillery training purposes of New Popular Edition sheet 167 *Salisbury*, printed in 1945 with a graticule reference system, overprinted in purple. In this each degree of latitude and longitude was divided into 100, and a six-figure 'grid reference' could be given by dividing the distance between the grid lines into tenths. The finally approved version had each degree of latitude and longitude divided into minutes, and was published with the heading *D.R.A's investigation of graticules*. See page 254.

*One-inch Popular Edition
map of Scotland
GSGS 3908 and GSGS 4639*

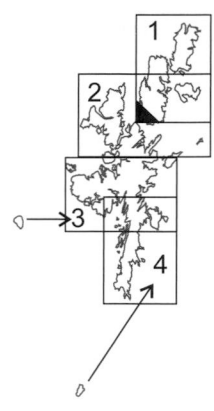

				1	
		2			
			3→		
				4	

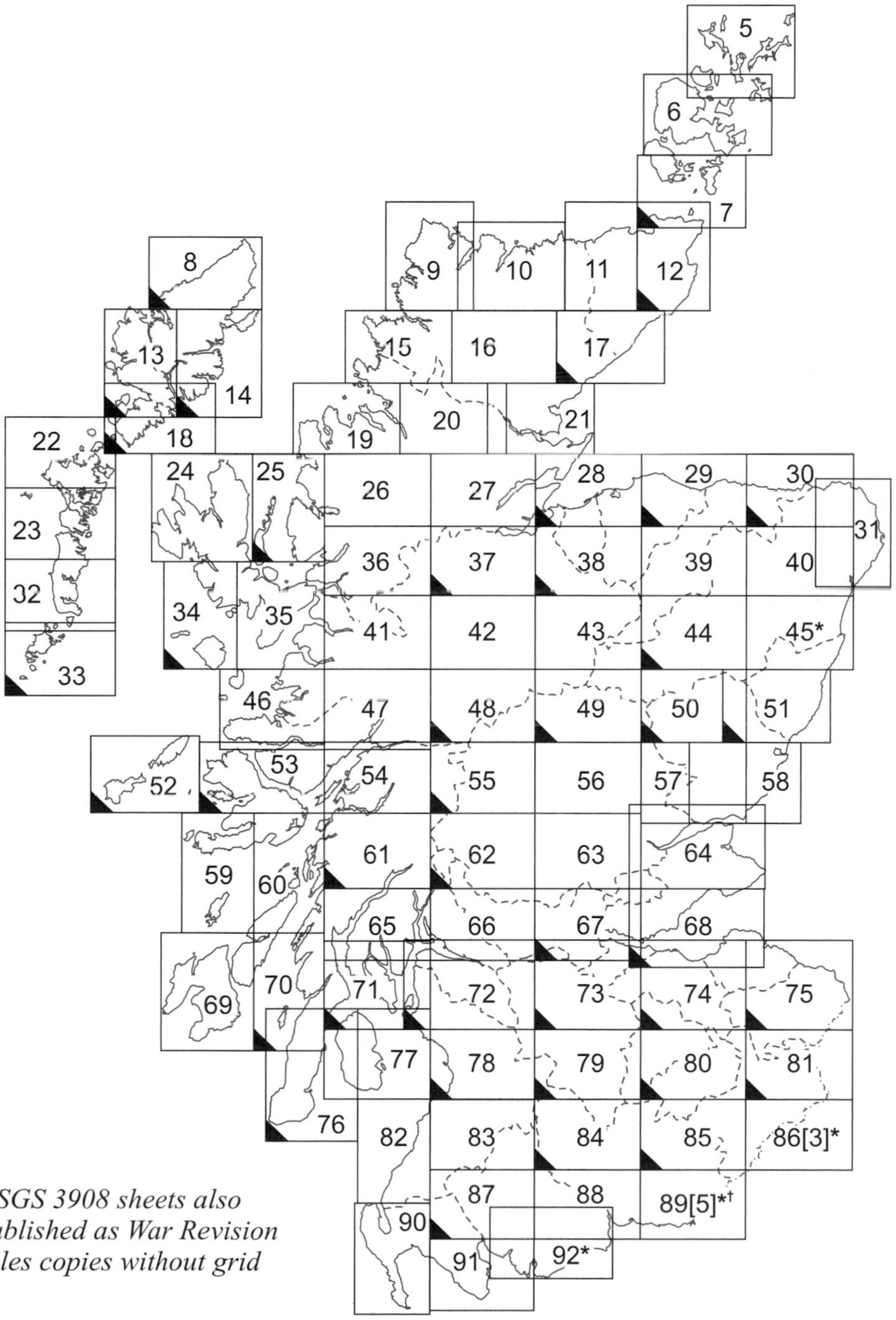

5

6

7

8	9	10	11	12

13		15	16	17
	14			

22	18	19	20	21
23	24	25	26	27

28	29	30
38	39	40

31

32	34	35	36	37
33			41	42

43	44	45*

46	47	48	49	50	51
52	53	54	55	56	57	58

59	60	61	62	63	64
69	70	65	66	67	68

71	72	73	74	75
76	77	78	79	80	81

82	83	84	85	86[3]*
90	87	88	89[5]*†	
91	92*			

| 49 | *GSGS 3908 sheets also
published as War Revision
sales copies without grid* |
|---|---|

| 45* | *GSGS 3908 sheets
also published as
Second War Revision* |
|---|---|

| 89† | *Sheet not published
in GSGS 4639* |
|---|---|

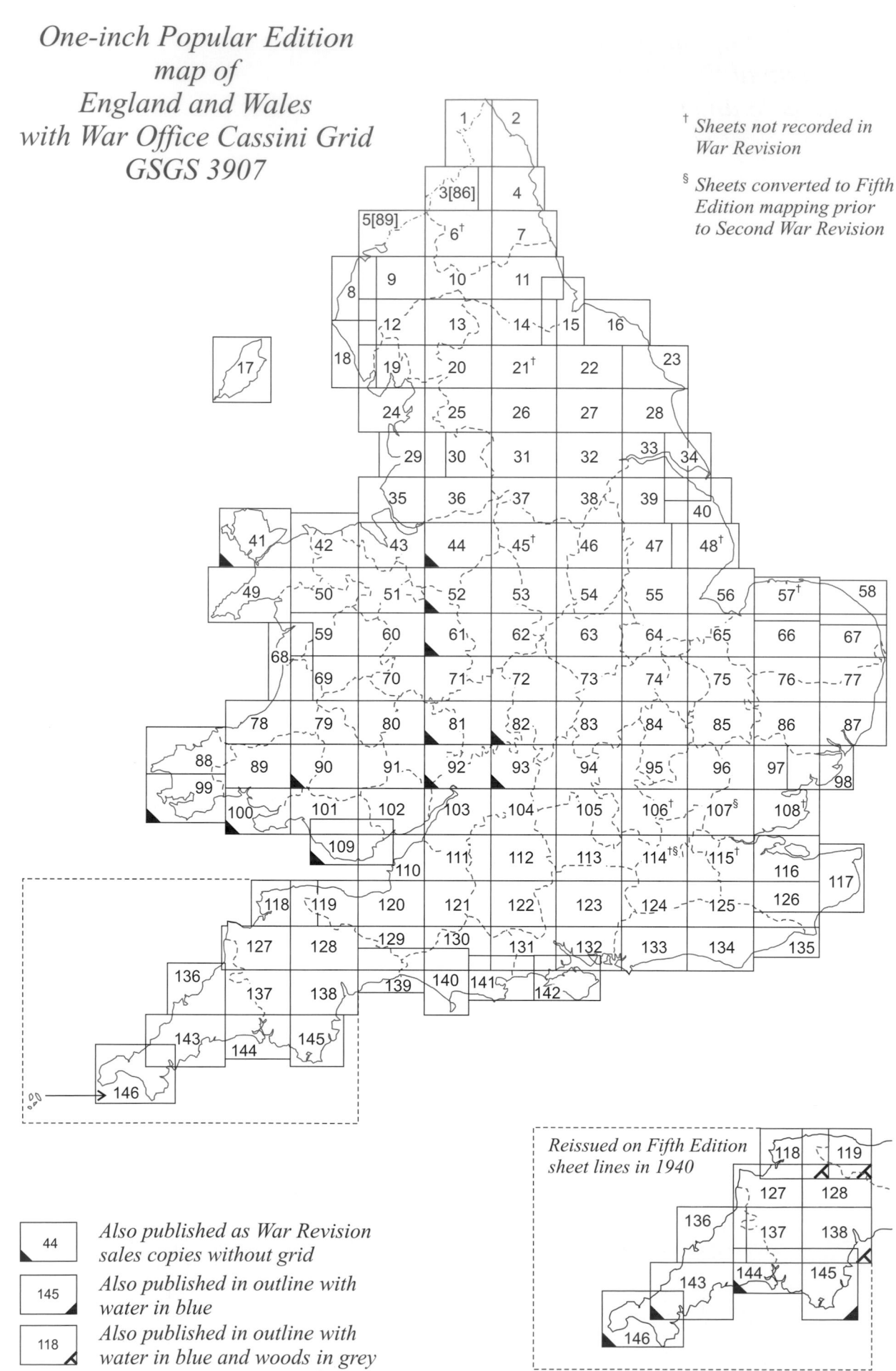

One-inch Popular Edition
map of
England and Wales
with War Office Cassini Grid
GSGS 3907

† *Sheets not recorded in War Revision*

§ *Sheets converted to Fifth Edition mapping prior to Second War Revision*

Reissued on Fifth Edition sheet lines in 1940

44   *Also published as War Revision sales copies without grid*

145   *Also published in outline with water in blue*

118   *Also published in outline with water in blue and woods in grey*

Second War Revision
map of
England and Wales
GSGS 3907

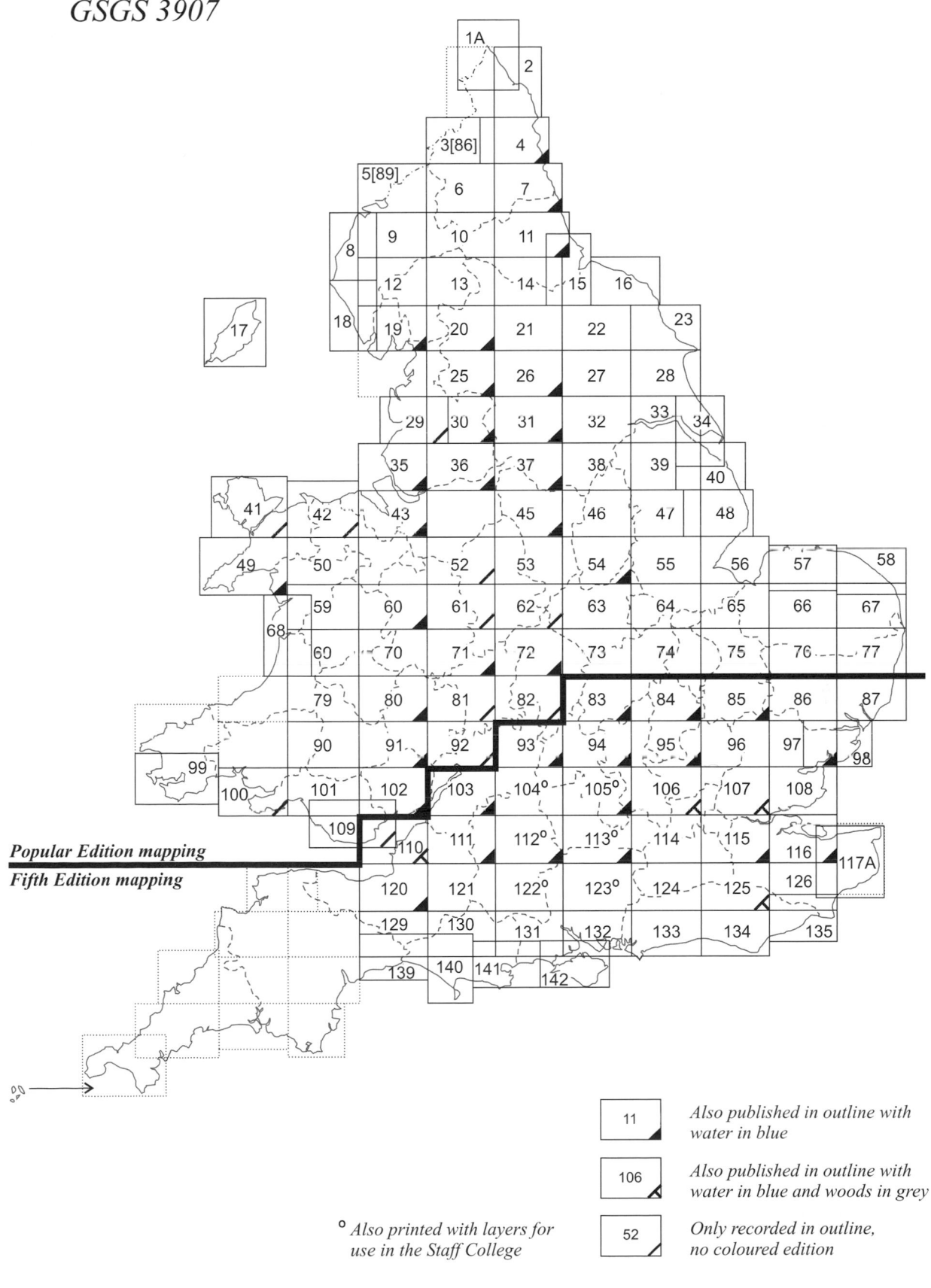

1A
2
3[86]
4
5[89]
6
7
8
9
10
11
12
13
14
15
16
17
18
19
20
21
22
23
25
26
27
28
29
30
31
32
33
34
35
36
37
38
39
40
41
42
43
45
46
47
48
49
50
52
53
54
55
56
57
58
59
60
61
62
63
64
65
66
67
68
69
70
71
72
73
74
75
76
77
79
80
81
82
83
84
85
86
87
90
91
92
93
94
95
96
97
98
99
100
101
102
103
104°
105°
106
107
108
109
110
111
112°
113°
114
115
116
117A
120
121
122°
123°
124
125
126
129
130
131
132
133
134
135
139
140
141
142

Popular Edition mapping

Fifth Edition mapping

11	*Also published in outline with water in blue*
106	*Also published in outline with water in blue and woods in grey*
52	*Only recorded in outline, no coloured edition*

° *Also printed with layers for use in the Staff College*

81

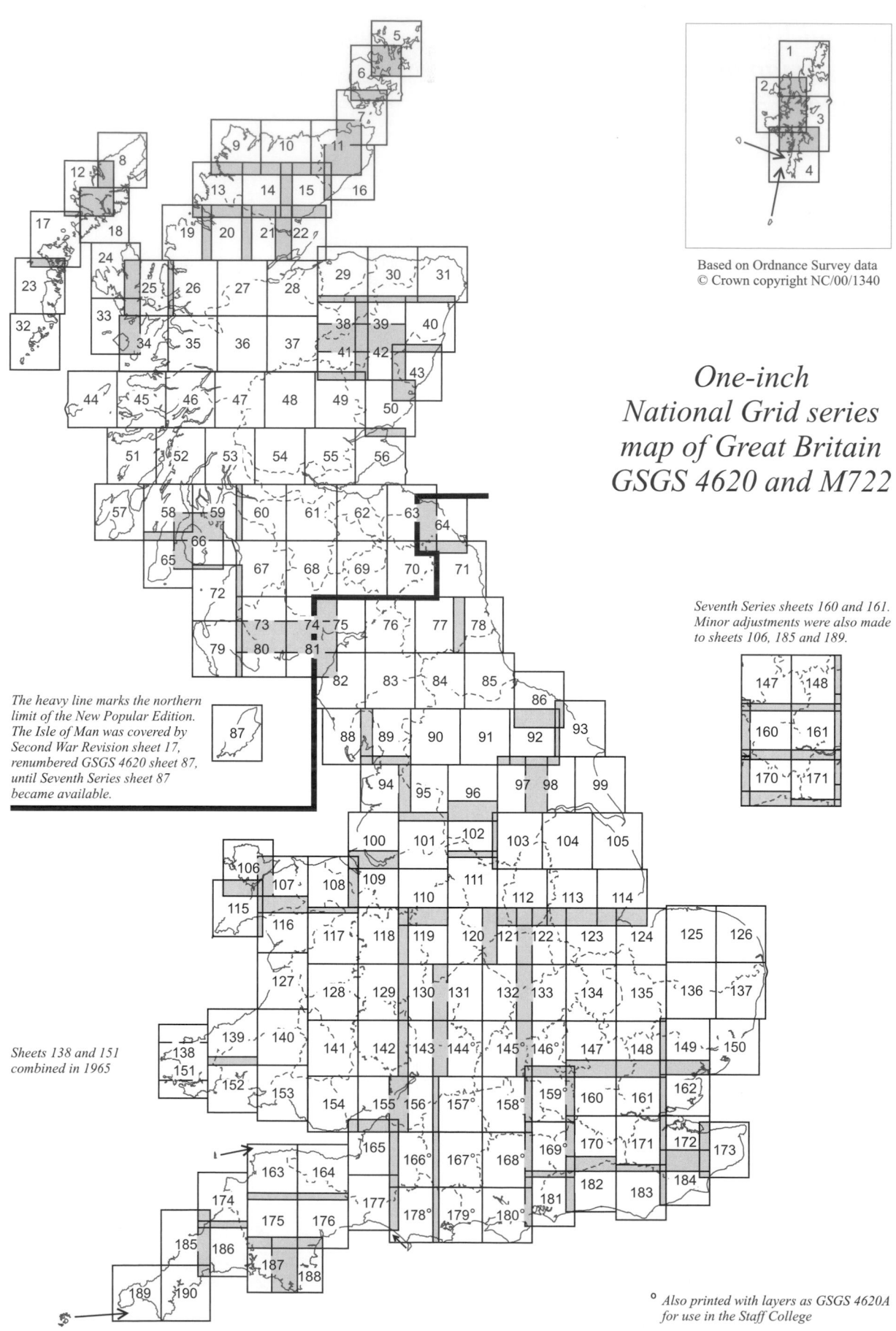

Based on Ordnance Survey data
© Crown copyright NC/00/1340

One-inch
National Grid series
map of Great Britain
GSGS 4620 and M722

Seventh Series sheets 160 and 161.
Minor adjustments were also made
to sheets 106, 185 and 189.

The heavy line marks the northern
limit of the New Popular Edition.
The Isle of Man was covered by
Second War Revision sheet 17,
renumbered GSGS 4620 sheet 87,
until Seventh Series sheet 87
became available.

Sheets 138 and 151
combined in 1965

° *Also printed with layers as GSGS 4620A*
for use in the Staff College

One-inch maps of Ireland with War Office Irish Grid
GSGS 3917 and GSGS 3943

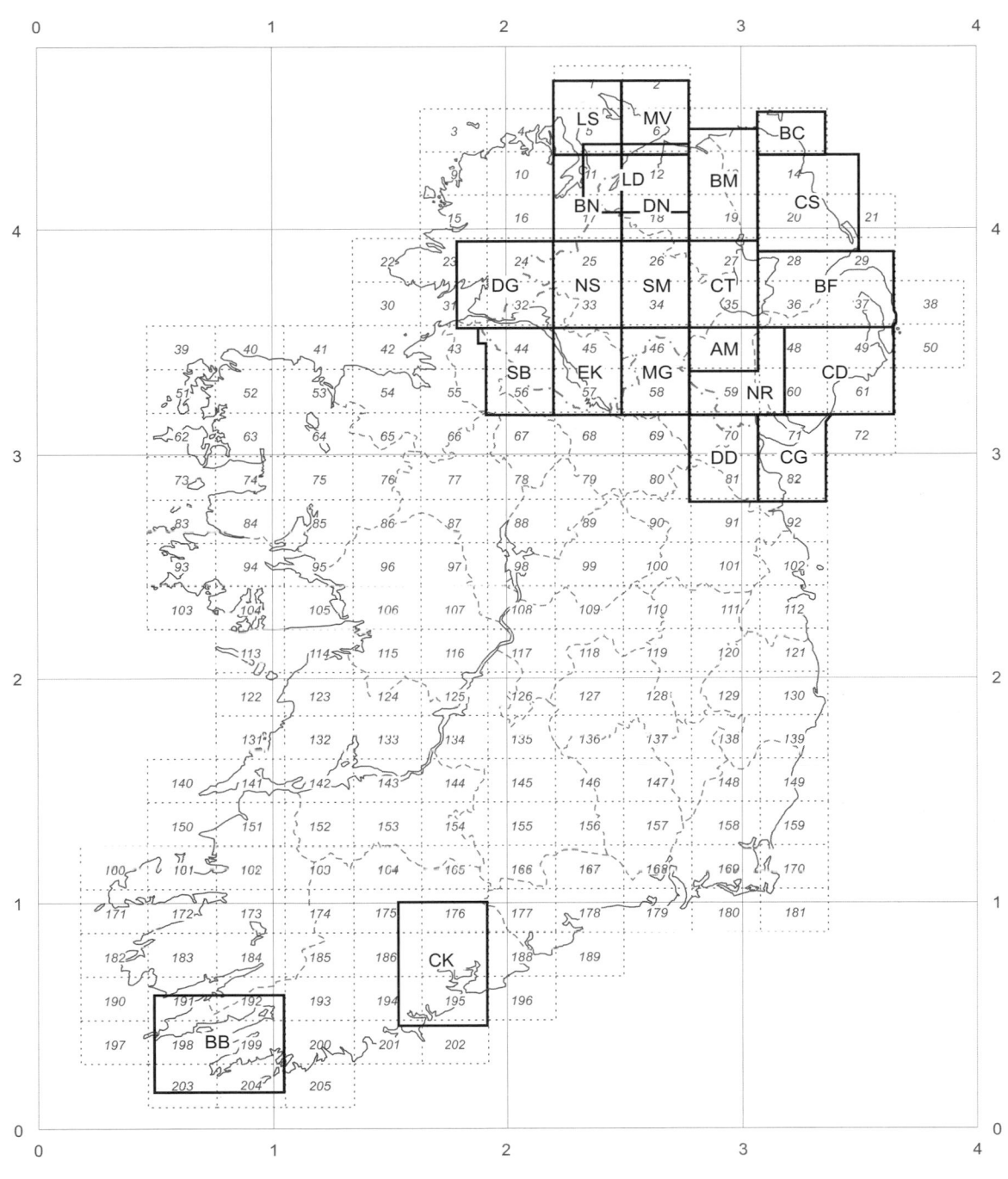

GSGS 3943

BB *Bantry Bay*
CK *Cork*

GSGS 3917
coloured sheets

AM *Armagh*
BF *Belfast*
CD *County Down S.E.*
LD *Londonderry*
LS *Lough Swilly*

GSGS 3917 *outline sheets*

BC *Ballycastle*
BM *Ballymoney*
BN *Buncrana*
CG *Clogher*
CT *Cookstown*
CS *Cushendall*

DG *Donegal*
DD *Dundalk*
DN *Dungiven*
EK *Enniskillen*
MG *Monaghan*

MV *Moville*
NR *Newry*
NS *Newtown Stewart*
SM *Six Mile Cross*
SB *Swanlinbar*

One-inch map of Ireland with War Office Irish Grid large sheet series, GSGS 4136

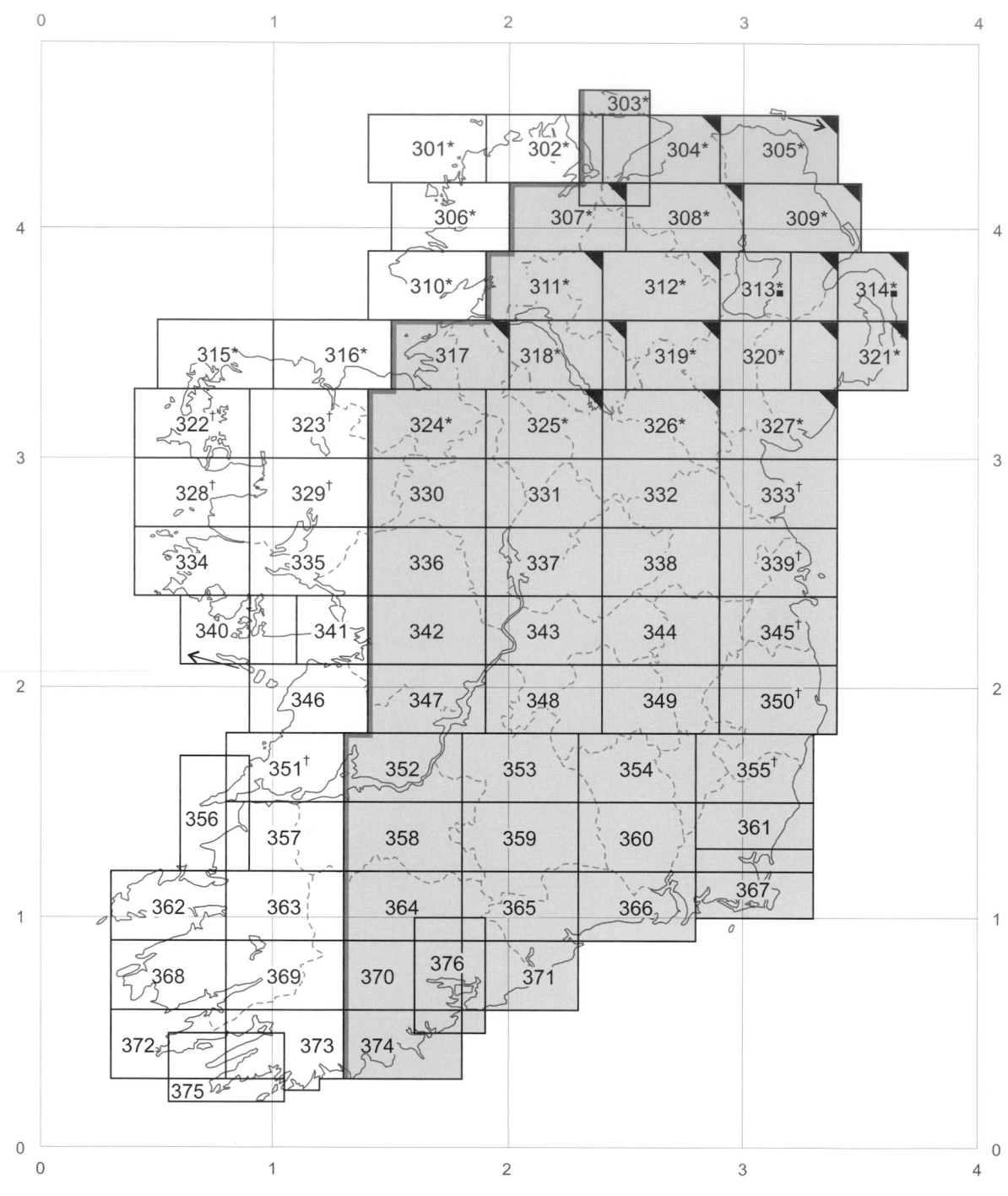

		Sheets in this area also published with layers
330		

		Also published with training areas overprinted
317		

Post-war reprints

* coloured sheet reprinted 1952-54
† coloured sheet reprinted 1959
■ layered sheet reprinted 1962

One-inch map of Northern Ireland, National Grid series, M723

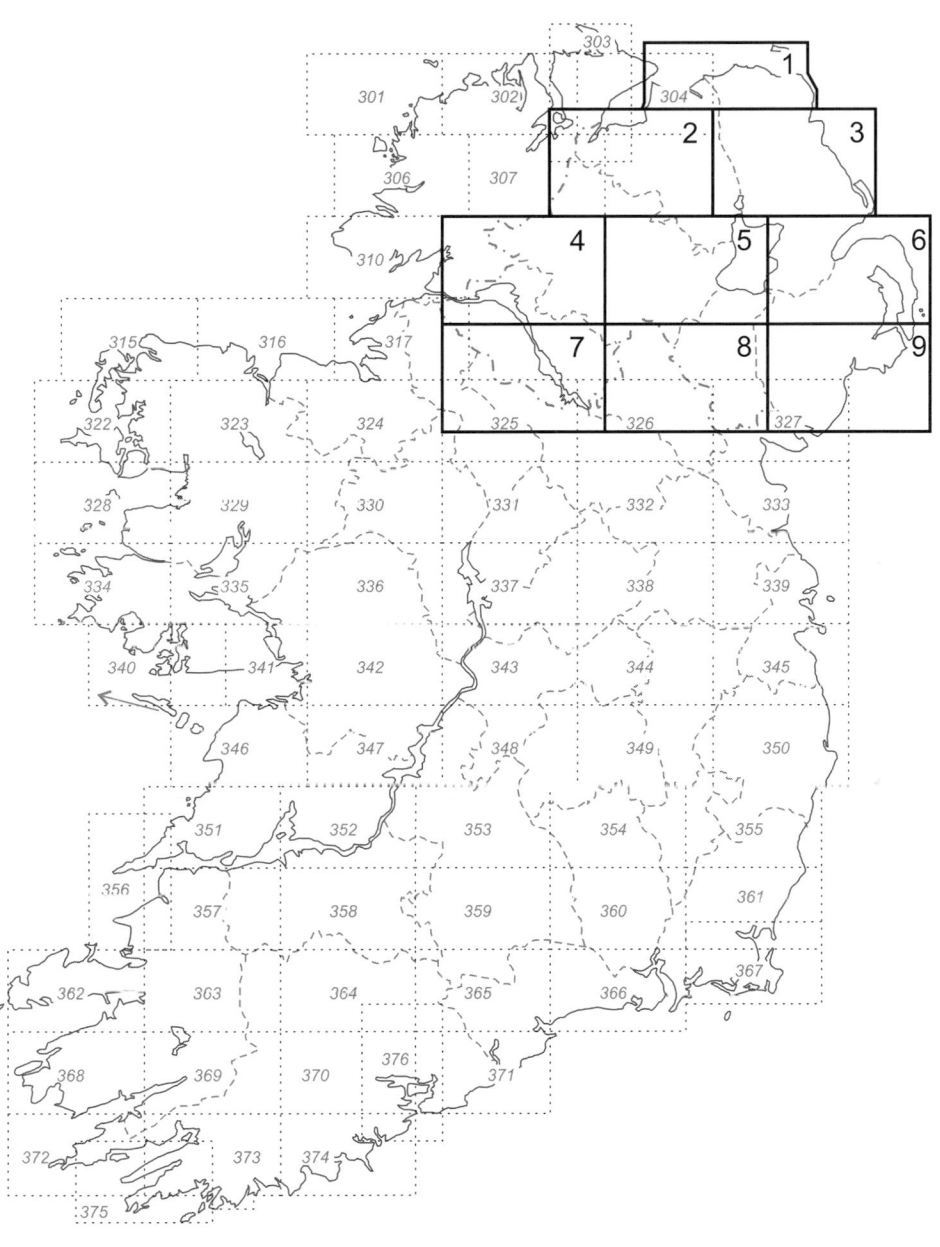

One-inch map of Northern Ireland, National Grid series, M723

Sheets of GSGS 4136 which remained in print

Cassini Grid series, 1923-1962

This is a cartobibliography in two parts, the first covering Cassini gridded maps and the second National Grid maps. The two parts have necessarily been organised in fundamentally different ways, but within each a consistency of method has been attempted in the numbering of columns, so that the numbers themselves and their functions may quickly become familiar to the user. No single map requires data in every column, and only the numbers relevant to the current map appear at the top of every page of its listing. The following is a description of the use of all headings and columns that appear in sections 1 to 6 of the book. The layout of the cartobibliography of National Grid series is described beginning on page 196.

Sections 1 to 6.

The headings contain three elements, not always used:

1.	Sheet number and name, or, in the case of district maps, sheet title, together with any sheet numbers quoted. Where the title is altered during the life of the map, the alternative forms are noted, with cross reference letters to column 10.

2.	First use: date of revision, as printed on the map. This is in fact reserved for certain district maps in this list. For the revision dates of Popular Edition series sheets, the reader is referred to Hodson (1999) (England and Wales) and Oliver (2000b) (Scotland); for those of the Fifth Edition to Oliver (2000a).

	Second use: the heading date on all War Revisions is 1940, it is also 1940 on all but four Second War Revision sheets: Scotland 45, 92, England and Wales 7, 117A. These exceptional cases only are noted here.

3.	Sheet dimensions. The coverage of the sheet is given, width by height. (The information is not offered in cases where sheets of more than one size are being described, when the information can often be calculated from details given in footnotes.) Users may need to compensate for the one mile overlap on the east and south sides of many sheets in the Scotland Popular Edition and the 2000 yard overlap on England and Wales Fifth Edition, which are included in the dimensions offered here. Sheet dimensions may be given in miles, kilometres or yards, depending on the base map used. Accuracy seems more valuable than consistency. Where the dimensions of specially made sheets are a product of the grid, details are given in the sheet footnotes in the form (144-156, 244-256) representing in most cases War Office Cassini Grid eastings, then northings, in kilometres. Some sheets have sheet lines partly based on those of the base map, partly on the grid, which in Great Britain lies at an angle to the sheet lines. Such sheets are thus not rectangular. These are described as concisely as possible.

The lists contain up to fifteen columns:

1.	Sheet edition.
	GSGS 3907, 3908: in their Popular Edition phase (as these maps were identified prior to War Revision), the sheet usually carried the War Office Cassini Grid in one of two styles – the British System "BS", from 1923 to *circa* 1931-3, then the Modified British System "MBS". This subdivision is used here. In 1940 conversion to *War Revision* "WR" began; later in 1940 *Second War Revision* "2WR" was introduced. For a description of the abbreviations relevant to the National Grid states of England and Wales sheet 17, see page 197, section 8.
	GSGS 3917, 3943: no pre-1931 maps are known, nor was there War Revision. All known sheets carried the War Office Irish Grid, listed here as "IG".
	GSGS 4136: defined by its edition number. First Editions probably had no edition heading.

2.	War Office publication date. A date given here will also imply the presence of the GSGS imprint, including series number, introduced in 1931-3, unless specifically noted. A sheet carrying the War Office imprint but lacking a publication date is listed "nd". The publication dates offered on War Revision and Second War Revision sheets are those which usually appear in the bottom left hand corner. War Revisions were in fact all published in 1940-41; however the dates in the bottom left hand corner usually remain those applied in 1931-3, sometimes qualified with the addition of the word *First* before *Published.....*

3.   GSGS 4136 only: publication date of specific edition. Some dates offered for unrecorded sheets in the second edition are taken from documentary evidence.

4.   Military print code (using, where lack of space demands, a system of + signs to indicate the accumulation of previous codes; _+ means overlook the previous to the one before that). The letter codes involved are explained in appendix 4. In supplements the sheet number may be given before the print code. The colour is noted, if not black, for printings retaining the original Popular or Fifth Edition marginalia (see column 10); blue is also disregarded on printings using the new style marginalia where it is as common as black. The colour of print codes on the green, purple or brown plates is always noted. Print codes are listed here conventionally: commas and full stops present in print codes are usually ignored; slashes (and full stops when they appear where slashes might be expected), are recorded. Four figure numbers are listed without commas, five or more figures with a comma before the last three digits, however they are presented in the original. The location of print codes is only occasionally noted. Mostly they are in the left corner, below the frame or below the legend (or both); a few printers chose to enter these codes in the bottom right hand corner. In longer strings, some elements may be moved from their original locations and redrawn, not always precisely as before. Further detail may exceptionally be given where it might help the user to identify the printing. A case such as England and Wales sheet 70, where two different printings exist with the same print code, but for the addition of a comma, is strong support for the view that all print codes should have been copied exactly as printed, including all full stops, commas and spaces. But there is good reason to take the opposite view. So many print codes are poorly printed that punctuation features are often indistinct and even lacking on some copies, and to have determined as two different printings two sheets that could not be compared side by side on the basis of print code difference alone was felt to be unjustified. No doubt this has caused the omission of some perfectly valid additional states, but equally kept some out that might have been entered erroneously. Printings guarded by question marks have not been recorded, but may be assumed, usually by their presence in the print code strings of other states.

5.   GSGS 3917, 3943 only: Ordnance Survey revision date.

6.   First use: GSGS 3907, 3908, 3917, 3943: Ordnance Survey publication date or, where it survives, print code. The use of "+" symbols on England and Wales Popular Edition maps implies a string of print codes, which will be as listed in Hodson (1999) unless noted otherwise. In cases where the date offered is a printing rather than publication date, the letter "p" is added in the form "1925p". Until 1940 it is assumed on Popular Edition sheets that the place of publication is Southampton. Second War Revision sheets with Popular Edition or Fifth Edition marginalia may have an imprint *Ordnance Survey Office, Southampton*. The assumed imprint for Fifth Edition sheets is *Published at the Ordnance Survey Office, [date]*. These dates are given in the form "1933.s" if *Southampton* survives in the imprint. The Ordnance Survey imprint was partially deleted or in some cases disappeared altogether in 1940, presumably following the bombing of Southampton in November 1940 which rendered the traditional imprint inaccurate. The default imprint on sheets with the new style marginalia introduced in 1941 is *Published at the Ordnance Survey, [date]*, in the bottom right hand corner. The date is often lacking. Sometimes minor correction dates or even civilian print codes exist on military printings that were not used on civilian printings. For further information on the civilian maps from which the military may be derived the reader is referred to Hodson (1999) and Oliver (2000a and 2000b).

      Second use: GSGS 4136: Printer information appearing bottom right.

7.   Ordnance Survey minor correction date, or the catchall expression *with periodical corrected reprints* "pcr", which first appeared on Popular Edition maps in November 1934. Not relevant on GSGS 4136. In supplement 1 to section 2, the otherwise unused space provides the opportunity of offering print run totals, derived from documentary sources.

8.   First use: England and Wales, Scotland Popular Edition sheets: Ordnance Survey road revision date. In many cases a road revision date, present in the civilian edition, has been deleted from the military in order to make space for additional marginalia.

      Second use: England and Wales Fifth Edition sheets: Ordnance Survey boundary revision date.

      Third use: GSGS 4136: date of military road classification, where offered. Some second edition sheets have a four part military road classification, undated, listed here as "m4".

9.   First use: England and Wales, Scotland: Ordnance Survey railway insertion date (sheets printed during the 1920s), railway revision date (sheets printed during the 1930s).

Second use: Training area maps in supplement 4: date of revision of War Department information.

Third use: GSGS 4136: date of overprinted information, where supplied.

10.   Margins and marginalia.
    GSGS 3907, 3908: Popular Edition "P", Fifth Edition "5", or new style, narrow "N" marginalia (see page 31). On War Revision and some special maps the marginalia that remains may be very fragmentary; how much of it survives is not described here. Some states have a suffix letter:
    a, b, c: alterations to sheet name (cross referring to the heading).
    o: no grid. † symbols in column 15 denote printings with OSPR references in appendix 3.
    p: grid in black (or the colour of the outline plate), numbered in blue. This was a format used on some special maps from 1933 onwards. The imprint on such issues may also be blue. It became standard on Second War Revision issues where the values joined the water plate; on these issues its presence is assumed, so not noted.
    q: grid in blue, numbered in blue; used on some mid-1930s manoeuvre maps.
    "v" to "z" relate to the note, introduced apparently in March 1941, concerning the currency of different military editions. See *Standardisation of editions GSGS 3907* (appendix 2). The note was usually printed in the top right margin of sheets which were little revised.
    v: the currency of both Popular Edition and War Revision is noted in *Standardisation of editions GSGS 3907*, but no such note appears on the map.
    w: with a note that a War Revision *may be used along with Popular (1932) Edition*, in purple, sometimes red.
    x: with a note that a Second War Revision *may be used along with Popular (1932) or War Revision (1940) Editions*, in blue. There are various wordings.
    y: with a note that a Second War Revision *may be used along with War Revision (1940) Edition*, in blue.
    z: with a note that a Second War Revision *may be used along with Popular (1932) Edition*, in blue.
    GSGS 3917, 3943: Third Edition: small sheet series "3", large sheet series "3L".
    GSGS 4136 not relevant.

11.   Sheet lines.
    GSGS 3907, 3908: Popular "P", Fifth "5", New Popular "6" Edition sheet lines; some sheets may use civilian tourist "T" or district "D" map sheet lines.
    GSGS 3917, 3943: Third Edition, small sheet series "3"; composite of Third Edition small sheets "33"; Third Edition, large sheet series "3L"; Third Edition small sheets and War Office Irish Grid sheet lines combined "3G"; Third Edition small sheets extended at the coast "3+".
    GSGS 4136 not relevant.

12.   Mapping.
    GSGS 3907, 3908: Popular "P" or Fifth "5" Edition.
    GSGS 3917, 3943: Third Edition "3".
    GSGS 4136 not relevant.

13.   Colours.
    GSGS 3907, 3908, 3917, 3943: C: coloured edition; Co: coloured edition without green plate; C+: coloured edition with green, where the presence of the green plate may be in doubt; Cr: War Revision sheets with red main roads; Cb: coloured edition with roads and contours in Air Force brown; CL: coloured edition with layers. O: outline edition; Ow: outline edition with water in blue; Ox: outline edition with water in blue, woods in grey; Oy: outline edition with water in blue, contours in red or brown; Oz: outline edition with orange plate.[255] ‡ symbols in column 15 denote outline editions to which there are OSPR references in appendix 3.

---

[255] British System maps were printed in up to seven colours, as with civilian maps – two for roads, one or two for water, woods, contours and the black plate. An additional purple plate contained the supplementary military information. Between 1931 and 1933 the War Office wanted coloured printings without a green plate for woodland, so it is probable that all Modified British System sheets were first issued in this form, also the last of the British System printings. With the introduction of the Modified British System the red plate was discontinued

GSGS 4136: O: outline edition; C: coloured edition; CL: coloured edition with layers; CLo: coloured edition with layers, without green plate; CB: coloured edition with bog overprint; CT: coloured edition with training areas overprint. Maps are presented in chronological sequence, irrespective of the overprint.

14. Location of copy. Copies in the Defence Geographic Centre (previously Military Survey) Superseded Collection, now in the British Library, are given preference, and are cited BL-d. Textual references to this collection are in the form "DGC Superseded". References to "book" imply inclusion of that map in a book, usually a report on an exercise or an examination: further details may be found via the footnote reference to supplement 7 or 9. "Card" references give details taken from catalogue cards, once in use by Military Survey, of so far unrecorded printings. "Dealer" references give details taken from copies noted in the stock or catalogues of map dealers, of which no copy has been traced for further inspection. Printings listed without a source were recorded in the early years of the investigation, but it is not known where and thus remain subject to confirmation. Owing to the closure of the collections in the final months of preparation of this book, it was impossible to confirm the detail of some states held by the RGS.

15. Cross reference, usually to footnotes following each sheet list. Symbols are used to refer to sales copy lists in OSPR and OS Reports (appendix 3): † to coloured ungridded War Revisions and ‡ to outline editions.

---

and road colours were reduced to one. The water tint plate was discontinued starting in 1940, even before War Revision, and was replaced by screening the solid blue plate. Thus the standard War Revision was in five colours, black, blue, green, orange (contours) and sienna (from December 1940 red) (roads and railway station infill), with the addition of the purple military plate. On Second War Revision the number of colours was reduced to four – black for outline and grid, blue for water and grid values, green for woods and orange for road fill and contours. This last was altered to Air Force Brown in May 1944, though it was not retained on all post-war printings.

Compiler's notes to sections 1 and 2

England and Wales, and Scotland

The British System of the War Office Cassini Grid came into use in 1918 on provisional issues of the 1:20,000 map of Great Britain (GSGS 2748), but it would be several years more before the one-inch was adopted as the basic scale for training. The maps chosen were the Popular Editions in England and Wales, and Scotland, overprinted with the Cassini Grid. At the time publication of the map in England and Wales was not complete, and that in Scotland not even begun. But there was no immediate requirement for national coverage, and no sheet of the current third edition maps was, so far as is known, ever associated with the grid. Publication of the Popular Edition in England and Wales was complete by 1926, and gridded editions for military use probably within a year of that. However, publication of the map in Scotland ran on into 1932, and, with the grid itself being transformed from the British System (BS) to the Modified British System (MBS) between 1931 and 1933,[256] it would seem certain that some Scotland Popular Edition sheets were never issued at all with the earlier system. But unless some printing record is discovered, we are unlikely ever to know which they were or the true extent of the map in this period. Once the process of grid change was complete, the official policy was to destroy earlier printings, if only to avoid confusion between grid systems. Early MBS issues were made in short print runs, as with BS printings, rarely more than a thousand in number, and often just a few hundred. The existence of many unrecorded states may be deduced from print code strings; others must have existed of which we are wholly unaware.

As the threat of war became reality, there was in 1939 and 1940 an exponential increase in the length of print runs of late MBS printings to many thousands. But such an increase in quantities proved an insufficient response to the crisis. The need speedily to incorporate up-to-date ARP revision into mapping which was by then already between twenty and thirty years out of date was the immediate reason for the publication of War Revision, then Second War Revision.[257] Nine English sheets still have not been recorded in War Revision; there is no conclusive proof that they were not made, but the incidence of printings before and after coupled with what documentary evidence does survive offers a range of probability from unlikely to virtually certain. Four other War Revision sheets, 16, 74, 84, 117, are only recorded as single copies, and sheet 116 in only two; the possibility arises that even though they were given print codes (even suggesting 20,000 copies) that they may have been proof copies or had extremely limited distribution before being superseded by a Second War Revision.

Second War Revision coverage was deemed unnecessary in some areas of England and Wales and never completed. It appears that these were areas where little ARP revision had been incorporated, thus War Revision satisfied military requirements and there were by then adequate stocks of the sheets involved. In Scotland only two Second War Revision sheets were issued, plus the two border sheets that also appear in GSGS 3907. A new variant was the appearance of many GSGS 3907 Second War Revision sheets in outline editions, with water in blue, or, from 1944, water in blue and woods in grey. Eleven of them were issued only in outline format, and were never published as coloured maps at all. All outline copies so far recorded were made for public sale rather than military use.

As far as possible Fifth Edition mapping was employed for the Second War Revision, being produced from the uncompleted fourth national revision, and thus more up to date. By the outbreak of war it had been prepared throughout southern England, as far north as Coventry. The first steps had been taken to incorporate it as early as 1938 on an MBS sheet 107, followed by 114 in 1940. Sheet 114 was at the same time injected with additional detail derived from ARP sources, and it was to all intents and purposes the first Second War Revision sheet. For some reason also it retained its Popular Edition marginalia. These two sheets were known as "Special Popular Edition". Sheet 107 was converted to War Revision when a massive amount of ARP revision was added to it in 1941. Second War Revision was to follow for both sheets, along with the remainder of southern England. But there could be no general conversion to Fifth Edition sheet lines – the risk of confusion was considered too great. Thus

---

[256] Richard Oliver discusses this matter on page 16.
[257] For a fuller account of this, see the section starting on page 25.

Fifth Edition mapping used for Second War Revision had to be recast within the existing Popular Edition sheet lines. However, the eleven sheets covering the south west, 118, 119, 127, 128, 136, 137, 138, 143, 144, 145, 146, could be converted to Fifth Edition mapping within Fifth Edition sheet lines without risk of confusion or interruption in coverage, since these were a self-contained block which conveniently overlapped Popular Edition sheets to the east. All eleven were converted by August 1940, first as MBS sheets, then as War Revision with apparently identical mapping; they were considered equally up to date whichever heading they carried. Their revision status was such that in their case Second War Revision was irrelevant. Two of these sheets also appeared in outline editions. Sheets with fifth edition mapping are listed "5" in column 12. Sheets which are truly Fifth Edition, with Fifth Edition sheet limits as well (including district maps) are listed "5" in column 11.

The issue of one-inch maps with new style marginalia began in October 1941. Two Scottish sheets, 51 and 55, do in fact have September print codes, but it appears that they were not actually printed until October. The new style sheets have no legends at the foot; these were replaced by conventional sign cards which were issued from December. 5000 copies of these were sent to each army command in the initial distribution. Instructions on how to give a grid reference also passed on to the cards. The other principal characteristic of the new style margins is a large black arrow printed across the map face as part of the magnetic variation apparatus. The new design was applied to all Second War Revision sheets, to all Scottish War Revision sheets, and to at least four English War Revision sheets. It is still unclear whether this was a War Office or an Ordnance Survey initiative,[258] but its purpose was indeed to save paper. The idea was approved by the General Staff who agreed that trained soldiers did not require conventional signs and grid reference boxes, at any rate on the map itself. For want of an official designation (the expressions "new style" and "sheets published with reduced margins" have been noted in official documents) they are noted "N" in column 10. Earlier Second War Revision printings, which retained elements of Popular or Fifth Edition marginalia, are marked "P" or "5". The situation is still not wholly clear in Scotland where it would appear that the earliest War Revision printings of sheets 4, 18, 30, 51, 65, 92 have yet to be recorded.

No BS sheet carries a GSGS number or imprint. England and Wales sheets were published as GSGS 3907 from 1931, starting slightly later than the introduction of the MBS, and Scotland sheets as 3908 from 1933 (the numbers were allocated on 15 January 1931). The two border sheets (Scotland 86/England 3 and Scotland 89/England 5) were members of both series. Four England MBS sheets have so far been recorded whose first issue preceded the application of the War Office imprint and GSGS number 3907; there may well have been others, probably in areas of high military concentration. These four are listed as without a date in column 2. Several district and extract maps carry no GSGS number. These are noted. Three Popular Edition based Second War Revision printings are erroneously headed *5th Edition style*. These are noted. Ordnance Survey imprint details are also noted where they survive; it is interesting that in many cases there is no directly equivalent civilian printing.

For completeness sake, three sheets printed after the Second World War which still retain the Cassini Grid are listed in this section, though two of them (both on New Popular, or Sixth, Edition sheet lines) are given the GSGS number 4620, later used for the National Grid Military System one-inch map. Also some Isle of Man maps (sheet 17) in postwar versions are listed, because their source is the Second War Revision map. Some maps in the GSGS miscellaneous sequence are also listed which derive from GSGS 3907. Both GSGS 3908 and 3907 were declared obsolete in 1950 once GSGS 4639 in Scotland and GSGS 4620 in England and Wales had become operational, and the fundamental change from Cassini to National Grid complete.

The training, exercise and manoeuvre area maps so far recorded are listed in the supplements which follow the principal sequence, together with many extract maps. Other maps or printings which are presumed (perhaps from indexes, or print code strings) are listed, but lack detail. There must also have been a whole class of maps with confidential overprints, about which I know nothing. Some of the manoeuvre maps made in the 1920s and 1930s have also so far evaded detection; their existence is suspected thanks to the *London Gazette* record of Orders in Council which notified forthcoming manoeuvres. In some cases the issue of maps was noted, though since the scale may not have been not given, it is possible that such unrecorded maps do not in fact belong here.

---

[258] 'Report on the work of Home Forces Survey Service during the year 1941', PRO WO 252/1412: ".....another proposal was being investigated to save paper by the reduction of the size of the margins around the edge of each map sheet." The use of the passive form keeps the identity of the mind behind the idea anonymous.

During the 1920s and 1930s standard sheets were often used for examinations, mostly relating to the admission and promotion of officers in the Staff College. Those with standard specification (though with the addition of a heading) are entered into the lists as usual – indeed sheets overprinted for examination use are in many cases apparently taken from normal print runs. Where it seems probable that they were printed specially, such as those with abnormal specification (perhaps with an unusual imprint, or in the colours of the civilian map), they are in supplement 8. There are likely to have been many more of these than those so far recorded.

The US Army Map Service (AMS) number M721 was allocated to GSGS 3907, and M722 (or M724) to GSGS 3908.[259] Neither ever appeared on a map (unless there be so far unrecorded AMS printings), and both numbers were later reallocated, as NATO SSD numbers – M721 to GSGS 4136, and M722 to GSGS 4620. Again, M721 appears to have been unused.

An artillery trace, GSGS 3851, was issued for the one-inch "Popular Gridded Edition" in 1927.

Sources

This list of printings of GSGS 3908 and 3907 has grown from a check list first put together in about 1983 by Richard Oliver, with some assistance by the late Guy Messenger. At that point little more was recorded than the heading and publication date, print code, and any other features of interest such as whether the green plate was present or not, and if a printing was on Place's waterproof paper. Non-standard features in the lower margin were noted. A record was unfortunately not maintained of where printings were located. When Richard presented me with a copy of the list in 1995 I continued to collect information very much in the same manner for some time, and only gradually, as publication became a possibility did I think it necessary to include details of the base map and a standardised procedure for dealing with changes in the mapping used, the marginalia, and a record of where printings of each sheet were seen. Such haphazard practices have resulted, I fear, in a less than perfect listing: it has proved impossible to confirm the details of all states since we still do not know where some of those recorded in the early days were found.

Much the largest surviving collection of these maps used to be held by Military Survey at Tolworth. The Defence Geographic Centre transferred the collection in 2001 to the British Library.[260] Particularly strongly represented are the printings of the Second War Revision and, to a lesser extent, War Revision. But we know from documentary evidence that several early printings of sheets in War Revision have yet to be located, and it is quite clear that the further back one goes, the rarer become the states that survive even in the Military Survey collection, never mind elsewhere, to the point, one suspects, where none at all do. Initially there was no organised attempt by Military Survey to retain a record copy of every state printed, and, by the time there was, the Second World War was history. It was only in the later years that copies of each printing were systematically retained as and when they were identified. A significant proportion of the sheets in the Military Survey collection were in fact Ordnance Survey file copies; more of these are also to be found in the collection in the School of Geography, University of Oxford. A similar gradual increase in rarity among the early printings is true also of other collections. These maps were never sent to the legal deposit libraries under copyright procedure, though many publicly accessible libraries have over the years acquired quite large collections, usually from periodic disposals by Military Survey.

---

[259] There is an apparent inconsistency in the lists of AMS numbers provided in the National Archives & Records Administration in College Park, Maryland, in that the one-inch map of Scotland is given against both M722 and M724, both specifically dated 1940-42. Since neither number is known to have appeared on a map it is really a hypothetical matter, and it is possibly an irrelevant coincidence that M724 would later be the SSD allocation for the one-inch National Grid map of Scotland, GSGS 4639.

[260] The Defence Geographic and Imagery Intelligence Agency (DGIA) was formed in 2000 by the merging of Military Survey and the Joint Air Reconnaissance Intelligence Centre (JARIC (UK)). The Defence Geographic Centre (DGC) is its largest business unit and shares the same site at Feltham. Among its other responsibilities DGC houses the Map Library. This was moved from Tolworth to Feltham in 2003. The part of the Superseded Collection that is no longer required for reference has been transferred to the British Library (Maps MOD). The complete list of series relevant to this book that have been transferred is GSGS 3907, 3908, 3917, 3943, 4136, 4620, 4620A, 4639; at present (2004) M722, M723 and post-war training area maps are retained by DGC. The process of transferring the GSGS miscellaneous sequence to the British Library has begun. See also page 294.

1. GSGS 3908 *Scotland*

For a explanation of the detail in each column see pages 86 to 89.

Sheet 1 *Yell & Unst (Shetland Islands)*   18 by 27 miles
BS was probably not published.

1	2	4	6	7	10	11	12	13	14	15
MBS	1933	?WO 500/33			P	P	P	Co		
MBS	1933	WO 500/33. 1000/35	1931		P	P	P	C	Wc	
MBS	1933	9500/40/J	1931		P	P	P	C	PC	
WR	1933	WO 10,000/40. 5000/3/41/F	1931		Pw	P	P	Cr	Cu	
WR	1933	10,000/2/42 W	1942		Nw	P	P	Cor	BL-d	
WR	1933	10,000/2/43 LR	-		Nw	P	P	Cor	BL-d	
WR	1933	10,000/2/43 LR	-		No	P	P	Cor	NLS	†

Sheet 2 *North Mainland (Shetland Islands)*   32 by 21 miles
BS was probably not published.

1	2	4	6	7	10	11	12	13	14
MBS	1933	WO 500/33	1931		P	P	P	Co	PC
MBS	1933	WO 500/33. 1000/35	1931		P	P	P	Co	RGS
MBS	1933	WO 4000/39	1931		P	P	P	Co	Wc
WR	1933	WO 10,000/40	1931		P	P	P	Co-	PC
WR	1933	10,000/2/42 LR	1942		Nw	P	P	Cor	BL-d

Sheet 3 *Central Mainland (Shetland Islands)*   27 by 18 miles
BS was probably not published.

1	2	4	6	7	10	11	12	13	14
MBS	1933	WO 500/33	1931		P	P	P	Co	PC
MBS	1933	WO 500/33. 1000/35	1931		P	P	P	C	Ag
MBS	1933	9500/40/J	1931		P	P	P	C	BL-d
WR	1933	5000/3/41/F	1931		Pw	P	P	Cr	NLS
WR	1933	10,000/2/42 W	1941		Nw	P	P	Cor	BL-d

Sheet 4 *South Mainland (Shetland Islands)*   18 by 27 miles
BS was probably not published.

1	2	4	6	7	10	11	12	13	14	15
MBS	1933	WO 500/33	1931		P	P	P	Co	Wc	
MBS	1933	WO 9500/40	1929	pcr	P	P	P	Co	BL-d	
WR					P	P	P	C		1
WR	1933	10,000/3/42 A	1942		Nw	P	P	Cor	BL-d	

1. *GSGS 3908 current edition*, 8 July 1941 lists this sheet as War Revision (see appendix 1). At this date this would have had Popular Edition marginalia.

Sheet 5 *Orkney Islands (North)*   27 by 23 miles
BS was probably not published.

1	2	4	6	7	10	11	12	13	14
MBS	1933	WO 500/33	1931		P	P	P	Co	PC
MBS	1933	WO 4000/39	1931		P	P	P	C	Wc
WR	1933	WO 10,000/40. 10,000/40 B	1931		P	P	P	C	BL-d
WR	1933	10,000/1/42 LR	1941		Nw	P	P	Cr	BL-d
WR	1933	10,000-9/42 C	-		Nw	P	P	Cr	BL-d

Sheet 6 *Orkney Islands (Mainland)*   32 by 21 miles
BS was probably not published.

1	2	4	6	7	10	11	12	13	14
MBS	1933	WO 500/33	1931		P	P	P	Co	BL-d
MBS	1933	WO 8000/39	1932	pcr	P	P	P	C	BL-d
MBS	1933	WO 5100/40	1932	pcr	P	P	P	C	BL-d
WR	1933	WO 10,000/40. 5000/3/41/F	1932	pcr	Pw	P	P	Cr	PC
WR	1933	10,000/1/42 LR	1942		Nw	P	P	Cr	BL-d
WR	1933	10,000/10/42 McL	1941		Nw	P	P	Cr	BL-d

1	2	4	6	7	8	9	10	11	12	13	14	15
Sheet 7 *Orkney Islands (South)*							27 by 18 miles					
BS was probably not published.												
MBS							P	P	P	Co		
MBS	1933	WO 8000/39. 8000/39 M	1931				P	P	P	C	BL-d	
WR	1933	10,000/40/J	1931	pcr			P	P	P	C	BL-d	
WR	1933	10,000/2/42 LR	1942				Nw	P	P	Cr	BL-d	
WR	1933	10,000/1/43 J	1942				Nw	P	P	Cr	BL-d	
WR	1933	350/1/43 J	1942				No	P	P	Cr	NLS	†
Sheet 8 *Butt of Lewis*							28 by 19 miles					
BS was probably not published.												
MBS	1933	WO 500/33	1930				P	P	P	Co	PC	
MBS	1933	WO 500/33. 1000/35	1930				P	P	P	Co	PC	
MBS	1933	WO 4000/39	1931				P	P	P	Co	BL-d	
WR		5000/3/41 F					P	P	P	Co	dealer	
WR	1933	10,000/3/42 LR	1941				Nw	P	P	Cor	BL-d	
WR	1933	10,350/11/42 B	1941				Nw	P	P	Cor	BL-d	
WR	1933	10,350/11/42 B	1941				No	P	P	Cor	NLS	†
Sheet 9 *Cape Wrath*							22 by 28 miles					
BS												
MBS	1933	WO 800/33	1930				P	P	P	Co	Wc	
MBS	1933	WO 8500/40	1930				P	P	P	C	BL-d	
WR	1933	10,000/11/40 L	1930				P	P	P	C	BL-d	
WR	1933	5000/2/42 LR	1942				Nw	P	P	Cr	BL-d	
WR	1933	15,000/6/42 LR	-				Nw	P	P	Cr	BL-d	
Sheet 10 *Tongue*							28 by 23 miles					
BS												
MBS	1933	WO 800/33	1930				P	P	P	Co	PC	
MBS	1933	WO 4000/39	1930				P	P	P	C	BL-d	
MBS	1933	6000/40/R	1930				P	P	P	C	Cu	1
WR	1933	WO 5000/5/41	none				Pw	P	P	Cr	BL-d	
WR	1933	5000/4/42 LR	1942				Nw	P	P	Cr	BL-d	
WR	1933	15,000/6/42 LR	-				Nw	P	P	Cr	BL-d	

1. The water infill plate is lacking.

1	2	4	6	7	8	9	10	11	12	13	14	15
Sheet 11 *Thurso & Reay*							19 by 28 miles					
BS was probably not published.												
MBS		?WO 500/33					P	P	P	Co		
MBS	1933	WO 500/33. 1000/35	1930				P	P	P	C	dealer	
MBS	1933	WO 8000/39. 8000/39 M	1930				P	P	P	C	BL-d	
WR	1933	10,000/10/40 L	1930				P	P	P	C	BL-d	
WR	1933	15,000/3/42 W	1942				Nv	P	P	Cr	BL-d	
Sheet 12 *Wick*							18 by 28 miles					
BS was probably not published.												
MBS		?WO 500/33					P	P	P	Co		
MBS	1933	WO 500/33. 1000/35	1930				P	P	P	C	BL-d	
MBS	1933	WO 8000/39. 8000/39 M	1930	pcr			P	P	P	C	BL-d	
WR	1933	WO 10,000/40. 10,000 40/B	1930	pcr			P	P	P	C	BL-d	
WR	1933	15,000/12/41 LR	1941				Nw	P	P	Cr	BL-d	
WR	1933	10,000/1/43 J	1942				Nw	P	P	Cr	BL-d	
WR	1933	450/1/43 J	1942				No	P	P	Cr	NLS	†

Sheet 13 *Loch Roag & Tarbert* — 19 by 27 miles
BS was probably not published.

1	2	4	6	7	8	9	10	11	12	13	14	15
MBS	1933	WO 500/33	1930				P	P	P	Co	PC	
MBS	1933	WO 500/33. 1000/35	1930				P	P	P	C+	BL-d	
MBS	1933	7500/40/J	1930				P	P	P	Co	BL-d	
WR	1933	5000/4/41 J	1930				P	P	P	Cr	OS	
WR	1933	10,000/3/42/J	1942				Nw	P	P	Cor	BL-d	
WR	1933	10,450/11/42 B	1942				Nw	P	P	Cor	BL-d	
WR	1933	10,450/11/42 B	1942				No	P	P	Cor	NLS	†

Sheet 14 *Stornoway* — 21 by 27 miles
BS was probably not published.

1	2	4	6	7	8	9	10	11	12	13	14	15
MBS	1933	WO 500/33	1930				P	P	P	Co	PC	
MBS	1933	WO 4000/39	1931				P	P	P	C	BL-d	
WR	1933	10,000/10/40 L	1931				P	P	P	C	BL-d	
WR	1933	10,000/2/42 LR	1942				Nw	P	P	Cr	BL-d	
WR	1933	10,000/11/42 J	1941				Nw	P	P	Cr	BL-d	
WR	1933	350/11/42 J	1941				No	P	P	Cr	NLS	†

Sheet 15 *Lochinver & Loch Assynt* — 28 by 19 miles
BS

1	2	4	6	7	8	9	10	11	12	13	14	15
MBS		?WO 500/33					P	P	P	Co		
MBS	1933	WO 500/33. 1000/35	1930				P	P	P	C	BL-d	
MBS	1933	7500/40/J	1930				P	P	P	C	NLS	
WR	1933	WO 10,000/40. 10,000/40/J	1930				P	P	P	C	BL-d	
WR	1933	5000/2/42 LR	1942				Nw	P	P	Cr	BL-d	
WR	1933	15,000/6/42 LR	-				Nw	P	P	Cr	BL-d	

Sheet 16 *Lairg & Loch Shin* — 28 by 19 miles
BS

1	2	4	6	7	8	9	10	11	12	13	14	15
MBS	1933	WO 800/33	1930				P	P	P	Co	Wc	
MBS	1933	WO 4000/39	1930				P	P	P	C	NLS	
MBS	1933	6000/40/R	1930				P	P	P	C	BL-d	
WR	1933	10,000/11/40 L	1930				P	P	P	C	BL-d	
WR	1933	WO 5000/5/41	none				Pw	P	P	Cr	BL-d	
WR	1933	5000/2/42 LR	1942				Nw	P	P	Cr	BL-d	
WR	1933	15,000/6/42 LR	-				Nw	P	P	Cr	BL-d	

Sheet 17 *Helmsdale* — 27 by 19 miles
BS

1	2	4	6	7	8	9	10	11	12	13	14	15
MBS	1933	WO 500/33	1930				P	P	P	Co	PC	
MBS	1933	WO 500/33. 1000/35	1930				P	P	P	C	NLS	
MBS	1933	7500/40/J	1930				P	P	P	C	BL-d	
WR	1933	10,000/11/40 L	1930				P	P	P	C	Wc	
WR	1933	WO 10,000/40. 5000/5/41	none				Pw	P	P	Cr	BL-d	
WR	1933	10,000/2/42 W	1941				Nw	P	P	Cr	BL-d	
WR	1933	10,000/11/42 J	1941				Nw	P	P	Cr	BL-d	
WR	1933	350/11/42 J	1941				No	P	P	Cr	NLS	†

Sheet 18 *Harris* — 27 by 19 miles
BS was probably not published.

1	2	4	6	7	8	9	10	11	12	13	14	15
MBS	1933	WO 500/33	1930				P	P	P	Co	PC	
MBS	1933	WO 500/33. 1000/35					P	P	P	C		
MBS	1933	7500/40/J	1929	pcr			P	P	P	C	BL-d	
WR							P	P	P	C		1
WR	1933	10,000/3/42 A	1942				Nw	P	P	Cor	BL-d	
WR	1933	10,350/11/42 B	1941				Nw	P	P	Cor	BL-d	
WR	1933	10,350/11/42 B	1941				No	P	P	Cor	NLS	†

1. *GSGS 3908 current edition*, 8 July 1941 lists this sheet as War Revision (see appendix 1). At this date this would have had Popular Edition marginalia.

1	2	4	6	7	8	9	10	11	12	13	14	15

Sheet 19 *Ullapool & Loch Ewe* — 28 by 19 miles

1	2	4	6	7	8	9	10	11	12	13	14	15
BS												
MBS	1933	WO 500/33	1930				P	P	P	Co	PC	
MBS	1933	WO 500/33. 1000/35	1930				P	P	P	C	Wc	
MBS	1933	WO 7500/40	1930				P	P	P	C	BL-d	
WR	1933	WO 10,000/40. 10,000/40/J	1930				P	P	P	C	Og	
WR	1933	5000/3/42 McL	1942				Nw	P	P	Cr	BL-d	
WR	1933	15,000/6/42 LR	-				Nw	P	P	Cr	BL-d	

Sheet 20 *Strath Oykell* — 27 by 19 miles

1	2	4	6	7	8	9	10	11	12	13	14	15
BS												
MBS	1933	WO 500/33	1930				P	P	P	Co	Wc	
MBS	1933	WO 500/33. 1000/35					P	P	P	C		
MBS	1933	WO 4000/39	1930				P	P	P	C	BL-d	
WR	1933	WO 10,000/40. 10,000/40/J	1930				P	P	P	C	BL-d	
WR	1933	5000/5/41	none				Pw	P	P	Cr	BL-d	
WR	1933	10,000/4/42 LR	-				Nw	P	P	Cr	BL-d	

Sheet 21 *Dornoch* — 27 by 19 miles

1	2	4	6	7	8	9	10	11	12	13	14	15
BS	-	?WO 450.30					P	P	P	C		
MBS		?WO 450.30. ?code/33					P	P	P	Co		
MBS	-	WO 450/30. 1500/35	1930				P	P	P	C	BL-d	1
MBS	-	WO 450/30. 1500/35. 200/38	1930				P	P	P	C	Wc	1
MBS	-	WO 16,000/39 C	1930				P	P	P	C	Ag	1,2
WR	1933	WO 10,000/40. 5000/3/41/F	1930				Pw	P	P	Cr	NLS	
WR	1933	15,000/12/41 LR	1941				Nw	P	P	Cr	BL-d	

1. The GSGS imprint is lacking. 2. This is the only Popular Edition sheet (i.e. pre-War Revision) in either GSGS 3907 or 3908 of which some copies have been recorded carrying Sales Copy stickers.

Sheet 22 *Sollas* — 27 by 19 miles

BS was probably not published.

1	2	4	6	7	8	9	10	11	12	13	14	15
MBS	1933	WO 500/33	1931				P	P	P	Co	PC	
MBS	1933	WO 500/33. 1000/35	1931				P	P	P	Co	Wc	
MBS	1933	WO 4000/39	1929	pcr			P	P	P	Co	BL-d	
WR	1933	WO 10,000/40. 10,000/40/J	1929	pcr			P	P	P	Co	BL-d	
WR	1933	10,000/3/42/J	1942				Nw	P	P	Cor	BL-d	

Sheet 23 *Benbecula* — 27 by 19 miles

BS was probably not published.

1	2	4	6	7	8	9	10	11	12	13	14	15
MBS	1933	WO 500/33	1931				P	P	P	Co	Wc	
MBS	1933	WO 500/33. 1000/35					P	P	P	C		
MBS	1933	WO 4000/39	1929	pcr			P	P	P	C	BL-d	
WR	1933	WO 10,000/40. 10,000/40/J	1929	pcr			P	P	P	C	BL-d	
WR	1933	10,000/2/42 W	1942				Nw	P	P	Cor	BL-d	

Sheet 24 *Portree & Dunvegan* — 25 by 28 miles

1	2	4	6	7	8	9	10	11	12	13	14	15
BS	-	WO 6.30. 200/30	nd				P	P	P	C	PC	
MBS		?WO 350/33					P	P	P	Co		
MBS	1933	WO 350/33. 1000/35	nd				P	P	P	C	BL-d	
MBS	1933	WO 4000/39	nd	1931			P	P	P	C	Og	
WR	1933	10,000/40 B	nd	1931			P	P	P	C	BL-d	
WR	1933	10,000/3/42 LR	1941				Nw	P	P	Cr	BL-d	

1	2	4	6	7	8	9	10	11	12	13	14	15

Sheet 25 *Raasay & Applecross* — 23 by 28 miles

1	2	4	6	7	10	11	12	13	14	15
BS										
MBS		?WO 350/33			P	P	P	Co		
MBS	-	WO 350/33. 1000/35	1930		P	P	P	C	BL-d	1
MBS		WO 4000/39			P	P	P	C	card	
WR	1933	WO 12,000/5/41	none		Pw	P	P	Cr	BL-d	
WR	1933	5000/3/42 A	1942		Nw	P	P	Cr	BL-d	
WR	1933	10,450/1/43 McL	-		Nw	P	P	Cr	BL-d	
WR	1933	10,450/1/43 McL	-		No	P	P	Cr	NLS	†

1. The GSGS imprint is lacking.

Sheet 26 *Loch Maree & Achnasheen* — 28 by 19 miles

1	2	4	6	7	10	11	12	13	14
BS	-	WO 11.28. 450/29	1928		P	P	P	C	PC
MBS	1933	WO 600/33	1928		P	P	P	Co	PC
MBS	1933	WO 4000/39	1928	pcr	P	P	P	C	BL-d
MBS	1933	6000/40/R	10/36 M36 R33	pcr	P	P	P	C	NLS
WR	1933	WO 10,000/40. 10,000/3/41	1928	pcr	P	P	P	Cr	BL-d
WR	1933	10,000/2/42 W	1942		Nw	P	P	Cr	BL-d
WR	1933	15,000/8/42 B	1941		Nw	P	P	Cr	BL-d

Sheet 27 *Strathpeffer & Invergordon* — 28 by 19 miles

1	2	4	6	7	10	11	12	13	14	15
BS	-				P	P	P	C		
MBS	1933	WO 2600/33	1929		P	P	P	Co	PC	
MBS	1933	WO 8000/39. 8000/39 M	1927	pcr	P	P	P	C	NLS	
WR	1933	10,000/40 B	1927	pcr	P	P	P	C	BL-d	
WR	1942	20,000/3/42 B	1942		Nw	P	P	Cr	BL-d	1

1. An updated imprint on a War Revision printing was very unusual.

Sheet 28 *Nairn & Cromarty* — 28 by 19 miles

1	2	4	6	7	10	11	12	13	14	15
BS	-	WO 10.29. 450/29	1929		P	P	P	C	PC	
MBS	1933	WO 2600/33	1929		P	P	P	Co	BL-d	
MBS	1933	WO 16,000/39	1929	pcr	P	P	P	C	BL-d	
WR	1933	WO 25,000/9/41/LR	none		P	P	P	Cr	BL-d	1
WR	1933	10,000/4/42 LR	-		N	P	P	Cr	BL-d	
WR	1933	10,000/1/43 J	1942		N	P	P	Cr	BL-d	
WR	1933	550/1/43 J	1942		No	P	P	Cr	NLS	†

1. This was apparently the last Scottish sheet to be published in War Revision.

Sheet 29 *Elgin & Keith* — 28 by 19 miles

1	2	4	6	10	11	12	13	14	15
BS	-			P	P	P	C		
MBS				P	P	P	Co		
MBS	1933	WO 4000/39	1929	P	P	P	C	Wc	
WR	1933	10,000/40 B	1929	P	P	P	C	BL-d	
WR	1933	WO 16,000/8/41 LR	none	P	P	P	Cr	BL-d	
WR	1933	10,000/12/41 LR	1942	N	P	P	Cr	BL-d	
WR	1933	10,000/11/42 J	1942	N	P	P	Cr	BL-d	
WR	1933	550/11/42 J	1942	No	P	P	Cr	NLS	†

Sheet 30 *Banff & Fraserburgh* — 27 by 19 miles

1	2	4	6	10	11	12	13	14	15
BS	-	WO 1/30. 400/30	1930	P	P	P	C	PC	
MBS	1933	WO 600/33	1930	P	P	P	Co	Wc	
MBS	1933	WO 4000/39	1930	P	P	P	C	PC	
MBS	1933	10,000/40/J	1930	P	P	P	C	PC	
MBS	1933	16,000/40/R	1930	P	P	P	C	BL-d	1
WR				P	P	P	C		2
WR	1933	10,000/2/42 LR	1942	Nv	P	P	Cr	BL-d	
WR	1933	10,000/11/42 J	1941	Nv	P	P	Cr	BL-d	
WR	1933	550/11/42 J	1941	No	P	P	Cr	NLS	†

1. The water infill plate is lacking. 2. *GSGS 3908 current edition*, 8 July 1941 lists this sheet as War Revision (see appendix 1). At this date this would have had Popular Edition marginalia.

1	2	4	6	7	8	9	10	11	12	13	14	15

Sheet 31 *Peterhead* — 19 by 27 miles

1	2	4	6	7	10	11	12	13	14	15
BS	-				P	P	P	C		
MBS	1933	WO 600/33	1930		P	P	P	C	Wc	
MBS	1933	WO 16,000/39	1930		P	P	P	C	BL-d	
MBS	1933	no code	1930		P	P	P	C	BL-d	1
WR	1933	10,000/8/41 LR	none		Pv	P	P	Cr	BL-d	
WR	1933	10,000/12/41 LR	1941		Nv	P	P	Cr	BL-d	
WR	1933	15,000/9/42 C	-		Nv	P	P	Cr	NLS	
WR	1933	15,000/9/42 C. 5000/10/42 C	-		Nv	P	P	Cr	BL-d	

1. The water infill plate is lacking.

Sheet 32 *Lochboisdale & Eriskay* — 27 by 18 miles

BS was probably not published.

1	2	4	6	10	11	12	13	14
MBS	1933	WO 800/33	1930	P	P	P	Co	BL-d
MBS	1933	WO 4000/39	1930	P	P	P	Co	PC
WR	1933	10,000/10/40 L	1930	P	P	P	Co-	BL-d
WR	1933	5000/2/42 LR	1942	Nw	P	P	Cor	BL-d
WR	1933	15,000/6/42 A	-	Nw	P	P	Cor	BL-d

Sheet 33 *Barra & Mingulay* — 27 by 20 miles

BS was probably not published.

1	2	4	6	10	11	12	13	14	15
MBS	1933	WO 500/33	1930	P	P	P	Co	BL-d	
MBS	nd	WO 7500/40	1930	P	P	P	Co	BL-d	
MBS	1938	4600/40 W	1930	P	P	P	Co	BL-d	1
WR	1933	WO 5000/5/41	none	Pw	P	P	Cr+	BL-d	
WR	1933	5000/2/42 LR	1942	Nw	P	P	Cor	BL-d	
WR	1933	10,350/1/43 B	1941	Nw	P	P	Cor	BL-d	
WR	1933	10,350/1/43 B	1941	No	P	P	Cor	NLS	†

1. There is no apparent logic to the new publication date.

Sheet 34 a. *The Cuillins, Rhum and Canna* b. *Cuillins, Rhum & Canna* — 19 by 28 miles

1	2	4	6	7	10	11	12	13	14	15
BS	-	WO 9.29. 300/29	1929		Pa	P	P	C	BL-d	
MBS	1933	WO 350/33	1929		Pa	P	P	Co	PC	
MBS	1933	WO 4000/39. 4000/39 M	1929	pcr	Pa	P	P	C	BL-d	
WR	1933	WO 10,000/40. 10,000/40/J	1035	pcr	Pa	P	P	C	BL-d	
WR	1933	10,000/2/42 W	1942		Nbw	P	P	Cr	BL-d	
WR	1933	10,550/1/43 B	1941		Nbw	P	P	Cr	BL-d	
WR	1933	10,550/1/43 B	1941		Nbo	P	P	Cr	NLS	†

Sheet 35 *Sound of Sleat* — 23 by 28 miles

1	2	4	6	7	10	11	12	13	14
BS	-	?WO 9.29. 300/29			P	P	P	C	
MBS		?WO 9.29. 300/29. 350/33			P	P	P	Co	
MBS	1933	WO 9.29. 300/29. 350/33. 1000/35	1929		P	P	P	C	Wc
MBS	1933	WO 4000/39	M39 R39 1038	pcr	P	P	P	C	Cu
WR	1933	10,000/40/B	1929	pcr	P	P	P	C	BL-d
WR	1933	10,000/1/42 LR	1941		Nw	P	P	Cr	BL-d
WR	1933	15,000/9/42 McL	-		Nw	P	P	Cr	BL-d

Sheet 36 *Lochcarron & Dornie* — 28 by 19 miles

1	2	4	6	7	10	11	12	13	14
BS	-	WO 6/29. 300/29	1929		P	P	P	C	PC
MBS	1933	WO 600/33	1929		P	P	P	Co	Wc
MBS	1933	WO 8000/40	1929	pcr	P	P	P	C	BL-d
WR	1933	10,000/10/40 L	1038 M37 R37	pcr	P	P	P	C	BL-d
WR	1933	15,000/3/42 B	1942		Nw	P	P	Cr	BL-d

1	2	4	6	7	8	9	10	11	12	13	14	15
Sheet 37 *Inverness*							28 by 19 miles					
BS	-						P	P	P	C		
MBS	1933	WO 1600/33	1929				P	P	P	Co	BL-d	
MBS	1933	WO 4000/39	1928	pcr			P	P	P	C	BL-d	
WR	1933	10,000/40 B	1928	pcr			P	P	P	C	BL-d	
WR	1933	15,000/2/42 W	1941				Nv	P	P	Cr	BL-d	
WR	1933	10,550/1/43 B	1941				Nv	P	P	Cr	BL-d	
WR	1933	10,550/1/43 B	1941				No	P	P	Cr	NLS	†
Sheet 38 *Grantown-on-Spey & Strath Dearn*							28 by 19 miles					
BS	-	?WO 7.29. 400/29					P	P	P	C		
BS	-	WO 7.29. 400/29. 300/31	1929				P	P	P	Co	PC	
MBS	1933	WO 1600/33	1929				P	P	P	Co	PC	
MBS	1933	WO 1600/33. 2000/36	1929				P	P	P	C	Wc	
MBS	1933	WO 8000/39	1929	pcr			P	P	P	C	BL-d	
WR	1933	10,000/10/40 L	1929	pcr			P	P	P	C	BL-d	
WR	1933	15,000/2/42 LR	1942				Nv	P	P	Cr	BL-d	
WR	1933	10,550/1/43 B	1941				Nv	P	P	Cr	BL-d	
WR	1933	10,550/1/43 B	1941				No	P	P	Cr	NLS	†
Sheet 39 *Dufftown & Huntly*							28 by 19 miles					
BS	-	WO 9/29. 300/29	19xx [trimmed]				P	P	P	C	PC	
MBS	1933	WO 850/33	1929				P	P	P	Co	Wc	
WR	1933	10,000/4/41 B	1929				Pw	P	P	Cr	PC	
WR	1933	WO 20,000/8/41 LR	none				Pw	P	P	Cr	BL-d	
WR	1933	10,000/8/42 C	-				Nw	P	P	Cr	BL-d	
Sheet 40 *Inverurie & Ellon*							27 by 19 miles					
BS	-						P	P	P	C		
MBS		?WO 600/33					P	P	P	Co		
MBS	1933	WO 600/33. 1000/35	1929				P	P	P	C	NLS	
MBS	1933	WO 12,000/39	1929				P	P	P	C	BL-d	
WR	1940	10,000/1/41 L	1929				P	P	P	C	BL-d	1
WR	1940	WO 10,000/41. 5000/6/41	none				Pv	P	P	Cr	BL-d	1
WR	1933	M 15,000/2/42	1942				Nv	P	P	Cr	BL-d	

1. An updated imprint on a War Revision printing was very unusual.

1	2	4	6	7	8	9	10	11	12	13	14	15
Sheet 41 *Glen Shiel & Glen Garry*							28 by 19 miles					
BS	-	WO 2.29. 350.29	1928				P	P	P	C	PC	
MBS							P	P	P	Co		
MBS	1933	WO 4000/39	836	pcr			P	P	P	C	PC	
MBS	1933	WO 6000/40 W	836	pcr			P	P	P	C	BL-d	
WR	1933	10,000/10/40 L	1929	pcr			P	P	P	C	BL-d	
WR	1933	15,000/3/42 A	1942				Nw	P	P	Cr	BL-d	
Sheet 42 *Fort Augustus*							28 by 19 miles					
BS	-						P	P	P	C		
MBS	1933	WO 850/33	1929				P	P	P	Co	BL-d	
WR	1933	WO 10,000/40. 10,000/41/J	1928		1932	12.32	P	P	P	C	NLS	
WR	1933	WO 17,000/10/41 LR	1941				N	P	P	Cr	BL-d	
WR	1933	10,000/8/42 J	1941				N	P	P	Cr	BL-d	
Sheet 43 *Kingussie*							28 by 19 miles					
BS	-	?WO 12.28. 450/29					P	P	P	C		
BS	-	WO 12.28. 450/29. 200/31	1928				P	P	P	Co	PC	
MBS	1933	WO 1600/33	1928		1931		P	P	P	Co	PC	
MBS	1933	WO 7000/40	1928	pcr			P	P	P	C	Wc	
MBS	1933	13,000/40 W	1928	pcr			P	P	P	C	BL-d	
WR	1933	10,000/40 B	1928	pcr			P	P	P	C	BL-d	
WR	1933	15,000/7/42 LR	-				Nv	P	P	Cr	BL-d	

1	2	4	6	7	8	9	10	11	12	13	14	15

Sheet 44 *Ballater & Strathdon* — 28 by 19 miles

1	2	4	6	7	8	9	10	11	12	13	14	15
BS	-						P	P	P	C		
MBS	1933	WO 850/33	1929				P	P	P	Co	PC	
MBS	1933	200/39 C	1929				P	P	P	C	BL-d	
MBS	1933	10,000/40 W	1929				P	P	P	C	RGS	1
WR	1933	WO 10,000/3/41	1929				Pw	P	P	Cr	BL-d	
WR	1933	5000/3/42 McL	1942				Nw	P	P	Cr	BL-d	
WR	1933	10,000/1/43 J	1942				Nw	P	P	Cr	BL-d	
WR	1933	350/1/43 J	1942				No	P	P	Cr	NLS	†

1. The water infill plate is lacking.

Sheet 45 *Aberdeen* — WR 1940; 2WR 1942 — 27 by 19 miles

1	2	4	6	7	8	9	10	11	12	13	14	15
BS	-						P	P	P	C		
MBS		?WO 850/33					P	P	P	Co		
MBS	1933	WO 850/33. 1000/35	1929				P	P	P	C	BL-d	
MBS	1933	16,500/39 C	1929				P	P	P	C	Wc	
?	1933	WO 10,000/40	1929				P	P	P	C		1
WR	1933	WO 10,000/40. WO 10,000/3/41	1929				P	P	P	Cr	BL-d	
WR	1933	WO 15,000/5/41	1929				P	P	P	Cr	BL-d	
WR	1933	5000/4/42 LR	-				N	P	P	Cr	BL-d	
2WR	1933	50,550/11/42 Wa	-				N	P	P	C	BL-d	1

1. This print code appears very faintly under the left hand legend box of the next printing in the list. It has not been recorded independently. 2. It was usual for Second War Revision printings to have updated imprints.

Sheet 46 *Ardnamurchan & Loch Shiel* — 28 by 20 miles

1	2	4	6	7	8	9	10	11	12	13	14	15
BS	-	WO 3.29. 300/29	1929				P	P	P	C	PC	
MBS	1933	WO 350/33	1929				P	P	P	Co	BL-d	
MBS	1933	WO 350/33. 1000/35	1929				P	P	P	C	Wc	
MBS	1933	WO 350/33. 1000/35. 4000/36	1929				P	P	P	C	PC	
WR	1933	WO 10,000/40. 10,000/40/J	1929	pcr			P	P	P	C	BL-d	
WR	1933	10,000/10/41 LR	1941				Nw	P	P	Cr	BL-d	1
WR	1933	10,000/12/41 LR	1941				Nv	P	P	Cr	BL-d	
WR	1933	15,000/10/42 McL	1941				Nv	P	P	Cr	RGS	

1. The current editions note (see page 88) is present, but crossed out. It is omitted on the next state.

Sheet 47 *Ben Nevis & Fort William* — 28 by 20 miles

1	2	4	6	7	8	9	10	11	12	13	14	15
BS	-	WO 1.29. 450/29	1928				P	P	P	C	PC	
MBS							P	P	P	Co		
MBS	1933	4000/39	1928	pcr			P	P	P	C	Wc	
MBS	1933	no code	1928	pcr			P	P	P	C	OS	
WR	1933	10,000/40 B	1928	pcr			P	P	P	C	BL-d	
WR	1933	WO 10,000/8/41 LR	none				Pv	P	P	Cr	BL-d	
WR	1933	10,000/1/42 LR	1941				Nv	P	P	Cr	BL-d	
WR	1933	20,000/9/42 McL	-				Nv	P	P	Cr	BL-d	

Sheet 48 *Loch Ericht & Loch Laggan* — 28 by 19 miles

1	2	4	6	7	8	9	10	11	12	13	14	15
BS	-						P	P	P	C		
MBS	1933	WO 850/33	1928				P	P	P	Co	PC	
MBS	1933	2000/40 W	1928	pcr			P	P	P	C	RGS	
MBS	1933	WO 8000/40	1928	pcr			P	P	P	C	BL-d	
WR	1933	10,000/40 B	1928	pcr			P	P	P	C	BL-d	
WR	1933	15,000/2/42 W	1942				Nw	P	P	Cr	BL-d	
WR	1933	10,450/1/43 McL	-				Nw	P	P	Cr	BL-d	
WR	1933	10,450/1/43 McL	-				No	P	P	Cr	NLS	†

Sheet 49 *Grampian Mountains & Blair Atholl* — 28 by 19 miles

1	2	4	6	7	8	9	10	11	12	13	14	15
BS	-						P	P	P	C		
MBS							P	P	P	Co		
MBS	1933	WO 7500/40	1927	pcr			P	P	P	C	BL-d	
MBS	1933	10,000/40 W	1927	pcr			P	P	P	C	PC	
WR	1933	WO 20,000/40	1927	pcr			P	P	P	Cr	RGS	

1	2	4	6	7	8	9	10	11	12	13	14	15
WR	1933	15,000/7/42 TL	-				Nw	P	P	Cr	BL-d	
WR	1933	20,000/9/43 Ch	-				Nw	P	P	Cr	BL-d	
WR	1933	20,000/9/43 Ch	-				No	P	P	Cr	NLS	†

Sheet 50 *Glen Clova & Lochnagar* — 27 by 19 miles

1	2	4	6	7	8	9	10	11	12	13	14	15
BS	-						P	P	P	C		
MBS	1933	WO 600/33	1927	1929			P	P	P	Co	PC	
MBS	1933	WO 600/33. 1000/35					P	P	P	C		
MBS	1933	WO 12,000/39	1927	pcr			P	P	P	C	BL-d	
WR	1933	WO 10,000/40. 10,000/40/J	1927	pcr			P	P	P	C	BL-d	
WR	1933	20,000/2/42 McL	1942				Nw	P	P	Cr	BL-d	
WR	1933	10,450/1/43 McL	-				Nw	P	P	Cr	BL-d	
WR	1933	10,450/1/43 McL	-				No	P	P	Cr	NLS	†

Sheet 51 *Stonehaven & Brechin* — 27 by 19 miles

1	2	4	6	7	8	9	10	11	12	13	14	15
BS	-	WO 500/30. 500/31	1928				P	P	P	Co	PC	
MBS	1933	WO 1600/33	1928				P	P	P	Co	PC	
MBS	1933	200/39	1928	1931			P	P	P	C	Cu	
MBS	1933	no code	1928	pcr			P	P	P	C	BL-d	1
MBS	1933	10,000/40/J	1928	pcr			P	P	P	C	BL-d	
WR							P	P	P	C		2
WR	1933	15,000/9/41 LR	1941				Nw	P	P	Cr	BL-d	3
WR	1933	15,000/4/42 LR	1942				Nw	P	P	Cr	BL-d	
WR	1933	10,000/5/43/M (purple)	1941				Nw	P	P	Cr	BL-d	
WR	1933	450/5/43/M	1941				No	P	P	Cr	NLS	†

1. The water infill plate is lacking. 2. *GSGS 3908 current edition*, 8 July 1941 lists this sheet as War Revision (see appendix 1). At this date this would have had Popular Edition marginalia. 3. If printed in September 1941 this would be one of the first sheets with new style marginalia, though the OS file copy in BL-d has the handwritten date 23 October 1941.

Sheet 52 *Coll & Tiree* — 28 by 19 miles

1	2	4	6	7	8	9	10	11	12	13	14	15
BS	-	WO 10.27. 500/28	1927				P	P	P	C	PC	
MBS	1933	WO 350/33	1927				P	P	P	Co	PC	
MBS	1933	WO 1035	1927	pcr			P	P	P	C	Wc	
MBS	1933	WO 4000/40	1927	pcr			P	P	P	C+	BL-d	
WR	1933	10,000/11/40 L	1927	pcr			P	P	P	Co-	BL-d	
WR	1933	10,000/3/42 W	1941				Nw	P	P	Cor	BL-d	
WR	1933	10,000/1/43 LR	-				Nw	P	P	Cor	BL-d	
WR	1933	10,000/1/43 LR	-				No	P	P	Cor	NLS	†

Sheet 53 *Sound of Mull* — 32 by 19 miles

1	2	4	6	7	8	9	10	11	12	13	14	15
BS	-	WO 28. 350/28	1927				P	P	P	C	PC	1
MBS	1933	WO 350/33	1927				P	P	P	Co	BL-d	
MBS	1933	WO 350/33. 1000/35	1927				P	P	P	C	Wc	
WR	1933	WO 10,000/40	1927	pcr			P	P	P	Cr	NLS	
WR	1933	WO 5000/5/41	none				Pw	P	P	Cr	BL-d	
WR	1933	10,000/4/42 Cr	1942				Nw	P	P	Cr	BL-d	2
WR	1933	10,000/8/42 B	1942				Nw	P	P	Cr	BL-d	
WR	1933	15,000/9/43 Ch	-				Nw	P	P	Cr	BL-d	
WR	1933	15,000/9/43 Ch	-				No	P	P	Cr	NLS	†

1. This printing is recorded on Place's waterproof paper, one of the earliest known. 2. A print code 10,000/3/42 LR in blue has been deleted with a purple line.

Sheet 54 *Loch Etive & Glen Coe* — 28 by 19 miles

1	2	4	6	7	8	9	10	11	12	13	14	15
BS	-	WO 11.27. 500.28	1927				P	P	P	C	PC	
MBS	1933	WO 600/33	1927				P	P	P	Co	PC	
MBS	1933	WO 1035	1927	pcr			P	P	P	C	BL-d	
MBS	1933	WO 4000/39	1927	pcr			P	P	P	C	BL-d	
WR	1933	WO 10,000/40. 10,000/40 B	1927	pcr			P	P	P	C	Cu	
WR	1933	15,000/10/41 LR	1941				Nw	P	P	Cr	BL-d	
WR	1933	20,000/8/42 W	-				Nw	P	P	Cr	BL-d	

Sheet 55 *Killin & Loch Rannoch* — 28 by 19 miles

1	2	4	6	7	8	9	10	11	12	13	14	15
BS	-	WO 11.27. 350/28	1927				P	P	P	C	PC	
MBS	1933	WO 600/33	1927				P	P	P	Co	PC	
MBS	1933	WO 1000/35	1927	1934	12.32		P	P	P	C	BL-d	
MBS	1933	WO 4000/39	1927	pcr			P	P	P	C	BL-d	
WR	1933	WO 10,000/40. 10,000/40/B	1927	pcr			P	P	P	C	BL-d	
WR	1933	WO 10,000/9/41 LR	1941				Nw	P	P	Cr	BL-d	1
WR	1933	10,000/5/42 LR	-				Nw	P	P	Cr	BL-d	
WR	1933	10,000/8/42 W	-				Nw	P	P	Cr	BL-d	
WR	1933	20,450/2/43 E	1941				Nw	P	P	Cr	BL-d	2
WR	1933	20,450/2/43 E	1941				No	P	P	Cr	NLS	†

1. If printed in September 1941 this would be one of the first sheets with new style marginalia, though the OS file copy now in BL-d has the handwritten date 13 October 1941. 2. The current editions note is in red, not purple (see page 88).

Sheet 56 *Dunkeld & Pitlochry* — 28 by 19 miles

1	2	4	6	7	8	9	10	11	12	13	14	15
BS	-						P	P	P	C		
MBS	1933	WO 1600/33	1927				P	P	P	Co	PC	
MBS	1933	WO 4000/39	1927	pcr			P	P	P	C	BL-d	
MBS	1933	13,000/40/R	1539 M38 R38	pcr			P	P	P	C	NLS	
MBS	1933	10,000/9/40 L	1927	pcr			P	P	P	C	Cu	
WR	1933	WO 10,000/8/41 LR	none				Pw	P	P	Cr	BL-d	
WR	1933	15,000/12/41 LR	1941				Nw	P	P	Cr	BL-d	
WR	1933	20,000/8/42 W	-				Nw	P	P	Cr	BL-d	

Sheet 57 *Forfar & Dundee* — 27 by 20 miles

1	2	4	6	7	8	9	10	11	12	13	14	15
BS	-						P	P	P	C		
MBS	1933	WO 1600/33	1927				P	P	P	Co	Wc	
MBS	1933	239	1927	pcr			P	P	P	C	BL-d	
WR	1933	WO 10,000/40. 10,000/40/J	1927	pcr			P	P	P	C	BL-d	1
WR	1933	WO 20,000/8/41 LR	none				P	P	P	Cr	BL-d	
WR	1933	10,000/4/42 LR	1941				N	P	P	Cr	BL-d	
WR	1933	5000/6/42 LR	-				N	P	P	Cr	BL-d	
WR	1933	10,000/9/42 McL	-				N	P	P	Cr	BL-d	

1. The adjoining sheet diagram is on the contour plate.

Sheet 58 *Arbroath & Montrose* — 28 by 20 miles

1	2	4	6	7	8	9	10	11	12	13	14	15
BS	-	?WO 3.28. 750/28					P	P	P	C		
BS	-	?500/30+					P	P	P	C		
BS	-	1000/31++	1927	1928			P	P	P	C+	PC	
MBS	1933	WO 3100/33	1927				P	P	P	Co	PC	
MBS	1933	WO 3100/33. 4000/36	1927				P	P	P	C	NLS	
MBS	1933	WO 8000/40	1927	pcr			P	P	P	C	OS	
MBS	1933	10,000/9/40 L	1927	pcr			P	P	P	C	BL-d	
WR	1933	WO 25,000/5/41	none				P	P	P	Cr	BL-d	
WR	1933	10,000/4/42 LR	1941				N	P	P	Cr	BL-d	
WR	1933	10,000/9/42 McL	-				N	P	P	Cr	BL-d	

Sheet 59 *Iona & Colonsay* — 19 by 31 miles

1	2	4	6	7	8	9	10	11	12	13	14	15
BS	-						P	P	P	C		
MBS	1933	WO 350/33	1927				P	P	P	Co	BL-d	
MBS	1933	WO 8000/39	1927				P	P	P	C	BL-d	
WR	1933	10,000/4/41 J	1927				Pw	P	P	Cr	BL-d	
WR	1933	5000/3/42 LR (purple)	1942				Nw	P	P	Cr	BL-d	
WR	1933	15,000/7/42 LR	-				Nw	P	P	Cr	BL-d	

Sheet 60 *North Jura & Firth of Lorne* — 19 by 31 miles

1	2	4	6	7	8	9	10	11	12	13	14	15
BS	-	WO 500/27	1927				P	P	P	C	PC	
MBS	1933	WO 350/33	1927				P	P	P	Co	BL-d	
MBS	1933	WO 4000/39	1927				P	P	P	C	PC	
WR	1933	WO 10,000/40. 10,000/40 B	1927				P	P	P	C	BL-d	
WR	1933	10,000/4/42 LR	1942				Nv	P	P	Cr	BL-d	
WR	1933	15,000/7/42 McL	-				Nv	P	P	Cr	BL-d	

Sheet 61 *Oban & Loch Awe* — 28 by 19 miles

1	2	4	6	7	8	9	10	11	12	13	14	15
BS	-						P	P	P	C		
MBS	1933	WO 600/33	1927				P	P	P	Co	BL-d	
MBS	1933	WO 600/33. 1000/35	1927				P	P	P	C	Wc	
MBS	1933	WO 4000/39. 4000/39 M	1927	pcr			P	P	P	C	OS	
WR	1933	10,000/41 B	1927	pcr			P	P	P	C	BL-d	1
WR	1933	WO 7000/8/41 LR	none				P	P	P	C	BL-d	1
WR	1941	5000/1/42 LR	1942				N	P	P	Cr	BL-d	
WR	1941	10,000/6/42 LR	-				N	P	P	Cr	BL-d	
WR	1941	10,000/8/42/C	-				N	P	P	Cr	BL-d	2
WR	1941	10,000/5/43/M (purple)	1941				N	P	P	Cr	BL-d	
WR	1941	550/5/43/M	1941				No	P	P	Cr	NLS	†

1. Main roads would usually be coloured red at this date, but in fact they are still sienna. 2. The incorrect GSGS number 3907 is crossed through, and 3908 applied with a stamp.

Sheet 62 *Loch Katrine & Loch Earn* — 28 by 19 miles

1	2	4	6	7	8	9	10	11	12	13	14	15
BS	-	WO 9/27. 1000/27	1927				P	P	P	C	PC	
MBS	1933	WO 1600/33	1927				P	P	P	Co	PC	
MBS	1933	12,000/39 C	1927		1933		P	P	P	C	BL-d	
WR	1933	WO 10,000/40. 10,000/40/J	1927				P	P	P	C	BL-d	
WR	1933	10,000/1/42 LR	1942				Nv	P	P	Cr	BL-d	
WR	1933	10,000/6/42 LR	-				Nv	P	P	Cr	BL-d	
WR	1933	10,000/8/42 B	1941				Nv	P	P	Cr	BL-d	
WR	1933	15,000/2/43 LR	-				Nv	P	P	Cr	BL-d	
WR	1933	15,000/2/43 LR	-				No	P	P	Cr	NLS	†

Sheet 63 *Perth & Strath Earn* — 27 by 19 miles

1	2	4	6	7	8	9	10	11	12	13	14	15
BS	-	?WO 10.27. 1000/27					P	P	P	C		
BS	-	WO 10.27. 1000/27. 200/31	1927				P	P	P	Co	PC	1
MBS		?WO 1600/33					P	P	P	Co		
MBS	1933	WO 1600/33. 500/37	1927				P	P	P	C	Ag	
MBS	1933	WO 12,000/39	1927	pcr			P	P	P	C	Wc	
MBS	1933	no code	1927	pcr			P	P	P	C	NLS	
WR	1933	10,000/40 B	1927	pcr			P	P	P	C	BL-d	
WR	1933	WO 10,000/40. 15,000/5/41	1927	pcr			P	P	P	Cr	BL-d	
WR	1933	15,000/2/42 LR	1942				N	P	P	Cr	BL-d	
WR	1933	20,000/8/42 W	1942				N	P	P	Cr	BL-d	

1. See figure 1.

Sheet 64 *Dundee & St. Andrews* — 34 by 21 miles

1	2	4	6	7	8	9	10	11	12	13	14	15
BS	-						P	P	P	C		
MBS		[?WO] 2300/33					P	P	P	Co	dealer	1
MBS	1933	WO 16,200/39	1927	pcr			P	P	P	C	NLS	2
WR	1933	10,000/40 B	1927	pcr			P	P	P	C	BL-d	3
WR	1933	10,000/4/41 A	1927	pcr			P	P	P	Cr	BL-d	
WR	1933	10,000/6/41/A	1927	pcr			P	P	P	Cr	BL-d	
WR	1933	10,000/2/42 A	1942				N	P	P	Cr	BL-d	
WR	1933	15,000/8/42 McL	-				N	P	P	Cr	BL-d	

1. A defective copy only has been recorded. 2. The civilian 5000/28 printing has "RAF Aerodrome (Wireless Tel. Sta.)" at Leuchars, together with a railway connection – "RAF" is usually scratched out. This printing just has "Aerodrome" marked (south of Leuchars), with no sign of the railway. 3. All indications of the aerodrome have been deleted.

1	2	4	6	7	8	9	10	11	12	13	14	15

Sheet 65 *Dunoon & Loch Fyne* — 28 by 18 miles

1	2	4	6	7	10	11	12	13	14	15
BS	-	WO 2.27	1927		P	P	P	C	BL-d	
MBS					P	P	P	Co		
MBS	1933	WO 16,000/39	1927	pcr	P	P	P	C	BL-d	
MBS	1933	no code	1927	pcr	P	P	P	C	NLS	1
WR					P	P	P	C		2
WR	1933	12,000/10/41 LR	1941		N	P	P	Cr	BL-d	
WR	1933	10,000/3/42 LR	1942		N	P	P	Cr	BL-d	
WR	1933	30,000/10/42/J	1941		N	P	P	Cr	BL-d	

1. The water infill plate is lacking. 2. *GSGS 3908 current edition*, 8 July 1941 lists this sheet as War Revision (see appendix 1). At this date this would have had Popular Edition marginalia.

Sheet 66 *Loch Lomond* — 28 by 18 miles

1	2	4	6	7	10	11	12	13	14
BS	-				P	P	P	C	
MBS					P	P	P	Co	
MBS	1933	WO 16,000/39	4000/27	1931	P	P	P	C	BL-d
WR	1933	WO 25,000/6/41	none		P	P	P	Cr	BL-d
WR	1933	10,000/3/42 LR	1942		N	P	P	Cr	BL-d
WR	1933	20,000/10/42 McL	1941		N	P	P	Cr	BL-d

Sheet 67 *Stirling & Dunfermline* — 27 by 18 miles

1	2	4	6	7	10	11	12	13	14	15
BS	-				P	P	P	C		
MBS	1933	WO 3100/33	1927	1930	P	P	P	Co	Mg-d	
MBS	1933	WO 16,000/39 C	1927	pcr	P	P	P	C	BL-d	
WR	1933	10,000/10/40 L	1927	pcr	P	P	P	C	BL-d	
WR	1933	10,000/41 B	1927	pcr	P	P	P	C	NLS	1
WR	1933	WO 6000/6/41	none		P	P	P	Cr	BL-d	
WR	1933	15,000/3/42 LR	1942		N	P	P	Cr	BL-d	
WR	1933	15,000/8/42 J	1941		N	P	P	Cr	BL-d	
WR	1933	20,000/9/43 Ch	1941		N	P	P	Cr	BL-d	
WR	1933	20,000/9/43 Ch	1941		No	P	P	Cr	NLS	†

1. The roads remain sienna.

Sheet 68 *Firth of Forth* — 34 by 20 miles

1	2	4	6	7	10	11	12	13	14	15
BS	-	WO 2.28. 650/28	1928		P	P	P	C	PC	
BS	-	WO 500/31	1928		P	P	P	C+	PC	
?		?WO 500/31. 500/33			P	P	P	Co		
MBS	1933	WO 500/31. 500/33. 3100/33	1928		P	P	P	Co	NLS	
MBS	1933	4300/39	1928	pcr	P	P	P	C	BL-d	
WR	1933	10,000/40 B	1928	pcr	P	P	P	C	BL-d	
WR	1933	WO 10,000/40. 16,000/5/41	none		P	P	P	Cr	BL-d	
WR	1933	10,000/2/42 A	1941		N	P	P	Cr	BL-d	
WR	1933	15,000/6/42 LR	-		N	P	P	Cr	Cu	
WR	1933	25,000/1/43 LR	-		N	P	P	Cr	BL-d	
WR	1933	25,000/1/43 LR	-		No	P	P	Cr	NLS	†
WR	1933	20,000/2/43 LR	-		N	P	P	Cr	BL-d	

Sheet 69 *Islay* — 25 by 30 miles

1	2	4	6	7	10	11	12	13	14	15
BS	-				P	P	P	C		
MBS	1933	WO 350/33	1926		P	P	P	Co	BL	1
MBS	1933	WO 4000/39	1926	pcr	P	P	P	C	BL-d	
WR	1933	10,000/40 B	1926	pcr	P	P	P	C	RGS	
WR	1933	10,000/2/42 J	1941		Nw	P	P	Cr	BL-d	
WR	1933	15,000/6/42 LR	-		Nw	P	P	Cr	BL-d	

1. The British Library copy is at Maps 7705(1).

Sheet 70 *Sound of Jura* — 19 by 30 miles

1	2	4	6	10	11	12	13	14
BS	-			P	P	P	C	
MBS	1933	WO 350/33	1926	P	P	P	Co	Wc
MBS	1933	WO 4000/39	1926	P	P	P	C	BL-d

104

1	2	4	6	7	8	9	10	11	12	13	14	15
WR	1933	10,000/41 B	1926				P	P	P	C	BL-d	
WR	1933	10,000/10/41 LR	1941				Nw	P	P	Cr	BL-d	
WR	1933	15,000/6/42 LR	-				Nw	P	P	Cr	BL-d	
WR	1933	10,000/1/43 LR	-				Nw	P	P	Cr	BL-d	
WR	1933	10,000/1/43 LR	-				No	P	P	Cr	NLS	†

Sheet 71 *Island of Bute*   27 by 23 miles

1	2	4	6	7	8	9	10	11	12	13	14	15
BS	-						P	P	P	C		
MBS							P	P	P	Co		
MBS	1933	200/39	1925	1929			P	P	P	C	BL-d	
WR	1933	WO 15,000/6/41	none				P	P	P	Cr	BL-d	
WR	1933	10,000/2/42 LR	1942				N	P	P	Cr	BL-d	
WR	1933	15,000/5/42 LR	-				N	P	P	Cr	BL-d	
WR	1933	10,000/1/43 LR	-				N	P	P	Cr	BL-d	
WR	1933	10,000/1/43 LR	-				No	P	P	Cr	NLS	†
WR	1933	10,000/5/43/M	1942				N	P	P	Cr	BL-d	
WR	1933	20,000/1/44 Wa	1942				N	P	P	Cr	BL-d	

Sheet 72 *Glasgow*   34 by 24 miles

1	2	4	6	7	8	9	10	11	12	13	14	15
BS	-						P	P	P	C		
MBS	1933	WO 1600/33	1925	1931			P	P	P	Co	Cu-m	
MBS	1933	WO 1600/33. 1000/35	1925	1931			P	P	P	C	BL-d	
MBS	1933	WO 16,000/39	1925	pcr			P	P	P	C	BL-d	
WR	1933	WO 10,000/40. 10,000/40/J	1925	pcr			P	P	P	C	BL-d	
WR	1933	WO 10,000/40. 10,000/4/41 A	1925	pcr			P	P	P	Cr	BL-d	
WR	1933	WO 10,000/40. 6000/6/41 A	1925	pcr			P	P	P	Cr	BL-d	
WR	1933	15,000/3/42 LR	1942				N	P	P	Cr	BL-d	
WR	1933	20,000/6/42 LR	-				N	P	P	Cr	BL-d	
WR	1933	10,000/10/42 F	-				N	P	P	Cr	Cu	
WR	1933	20,000/2/43 LR	-				N	P	P	Cr	BL-d	
WR	1933	20,000/2/43 LR	-				No	P	P	Cr	NLS	†
WR	1933	15,000/1/44 Wa	-				N	P	P	Cr	BL-d	

Sheet 73 *Falkirk & Motherwell*   28 by 24 miles

1	2	4	6	7	8	9	10	11	12	13	14	15
BS	-						P	P	P	C		
MBS	1933	WO 3100/33	1926	1932	8.32		P	P	P	Co	PC	
MBS	1933	WO 16,000/39 C	1926	-			P	P	P	C	BL-d	
WR	1933	10,000/40 B	1926	pcr			P	P	P	C	NLS	
WR	1933	WO 10,000/40. 10,000/4/41/A	1926	pcr			P	P	P	Cr	BL-d	
WR	1933	WO 10,000/5/41	none				P	P	P	Cr	Og	
WR	1933	10,000/2/42 LR	1942				N	P	P	Cr	BL-d	
WR	1933	15,000/4/42 LR	1942				N	P	P	Cr	BL-d	
WR	1933	10,000/5/43/M (purple)	1942				N	P	P	Cr	BL-d	
WR	1933	850/5/43/M	1942				No	P	P	Cr	NLS	†
WR	1933	20,000/10/43 Ch	-				N	P	P	Cr	BL-d	
WR	1933	20,000/10/43 Ch	-				No	P	P	Cr	OS	

Sheet 74 *Edinburgh*   28 by 24 miles

1	2	4	6	7	8	9	10	11	12	13	14	15
BS	-	WO 1500/27	1926				P	P	P	C	PC	
MBS		?WO 3100/33					P	P	P	Co		
MBS	1933	WO 3100/33. 2300/38	1926				P	P	P	C	NLS	
MBS	1933	WO 16,000/39 C	1928	pcr			P	P	P	C	BL-d	
WR	1933	10,000/40 C	1928	pcr			P	P	P	Cr	BL-d	
WR		13,000/40 J					P	P	P	C	card	
WR	1933	WO 5000/5/41	none				P	P	P	Cr	BL-d	
WR	1933	15,000/12/41 LR	1941				N	P	P	Cr	BL-d	
WR	1933	15,000/6/42 LR	-				N	P	P	Cr	BL-d	
WR	1933	20,000/1/43 LR	-				N	P	P	Cr	BL-d	
WR	1933	20,000/1/43 LR	-				No	P	P	Cr	NLS	†

Sheet 75 *Dunbar & Lammermuir* — 27 by 24 miles

1	2	4	6	7	8	9	10	11	12	13	14	15
BS	-	?WO 11.26. 500/27					P	P	P	C		
BS	-	Reprint 1000/27+	1926				P	P	P	C	PC	
MBS	1933	WO 1600/33	1926	1932	9.32		P	P	P	Co	BL-d	
MBS	1933	WO 16,750/39	1926	pcr			P	P	P	C	BL-d	
MBS	1933	10,000/40 B	1038 M38 R37	pcr			P	P	P	C	NLS	1
WR	1933	WO 10,000/40. 13,000/40/J	1926	pcr			P	P	P	C	RGS	
WR	1933	WO 10,000/40 C	1926	pcr			P	P	P	Cr	BL-d	
WR	1933	WO 10,000/40. 5000/6/41	none				P	P	P	Cr	NLS	
WR	1933	15,000/2/42 H	1941				N	P	P	Cr	BL-d	
WR	1933	15,000/7/42 F	-				N	P	P	Cr	BL-d	
WR	1933	20,000/1/43 LR	-				N	P	P	Cr	BL-d	
WR	1933	20,000/1/43 LR	-				No	P	P	Cr	NLS	†

1. A copy of this state is recorded with the signature "J.B.& Son, Ltd, 2nd July 1940" (a Bartholomew copy).

Sheet 76 *Kintyre* — 24 by 34 miles

1	2	4	6	7	8	9	10	11	12	13	14	15
BS	-						P	P	P	C		
MBS	1933	WO 850/33	1926				P	P	P	Co	BL-d	
MBS	1933	WO 8000/39	1926	pcr			P	P	P	C	Wc	
WR	1933	WO 10,000/41. 5000/4/41 A	1926	pcr			P	P	P	Cr	Og	
WR	1933	no code	1941				N	P	P	Cr	BL-d	
WR	1933	15,000/5/42 LR	-				N	P	P	Cr	BL-d	
WR	1933	10,000/1/43 LR	-				N	P	P	Cr	BL-d	
WR	1933	10,000/1/43 LR	-				No	P	P	Cr	NLS	†

Sheet 77 *Island of Arran* — 28 by 24 miles

1	2	4	6	7	8	9	10	11	12	13	14	15
BS	-						P	P	P	C		
MBS	1933	WO 850/33	1926				P	P	P	Co	BL-d	
MBS	1933	WO 4000/39	1926				P	P	P	C	Wc	
WR	1933	10,000/41/J	1926	pcr			P	P	P	C	PC	
WR	1933	15,000/10/41 LR	1941				N	P	P	Cr	BL-d	
WR	1933	20,000/6/42 LR	-				N	P	P	Cr	BL-d	
WR	1933	10,000/10/42 A	-				N	P	P	Cr	BL-d	

Sheet 78 *Kilmarnock & Ayr* — 28 by 19 miles

1	2	4	6	7	8	9	10	11	12	13	14	15
BS	-	?WO 8.26. 1000/26					P	P	P	C		
BS	-	?750/28+					P	P	P	C		
MBS	1933	3100/33++					P	P	P	Co		
MBS	1933	WO 12,000/39 C	1926	1931		1926	P	P	P	C	BL-d	
WR	1933	10,000/40 J					P	P	P	C	card	
WR	1933	10,000/2/41 L	1926	1931		1926	P	P	P	Cr	BL-d	
WR	1933	15,000/10/41 LR	1941				N	P	P	Cr	BL-d	1
WR	1933	15,000/5/42 LR	-				N	P	P	Cr	BL-d	
WR	1933	20,000/8/42 LR	-				N	P	P	Cr	BL-d	
WR	1933	20,000/2/43 LR	-				N	P	P	Cr	BL-d	
WR	1933	20,000/2/43 LR	-				No	P	P	Cr	NLS	†
WR	1933	10,000/10/43 Wa	-				N	P	P	Cr	BL-d	

1. The same print code appears on a civilian outline and water printing.

Sheet 79 *Lanark* — 28 by 19 miles

1	2	4	6	7	8	9	10	11	12	13	14	15
BS	-	?WO 8.26. 1000/26					P	P	P	C		
BS	-	?750/28+					P	P	P	C		
MBS	1933	3100/33++	1926				P	P	P	Co	BL-d	
MBS	1933	12,000/39	M36 R32	pcr			P	P	P	C	BL-d	
MBS	1933	10,000/40 J	10/37 M36 R32	pcr			P	P	P	C	BL	
WR		?WO 10,000/40. 10,000/41					P	P	P	C		
WR	1933	10,000/41/J+	1926	pcr			P	P	P	C	NLS	
WR	1933	15,000/5/42 LR	-				Nv	P	P	Cr	BL-d	
WR	1933	30,000/8/42 LR	-				Nv	P	P	Cr	BL-d	
WR	1933	15,600/11/43 Wa	-				Nv	P	P	Cr	BL-d	
WR	1933	15,600/11/43 Wa	-				No	P	P	Cr	NLS	†

1	2	4	6	7	8	9	10	11	12	13	14	15

Sheet 80 *Peebles & Galashiels* — 28 by 19 miles

1	2	4	6	7	8	9	10	11	12	13	14	15
BS	-						P	P	P	C		
MBS	1933	WO 3100/33	1926				P	P	P	Co	BL-d	
MBS	1933	no code	1926	pcr			P	P	P	C	BL-d	
WR	1933	WO 10,000/40. 10,000/40/J	1926	pcr			P	P	P	C	RGS	1
WR	1933	15,000/3/42 B	1942				Nv	P	P	Cr	BL-d	
WR	1933	15,000/7/42 F	-				Nv	P	P	Cr	BL-d	
WR	1933	10,650/1/43 McL	-				Nv	P	P	Cr	PC	
WR	1933	10,650/1/43 McL	-				No	P	P	Cr	NLS	†
WR	1933	10,000/7/43 Ch	-				Nv	P	P	Cr	BL-d	

1. The adjoining sheet diagram is on the contour plate.

Sheet 81 *Kelso* — 27 by 19 miles

1	2	4	6	7	8	9	10	11	12	13	14	15
BS	-						P	P	P	C		
MBS	1933	WO 1600/33	1926	1932	9.32		P	P	P	Co	BL-d	
MBS	1933	no code	1926	1932	9.32		P	P	P	C	BL-d	
MBS	1933	13,000/40 B	1926	1932	9.32		P	P	P	C	NLS	
WR	1933	WO 10,000/41. 10,000/41 B	1926	1932	9.32		P	P	P	C	PC	
WR	1933	WO 10,000/41 C	1926	1932	9.32		P	P	P	Cr	BL-d	
WR	1933	20,000/1/42 LR	1942				Nv	P	P	Cr	BL-d	
WR	1933	20,000/8/42 J	1942				Nv	P	P	Cr	BL-d	
WR	1933	20,000/9/43 Ch	1941				Nv	P	P	Cr	BL-d	
WR	1933	20,000/9/43 Ch	1941				No	P	P	Cr	NLS	†

Sheet 82 *Ailsa Craig & Girvan* — 19 by 28 miles

1	2	4	6	7	8	9	10	11	12	13	14	15
BS	-	WO 7.26. 1000/26	1925				P	P	P	C	PC	
MBS	1933	WO 1600/33	1925				P	P	P	Co	BL-d	
MBS	1933	WO 16,000/39 C	1925	1931			P	P	P	C	BL-d	
WR	1933	WO 5000/5/41	none				Pw	P	P	Cr	BL-d	
WR	1933	15,000/11/41 LR	1941				Nw	P	P	Cr	BL-d	
WR	1933	45,000/7/42 F	-				Nw	P	P	Cr	BL-d	

Sheet 83 *Loch Doon* — 28 by 19 miles

1	2	4	6	7	8	9	10	11	12	13	14	15
BS	-						P	P	P	C		
MBS	1933	WO 1600/33	1926				P	P	P	Co	PC	
MBS	1933	WO 11,500/40 C	1926	pcr			P	P	P	C	BL	
WR	1933	10,000/11/40 L	1926	pcr			P	P	P	C	BL-d	
WR	1933	WO 6000/6/41	none				P	P	P	Cr	BL-d	
WR	1933	WO 11,000/7/41	none				P	P	P	Cr	BL-d	
WR	1933	15,000/5/42 A	-				N	P	P	Cr	BL-d	
WR	1933	25,000/8/42 B	1941				N	P	P	Cr	BL-d	

A grid error was reported on 10 June 1941, that the repeat references for northing 35 had been placed along grid line 36. The error was apparently present on pre-war Popular Edition and War Revision printings up to that date.

Sheet 84 *Nithsdale & Moffat* — 28 by 19 miles

1	2	4	6	7	8	9	10	11	12	13	14	15
BS	-						P	P	P	C		
MBS	1933	WO 850/33	1926				P	P	P	Co	PC	
MBS	1933	WO 16,000/39 C	1926	1932			P	P	P	C	BL-d	1
WR	1933	WO 10,000/3/41	1926	-			Pw	P	P	Cr	BL-d	
WR	1933	5000/10/41 LR	1941				Nw	P	P	Cr	BL-d	
WR	1933	15,000/4/42 LR	-				Nw	P	P	Cr	BL-d	
WR	1933	25,000/7/42 F	-				Nw	P	P	Cr	BL-d	
WR	1933	10,000/2/43 LR	-				Nw	P	P	Cr	BL-d	
WR	1933	10,000/2/43 LR	-				No	P	P	Cr	NLS	†
WR	1933	10,000/11/43 Wa	-				Nw	P	P	Cr	BL-d	

1. Also recorded with "Proof for Registration. Received from Sc[ottish]. Com[man]d. 24.10.40" stamped in red (copy NLS).

1	2	4	6	7	8	9	10	11	12	13	14	15

Sheet 85 *Hawick & Eskdale* — 28 by 19 miles

1	2	4	6	7	8	9	10	11	12	13	14	15
BS	-	?WO 8.26. 1000/26					P	P	P	C		
BS	-	1000/27+	1926				P	P	P	C	PC	
MBS	1933	3100/33++	1926				P	P	P	Co	BL-d	
MBS	1933	no code	1926	pcr			P	P	P	C	BL-d	
MBS		12,000/39					P	P	P	C	card	
WR	1933	10,000/11/40 L	1926	pcr			P	P	P	C	PC	
WR	1933	15,000/10/41 L/R	1941				Nv	P	P	Cr	BL-d	1
WR	1933	20,000/4/42 LR	1941				Nv	P	P	Cr	BL-d	
WR	1933	10,000/8/42 J	1941				Nv	P	P	Cr	BL-d	
WR	1933	20,000/7/43 Ch	-				Nv	P	P	Cr	BL-d	
WR	1933	20,000/7/43 Ch	-				No	P	P	Cr	NLS	†

1. On some copies the northing number 38 was omitted from the western margin near the top. It is unclear whether "L/R" refers to an otherwise unrecorded printing company, or is a unique way of expressing "London Road" (see appendix 4).

Sheet 86 (Scotland), **Sheet 3** (England & Wales) *The Cheviot Hills* — 27 by 18 miles

1	2	4	6	7	8	9	10	11	12	13	14	15
BS	-	?WO 1/26. 2000/27					P	P	P	C		
BS	-	WO 1/26. 2000/27. 500/28	1925				P	P	P	C	PC	
MBS	1933	WO 3400/32	1925		1930	8.29E	P	P	P	Co	BL-d	
MBS	1933	WO 3400/32. 1000/34	1925		1930	8.29E	P	P	P	C	BL-d	
MBS	1932	no code	3038 M38 R37	pcr			P	P	P	C	BL-d	
MBS	1933	WD 12,000/39 C. 10,000/39 C	1925		pcr		P	P	P	C	BL-d	
MBS	1932	WO 12,000/40	1925		pcr		P	P	P	C	Wc	
WR	1932	10,000/40/J	3038 M38 R37	pcr			P	P	P	C	BL-d	
WR	1932	WO 12,000/40. 20,000/3/41	1925		pcr		Pv	P	P	Cr	BL-d	
WR	1932	10,000/2/42 B	1925		pcr		Pv	P	P	Cr	BL-d	
2WR	1942	72,000/7/42 LR	-				N	P	P	C	BL-d	1
2WR	1942	40,000/10/42/M	-				N	P	P	C	BL-d	
2WR	1942	10,000/12/43 Ch	-				N	P	P	C	BL-d	

This sheet has the heading *Ordnance Survey of Great Britain*. From 1933 it was a member of both GSGS 3907 and 3908. 1. Used also for *Redesdale & Otterburn ranges*. See supplement 4.

Sheet 87 *Newton Stewart* — 28 by 19 miles

1	2	4	6	7	8	9	10	11	12	13	14	15
BS	-						P	P	P	C		
MBS	1933	WO 850/33	1925				P	P	P	Co	PC	
MBS	1933	WO 8000/40	1925				P	P	P	C	BL-d	
MBS	1933	6000/40 W	1040 M39 R39				P	P	P	C	BL-d	
WR	1933	WO 10,000/40. 10,000/40/J	1925				P	P	P	C	BL-d	
WR	1933	15,000/5/42 LR	-				Nw	P	P	Cr	BL-d	
WR	1933	10,000/10/42 B	1942				Nw	P	P	Cr	BL-d	
WR	1933	20,000/2/43 LR	-				Nw	P	P	Cr	BL-d	
WR	1933	20,000/2/43 LR	-				No	P	P	Cr	NLS	†

Sheet 88 *Dumfries* — 28 by 18 miles

1	2	4	6	7	8	9	10	11	12	13	14	15
BS	-	?WO 8.25					P	P	P	C		
BS	-	WO 8.25. Reprint 1000/26	1925				P	P	P	C	PC	
MBS	1933	850/33+	1925				P	P	P	Co	BL-d	
MBS	1933	16,200/39 C	1925	1926			P	P	P	C	BL-d	
WR	1933	WO 5000/5/41	none				P	P	P	Cr	BL-d	
WR	1933	WO 12,000/10/41 LR	1941				N	P	P	Cr	BL-d	
WR	1933	20,000/4/42 LR	1941				N	P	P	Cr	BL-d	
WR	1933	35,000/7/42 McL	-				N	P	P	Cr	BL-d	

Sheet 89 (Scotland), **Sheet 5** (England & Wales) *Solway Firth & River Esk*   27 by 18 miles

1	2	4	6	7	8	9	10	11	12	13	14	15
BS	-						P	P	P	C		
MBS	1932	WO 1500/32	1925	1931	9.29E		P	P	P	Co	BL-d	
MBS	1933	WO 1500/32. 1000/36	1925	1931	9.29E		P	P	P	C	BL-d	
MBS	1933	13,000/39 C	1925	1931	9.29E		P	P	P	C	BL-d	
WR	1932	WO 6000/40	1925	1931	9.29E		P	P	P	C	BL-d	
WR	1932	WO 6000/40. 10,000/41	1925	1931	9.29E		P	P	P	Cr	Og	
2WR	1941	WO 10,000/7/41	none				Py	P	P	C	BL-d	
2WR	1941	50,000/10/41 LR	none				Py	P	P	C	Cu	
2WR	1941	16,050/1/43 CK	-				Ny	P	P	C	NLS	
2WR	1941	20,000/5/43/C	-				Ny	P	P	C	BL-d	

This sheet has the heading *Ordnance Survey of Great Britain*. From 1932 it was a member of both GSGS 3907 and 3908.

Sheet 90 *Stranraer*   20 by 28 miles

1	2	4	6	7	8	9	10	11	12	13	14	15
BS	-	?WO 2.25					P	P	P	C		
BS	-	WO 2.25. Reprint 600/26					P	P	P	C		
MBS	1933	WO 600/33	1924				P	P	P	Co	Cu-m	
MBS	1933	WO 1300/38	1924				P	P	P	C	PC	1
MBS	1933	WO 12,000/40	1924				P	P	P	C	BL-d	1
WR	1933	10,000/40 B	1924				P	P	P	C	Og	2
WR	1933	15,000/5/42 LR	1941				Nv	P	P	Cr	BL-d	
WR	1933	40,000/7/42 F	-				Nv	P	P	Cr	BL-d	

1. The imprint erroneously gives the GSGS number as 3907. 2. The GSGS number is still 3907; there is a note on an OS file copy, now in Og, that the plates were amended on 22 March 1941.

Sheet 91 *Wigtown*   27 by 18 miles

1	2	4	6	7	8	9	10	11	12	13	14	15
BS	-	?WO 2.25					P	P	P	C		
BS	-	WO 2.25. Reprint 600/26	1924				P	P	P	C	BL-d	
MBS	1933	600/33+	1924				P	P	P	Co	BL-d	
MBS	1933	1000/35++	1924				P	P	P	C	NLS	
MBS	1933	WO 12,000/39 C	1924				P	P	P	C	BL-d	
WR	1933	10,000/41 B	1924				P	P	P	C	BL-d	1
WR	1933	15,000/4/42 LR	1941				Nw	P	P	Cr	BL-d	
WR	1933	30,000/7/42 McL	-				Nw	P	P	Cr	BL-d	

1. The two-inch alpha-numeric squaring system was not deleted from this printing.

Sheet 92 *Castle Douglas & Kirkcudbright*   WR 1940; 2WR 1942   32 by 18 miles

1	2	4	6	7	8	9	10	11	12	13	14	15
BS	-	WO 2.25	1925				P	P	P	C	PC	
MBS	1933	WO 600/33	1925				P	P	P	Co	BL-d	
MBS	1933	WO 4000/39	1925				P	P	P	C	OS	
WR							P	P	P	C		1
WR	1933	10,000/6/42 LR	-				Nw	P	P	Cr	BL-d	
WR	1933	15,000/7/42 LR	-				Nw	P	P	Cr	BL-d	
2WR	1943	50,000/3/43 LR	-				N	P	P	C	BL-d	

1. *GSGS 3908 current edition*, 8 July 1941 lists this sheet as War Revision (see appendix 1). At this date this would have had Popular Edition marginalia.

Maps of Scotland in supplement 4 are listed following section 2.

2. GSGS 3907 *England and Wales*

For a explanation of the detail in each column see pages 86 to 89.

Sheet 1 *River Tweed* — 18 by 27 miles

1	2	4	6	7	10	11	12	13	14
BS	-				P	P	P	C	
MBS	1932	750/32	1926		P	P	P	Co	BL-d
MBS	1932	1750/38	1926	pcr	P	P	P	C	PC
MBS	1932	WO 1750/38. 7000/39	1926	pcr	P	P	P	C	BL-d
WR	1932	WO 15,000/40	1926	pcr	P	P	P	C	BL-d

2WR see sheet 1A.

Sheet 1A *Berwick upon Tweed* — c.22½ by c.26¾ miles

BS, MBS, WR see sheet 1

1	2	4	6	10	11	12	13	14
2WR	1941	50,000/10/41 LR	1941	P	-	P	C	BL-d
2WR	1941	26,050.12/42/M	-	N	-	P	C	RGS
2WR	1941	10,000/12/43 Ch	-	N	-	P	C	BL-d

Berwick upon Tweed lay uncomfortably on the join between sheets 1 and 2, and was similarly positioned at the edge of Scotland sheet 75. With the sheet 1 area entirely covered by Scotland sheets 75 and 81, the decision was taken to replace it with a sheet that showed Berwick centrally, so offering a long stretch of coast line north and south of it, even though this left part of England no longer covered in GSGS 3907. Sheet lines are parallel with and perpendicular to those of Popular Edition sheets.

Sheet 2 *Holy Island* — 18 by 27 miles

1	2	4	6	7	10	11	12	13	14	15
BS	-	WO 2.26	1925	1926	P	P	P	C	PC	
MBS	1932	WO 350/32. WO 750/32	3000/32	1931	P	P	P	Co	BL-d	
MBS	1932	1000/35+	3000/32	1931	P	P	P	C	Wc	
MBS	1932	WO 3750/39	1925	pcr	P	P	P	C	BL-d	
MBS	1932	WO 17,000/40 C	1925	pcr	P	P	P	C	Bg	
MBS	1932	WO 17,000/40 C. 20,000/40 M	1925	pcr	P	P	P	C	Cu	
WR	1932	WO 20,000/3/41	1925	pcr	Pw	P	P	Cr	BL-d	
2WR	1941	20,000/11/41 LR	1941		Nx	P	P	C	BL-d	1
2WR	1941	20,000/6/42 LR	-		Nx	P	P	C	BL-d	
2WR	1941	21,050/11/42 Wa	-		Nx	P	P	C	BL-d	

1. Lacking the *Popular Edition style* heading.

Sheet 3 (England & Wales), **Sheet 86** (Scotland) *The Cheviot Hills* — 27 by 18 miles

1	2	4	6	7	8	9	10	11	12	13	14	15
BS	-	?WO 1/26. 2000/27					P	P	P	C		
BS	-	WO 1/26. 2000/27. 500/28	1925				P	P	P	C	PC	
MBS	1933	WO 3400/32	1925		1930	8.29E	P	P	P	Co	BL-d	
MBS	1933	WO 3400/32. 1000/34	1925		1930	8.29E	P	P	P	C	BL-d	
MBS	1932	no code	3038 M38 R37	pcr			P	P	P	C	BL-d	
MBS	1933	WD 12,000/39 C. 10,000/39 C	1925	pcr			P	P	P	C	BL-d	
MBS	1932	WO 12,000/40	1925	pcr			P	P	P	C	Wc	
WR	1932	10,000/40/J	3038 M38 R37	pcr			P	P	P	C	BL-d	
WR	1932	WO 12,000/40. 20,000/3/41	1925	pcr			Pv	P	P	Cr	BL-d	
WR	1932	10,000/2/42 B	1925	pcr			Pv	P	P	Cr	BL-d	
2WR	1942	72,000/7/42 LR	-				N	P	P	C	BL-d	1
2WR	1942	40,000/10/42/M	-				N	P	P	C	BL-d	
2WR	1942	10,000/12/43 Ch	-				N	P	P	C	BL-d	

This sheet has the heading *Ordnance Survey of Great Britain*. From 1933 it was a member of both GSGS 3907 and 3908. 1. Used also for *Redesdale & Otterburn ranges*. See supplement 4.

1	2	4	6	7	8	9	10	11	12	13	14	15

Sheet 4 *Alnwick & Rothbury*   27 by 18 miles

1	2	4	6	7	8	9	10	11	12	13	14	15
BS	-						P	P	P	C		
MBS	1932	WO 900/32	1925	1929			P	P	P	Co	BL-d	
MBS		?WO 900/32. 1000/35					P	P	P	C		
MBS	1932	WO 900/32. 1000/35. 2000/39	1925	1929			P	P	P	C	BL-d	
MBS	1932	WO 8000/39	1925	pcr			P	P	P	C	BL-d	
MBS	1932	WO 12,500/40	1925	pcr			P	P	P	C	BL-d	
MBS	1932	20,000/40 M	1925	pcr			P	P	P	C	Bg	
WR	1932	WO 10,000/41	1925	pcr			P	P	P	Cr	BL-d	
2WR	1941	WO 50,000/5/41	nd	pcr			P	P	P	C	BL-d	
2WR	1940	30,000/2/42 LR. 30,000/3/42 A	1942				N	P	P	C	BL-d	1
2WR	1940	no code	-				N	P	P	C	NLS	
2WR	1940	600/11/43 Ch	-				N	P	P	Ow	NLS	‡
2WR	1940	10,000/12/43 Ch	1942				N	P	P	C	BL-d	

1. This printing has the erroneous heading *5th Edition style*. As with sheets 11 and 14, instructions were issued on 24 April 1942 that this be altered to *Popular Edition style* by the use of a rubber stamp which was circulated around the various map stores. Copies issued prior to the receipt of the stamp may be amended by hand in ink. Presumably some were in circulation even before that.

Sheet 5 (England & Wales), **Sheet 89** (Scotland) *Solway Firth & River Esk*   27 by 18 miles

1	2	4	6	7	8	9	10	11	12	13	14	15
BS	-						P	P	P	C		
MBS	1932	WO 1500/32	1925	1931	9.29E		P	P	P	Co	BL-d	
MBS	1933	WO 1500/32. 1000/36	1925	1931	9.29E		P	P	P	C	BL-d	
MBS	1933	13,000/39 C	1925	1931	9.29E		P	P	P	C	BL-d	
WR	1932	WO 6000/40	1925	1931	9.29E		P	P	P	C	BL-d	
WR	1932	WO 6000/40. 10,000/41	1925	1931	9.29E		P	P	P	Cr	Og	
2WR	1941	WO 10,000/7/41	none				Py	P	P	C	BL-d	
2WR	1941	50,000/10/41 LR	none				Py	P	P	C	Cu	
2WR	1941	16,050/1/43 CK	-				Ny	P	P	C	NLS	
2WR	1941	20,000/5/43/C	-				Ny	P	P	C	BL-d	

This sheet has the heading *Ordnance Survey of Great Britain*. From 1932 it was a member of both GSGS 3907 and 3908.

Sheet 6 *Hexham*   27 by 18 miles

1	2	4	6	7	8	9	10	11	12	13	14	15
BS	-						P	P	P	C		
MBS		?WO 1300/32					P	P	P	Co		
MBS	1932	1000/35+	3500/32	1930			P	P	P	C	Mg-d	
MBS	1932	4000/36++	3500/32	1930			P	P	P	C	PC	
MBS	1932	4000/39+++	3500/32	1930			P	P	P	C	BL-d	
MBS	1932	WO 21,000/40	1925	pcr			P	P	P	C	Bg	

WR was probably not published.

1	2	4	6	7	8	9	10	11	12	13	14	15
2WR	1940	WO 45,000/4/41 M	none				P	P	P	C	PC	1
2WR	1940	WO 45,000/4/41	none				P	P	P	C	BL-d	2
2WR	1941	20,000/10/41 LR	none				P	P	P	C	BL-d	
2WR	1941	20,000/8/42 A	-				N	P	P	C	BL-d	
2WR	1941	11,050/5/43/C	-				N	P	P	C	BL-d	
2WR	1941	10,000/12/43 HAY	-				N	P	P	C	BL-d	

War Revision never appears on a *GSGS 3907 current edition* statement (see appendix 1), strong evidence that it was not issued (but see sheet 134). 1. The "M" in the print code is faint. 2. There is apparently no "M" at all in the print code.

Sheet 7 *Newcastle upon Tyne*   WR 1940; 2WR no date   27 by 18 miles

1	2	4	6	7	8	9	10	11	12	13	14	15
BS	-	WO 12.25	1925				P	P	P	C	PC	
MBS		?WO 1250/32					P	P	P	Co		
MBS	1932	WO 1250/32. 1000/33	3500/32++	1929			P	P	P	Co	BL-d	
MBS	1932	1500/36	3500/32++	1929			P	P	P	C	PC	
MBS	1932	1500/36. 1000/38	3500/32++	1929			P	P	P	C	BL-d	
MBS	1932	1500/36. 1000/38. 6000/39	3500/32++	1929			P	P	P	C	BL-d	
MBS	1932	WO 15,000/40	1925	pcr			P	P	P	C	Bg	

1	2	4	6	7	8	9	10	11	12	13	14	15
WR	1932	WO 20,000/40	1925	pcr			P	P	P	Cr	BL-d	
WR	1932	40,000/5/41 F	1925	pcr			P	P	P	Cr	BL-d	
WR	1932	10,000/10/41 LR (blue)	none				P	P	P	Cr	BL-d	
2WR	1941	70,000/12/41 LR	1941				N	P	P	C	BL-d	
2WR	1941	35,000/9/42/M	-				N	P	P	C	BL-d	
2WR	1941	600/9/43 Ch	1941				N	P	P	Ow	BL-d	‡

The Second War Revision heading was, presumably erroneously, undated. See also supplement 8.

Sheet 8 *Workington & Cockermouth* — 18 by 27 miles

1	2	4	6	7	8	9	10	11	12	13	14	15
BS	-						P	P	P	C		
MBS	1932	WO 800/32	3000/31	1931			P	P	P	Co	BL-d	
MBS	1932	WO 800/32. 1000/36	1925	1931			P	P	P	C	BL-d	
MBS	1932	WO 800/32. 1000/36. 4000/39	1925	1931			P	P	P	C	BL-d	
WR	1932	WO 10,000/40	1925	pcr			P	P	P	C	Cu	1
WR	1932	WO 10,000/40. 20,000/40/R	1925	pcr			P	P	P	Cr	BL-d	1,2
2WR	1940	70,000/4/42 LR	1942				N	P	P	C	BL-d	
2WR	1940	no code	1942				N	P	P	Oz	BL	3

This sheet had the heading *Ordnance Survey of Great Britain* until altered to *Ordnance Survey of England & Wales* on Second War Revision. Although with coverage of Scotland, it was not required as a member of GSGS 3908 since the relevant area was also covered by Scotland sheet 92. 1. A grid error on War Revision printings was reported on 26 July 1941, that along northing 570 the 50 and 60 easting values had been reversed. 2. In this case it is the contours, not the roads, that appear to be red. 3. This state was printed from the black and orange plates only, perhaps for the use of the Ministry of Town and Country Planning, for whom the Ordnance Survey provided copies of all sheets in the New Popular Edition in this style. The British Library accession date was 1 May 1946.

Sheet 9 *Carlisle* — 27 by 18 miles

1	2	4	6	7	8	9	10	11	12	13	14	15
BS	-						P	P	P	C		
MBS	1932	WO 800/32	1925				P	P	P	Co	BL-d	
MBS	1932	WO 800/32. 1000/36	1925				P	P	P	C	BL-d	
MBS	1932	WO 3750/40	1925	pcr			P	P	P	C	BL-d	
WR	1932	WO 9000/40	1925	pcr			P	P	P	C	Bg	
WR	1932	24,000/7/40 L	1925	pcr			P	P	P	C	BL-d	
2WR	1940	WO 45,000/3/41	1925.s	pcr			P	P	P	C	BL-d	
2WR	1940	45,000/4/41 CR	1925.s	pcr			P	P	P	C	BL-d	
2WR	1940	20,000/10/41 LR	none				P	P	P	C	BL-d	
2WR	1940	11,050/1/43 BJ	-				N	P	P	C	Lk	
2WR	1940	15,000/8/43 Mc	-				N	P	P	C	BL-d	

Sheet 10 *Alston & Weardale* — 27 by 18 miles

1	2	4	6	7	8	9	10	11	12	13	14	15
BS	-						P	P	P	C		
MBS	1932	WO 1300/32	1925				P	P	P	Co	BL-d	
MBS	1932	WO 1300/32. 4000/36	1925				P	P	P	C	BL-d	
MBS	1932	WO 1300/32. 4000/36. 4000/39	1925				P	P	P	C	BL-d	
MBS	1932	WO 6000/40	1925	pcr			P	P	P	C	Dtc	
MBS	1932	WO 6000/40. 26,000/40/R	1925	pcr			P	P	P	C	Mg-d	
WR	1932	WO 20,000/40	1925	pcr			P	P	P	Cr	BL-d	1
2WR	1940	no code	none				Px	P	P	C	Lk	
2WR	1940	20,000/10/41 LR	none				Px	P	P	C	BL-d	
2WR	1940	20,000/4/42 LR	-				Nx	P	P	C	BL-d	
2WR	1940	21,000/11/42 C	-				Nx	P	P	C	BL-d	
2WR	1940	10,000/7/43 Wa	-				Nx	P	P	C	BL-d	
2WR	1940	15,000/12/43 Wa	-				Nx	P	P	C	BL-d	

1. Copies have been recorded with roads clearly red, in others, rust rather than red.

1	2	4	6	7	8	9	10	11	12	13	14	15

Sheet 11 *Durham & Sunderland*   29 by 18 miles

1	2	4	6	7	8	9	10	11	12	13	14	15
BS	-	WO 2.26	1925				P	P	P	C	PC	
MBS	1932	WO 900/32	3000/32	1931			P	P	P	Co	PC	
MBS	1932	WO 900/32. 500/34	3000/32	1931			P	P	P	C	BL-d	
MBS	1932	WO 2500/37	3000/32	1931			P	P	P	C	BL-d	
MBS	1932	WO 12,000/39	1925	pcr			P	P	P	C	Rg	
MBS	1932	6000/40 C+	1925	pcr			P	P	P	C	BL-d	
MBS		?3000 C++					P	P	P	C		
MBS	1932	25,000/40/R+++	1925	pcr			P	P	P	C	Dtc	
WR	1932	20,000/41	1925	pcr			P	P	P	Cr	BL-d	
2WR	1941	70,000/2/42 LR	1942				N	P	P	C	BL-d	1
2WR	1941	21,050/11/42 Wa	-				N	P	P	C	BL-d	
2WR	1941	20,000/8/43 Mc	-				N	P	P	C	BL-d	
2WR	1941	644/Ch	1942				N	P	P	Ow	NLS	‡

1. This printing has the erroneous heading *5th Edition style*. Instructions were issued on 24 April 1942 that this be altered to *Popular Edition style* by the use of a rubber stamp which was circulated around the various map stores. Copies issued prior to the receipt of the stamp may be amended by hand in ink. Presumably some were in circulation even before the discovery was made. The same error affected sheet 14, and later sheet 4.

Sheet 12 *Keswick & Ambleside*   18 by 27 miles

1	2	4	6	7	8	9	10	11	12	13	14	15
BS	-						P	P	P	C		
MBS	1932	WO 800/32	2500/29	1930			P	P	P	Co	BL-d	
MBS	1932	WO 800/32. 1000/36	2500/29	1930			P	P	P	C	BL-d	
MBS	1932	5000/39 C	1925	pcr			P	P	P	C	BL-d	
WR	1932	WO 6000/40	1925	pcr			P	P	P	C	Cu	
WR	1932	24,000/7/40 L	1925	pcr			P	P	P	C	BL-d	
WR	1932	WO 6000/40. 20,000/41	1925	pcr			P	P	P	Cr	Ob	
2WR	1941	26,250/M/11/42	-				Nx	P	P	C	BL-d	

Sheet 13 *Kirkby Stephen & Appleby*   27 by 18 miles

1	2	4	6	7	8	9	10	11	12	13	14	15
BS	-	WO 9.25	1925				P	P	P	C	BL-d	
MBS		?WO 9.25. WO 1250/32					P	P	P	Co		
MBS	1932	WO 9.25. WO 1250/32. 1000/36	3300/30	1930			P	P	P	C	BL-d	
MBS	1932	WO 5000/39 C	1924	pcr			P	P	P	C	BL-d	
WR	1932	20,000/7/40/H	1924	pcr			P	P	P	C	BL-d	
WR	1932	WO 14,000/40	1924	pcr			P	P	P	C	BL-d	
WR	1932	WO 14,000/40. 10,000/4/41	1924	pcr			Pv	P	P	Cr	BL-d	
WR	1932	10,000/10/41 LR (blue)	1924	pcr			Pv	P	P	Cr	BL-d	
2WR	1940	20,000/5/42 LR	-				Nx	P	P	C	BL-d	
2WR	1940	25,000.11.42 H	-				Nx	P	P	C	BL-d	
2WR	1940	-/7/43 H.U.	-				Nx	P	P	C	BL-d	
2WR	1940	15,000/12/43 Ch	-				Nx	P	P	C	BL-d	

Sheet 14 *Darlington*   27 by 18 miles

1	2	4	6	7	8	9	10	11	12	13	14	15
BS	-	WO 9.25	1925				P	P	P	C	BL-d	
MBS	1932	WO 1350/32	1925	1930			P	P	P	Co	BL-d	
MBS	1932	WO 1350/32. 1000/36	1925	1930			P	P	P	Cr	BL-d	
MBS		?1000/37					P	P	P	C		
MBS		?1500/39+					P	P	P	C		
MBS	1932	7500/39 C++ (purple)	1925	pcr			P	P	P	C	PC	
MBS	1932	WO 11,500/40	2038 M40 R40	pcr			P	P	P	C	Ag	
WR	1932	WO 20,000/41	1925	pcr			P	P	P	Cr	BL-d	
WR	1932	10,000/10/41 LR (blue)	1925	pcr			P	P	P	Cr	BL-d	
2WR	1941	70,000/2/42 LR	1942				N	P	P	C	BL-d	1
2WR	1941	21,000/11/42/C	-				N	P	P	C	BL-d	
2WR	1941	15,000/7/43 Hu	-				N	P	P	C	BL-d	
2WR	1941	15,000/12/43 Wa	-				N	P	P	C	BL-d	

1. This printing has the erroneous heading *5th Edition style*. Instructions were issued on 24 April 1942 that this be altered to *Popular Edition style* by the use of a rubber stamp which was circulated around the various map stores. Copies issued prior to the receipt of the stamp may be amended by hand in ink. Some were in circulation before the discovery was made: one is in Cu Maps 34.034. The same error affected sheet 11, and later sheet 4.

1	2	4	6	7	8	9	10	11	12	13	14	15

Sheet 15 *Middlesbrough & Hartlepool*   19 by 27 miles

1	2	4	6	7	10	11	12	13	14	15
BS	-	WO 2.26	1925		P	P	P	C	BL-d	
MBS					P	P	P	Co		
MBS	1932	2500/39	1925	pcr	P	P	P	C	BL-d	
MBS	1932	WO 6000/40	1925	pcr	P	P	P	C	BL-d	
MBS	1932	WO 6000/40. 4000/40/R	1925	pcr	P	P	P	C	Wc	
WR	1932	WO 20,000/40	1925	pcr	P	P	P	C	BL-d	
WR	1932	WO 20,000/5/41	nd		P	P	P	Cr	BL-d	
2WR	1942	70,000/2/42 LR	1942		N	P	P	C	BL-d	
2WR	1942	21,000/11/42/C	-		N	P	P	C	BL-d	
2WR	1942	40,000/9/43 F	1942		N	P	P	C	BL-d	

Sheet 16 *Whitby & Saltburn*   27 by 18 miles

1	2	4	6	7	10	11	12	13	14	15
BS	-	WO 9.25	1925		P	P	P	C	BL-d	
MBS		?WO 1500/32			P	P	P	Co		
MBS		?1500/34+			P	P	P	C		
MBS		?1000/35++			P	P	P	C		
MBS		?1500/37+++			P	P	P	C		
MBS		?2000/39++++			P	P	P	C		
MBS	1932	6000/39 C+++++	3000/29	1929	P	P	P	C	BL-d	
MBS	1932	24,000/40 M++++++	3000/29	1929	P	P	P	C	PC	
MBS	1932	WO 8500/40	1925	pcr	P	P	P	C	BL-d	
WR	1932	WO 20,000/40. 20,000/12/40 F	1925	pcr	P	P	P	Cr	BL-d	1
2WR	1941	50,000/5/41/F	1925.s	pcr	P	P	P	C	BL-d	
2WR	1941	30,000/1/42 LR	1941		N	P	P	C	BL-d	
2WR	1941	21,250/11/42 W	-		N	P	P	C	BL-d	
2WR	1941	40,000,9/43 C&R Ltd	-		N	P	P	C	BL-d	

For *Yorkshire manoeuvre area*, 1939 see supplement 7. 1. The *relation of grid letters and sheet numbers* diagram lacks sheet lines and numbers.

Sheet 17 *Isle of Man*   24 by 27 miles

1	2	4	6	7	10	11	12	13	14	15
BS	-	WO 10.24	1921	1924	P	P	P	C	BL-d	
MBS	1932	WO 800/32	3750/31++	1931	P	P	P	Co	IWM	
MBS	1932	1000/35+	1921	pcr	P	P	P	C	BL-d	
MBS	1932	3000/38++	1921	pcr	P	P	P	C	PC	
MBS	1932	12,000/39 C+++	1921	pcr	P	P	P	C	Cu	
WR	1932	WO 20,000/40	1921	pcr	P	P	P	C	BL-d	
WR	1932	WO 20,000/40	1921	pcr	P	P	P	Cr	Wc	
WR	1932	10,000/9/41 LR	4038		Pv	P	P	Cr	BL-d	
WR	1932	10,000/3/42 LR (blue)	none		Pv	P	P	Cr	BL-d	
2WR	1942	10,000/1/43 LR	-		Nx	P	P	C	BL-d	
2WR	1942	no code	3268		Nx	P	P	C	BL-d	1

1. While there is no indication of this on the map, this printing was issued in 1948.

Dependent issues on Second War Revision

GSGS 4620 sheet 87, with National Grid military system

1	2	4	10	11	12	13	14	15
WOE	1949	15,000/10/49	N	P	P	C	BL-d	1
2-G	1952	10,000/9/52	N	P	P	C	BL-d	2
2-G	1952	20,000/8/55 OS	N	P	P	C	BL-d	

Elements of the new style marginalia survive, though not the black arrow. The military overprint is purple. 1. The sheet is numbered *National Grid sheet 87*. The GSGS 3907 heading *Second War Revision 1940 sheet 17* also survives. 2. The sheet number is now *England & Wales sheet 87*. The Second War Revision heading is deleted.

Civilian issues, still numbered *Second War Revision 1940 sheet 17*

1	2	6	10	11	12	13	14	15
-	1950	3494	N	P	P	C	PC	
-	1950	3494	N	P	P	O	OS	
-	nd	nc	-	P	-	y	EXg	1
-	1950	C	N	P	P	C	PC	2

With the heading: *Popular Edition style with National Grid*. Elements of the new style marginalia survive, though not the black arrow. 1. A physical features printing requiring the water and contours plates only. 2. This reprint was probably made in 1956 (MV 1956).

1	2	4	6	7	8	9	10	11	12	13	14	15

Sheet 18 *Wasdale* — 18 by 27 miles

1	2	4	6	7	8	9	10	11	12	13	14	15
BS	-						P	P	P	C		
MBS	1932	WO 1600/32	1925				P	P	P	Co	BL-d	
MBS	1932	WO 10,000/39 C	1925	pcr			P	P	P	C	BL-d	
WR	1932	WO 20,000/40	1925	pcr			P	P	P	C	BL-d	
WR	1932	24,000/7/40/CK	1925	pcr			P	P	P	C	BL-d	
2WR	1942	11,050/5/43/C	-				Nx	P	P	C	BL-d	

Sheet 19 *Windermere & Ulverston* — 27 by 18 miles

1	2	4	6	7	8	9	10	11	12	13	14	15
BS	-						P	P	P	C		
MBS	1932	WO 1600/32	2500/28	1928			P	P	P	Co	BL-d	
MBS	1932	WO 1600/32. 1000/38	2500/28	1928			P	P	P	C	BL-d	
MBS	1932	WO 1600/32. 1000/38. 8000/39	2500/28	1928			P	P	P	C	BL-d	
WR	1932	WO 4000/40	1925	pcr			P	P	P	C	Rg	
WR	1932	WO 4000/40. 20,000/40/R	1925	pcr			P	P	P	C	BL-d	
2WR	1940	WO 20,000/41	1925.s	pcr			Pv	P	P	C	BL-d	1
2WR	1941	30,000/7/42 LR	-				Nv	P	P	C	BL-d	1
2WR	1941	644/Ch	1941				N	P	P	Ow	NLS	‡

1. *Standardisation of editions GSGS 3907* (see appendix 2) provides the information that this sheet should have been published with a current editions note. It was not.

Sheet 20 *Kirkby Lonsdale & Hawes* — 27 by 18 miles

1	2	4	6	7	8	9	10	11	12	13	14	15
BS	-	WO 7.25	1925				P	P	P	C	BL-d	
MBS	1932	WO 2200/32	4000/29	1927			P	P	P	Co	PC	
MBS	1932	WO 10,000/39 C	1928	pcr			P	P	P	C	BL-d	
WR	1932	WO 5000/40	1928	pcr			P	P	P	C	LDg	
WR	1932	23,000/7/40 L	1928	pcr			P	P	P	C	BL-d	
WR	1932	WO 10,000/4/41	1928	pcr			Pv	P	P	Cr	BL-d	
WR	1932	WO 10,000/8/41	none				Pv	P	P	Cr	BL-d	
2WR	1942	20,000/4/42 LR	1942				Nx	P	P	C	BL-d	
2WR	1942	30,000/7/42 LR	-				Nx	P	P	C	BL-d	1
2WR	1942	800/11/43 Ch	-				Nx	P	P	Ow	NLS	2‡
2WR	1942	16,200/1/44 HAY	-				Nx	P	P	C	BL-d	3

1. The grid values in the *relation of grid letters and sheet numbers* diagram are incorrect; they should be 500 E-W and 400 S-N, not 400 and 500 as printed. There is a copy corrected by hand in the Library of Congress. 2. The incorrect values are still present. 3. The current edition note now just reads "No significant change" (see page 88).

Sheet 21 *Ripon & Northallerton* — 27 by 18 miles

1	2	4	6	7	8	9	10	11	12	13	14	15
BS	-						P	P	P	C		
MBS	1932	WO 3550/32	3000/29	27-9			P	P	P	Co	BL-d	
MBS		?1000/36+					P	P	P	C		
MBS		?1000/38++					P	P	P	C		
MBS	1932	4500/38+++	3000/29	27-9			P	P	P	C	BL-d	1
MBS	1932	6000/39 C++++	3000/29	27-9			P	P	P	C	BL-d	
MBS	1932	WO 19,500/40 M	1925	pcr			P	P	P	C	Rg	

WR was probably not published.

1	2	4	6	7	8	9	10	11	12	13	14	15
2WR	1932	WO 45,000/40	1925.s	pcr			P	P	P	C	BL-d	2
2WR	1941	20,000/6/41	none				P	P	P	C	BL-d	3
2WR	1941	30,000/3/42 LR	1942				N	P	P	C	BL-d	
2WR	1941	16,250/11/42 W	-				N	P	P	C	NLS	
2WR	1941	20,000/8/43/M	-				N	P	P	C	BL-d	

War Revision never appears on a *GSGS 3907 current edition* statement (see appendix 1), strong evidence that it was not issued (but see sheet 134). 1. See also supplement 8. 2. It was usual for Second War Revision printings to have updated imprints. 3. The print code is blue; a second print code, 50,000/6/41, has been blocked out.

1	2	4	6	7	8	9	10	11	12	13	14	15

Sheet 22 *Pickering & Thirsk*   27 by 18 miles

1	2	4	6	7	8	9	10	11	12	13	14	15
BS	-	WO 7.25	1924				P	P	P	C	PC	
MBS	1932	WO 2150/32	1924	1930			P	P	P	Co	BL-d	
MBS		?WO 2150/32. 1000/37					P	P	P	C		
MBS	1932	WO 2150/32. 1000/37. 2500/39	1924	1930			P	P	P	C	Mg-d	
MBS	1932	WO 400/39	1924	pcr			P	P	P	C	BL-d	
MBS	1932	WO 6000/40	1924	pcr			P	P	P	C	Rg	
WR	1932	20,000/40/R	1924	pcr			P	P	P	C	BL-d	
2WR	1940	WO 20,000/40	1924.s	pcr			P	P	P	C	BL-d	
2WR	1941	30,000/3/42 A	1942				Nv	P	P	C	BL-d	1
2WR	1941	21,250/11/42 W	-				Nv	P	P	C	NLS	1
2WR	1941	20,000/6/43 Ch	-				Nv	P	P	C	BL-d	1
2WR	1941	30,000/12/43 Ch	1941				Nv	P	P	C	BL-d	1

For *Yorkshire manoeuvre area*, 1939 see supplement 7. 1. *Standardisation of editions GSGS 3907* (see appendix 2) provides the information that this sheet should have been published with a current editions note. It was not.

Sheet 23 *Scarborough*   27 by 18 miles

1	2	4	6	7	8	9	10	11	12	13	14	15
BS	-						P	P	P	C		
BS	-	WO 400/30	1925	1929			P	P	P	C	BL-d	
BS	-	WO 7/30	1925	1929			P	P	P	C	PC	
MBS		?WO 2450/32					P	P	P	Co		
MBS		?500/34+					P	P	P	C		
MBS		?1000/35++					P	P	P	C		
MBS		?1000/37+++					P	P	P	C		
MBS	1932	1000/39++++	3000/32	1931			P	P	P	C	BL-d	
MBS	1932	WO 6000/40	1925	pcr			P	P	P	C	Rg	
WR	1932	20,000/40/R	1925	pcr			P	P	P	C	Wc	
WR	1932	WO 20,000/40	1925	pcr			P	P	P	Cr	PC	
WR	1932	WO 20,000/5/41	nd	pcr			P	P	P	Cr	BL-d	
2WR	1940	70,000/2/42 F	1942				N	P	P	C	Cu	
2WR	1940	21,250/11/42 W	-				N	P	P	C	NLS	
2WR	1940	20,000/7/43 E	-				N	P	P	C	BL-d	
2WR	1940	40,000/10/43 Ch	-				N	P	P	C	BL-d	

For *Yorkshire manoeuvre area*, 1939 see supplement 7.

Sheet 24 *Lancaster & Barrow*   27 by 18 miles

1	2	4	6	7	8	9	10	11	12	13	14	15
BS	-	WO 9.24	1924	1924			P	P	P	C	BL-d	
MBS		?WO 1600/32					P	P	P	Co		
MBS		?2000/36+					P	P	P	C		
MBS	1932	500/37++	3030/30	1930			P	P	P	C	IWM	
MBS	1932	1000/39+++	3030/30	1930			P	P	P	C	BL-d	
WR	1932	WO 7500/40	1925	pcr			P	P	P	C	Cu	
WR	1932	WO 20,000/41	1925	pcr			P	P	P	Cr	BL-d	
WR	1932	20,000/4/42 LR (blue)	nd	-			P	P	P	Cr	BL-d	

2WR was not published, though it was apparently ready had it been required.

Sheet 25 *Ribblesdale*   27 by 18 miles

1	2	4	6	7	8	9	10	11	12	13	14	15
BS	-						P	P	P	C		
MBS	1932	WO 2250/32	3500/32+	1930			P	P	P	Co	BL-d	
MBS	1932	WO 2250/32. 1000/37	1924	1930			P	P	P	C	BL-d	
MBS	1932	WO 2250/32. 1000/37. 1500/39	1924	1930			P	P	P	C	BL-d	
WR	1932	WO 6000/40	19--	pcr			P	P	P	C	BL-d	
WR	1932	WO 20,000/3/41	1924	pcr			P	P	P	Cr	BL-d	
2WR	1940	20,000/2/42 A	1942				Ny	P	P	C	BL-d	
2WR	1940	16,650/1/43 Wa	-				Ny	P	P	C	NLS	
2WR	1940	15,000/5/43/C	-				Ny	P	P	C	BL-d	
2WR	1940	600/9/43 Ch	1942				Ny	P	P	Ow	NLS	‡
2WR	1940	10,000/12/43 Wa	-				Ny	P	P	C	BL-d	

1	2	4	6	7	8	9	10	11	12	13	14	15

Sheet 26 *Harrogate* — 27 by 18 miles

1	2	4	6	7	8	9	10	11	12	13	14	15
BS	-	?WO 3.25					P	P	P	C		
BS	-	WO 3.25. 1000/27	1924				P	P	P	C	BL-d	
?BS		?WO 500/32					P	P	P	Co		
MBS	1932	WO 500/32. WO 2450/32	4500/31+++	1930			P	P	P	Co	BL-d	
MBS	1932	WO 1000/38	1924	pcr			P	P	P	C	Mg-d	
MBS	1932	WO 1000/38. 1500/39	1924	pcr			P	P	P	C	BL-d	
MBS	1932	WO 21,000/40/R	1924	pcr			P	P	P	C	RGS	
WR	1932	no code	1924	pcr			P	P	P	C	Lk	
WR	1932	WO 20,000/40	1924	pcr			P	P	P	Cr	BL-d	
2WR	1941	50,000/6/41	none				P	P	P	C	BL-d	
2WR	1941	30,000/3/42 LR	1942				N	P	P	C	BL-d	
2WR	1941	35,000/9/42/M	-				N	P	P	C	BL-d	
2WR	1941	30,000/10/43 Ch	-				N	P	P	C	BL-d	
2WR	1941	800/11/43 Ch	-				N	P	P	Ow	NLS	‡

For a 1928 special printing see supplement 7, and figure 18.

Sheet 27 *York* — 27 by 18 miles

1	2	4	6	7	8	9	10	11	12	13	14	15
BS	-	WO 10.24	1924				P	P	P	C	PC	
MBS	1932	WO 4500/32	3000/29	27-9		1926	P	P	P	Co	PC	
MBS	1932	WO 4500/32. 500/36	3000/29	27-9		1926	P	P	P	C	PC	
MBS	1932	1000/37	1924	pcr			P	P	P	C	Mg-d	
MBS	1932	1000/37. 12,500/39 C	1924	pcr			P	P	P	C	BL-d	
MBS	1932	WO 6000/40 C	1924	pcr			P	P	P	C	Wc	
WR	1932	WO 20,000/40	1924	pcr			P	P	P	Cr	PC	
WR	1932	WO 10,000/4/4/41 [sic]	nd	pcr			P	P	P	Cr	Ag	
WR	1932	20,000/6/41	none				P	P	P	Cr	BL-d	
WR	1932	10,000/6/41	none				P	P	P	Cr	BL-d	
2WR	1941	70,000/2/42 F	1941				N	P	P	C	BL-d	
2WR	1941	30,000.9.42 H	-				N	P	P	C	Cu-m	
2WR	1941	16,400/7/43 E	-				N	P	P	C	BL-d	
2WR	1941	30,000/10/43 Ch	-				N	P	P	C	BL-d	

For *Yorkshire manoeuvre area*, 1939 see supplement 7.

Sheet 28 *Great Driffield & Bridlington* — 27 by 18 miles

1	2	4	6	7	8	9	10	11	12	13	14	15
BS	-	?WO 8.24					P	P	P	C		
BS	-	WO 8.24. 1000/27	1924	1927			P	P	P	C	BL-d	
MBS	1932	WO 1250/33	2500/30	1930			P	P	P	Co	PC	
MBS	1932	WO 1250/33. 2000/34	2500/30	1930			P	P	P	C	Mg-d	
MBS	1932	WO 1250/33. 2000/34. 1000/37	2500/30	1930			P	P	P	C	PC	
MBS	1932	WO 6500/40	1924	pcr			P	P	P	C	Wc	
MBS	1932	20,000/40 M	1924	pcr			P	P	P	C	PC	
WR	1932	20,000/40/R	1924	pcr			P	P	P	C	PC	
WR	1932	WO 30,000/4/41	nd	pcr			P	P	P	Cr	BL-d	
WR	1932	20,000/8/41 LR	none				P	P	P	Cr	BL-d	
2WR	1941	70,000/5/42 LR	-				N	P	P	C	BL-d	
2WR	1941	11,050/12/42 Wa	-				N	P	P	C	NLS	
2WR	1941	25,000/7/43	-				N	P	P	C	BL-d	
2WR	1941	15,000/1/44 HAY	-				N	P	P	C	BL-d	

For *Yorkshire manoeuvre area*, 1939 see supplement 7. See also supplement 8.

Sheet 29 *Preston, Southport & Blackpool* — 27 by 18 miles

1	2	4	6	7	8	9	10	11	12	13	14	15
BS	-	WO 2.24	1924				P	P	P	C	BL-d	
MBS	1932	WO 1600/32	2250/30+	1930			P	P	P	Co	IWM	
MBS	1932	WO 5000/39	1921	pcr			P	P	P	C	BL-d	
WR	1932	WO 9000/40	1921	pcr			P	P	P	C	BL-d	
WR	1932	WO 9000/40. 20,000/8/40 Mc	1921	pcr			P	P	P	C	BL-d	
WR	1932	WO 9000/40. 10,000/6/41/F	1921	pcr			P	P	P	Cr	BL-d	
WR	1932	20,000/3/42 LR (blue)	none				P	P	P	Cr	BL-d	
2WR	1941	600/9/43 Ch	1941				N	P	P	Ow	NLS	‡

1	2	4	6	7	8	9	10	11	12	13	14	15
Sheet 30 *Blackburn*							27 by 18 miles					
BS	-						P	P	P	C		
MBS	1932	WO 1600/32	6000/29	1929	-		P	P	P	Co	BL-d	
MBS		?WO 1000/38					P	P	P	C		
MBS	1932	WO 1000/38. 2500/39	5000/33	1933	1933	1933	P	P	P	C	BL-d	
WR	1932	WO 6000/40	1924	pcr			P	P	P	C	BL-d	
WR	1932	WO 6000/40. C 6000/40	1924	pcr			P	P	P	C	Rg	
WR	1932	WO 6000/40. 20,000/8/40 Mc	1924	pcr			P	P	P	C	Cu	
WR	1932	WO 10,000/8/41	none				P	P	P	Cr	BL-d	
WR	1932	20,000/3/42 LR (blue)	none				P	P	P	Cr	BL-d	
2WR	1942	25,000.9.42 H	-				N	P	P	C	BL-d	
2WR	1942	62,000/6/43 Ch	-				N	P	P	C	BL-d	
2WR	1942	800/12/43 Ch	1942				N	P	P	Ow	NLS	‡
Sheet 31 *Leeds & Bradford*							27 by 18 miles					
BS	-						P	P	P	C		
?MBS		?WO 2250/32					P	P	P	Co		
BS	-	500/32+	3500/32++	1931			P	P	P	Co	BL-d	1
MBS	1932	1000/36++	1925	pcr			P	P	P	C	BL-d	
MBS	1932	1000/39 C+++	1925	pcr			P	P	P	C	BL-d	
WR	1932	WO 14,000/40	1925	pcr			P	P	P	C	RGS	
WR	1932	WO 14,000/40. 20,000/12/40/F	1925	pcr			P	P	P	Cr	BL-d	
WR	1933	WO 20,000/8/41 LR	none				P	P	P	Cr	BL-d	
2WR	1942	70,000/4/42 A	-				N	P	P	C	BL-d	
2WR	1942	30,000.9.42.H (green)	-				N	P	P	C	PC	
2WR	1942	15,000/11/43 Ch	-				N	P	P	C	BL-d	
2WR	1942	644	-				N	P	P	Ow	NLS	‡

1. An unusually late BS printing, without GSGS number or imprint.

1	2	4	6	7	8	9	10	11	12	13	14	15
Sheet 32 *Goole & Pontefract*							27 by 18 miles					
BS	-	WO 7.24	1924	1924			P	P	P	C	BL-d	
MBS	1932	WO 1450.32	1924	1924			P	P	P	Co	PC	
MBS	1932	WO 1000/36	2000/34	1933	1932		P	P	P	C	Mg-d	
MBS	1932	WO 1000/36. 1500/39	2000/34	1933	1932		P	P	P	C	BL-d	
WR	1932	WO 7000/40	1924	pcr			P	P	P	C	Bg	
WR	1932	WO 20,000/40	1924	pcr			P	P	P	C	BL-d	
WR	1932	WO 20,000/3/41	1924	pcr			P	P	P	Cr	Cu	
WR	1932	20,000/8/41 LR	none				P	P	P	Cr	BL-d	
2WR	1941	70,000/4/42 LR	1942				N	P	P	C	BL-d	
2WR	1941	20,000/3/43 Wa	-				N	P	P	C	PC	
2WR	1941	1200/3/43 Wa	-				N	P	P	C	NLS	
2WR	1941	10,000/5/43/C	-				N	P	P	C	BL-d	
2WR	1941	40,000/9/43 F	1942				N	P	P	C	BL-d	

For *Yorkshire manoeuvre area*, 1939 see supplement 7.

1	2	4	6	7	8	9	10	11	12	13	14	15
Sheet 33 *Hull*							27 by 18 miles					
BS	-	?WO 8.24					P	P	P	C		
BS	-	WO 8.24. 1000/27	1924	1924			P	P	P	C	BL-d	
MBS	1932	WO 1250/33	3000/31	1930			P	P	P	Co	PC	
MBS	1932	WO 1250/33. 1000/36	3000/31	1930			P	P	P	C	BL-d	
MBS	1932	WO 1250/33. 1000/36. 1000/37	3000/31	1930			P	P	P	C	Mg-d	
MBS	1932	WO 12,000/40	1924	pcr			P	P	P	C	Wc	
WR	1932	no code	1924	pcr			P	P	P	C	PC	
WR	1932	WO 26,000/40	1924	pcr			P	P	P	C	BL-d	

1	2	4	6	7	8	9	10	11	12	13	14	15
2WR	nd	WO 50,000/6/41	none				P	P	P	C	PC	1
2WR	1941	WO 50,000/6/41	none				P	P	P	C	Cu	2
2WR	1941	WO 50,000/6/41	none				P	P	P	C	BL-d	3
2WR	1941	30,000/1/42 LR	1941				N	P	P	C	BL-d	
2WR	1941	25,000.9.42 H	-				N	P	P	C	BL-d	
2WR	1941	16,050/7/43 Hu	-				N	P	P	C	BL-d	
2WR	1941	10,000/1/44 Wa	-				N	P	P	C	BL-d	

For [*Yorkshire manoeuvre area*], 1939 see supplement 7. This sheet evidently required no purple overprint plate and in this form is recognisable as a 1939 printing with grid in black with blue figures. 1. The GSGS imprint is lacking. 2. The GSGS imprint is blue. 3 The GSGS imprint is black.

Sheet 34 *Mouth of the Humber* — 18 by 27 miles

1	2	4	6	7	10	11	12	13	14
BS	-	?WO 8.24			P	P	P	C	
BS	-	WO 8.24. 1000/27	1924	24-7	P	P	P	C	BL-d
MBS		?WO 850/32			P	P	P	Co	
MBS	1932	WO 850/32. 2000/34	1924	1929	P	P	P	C	PC
MBS	1932	WO 850/32. 2000/34. 12,000/39	1924	1929	P	P	P	C	BL-d
MBS	1932	30,000/40/R	1923	pcr	P	P	P	C	Bg
MBS	1932	WO 6000/40	1923	pcr	P	P	P	C	Wc
WR	1932	WO 20,000/40	1923	pcr	P	P	P	C	BL-d
2WR	1941	50,000/5/41	none		P	P	P	C	BL-d
2WR	1941	20,000/10/41 LR	none		P	P	P	C	BL-d
2WR	1941	30,000/6/42 LR	-		N	P	P	C	BL-d
2WR	1941	21,050,12/43 C&R	-		N	P	P	C	BL-d

Sheet 35 *Liverpool & Birkenhead* — 27 by 18 miles

1	2	4	6	7	10	11	12	13	14	15
BS	-	WO 1.24	1923		P	P	P	C	BL-d	
MBS		?WO 1600/32			P	P	P	Co		
MBS	1932	1000/36+	3500/27	1927	P	P	P	C	Mg-d	
MBS		?500/36++			P	P	P	C		
MBS	1932	1000/39+++	3500/27	1927	P	P	P	C	BL-d	
WR	1932	WO 40,000/40	1923	pcr	P	P	P	C	BL-d	
WR	1932	WO 6500/40	1923	pcr	P	P	P	C	Bg	
WR	1932	WO 6500/40. 20,000/40 B	1923	pcr	P	P	P	C	BL-d	
WR	1932	WO 6500/40. 10,000/7/41	none		P	P	P	Cr	BL-d	
2WR	1942	70,000/8/42 A	-		N	P	P	C	BL-d	
2WR	1942	600/11/43 Ch	-		N	P	P	Ow	NLS	‡

Sheet 36 *Bolton & Manchester* — 27 by 18 miles

1	2	4	6	7	10	11	12	13	14	15
BS	-	WO 2.24	1924		P	P	P	C	BL-d	
MBS		?WO 1600/32			P	P	P	Co		
MBS	1932	1000/36+	2500/31++	1930	P	P	P	C	Mg-d	
MBS	1932	1500/38++	2500/31++	1930	P	P	P	C	PC	
MBS	1932	1500/39+++	2500/31++	1930	P	P	P	C	BL-d	
WR	1932	WO 20,000/40	1924	pcr	P	P	P	C	BL-d	
WR	1932	WO 10,250/40. 8000/8/40/T+	1924	pcr	P	P	P	C	BL-d	
WR	1932	20,000/8/40/A	1924	pcr	P	P	P	C	Ob	
WR	1932	20,000/8/41 LR	none		P	P	P	Cr	BL-d	
WR	1932	20,000/3/42 A (blue)	none		P	P	P	Cr	BL-d	
2WR	1942	70,000/8/42 F	-		N	P	P	C	Cu	
2WR	1942	600/11/43 Ch	-		N	P	P	Ow	NLS	‡
2WR	1942	11,600/1/44 HAY	-		N	P	P	C	BL-d	

1	2	4	6	7	8	9	10	11	12	13	14	15

Sheet 37 *Barnsley & Sheffield* — 27 by 18 miles

1	2	4	6	7	8	9	10	11	12	13	14	15
BS	-	WO 2.24	1924				P	P	C		BL-d	
MBS	1932	WO 1600/32	4000/31+	1931			P	P	P	Co	PC	
MBS	1932	1000/36+	4000/31+	1931			P	P	P	C	Mg-d	
MBS	1932	1000/38++	4000/31+	1931			P	P	P	C	BL-d	
MBS	1932	8000/39+++	4000/31+	1931			P	P	P	C	BL-d	
WR	1932	WO 20,000/40	1924	pcr			P	P	P	C	BL-d	
WR	1932	WO 20,000/3/41	1924	pcr			P	P	P	Cr	BL-d	
WR	1932	10,000/1/42 LR (blue)	1924				N	P	P	C	BL-d	1
2WR	1942	70,000/3/42 A	1942				N	P	P	C	BL-d	
2WR	1942	30,000/8/42 C	1942				N	P	P	C	BL-d	
2WR	1942	644/Ch	1942				N	P	P	Ow	NLS	‡

1. One of only four England and Wales War Revision sheets recorded with the new style marginalia. For some reason this printing does not have red main roads.

Sheet 38 *Doncaster* — 27 by 18 miles

1	2	4	6	7	8	9	10	11	12	13	14	15
BS	-	WO 12.26. 750/27	1923	1926			P	P	P	C	BL-d	
MBS	1932	WO 1000/32	3000/29	1929			P	P	P	Co	PC	
MBS	1932	WO 1000/32. 1000/36	3000/29	1929			P	P	P	C	PC	
MBS	1932	WO 1000/32. 1000/36. 1000/37	3000/29	1929			P	P	P	C	Mg-d	
MBS	1932	WO 5000/39 C	1923	pcr			P	P	P	C	BL-d	
MBS	1932	WO 6000/40	1923	pcr			P	P	P	C	RGS	
WR	1932	WO 10,000/40	1923	pcr			P	P	P	C	Bg	
WR	1932	WO 20,000/40	1923	pcr			P	P	P	C	BL-d	
2WR	1941	70,000/12/41 LR	1941				N	P	P	C	BL-d	
2WR	1941	30,000/8/42 C	1941				N	P	P	C	BL-d	
2WR	1941	10,000/11/43 Ch	-				N	P	P	C	BL-d	

Sheet 39 *Scunthorpe & Market Rasen* — 27 by 18 miles

1	2	4	6	7	8	9	10	11	12	13	14	15
BS	-	WO 1.27. 1000/27	1923	1926			P	P	P	C	BL-d	
MBS							P	P	P	Co		
MBS	1932	WO 1000/39 C	1923	pcr			P	P	P	C	BL-d	
MBS	1932	WO 28,500/40 C	1923	pcr			P	P	P	C	Wc	
WR	1932	no code	1923	pcr			P	P	P	C	PC	
2WR	1941	WO 45,000/4/41	none				P	P	P	C	BL-d	
2WR	1940	20,000/10/41 LR	nd	pcr			P	P	P	C	BL-d	
2WR	1940	20,000/4/42 LR	-				N	P	P	C	BL-d	
2WR	1940	21,250/12/42 Wa	-				N	P	P	C	BL-d	

Sheet 40 *Grimsby & Louth* — 27 by 18 miles

1	2	4	6	7	8	9	10	11	12	13	14	15
BS	-	WO 1.27. Reprint 1000/27	1923	1926			P	P	P	C	BL-d	
MBS	1932	WO 750/32	1923	1929			P	P	P	Co	Mg-d	
MBS	1932	WO 750/32. 500/32	1923	1929			P	P	P	Co	IWM	
MBS	1932	WO 1000/38	1923	pcr			P	P	P	C	BL-d	
MBS	1932	WO 1000/38. 500/39	1923	pcr			P	P	P	C	Mg-d	
MBS	1932	6000/39	1923	pcr			P	P	P	C	Cu-m	
MBS	1932	WO 6000/40. 6000/40/R	1923	pcr			P	P	P	C	PC	
WR	1932	no code	1923	pcr			P	P	P	C	Wc	
WR	1932	WO 20,000/40	1923	pcr			P	P	P	C	Bg	
2WR	1941	WO 45,000/4/41	1923s	pcr			P	P	P	C	BL-d	
2WR	1941	20,000/8/41 LR	none				P	P	P	C	BL-d	1
2WR	1941	20,000/4/42 LR	-				N	P	P	C	BL-d	
2WR	1941	10,000/11/42 LR	-				N	P	P	C	BL-d	

1. The War Office publication date is in blue.

1	2	4	6	7	8	9	10	11	12	13	14	15

Sheet 41 *Anglesey* — 29 by 24 miles

1	2	4	6	7	8	9	10	11	12	13	14	15
BS	-						P	P	P	C		
BS	-	WO 500/30	3500/27	24-7			P	P	P	C	BL-d	
MBS	1932	WO 1000/33	3750/31+	1931			P	P	P	Co	BL-d	
MBS		?WO 750/39					P	P	P	C		
MBS	1932	WO 750/39. 3000/39	3000/37++	1931			P	P	P	C	PC	1
MBS		WO 6000/40					P	P	P	C		2
WR	1932	28,000/40/R	1922	pcr			P	P	P	C	RGS	2
WR	1932	WO 10,000/3/41	1922	pcr			P	P	P	Cr	BL-d	2
WR	1932	10,000/6/41 A	1922	pcr			P	P	P	Cr	BL-d	2
WR		20,000/3/42 LR					P	P	P	C		2
WR	1932	11,450/1/43 W	none				P	P	P	Cr	BL-d	2
WR	nd	11,450/1/43 W	none				Po	P	P	Cr	PC	2†
2WR	1932	600/11/43 Ch	-				N	P	P	Ow	Wc	3‡

See also supplement 3. 1. The OS print code string is 3500/27. 3750/31. 3000/37, the last not recorded on a civilian map. 2. The words *Popular Edition* are deleted from the heading, leaving only *one-inch map*, in upper case lettering. 3. It was usual for Second War Revision printings to have updated imprints.

Sheet 42 *Llandudno & Denbigh* — 27 by 22 miles

1	2	4	6	7	8	9	10	11	12	13	14	15
BS	-						P	P	P	C		
MBS	1932	WO 1600/32	2500/30	1931			P	P	P	Co	IWM	
MBS	1932	WO 5000/39 C	1922	pcr			P	P	P	C	BL-d	
WR	1932	WO 9000/40	1922	pcr			P	P	P	C	PC	
WR	1932	WO 9000/40. 19,000 C	1922	pcr			P	P	P	C	BL-d	
WR	1932	WO 9000/40. 20,000/40 B	1922	pcr			P	P	P	C	BL-d	
WR	1932	20,000/4/42 LR (blue)	none				P	P	P	Cr	BL-d	
2WR	1941	no code	1941				N	P	P	Ow	NLS	‡
2WR	1941	644/Ch	1941				N	P	P	Ow	OS	

Sheet 43 *Chester* — 27 by 18 miles

1	2	4	6	7	8	9	10	11	12	13	14	15
BS	-	WO 2.24	1924				P	P	P	C	BL-d	
MBS							P	P	P	Co		
MBS		?WO 500/37					P	P	P	C		
MBS		?WO 500/37. 1000/37					P	P	P	C		
MBS	1932	WO 500/37. 1000/37. 7500/39	1924	pcr			P	P	P	C	BL-d	
MBS	1932	WO 14,000/40	1924	pcr			P	P	P	C	PC	
MBS	1932	WO 14,000/40. 10,000/40 R	1924	pcr			P	P	P	C	PC	
WR	1932	20,000/8/40/A	1924	pcr			P	P	P	C	Wc	
WR	1932	20,000/5/41 R_+	1924	pcr			P	P	P	Cr	BL-d	
2WR	1942	70,000/5/42 A	1942				N	P	P	C	BL-d	
2WR	1942	11,450/11/42/M	1942				N	P	P	C	BL-d	
2WR	1942	645/Ch	1942				N	P	P	Ow	NLS	‡

Sheet 44 *Northwich & Macclesfield* — 27 by 18 miles

1	2	4	6	7	8	9	10	11	12	13	14	15
BS	-	WO 8.25	1925				P	P	P	C	BL-d	
MBS	1932	WO 1800/32	500/30+	1930			P	P	P	Co	IWM	
MBS		?1000/36+					P	P	P	C		
MBS	1932	1000/38++	500/30+	1930			P	P	P	C	BL-d	
MBS	1932	12,000/39 C+++	500/30+	1930			P	P	P	C	BL-d	
MBS	1932	WO 13,000/40	1925	pcr			P	P	P	C	Wc	
WR	1932	20,000/8/40 L	1925	pcr			P	P	P	C	BL-d	
WR	1932	WO 30,000/8/41	none				P	P	P	Cr	BL-d	
WR	1932	20,000/5/42 LR (blue)	none				P	P	P	Cr	BL-d	
WR	1932	10,000/11/42/M (purple)	nd				P	P	P	Cr	BL-d	
WR	nd	1450/11/42/M	nd				Po	P	P	Cr	RGS	†

2WR was not published, though it was apparently ready had it been required.

1	2	4	6	7	8	9	10	11	12	13	14	15

Sheet 45 *Buxton & Matlock* — 27 by 18 miles

1	2	4	6	7	8	9	10	11	12	13	14	15
BS	-						P	P	P	C		
BS	-	WO Reprint 1000/29	1923	1928	2/28		P	P	P	C	PC	
BS	-	WO 3750/30	3000/30	1928	2/28		P	P	P	C	book	1
BS	-	WO 2000/31	3000/30	1928	2/28		P	P	P	Co	PC	
MBS	1932	WO 2650/32	3000/30	1928	-		P	P	P	Co	IWM	
MBS	1932	WO 1000/37	1928	pcr			P	P	P	C	Mg	
MBS	1932	WO 1000/37. 6000/39	1928	pcr			P	P	P	C	BL-d	
MBS	1932	WO 1000/37. 6000/39 Mc. 6000/40	1928	pcr			P	P	P	C	Ag	
MBS	1932	6000/40/R+	1928	pcr			P	P	P	C	Bg	
MBS	1932	28,000/40 M_+	1928	pcr			P	P	P	C	PC	2

WR was almost certainly not published.

1	2	4	6	7	8	9	10	11	12	13	14	15
2WR	1941	no code	none				P	P	P	C	Cu	3
2WR	1941	WO 50,000/5/41	none				P	P	P	C	Og	3,4
2WR	1941	WO 50,000/5/41	none				P	P	P	C	Wc	3,5
2WR	1941	20,000/2/42 F	none				P	P	P	C	BL-d	3,6
2WR	1941	45,000/8/42/M	-				N	P	P	C	BL-d	
2WR	1941	600/11/43 Ch	-				N	P	P	Ow	NLS	‡7
2WR	1941	644/Ch	1941				N	P	P	Ow	PC	7
2WR	1941	645/Ch	1941				N	P	P	Ow	Cu-m	7

1. See supplement 7. 2. *GSGS 3907 current edition,* 15 May 1941 (see appendix 1), still shows Popular Edition for sheet 45. With the Second War Revision first printed at latest the same month, it is almost inconceivable that War Revision would have been issued as well. 3. There was an error in the grid numbering in that the "01" value in the right hand margin was printed as "10". 4. The print code has tall figures. 5. The "0"s in the print code appear to be tapering. 6. This is a remarkably late printing still to have Popular Edition marginalia. 7. This is the only sheet for which three different outline and water printings have been recorded.

Sheet 46 *The Dukeries* — 27 by 18 miles

1	2	4	6	7	8	9	10	11	12	13	14	15
BS	-						P	P	P	C		
BS	-	WO 3500/31	500/30+	26-9	6.28		P	P	P	Co	book	1,2
MBS	1932	WO 900/32	500/30+	26-9	6.28		P	P	P	Co	PC	1
MBS	1932	500/34+	500/30+	26-9	6.28		P	P	P	C	Bg	1
MBS		?1000/36++					P	P	P	C		
MBS	1932	1000/39+++	500/30+	26-9	6.28		P	P	P	C	BL-d	1
MBS	1932	WO 15,000/39 C	1923	pcr			P	P	P	C	PC	
MBS	1932	6000/40+	1923	pcr			P	P	P	C	Wc	
MBS	1932	6000 C++	1923	pcr			P	P	P	C	Bg	
MBS	1932	20,000 C/40+++	1923	pcr			P	P	P	C	PC	
WR	1932	20,000/12/40/A	1923	pcr			P	P	P	Cr	BL-d	3
2WR	1932	50,000/6/41	none				P	P	P	C	BL-d	4
2WR	1941	30,000/3/42 LR	1942				N	P	P	C	BL-d	
2WR	1941	25,000/10/42 W	-				N	P	P	C	RGS	
2WR	1941	10,000/2/43 LR	-				N	P	P	C	BL-d	
2WR	1941	10,000/1/44 Ch	-				N	P	P	C	BL-d	

1. The OS print code string is 3000/30. 500/30, according to Hodson (1999) not seen on a civilian printing. 2. See supplement 8. 3. The *relation of grid letters and sheet numbers* diagram lacks sheet lines and numbers. 4. It was usual for Second War Revision printings to have updated imprints.

Sheet 47 *Lincoln* — 27 by 18 miles

1	2	4	6	7	8	9	10	11	12	13	14	15
BS	-	WO 1.27. Reprint 1000/27	1923	1926			P	P	P	C	BL-d	
MBS		?WO 800/32					P	P	P	Co		
MBS		?1000/35+					P	P	P	C		
MBS	1932	1000/38++	2250/30	1928			P	P	P	C	BL-d	
MBS	1932	8000/39 C+++	2250/30	1928			P	P	P	C	PC	
MBS	1932	WO 27,000/40 C	1923	pcr			P	P	P	C	Lk	
WR	1932	no code	19--	pcr			P	P	P	C	PC	
2WR	1940	WO 45,000/3/41	1923.s	pcr			P	P	P	C	BL-d	
2WR	1940	20,000/9/41 LR	none				P	P	P	C	BL-d	
2WR	1940	30,000/3/42 H	1942				N	P	P	C	BL-d	
2WR	1940	30,000/1/43 LR	-				N	P	P	C	BL-d	

Sheet 48 *Horncastle & Skegness* — 27 by 18 miles

1	2	4	6	7	8	9	10	11	12	13	14	15
BS	-	WO 1.27. 1000/27	1923	1926			P	P	P	C	BL-d	
MBS		?WO 700/32					P	P	P	Co		
MBS	1932	WO 700/32. 1000/36	1923	1929			P	P	P	C	BL-d	
MBS	1932	WO 12,500/40	1923	pcr			P	P	P	C	Wc	1
MBS	1932	WO 12,500/40. 20,000/40	1923	pcr			P	P	P	C	Bg	
MBS	1932	WO 12,500/40. 10,000/40	1923	pcr			P	P	P	C	Lk	

WR was almost certainly not published.

1	2	4	6	7	8	9	10	11	12	13	14	15
2WR	1940	WO 45,000/41	1923.s	pcr			P	P	P	C	BL-d	2,3
2WR	1940	20,000/6/41	none				P	P	P	C	BL-d	3
2WR	1940	30,000/3/42 J	1942				N	P	P	C	BL-d	
2WR	1940	10,000/11/42 LR	-				N	P	P	C	BL-d	
2WR	1940	10,000/2/43 LR	-				N	P	P	C	BL-d	

1. The heading *relation of grid letters and sheet numbers* is blue, the diagram purple. 2. Popular Edition was noted as the only alternative to Second War Revision when it made its first appearance in *GSGS 3907 current edition,* 1 February 1941 (see appendix 1). This would make a War Revision edition of this sheet highly improbable. 3. A grid error was reported on 12 May 1941, that at two places along easting line 601, at northing 380 and 390, the value 10 was printed in place of 01. The magnetic variation diagram is undated on the WO 45,000/41 printing.

Sheet 49 *Portmadoc & Criccieth* — 34 by 22 miles

1	2	4	6	7	8	9	10	11	12	13	14	15
BS	-	WO 1.24	1922			1923	P	P	P	C	Lk	
MBS	1932	WO 600/32	3500/30+	1929	11.29	1928	P	P	P	Co	BL-d	
MBS	1932	WO 600/32. 1000/33	3500/30+	1929	11.29	1928	P	P	P	Co	PC	
MBS	1932	WO 6000/39	1922	pcr			P	P	P	C	BL-d	
WR	1932	WO 3000/40	1922	pcr			P	P	P	C	BL-d	
WR	1932	WO 20,000/40	1922	pcr			P	P	P	Cr	Lu	
2WR	1941	10,000/12/42 LR	-				Nx	P	P	C	BL-d	
2WR	1941	2000/10/43 Ch	-				Nx	P	P	C	RGS	
2WR	1941	2000/10/43 Ch	-				Nx	P	P	Ow	NLS	‡

Sheet 50 *Bala* — 27 by 18 miles

1	2	4	6	7	8	9	10	11	12	13	14	15
BS	-	WO 1.24	1921	1923			P	P	P	C	BL-d	
MBS	1932	WO 1400/32	1921	1929			P	P	P	Co	BL-d	
MBS	1932	WO 1000/36	50/33	1929			P	P	P	C	Mg-d	
MBS	1932	500/37	1921	pcr			P	P	P	C	PC	
MBS	1932	1000/37	1921	pcr			P	P	P	C	BL-d	
MBS	1932	1000/37. 4000/39	1921	pcr			P	P	P	C	BL-d	
WR	1932	WO 9000/40	1921	pcr			P	P	P	C	BL-d	
WR	1932	24,000/7/40 L	1921	pcr			P	P	P	C	BL-d	
WR	1932	WO 10,000/6/41	none				Pw	P	P	Cr	BL-d	
2WR	1941	20,000/5/42 LR	-				Nx	P	P	C	BL-d	
2WR		proofs					N	P	P	Cb		1

1. Proof copies of this sheet were distributed early in 1944 to the Directorate of Military Survey and GHQ Home Forces with roads and contours coloured Air Force brown, Griblets brown, blue grey tint, and third layer violet. Air Force brown was preferred, and came into use (on other sheets) in May 1944.

Sheet 51 *Wrexham & Oswestry* — 27 by 18 miles

1	2	4	6	7	8	9	10	11	12	13	14	15
BS	-	WO 1.24	1921	1923			P	P	P	C	IWM	
MBS		?WO 800/32					P	P	P	Co		
MBS		?1000/36+					P	P	P	C		
MBS		500/37++					P	P	P	C	RAF	
MBS		750/39+++					P	P	P	C	DGC	1
WR	1932	WO 20,000/40	1921	pcr			P	P	P	C	Lk	
WR	1932	WO 8000/40	1921	pcr			P	P	P	C	BL-d	
WR	1932	WO 8000/40. 20,000/40 M	1921	pcr			P	P	P	C	BL-d	
WR	1932	20,000/5/42 LR (blue)	none				P	P	P	Cr	BL-d	

2WR was not published, though it was apparently ready had it been required.

1. The only copy recorded was held by DGC, but apparently not transferred to the British Library.

1	2	4	6	7	8	9	10	11	12	13	14	15

Sheet 52 *Stoke on Trent* — 27 by 18 miles

1	2	4	6	7	8	9	10	11	12	13	14	15
BS	-	?WO 6.25					P	P	P	C		
BS	-	WO 6.25. 600/27	1921	25-6			P	P	P	C	BL-d	
MBS		?WO 1600/32					P	P	P	Co		
MBS		?500/34+					P	P	P	C		
MBS	1932	1000/36++	1921	25-8			P	P	P	C	Bg	
MBS		?1000/38+++					P	P	P	C		
MBS	1932	8000/39++++	1921	25-8			P	P	P	C	Cu-m	
WR	1932	WO 3000/40	1921	pcr			P	P	P	C	Wc	
WR	1932	WO 30,000/40	1921	pcr			P	P	P	C	BL-d	1
WR	1932	26,000/8/40 W	1921	pcr			P	P	P	C	Cu	
WR	1932	15,000/11/42/M (purple)	1921	pcr			P	P	P	Cr	RGS	
WR	nd	1450/11/42/M	1921	pcr			Po	P	P	Cr	NLS	†
WR	1932	25,000/1/43 LR (blue)	none				P	P	P	Cr	BL-d	
2WR	1942	600/11/43 Ch	-				N	P	P	Ow	NLS	‡

1. Some printings show evidence of the deleted print code WO 3000/40 beneath the replacement – the "WO" has been moved left.

Sheet 53 *Derby* — 27 by 18 miles

1	2	4	6	7	8	9	10	11	12	13	14	15
BS	-						P	P	P	C		
BS	-	WO 1000/26	1921	1924			P	P	P	C	BL-d	
MBS		?WO 950/32					P	P	P	Co		
MBS	1932	WO 950/32. 1500/34	3500/31	1931			P	P	P	C	PC	1
MBS	1932	WO 5000/39 C	1921	pcr			P	P	P	C	BL-d	
MBS	1932	WO 7500/40	1921	pcr			P	P	P	C	BL-d	
MBS		?WO 7500/40. 5000/40					P	P	P	C		
MBS	1932	WO 7500/40. 5000/40. 26,000/40	1921	pcr			P	P	P	C	Bg	
WR	1932	WO 20,000/40	1921	pcr			P	P	P	Cr	BL-d	
2WR	1942	70,000/3/42 F	1942				N	P	P	C	BL-d	
2WR	1942	35,000/10/42 A	-				N	P	P	C	BL-d	

1. The OS print code 3500/31 is not recorded on a civilian map; doubtless it was replaced in the event by 3500/32.

Sheet 54 *Nottingham* — 27 by 18 miles

1	2	4	6	7	8	9	10	11	12	13	14	15
BS	-	WO 1.27. 1000/27	1921			1926	P	P	P	C	BL-d	
MBS		?WO 1000/32					P	P	P	Co		
MBS		?500/34+					P	P	P	C		
MBS	1932	1000/36++	3000/31	1930		1928	P	P	P	C	Bg	
MBS	1932	3000/39+++	3000/31	1930		1928	P	P	P	C	BL-d	
MBS	1932	WO 15,000/39	1921	pcr			P	P	P	C	BL-d	
WR	1932	WO 19,000/40	1921	pcr			P	P	P	C	Bg	
WR	1932	WO 10,000/3/41	1921	pcr			P	P	P	Cr	BL-d	
WR	1932	WO 20,000/6/41	none				P	P	P	Cr	Cu	
2WR	1942	70,000/4/42 LR	1942				N	P	P	C	BL-d	
2WR	1942	21,650/11/42/M	1942				N	P	P	C	NLS	
2WR	1942	15,000/1/43 LR	-				N	P	P	C	BL-d	
2WR	1942	600/11/43 Ch	-				N	P	P	Ow	NLS	‡
2WR	1942	644/Ch	-				N	P	P	Ow	BL-d	

Sheet 55 *Grantham* — 27 by 18 miles

1	2	4	6	7	8	9	10	11	12	13	14	15
BS	-	WO 5.26	1922	1926			P	P	P	C	BL-d	
MBS	1932	WO 900/32	3800/30	1930			P	P	P	Co	Bc	
MBS		?500/34+					P	P	P	C		
MBS		?1000/36++					P	P	P	C		
MBS		?1750/39+++					P	P	P	C		
MBS	1932	6000/39 C++++	3800/30	1930			P	P	P	C	BL-d	
MBS	1932	WO 6000/40. 5000/40/R	1922	pcr			P	P	P	C	Wc	
MBS	1932	WO 6000/40. 20,000/40/R	1922	pcr			P	P	P	C	Cu-m	
WR	1932	30,000/40 M	1922	pcr			P	P	P	C	BL-d	

1	2	4	6	7	8	9	10	11	12	13	14	15
2WR	1941	WO 50,000/7/41	none				P	P	P	C	BL-d	
2WR	1941	30,000/1/42 LR	1942				N	P	P	C	BL-d	
2WR		20,000/4/42 LR					N	P	P	C	dealer	
2WR	1941	21,050/12/42 Wa	-				N	P	P	C	BL-d	
2WR	1941	20,000/12/42 LR	-				N	P	P	C	Cu	
2WR	1941	35,000/1/43 LR	-				N	P	P	C	BL-d	

Sheet 56 *Boston*   27 by 18 miles

1	2	4	6	7	8	9	10	11	12	13	14	15
BS	-						P	P	P	C		
MBS	1932	WO 600/32	1922	1928			P	P	P	Co	BL-d	
MBS		?1500/33+					P	P	P	C		
MBS		?1000/37++					P	P	P	C		
MBS	1932	6000/39+++	1922	1928			P	P	P	C	BL-d	
MBS	1932	WO 6000/40	1922	pcr			P	P	P	C	PC	
MBS		20,000/40/R					P	P	P	C	dealer	
WR	1932	30,000/40 M	1922	pcr			P	P	P	C	BL-d	
2WR	1940	WO 45,000/4/41	1922.s	pcr			P	P	P	C	BL-d	
2WR	1940	20,000/7/41	none				P	P	P	C	BL-d	
2WR	1940	30,000/2/42 LR	1942				N	P	P	C	BL-d	
2WR	1940	30,000/2/42 LR. 30,000/6/42 R	-				N	P	P	C	BL-d	
2WR	1940	25,000/10/42 McL	1942				N	P	P	C	BL-d	
2WR		12-43 Hay					N	P	P	C	card	1
2WR	1940	20,000/8/44 Wa	-				N	P	P	Cb	BL-d	

1. Added in pencil in a Military Survey card catalogue. It was confirmed by a tick, though is no longer in DGC Superseded.

Sheet 57 *Fakenham*   27 by 18 miles

1	2	4	6	7	8	9	10	11	12	13	14	15
BS	-						P	P	P	C		
MBS		?WO 900/32					P	P	P	Co		
MBS	1932	WO 900/32. 1000/36	1921	25-8			P	P	P	C	BL-d	
MBS	1932	1000/36. 3500/39	1921	pcr			P	P	P	C	Lu	
MBS	1932	1000/36. 3500/39. 6000/39 C	1921	pcr			P	P	P	C	Cu	
MBS	1932	WO 6000/40	1921	pcr			P	P	P	C	Bg	
MBS	1932	WO 6000/40. 20,000/40/R	1921	pcr			P	P	P	C	Cu-m	
MBS		?WO 6000/40. 5000/40/R					P	P	P	C		
MBS	1932	30,000/40/R+	1921	pcr			P	P	P	C	RGS	
WR was not published.												
2WR	1941	WO 20,000/4/41	none				Pz	P	P	C	BL-d	1
2WR	1940	20,000/9/41 B	nd	pcr			Pz	P	P	C	BL-d	
2WR	1940	30,000/5/42 LR	-				Nz	P	P	C	BL-d	
2WR	1940	20,000/11/42 LR	-				Nz	P	P	C	BL-d	
2WR	1940	25,000/12/43 HAY	-				Nz	P	P	C	BL-d	

1. The note advises the use of Second War Revision and Popular Edition as equally valid. Its lack of reference to War Revision is strong evidence that this was not issued, so too its absence on its first appearance in *GSGS 3907 current edition,* 15 May 1941 (see appendix 1), where Popular Edition is noted as the only alternative to Second War Revision.

Sheet 58 *Cromer*   27 by 18 miles

1	2	4	6	7	8	9	10	11	12	13	14	15
BS	-	WO 3.25	1922	24-5			P	P	P	C	PC	
MBS	1932	WO 850/32	3500/29	1928			P	P	P	Co	BL-d	
MBS		?WO 1000/37					P	P	P	C		
MBS	1932	WO 1000/37. 1000/39 C	1922	pcr			P	P	P	C	Mg-d	
MBS	1932	WO 7500/40	1922	pcr			P	P	P	C	Wc	
WR	1932	WO 6000/40	1922	pcr			P	P	P	C	PC	
WR	1932	WO 6000/40. 30,000/40/R	1922	pcr			P	P	P	C	BL-d	
2WR	1941	WO 50,000/5/41	none				P	P	P	C	Cu	
2WR	1941	30,000/12/41 LR	none				P	P	P	C	BL-d	
2WR	1941	40,000/7/42 LR	-				N	P	P	C	BL-d	
2WR	1941	16,000/4/44 Mc	-				N	P	P	C	BL-d	

1	2	4	6	7	8	9	10	11	12	13	14	15
Sheet 59 *Dolgelley & Lake Vyrnwy*							27 by 18 miles					
BS	-						P	P	P	C		
MBS	1932	WO 600/32	1921				P	P	P	Co	BL-d	
MBS		?WO 600/32. 1000/36					P	P	P	C		
MBS	1932	WO 600/32. 1000/36. 4000/39	1921				P	P	P	C	BL-d	
WR	1932	WO 6000/40	1921	pcr			P	P	P	C	Wc	
WR	1932	WO 6000/40. 20,000/9/40/F	1921	pcr			P	P	P	C	BL-d	
WR	1932	24,000/40 W	1921	pcr			P	P	P	C	BL-d	
2WR	1942	20,000/12/42 LR	-				Ny	P	P	C	BL-d	
Sheet 60 a. *Shrewsbury* b. *Shrewsbury & Welshpool*							27 by 18 miles					
BS	-	WO 1.24	1921	1923			Pa	P	P	C	BL-d	
MBS	1932	WO 1200/32	1921	1923			Pa	P	P	Co	IWM	
MBS	1932	?1000/36+					Pa	P	P	C		
MBS	1932	750/38++	1921	1923			Pa	P	P	C	BL-d	
MBS	1932	6000/40 C+++	1921	1923			Pa	P	P	C	BL-d	
MBS	1932	5000 C++++	1921	1923			Pa	P	P	C	Wc	
WR	1932	WO 20,000/40	1921	pcr			Pb	P	P	C	BL-d	
WR	1932	24,000/7/40/F	1921	pcr			Pb	P	P	C	BL-d	
2WR	1942	70,000/3/42 F	1942				Nb	P	P	C	BL-d	
2WR	1942	600/11/43 Ch	-				Nb	P	P	Ow	BL-d	‡
Sheet 61 *Wolverhampton*							27 by 18 miles					
BS	-						P	P	P	C		
BS	-	WO 1200/29	1921	1929			P	P	P	C	BL-d	
BS	-	WO 1000/29. 2275/30	1921	1929		11-26	P	P	P	C	book	1
MBS	1932	WO 2000/32	1921	1929			P	P	P	Co	PC	
MBS	1932	WO 2000/32. 1000/36	1921	1929			P	P	P	C	BL-d	
MBS	1932	WO 2000/32. 1000/36. 1000/39	1921	1929			P	P	P	C	BL-d	
MBS	1932	4000/39	1921	pcr			P	P	P	C	BL-d	
WR	1932	20,000/40/R	1921	pcr			P	P	P	C	Cu	
WR	1932	26,000/40/C	1921	pcr			P	P	P	C	BL-d	
WR	1933	WO 10,000/8/41 LR	none				P	P	P	Cr	PC	
WR	1933	20,000/4/42 A (blue)	none				P	P	P	Cr	BL-d	
WR	1933	20,000/4/42 A. 31,450/1/43 R	1921	pcr			P	P	P	Cr	BL-d	2
WR	nd	20,000/4/42 A. 31,450/1/43 R	1921	pcr			Po	P	P	Cr	NLS	†
2WR	1942	600/11/43 Ch	-				N	P	P	Ow	NLS	‡
2WR	1942	644/Ch	1941				N	P	P	Ow	BL-d	

1. See supplement 8. 2. The 20,000/4/42 A print code is now black, and redrawn.

1	2	4	6	7	8	9	10	11	12	13	14	15
Sheet 62 *Burton & Walsall*							27 by 18 miles					
BS	-	WO 1.24	1921	1923			P	P	P	C	BL-d	
MBS							P	P	P	Co		
MBS	1932	WO 1000/34	2700/33	1932	1931	1932	P	P	P	C	BL-d	
MBS	1932	WO 1000/34. 1500/37	2700/33	1932	1931	1932	P	P	P	C	PC	
MBS	1932	WO 1000/34. 1500/37. 5750/39	2700/33	1932	1931	1932	P	P	P	C	BL-d	
MBS	1932	WO 7000/40	1921	pcr			P	P	P	C	BL-d	
WR	1932	31,000/40 M	1921	pcr			P	P	P	C	IWM	
WR	1932	25,000/12/40/A	1921	pcr			P	P	P	Cr	BL-d	
WR	1932	25,000/12/40 A. 20,000/3/42 R	none				P	P	P	Cr	BL-d	
WR	1932	30,000/7/42 LR (blue)	none				P	P	P	Cr	BL-d	
WR	1932	30,000/8/42 LR (blue)	none				P	P	P	Cr	BL-d	
2WR	1941	600/9/43 Ch	1941				N	P	P	Ow	NLS	‡
2WR	1941	644/Ch	1941				N	P	P	Ow	BL-d	
Sheet 63 *Leicester*							27 by 18 miles					
BS	-						P	P	P	C		
MBS	1932	WO 1150/32	3000/30	1930			P	P	P	Co	PC	
MBS	1932	WO 1150/32. 1000/35	3000/30	1930			P	P	P	C	PC	
MBS	1932	1000/37	1921	pcr			P	P	P	C	BL-d	
MBS	1932	1000/37. 2000/39 C	1921	pcr			P	P	P	C	BL-d	

1	2	4	6	7	8	9	10	11	12	13	14	15
MBS	1932	WO 28,500/40 C	1921	pcr			P	P	P	C	Cu-m	1
WR	1933	10,000/8/41 LR	none				P	P	P	Cr	PC	2
2WR	1942	70,000/4/42 A	-				N	P	P	C	BL-d	
2WR	1942	11,650/11/42/M	1942				N	P	P	C	Og	
2WR	1942	9950/12/42/M	1942				N	P	P	C	Ob	
2WR	1942	10,000/1/43 LR	-				N	P	P	C	BL-d	

1. The "C" is faint in this print code. 2. This was the last sheet to be converted to War Revision.

Sheet 64 *Peterborough*   27 by 18 miles

1	2	4	6	7	8	9	10	11	12	13	14	15
BS	-						P	P	P	C		
MBS	1932	WO 2300/32	50/30+	28-9			P	P	P	Co	BL-d	1
MBS		?WO 1000/37					P	P	P	C		
MBS	1932	WO 1000/37. 1500/38	1922	pcr			P	P	P	C	Cu	
MBS	1932	WO 1000/37. 1500/38. 9000/39 C	1922	pcr			P	P	P	C	BL-d	
MBS	1932	WO 6000/40	1922	pcr			P	P	P	C	BL-d	
?		?WO 6000/40. 25,000/40/R					P	P	P	C		
WR	1932	30,000/40/R+	1922	pcr			P	P	P	C	BL-d	
WR	1932	35,000/4/41 R_+	1922	pcr			P	P	P	Cr	BL-d	
2WR	1940	50,000/9/41 LR	none				P	P	P	C	BL-d	
2WR	1940	30,000/4/42 F	1942				N	P	P	C	BL-d	2
2WR	1940	40,000/7/42 LR	-				N	P	P	C	BL-d	
2WR	1940	15,000/12/42 LR	-				N	P	P	C	BL-d	

1. The OS print code is 2500/30. 50/30, not recorded on a civilian map. 2. The reference 1/63360/225/27·048" is present, no doubt erroneously, in the bottom right corner.

Sheet 65 *Wisbech & King's Lynn*   27 by 18 miles

1	2	4	6	7	8	9	10	11	12	13	14	15
BS	-						P	P	P	C		
MBS	1932	WO 850/32	3500/32	1930			P	P	P	Co	BL-d	
MBS		?1000/35+					P	P	P	C		
MBS	1932	2000/38++	3500/32	1930			P	P	P	C	BL-d	
MBS	1932	2000/39 C+++	3500/32	1930			P	P	P	C	PC	
WR	1932	20,000/40/R	1922	pcr			P	P	P	C	Cu	
WR		?WO 6000/40. 6000/40/R					P	P	P	C		
WR	1932	30,000/40/R+	1922	pcr			P	P	P	C	BL-d	
WR	1932	WO 20,000/3/41	1922	pcr			P	P	P	Cr	BL-d	
WR	1932	20,000/5/41/A	1922	pcr			P	P	P	Cr	PC	
2WR	1942	70,000/2/42 LR	1942				N	P	P	C	BL-d	1
2WR	1942	70,000/2/42 LR	1942				N	P	P	C	BL-d	2
2WR	1942	40,000/7/42 LR	-				N	P	P	C	BL-d	
2WR	1942	15,000/1/43 LR	-				N	P	P	C	BL-d	
2WR	1942	25,000/10/43/14MRS/15	1942				N	P	P	C	BL-d	
2WR	1942	20,000/6/44 Ch	-				N	P	P	Cb	BL-d	

1. The print code is small. 2. The print code is very small.

Sheet 66 *Swaffham & East Dereham*   27 by 18 miles

1	2	4	6	7	8	9	10	11	12	13	14	15
BS	-						P	P	P	C		
MBS	1932	WO 1600/32	1921	1928			P	P	P	Co	BL-d	1
MBS		?WO 1000/37					P	P	P	C		
MBS	1932	WO 1000/37. 750/39 C	1921	1928			P	P	P	C	BL-d	
WR	1932	30,000/40/R	1921	1928			P	P	P	C	BL-d	
2WR	1941	WO 45,000/4/41	none				P	P	P	C	BL-d	
2WR	1941	20,000/7/41	none				P	P	P	C	BL-d	
2WR	1941	30,000/2/42 A	1942				N	P	P	C	BL-d	
2WR	1941	40,000/7/42 LR	-				N	P	P	C	BL-d	
2WR	1941	10,050/11/42 Wa	-				N	P	P	C	BL-d	
2WR	1941	30,000/11/43 Ch	-				N	P	P	C	BL-d	

1. There is only one civilian printing of this sheet recorded, so the minor corrections made in 1928 and a change in railway company names to reflect grouping in 1923, are present only in these military printings.

1	2	4	6	7	8	9	10	11	12	13	14	15

Sheet 67 *Norwich & Great Yarmouth* — 27 by 18 miles

1	2	4	6	7	8	9	10	11	12	13	14	15
BS	-						P	P	P	C		
MBS	1932	WO 1600/32	3750/31++	1930			P	P	P	Co	BL-d	
MBS		?WO 1000/37					P	P	P	C		
MBS	1932	WO 1000/37. 6000/39	1921	pcr			P	P	P	C	PC	
MBS		?WO 6000/40					P	P	P	C		
MBS	1932	WO 6000/40. 20,000/40	1921	pcr			P	P	P	C	BL-d	
WR	1932	30,000/40/R	1921	pcr			P	P	P	C	BL-d	
WR	1932	20,000/4/41/A		pcr			P	P	P	Cr	RGS	
WR	1932	20,000/8/41 LR	nd	pcr			P	P	P	Cr	BL-d	
2WR	1941	50,000/11/41 LR	1941				N	P	P	C	BL-d	
2WR	1941	30,000/3/42 LR	1941				N	P	P	C	BL-d	
2WR	1941	40,000/7/42 LR	-				N	P	P	C	BL-d	
2WR	1941	20,000/12/42 LR	-				N	P	P	C	BL-d	

Sheet 68 *Barmouth & Aberystwyth* — 18 by 32 miles

1	2	4	6	7	8	9	10	11	12	13	14	15
BS	-	WO 3.25	1922	23-5			P	P	P	C	PC	
BS	-	WO 2000/30	3000/29	23-9	9.29		P	P	P	C	PC	
MBS	1932	WO 600/32	3000/29	23-9	9.29		P	P	P	Co	BL-d	
MBS	1932	WO 600/32. 1000/36	3000/29	23-9	9.29		P	P	P	C	PC	
MBS	1932	WO 600/32. 1000/36. 6000/39	3000/29	23-9	-		P	P	P	C	BL-d	
WR	1932	WO 6000/40	1922	pcr			P	P	P	C	RGS	
WR	1932	WO 6000/40. 20,000/40	1922	pcr			P	P	P	C	BL-d	
2WR	1942	20,000/1/43 LR	-				Nx	P	P	C	BL-d	

Sheet 69 *Llanidloes* — 27 by 18 miles

1	2	4	6	7	8	9	10	11	12	13	14	15
BS	-						P	P	P	C		
BS	-	WO 2000/30					P	P	P	C		
MBS	1932	WO 600/32	1922	1928			P	P	P	Co	BL-d	
MBS		?WO 600/32. 1000/36					P	P	P	C		
MBS	1932	WO 600/32. 1000/36. 4000/39	1922	1928			P	P	P	C	BL-d	
WR	1932	26,000/40 W	1922	pcr			P	P	P	C	BL-d	
WR	1932	WO 6000/40	1922	pcr			P	P	P	C	Bg	
WR	1932	WO 6000/40. 20,000/41	1922	pcr			Pv	P	P	Cr	BL-d	
2WR	1942	11,250/1/43 CK	1942				Nx	P	P	C	NLS	
2WR	1942	15,000/9/43 C	-				Nx	P	P	C	BL-d	

Sheet 70 *Bishop's Castle* — 27 by 18 miles

1	2	4	6	7	8	9	10	11	12	13	14	15
BS	-						P	P	P	C		
MBS	1932	WO 600/32	1920	1923			P	P	P	Co	BL-d	
MBS	1932	WO 600/32. 1000/36	1920	1923			P	P	P	C	BL-d	
MBS	1932	WO 600/32. 1000/36. 3750/39	1920	1923			P	P	P	C	BL-d	
WR	1932	WO 9000/40	1920	pcr			P	P	P	C	BL-d	
WR	1932	WO 9000/40. 20000/40	1920	pcr			P	P	P	C	Og	1
WR	1932	WO 9000/40. 20,000/40	1920	pcr			P	P	P	Cr	BL-d	2
2WR	1941	20,000/4/42 LR	1942				Nx	P	P	C	BL-d	
2WR	1941	16,250,9/43 C	-				Nx	P	P	C	BL-d	

1. With no comma in the print code and sienna main roads. 2. With a comma in the print code and red main roads.

Sheet 71 *Kidderminster* — 27 by 18 miles

1	2	4	6	7	8	9	10	11	12	13	14	15
BS	-						P	P	P	C		
MBS	1932	WO 2350/32	1921	1928	24-6		P	P	P	Co	BL-d	
MBS	nd	WO 12,500/39 C	1921	pcr			P	P	P	C	BL-d	1

1	2	4	6	7	8	9	10	11	12	13	14	15
WR	1932	WO 20,000/40	1921	pcr			P	P	P	C	Cu	
WR	1932	WO 3000/40	1921	pcr			P	P	P	C	BL-d	
WR	1932	WO 3000/40. 20,000/7/40/BJ	1921	pcr			P	P	P	C	Wc	
WR	1932	WO 10,000/8/41 LR	1921	pcr			P	P	P	Cr	BL-d	
WR	1932	20,000/3/42 LR (blue)	none				P	P	P	Cr	BL-d	
2WR	1942	70,000/8/42/M	-				N	P	P	C	BL-d	
2WR	1942	10,000/1/43 LR	-				N	P	P	C	BL-d	
2WR	1942	600/9/43 Ch	1942				N	P	P	Ow	BL-d	‡
2WR	1942	645/Ch	1942				N	P	P	Ow	OS	

1. The War Office imprint is lacking.

Sheet 72 *Birmingham*   27 by 18 miles

1	2	4	6	7	8	9	10	11	12	13	14	15
BS	-						P	P	P	C		
MBS	1932	WO 1950/32	3500/31	1931			P	P	P	Co	BL-d	
MBS		?WO 1950/32. 1500/33					P	P	P	C		
MBS	1931	WO 1950/32. 1500/33. 1000/34	3500/31	1931			P	P	P	C	Mg-d	
MBS	1931	WO 2000/39	1921	pcr			P	P	P	C	PC	
MBS	1931	WO 2000/39. 8000/39	1921	pcr			P	P	P	C	BL-d	
WR	1931	no code	1921	pcr			P	P	P	C	BL-d	1
WR	1931	no code	1921	pcr			P	P	P	C	BL-d	2
WR	1931	WO 20,000/41	1921	pcr			P	P	P	Cr	BL-d	
WR	1931	10,000/11/41 LR (blue)	nd	pcr			P	P	P	Cr	BL-d	
2WR	1942	70,000/6/42 LR	-				N	P	P	C	BL-d	
2WR	1942	27,050/1/43 BJ	-				N	P	P	C	BL-d	3
2WR	1942	2500/10/43 Ch	-				N	P	P	C	Bg	
2WR	1942	644 Ch	-				N	P	P	Ow	BL-d	‡

See figure 22. 1. The woodland is blue-green. 2. The woodland is yellow-green. 3. The *relation of grid letters and sheet numbers* diagram incorrectly shows the 300 km northing as passing through sheets 81-83, instead of sheets 71-73.

Sheet 73 *Rugby*   27 by 18 miles

1	2	4	6	7	8	9	10	11	12	13	14	15
BS	-						P	P	P	C		
MBS	1932	WO 2250/32	3300/31	24-8			P	P	P	Co	BL-d	
MBS	1932	WO 1000/38	1920	pcr			P	P	P	C	BL-d	
MBS	1932	WO 1000/38. 1000/38	1920	pcr			P	P	P	C	Bg	
MBS	1932	WO 1000/38. 1000/38. 2000/39	1920	pcr			P	P	P	C	PC	
WR	1932	WO 5000/40	1920	pcr			P	P	P	C	Bg	
WR	1932	WO 5000/40. 26,000/40	1920	pcr			P	P	P	C	BL-d	
WR	1932	29,000/7/40/H (black)	1920	pcr			P	P	P	C	Cu	1
WR	1932	29,000/7/40/H (blue)	1920	pcr			P	P	P	C	PC	2
2WR	1941	WO 50,000/9/41 LR	1941				5	P	5	C	BL-d	
2WR	1941	WO 20,000/2/42	1941				5	P	5	C	BL-d	
2WR	1941	30,000/9/42 C	-				N	P	5	C	BL-d	
2WR	1941	25,000/1/43 LR	-				N	P	5	C	BL-d	
2WR	1941	10,000/2/43 LR	-				N	P	5	C	BL-d	

1. The black print code aligns with the left edge of the legend. 2. The blue print code is inset more to the right.

Sheet 74 *Kettering & Huntingdon*   27 by 18 miles

1	2	4	6	7	8	9	10	11	12	13	14	15
BS	-						P	P	P	C		
MBS	1932	WO 1600/32	2500/30	24-30			P	P	P	Co	BL-d	
MBS		?300/34+					P	P	P	C		
MBS		?500/37++					P	P	P	C		
MBS		?1000/38+++					P	P	P	C		
MBS	1932	2000/39++++	2500/30	24-30			P	P	P	C	BL-d	
MBS	1932	12,000/39+++++	2500/30	24-30			P	P	P	C	PC	
MBS		?WO 6000/40					P	P	P	C		
MBS	1932	WO 6000/40. 10,000/40/R	1923	pcr			P	P	P	C	BL-d	
MBS	1932	WO 6000/40. 40,000/7/40/F	1923	pcr			P	P	P	C	Bg	

1	2	4	6	7	8	9	10	11	12	13	14	15
WR	1932	no code	1923	pcr			P	P	P	C	Wc	1
2WR	1941	WO 50,000/4/41	1941				5	P	5	C	BL-d	
2WR	1941	WO 50,000/5/41	1941				5	P	5	C	BL-d	
2WR	1941	20,000/10/41 LR	1941				5	P	5	C	BL-d	
2WR	1940	30,000/4/42 LR	1942				N	P	5	C	BL-d	
2WR	1940	35,000/10/42/J	1942				N	P	5	C	BL-d	
2WR	1940	10,000/2/43 LR	-				N	P	5	C	BL-d	
2WR	1940	10,000/11/43 Wa	-				N	P	5	C	BL-d	

See figures 4 and 5. 1. *GSGS 3907 current edition*, 1 February 1941 still lists Popular Edition for sheet 74 (see appendix 1). The following list, for 15 May, offers both War Revision and Second War Revision. On the next, for 8 July 1941, War Revision has already disappeared from the record, suggesting that the stock had been turned to salvage. This unique sequence helps explain the rarity of this sheet, and so far the copy in the Library of Congress, Washington, D.C., acquired from the US War Department map collection, is the only one recorded.

Sheet 75 *Ely*   27 by 18 miles

1	2	4	6	7	8	9	10	11	12	13	14	15
BS	-						P	P	P	C		
MBS	1932	WO 1600/32	1920	26-8			P	P	P	Co	BL-d	
MBS	1921	WO 6000/40	1920	pcr			P	P	P	C	Wc	
MBS	1932	WO 6000/40. 10,000/40/R	1920	pcr			P	P	P	C	BL-d	
WR	1932	no code	1920	pcr			P	P	P	C	BL-d	
WR	1932	40,000/40/R	1920	pcr			P	P	P	C	BL-d	
WR	1932	WO 10,000/41	1920	pcr			P	P	P	Cr	BL-d	
2WR	1941	WO/50,000/6/41	1941				5	P	5	C	BL-d	
2WR	1941	30,000/2/42 H (blue)	1941				N	P	5	C	BL-d	
2WR	1941	30,000/6/42 R+ (black)	-				N	P	5	C	BL-d	1
2WR	1941	20,000/12/42 LR	-				N	P	5	C	BL-d	
2WR	1941	10,000/2/43 LR	-				N	P	5	C	BL-d	
2WR	1941	25,000/8/43/M	-				N	P	5	C	BL-d	
2WR	1941	20,000/8/44 Wa	1941				N	P	5	Cb	BL-d	

1. Both the 2/42 print code (which had been blue on the previous) and the 6/42 are black on this printing.

Sheet 76 *Thetford*   27 by 18 miles

1	2	4	6	7	8	9	10	11	12	13	14	15
BS	-						P	P	P	C		
MBS	1932	WO 1600/32	1920	23-8			P	P	P	Co	BL-d	
MBS	1932	WO 1000/38	1920	pcr			P	P	P	C	Lk	
MBS	1932	WO 1000/38. 7500/39 C	1920	pcr			P	P	P	C	BL-d	
WR	1932	no code	1920	pcr			P	P	P	C	Lk	
WR	1932	WO 20,000/41	1920	pcr			P	P	P	Cr	BL-d	
WR	1932	WO 20,000/4/41	nd	pcr			P	P	P	Cr	BL-d	
WR	1932	20,000/7/41	none				P	P	P	Cr	BL-d	
2WR	1942	30,000/1/42 LR. 30,000/2/42 F	1941				Nx	P	P	C	BL-d	
2WR	1942	30,000/6/42 F	-				Nx	P	P	C	BL-d	
2WR	1942	30,000/10/42/M	-				Nx	P	P	C	NLS	
2WR	1942	30,000/11/43 Ch	-				Nx	P	P	C	PC	1
2WR	1942	30,000/11/43 Ch	1941				Nx	P	P	C	BL-d	1
2WR	1942	10,000/11/43 CR	1941				Nx	P	P	C	PC	

1. Both forms, with and without the OS imprint date, do exist.

Sheet 77 *Lowestoft & Waveney Valley*   27 by 18 miles

1	2	4	6	7	8	9	10	11	12	13	14	15
BS	-	WO 1.24	1921				P	P	P	C	PC	
MBS	1932	WO 1600/32	1921	24-8			P	P	P	Co	BL-d	
MBS	1921	WO 6000/40 M	1921	pcr			P	P	P	C	Wc	
WR	1932	no code	1921	pcr			P	P	P	C	NLS	1
WR	1932	20,000/40/R	1921	pcr			P	P	P	C	Og	
WR	1932	WO 20,000/4/41	1921	pcr			P	P	P	Cr	BL-d	
WR	1932	20,000/7/41	none				P	P	P	Cr	BL-d	
WR	1932	10,000/1/42 LR (blue)	none				P	P	P	Cr	BL-d	
2WR	1942	70,000/3/42 LR	1941				N	P	P	C	BL-d	
2WR	1942	70,000/7/42 LR	-				N	P	P	C	BL-d	
2WR	1942	15,000/3/44 Ch	-				N	P	P	C	BL-d	

1. With the scale bar and all other centre marginalia in blue.

Sheet 78 *Lampeter* — 27 by 18 miles

1	2	4	6	7	8	9	10	11	12	13	14	15
BS	-						P	P	P	C		
MBS	1932	WO 500/32	1923	1929			P	P	P	Co	BL-d	
MBS		?WO 500/32. 1000/36					P	P	P	C		
MBS	1932	WO 500/32. 1000/36. 3750/39 C	1923	1929			P	P	P	C	BL-d	
WR	1932	WO 6000/40	1923	pcr			P	P	P	C	BL-d	
WR	1932	24,000/40 W	1923	pcr			P	P	P	C	BL-d	
WR	1932	WO 10,000/41	1923	pcr			Pv	P	P	Cr	BL-d	1
WR	1932	20,000/5/42 LR (blue)	none				Pv	P	P	Cr	BL-d	1

2WR was not published.

1. *Standardisation of editions GSGS 3907* (see appendix 2) provides the information that this sheet should have been published with a current editions note. It was not.

Sheet 79 *Llandrindod Wells* — 27 by 18 miles

1	2	4	6	7	8	9	10	11	12	13	14	15
BS	-						P	P	P	C		
MBS	1932	WO 500/32	1923	1929			P	P	P	Co	BL-d	
MBS		?WO 500/32. 1000/36					P	P	P	C		
MBS	1932	WO 500/32. 1000/36. 4750/39	1923	1929			P	P	P	C	BL-d	
MBS	1932	WO 5000/40	1922	pcr			P	P	P	C	Cu	1
WR	1932	WO 5000/40	1922	pcr			P	P	P	C	Cu	1
WR	1932	WO 5000/40. 20,000/41	1922	pcr			P	P	P	Cr	BL-d	
WR	1932	20,000/9/42 C (blue)	none				Pw	P	P	Cr	BL-d	
2WR	1942	15,150/9/43 C	-				Nx	P	P	C	BL-d	

A contour numbering error in square 4388 (contour 1300 should read 1400) was notified on 28 October 1941, with instructions that it be amended by deleting with a razor blade. It was later corrected. 1. An instance where the War Revision was apparently created by overprinting the MBS with the words *War Revision 1940*.

Sheet 80 *Kington* — 27 by 18 miles

1	2	4	6	7	8	9	10	11	12	13	14	15
BS	-						P	P	P	C		
MBS	1932	WO 1100/32	1920	1924			P	P	P	Co	BL-d	
MBS	1932	WO 1100/32. 1000/36	1920	1924			P	P	P	C	Bg	
MBS	1932	WO 1100/32. 1000/36. 4000/39	1920	1924			P	P	P	C	PC	
WR	1932	WO 9000/40	1920	pcr			P	P	P	C	BL-d	
WR	1932	24,000/7/40 W	1920	pcr			P	P	P	C	BL-d	
WR	1932	20,000/40/R++(sic)	1920	pcr			P	P	P	C	BL	
WR	1933	10,000/8/41 LR	none				P	P	P	Cr	BL-d	
WR	1933	20,000/9/42 C (blue)	none				P	P	P	Cr	BL-d	
2WR	1942	71,250/2/43 Wa	-				N	P	P	C	BL-d	
2WR	1942	645/Ch	1942				N	P	P	Ow	NLS	‡

Sheet 81 *Worcester* — 27 by 18 miles

1	2	4	6	7	8	9	10	11	12	13	14	15
BS	-						P	P	P	C		
BS	-	WO 1150/30	5000/28	1928			P	P	P	C	BL-d	
MBS	1932	WO 3100.32	5000/28	1928			P	P	P	Co	PC	
MBS	1932	1000/37+	5000/28	1928			P	P	P	C	PC	
MBS		?1000/37++					P	P	P	C		
MBS		?750/39+++					P	P	P	C		
MBS	1932	5000/39 C++++ (purple)	5000/28	1928			P	P	P	C	BL-d	
WR	1932	WO 6000/40	1920	pcr			P	P	P	C	Wc	
WR	1932	WO 6000/40. 20,000/40/R	1920	pcr			P	P	P	C	BL-d	
WR	1932	WO 6000/40. 20,000/12/40/F	1920	pcr			P	P	P	Cr	BL-d	
WR	1933	WO 6000/40. 10,000/3/41 LR	none				P	P	P	Cr	BL-d	
WR	1933	20,000/4/42 A (blue)	none				P	P	P	C	BL-d	1
WR	1933	25,000/1/43 LR (blue)	none				P	P	P	C	BL-d	1
WR	nd	25,000/1/43 LR (blue)	none				Po	P	P	C	Mg	1†
2WR	1942	600/11/43 Ch	-				N	P	P	Ow	BL-d	‡
2WR	1942	645/Ch	-				N	P	P	Ow	Rg	

1. Main roads revert to sienna.

1	2	4	6	7	8	9	10	11	12	13	14	15

Sheet 82 *Stratford on Avon* — 27 by 18 miles

1	2	4	6	7	10	11	12	13	14	15
BS	-				P	P	P	C		
MBS	1932	WO 2100/32	3500/29	1929	P	P	P	Co	BL-d	
MBS	1932	1000/35+	1919	1929	P	P	P	C	PC	
MBS	1932	1600/38++	1919	1929	P	P	P	C	Bg	
MBS	1932	17,000/39+++	1919	1929	P	P	P	C	BL-d	
WR	1932	WO 20,000/40	1919	pcr	P	P	P	C	Cu	
WR	1932	WO 3000/40	1919	pcr	P	P	P	C	BL-d	
WR	1932	WO 3000/40. 20,000/41	1919	pcr	P	P	P	Cr	BL-d	
WR	1933	WO 3000/40. 10,000/8/41 LR	none		P	P	P	Cr	Og	
WR	1933	20,000/11/41 LR (blue)	none		P	P	P	Cr	RGS	
WR	1932	45,000/12/42/M (purple)	none		P	P	P	Cr	BL-d	
WR	1932	2050/12/42/M+	none		P	P	P	Cr	PC	1
WR	nd	2050/12/42/M	none		Po	P	P	Cr	Wc	†
2WR	1942	644/Ch	-		N	P	P	Ow	NLS	‡

1. The print code is printed over the 45,000/12/42/M code.

Sheet 83 *Northampton* — 27 by 18 miles

1	2	4	6	7	10	11	12	13	14	15
BS	-	WO 1.24	1919		P	P	P	C	BL-d	
BS	-	?WO 900/28			P	P	P	C		
BS	-	WO 900/28. 2275/29	1919	1924	P	P	P	C	book	1
MBS	1932	WO 2600/32	3000/30	1928	P	P	P	Co	BL-d	
MBS		?WO 2600/32. 1000/35			P	P	P	C		
MBS	1932	WO 2600/32. 1000/35. 1600/38	3000/30	1928	P	P	P	C	Bg	
MBS	1932	WO 10,500/40	1919	pcr	P	P	P	C	BL-d	
MBS	1932	4000/40+	1919	pcr	P	P	P	C	BL-d	
MBS	1932	20,000/40++	1919	pcr	P	P	P	C	PC	
WR	1932	WO 20,000/40	1919	pcr	P	P	P	C	BL	
WR	1932	20,000/4/41/H	1919	pcr	P	P	P	Cr	Lk	
2WR	1941	WO 50,000/9/41 LR	1941		5	P	5	C	Cu	
2WR	1941	30,000/2/42 LR	1942		N	P	5	C	Og	2
2WR	1941	30,000/2/42 LR	1942		N	P	5	C	BL-d	3
2WR	1941	30,000/2/42 LR	1942		N	P	5	C	IWM	4
2WR	1941	30,000/12/42 LR	1942		N	P	5	C	BL-d	5
2WR	1941	15,000/1/43 LR	-		N	P	5	C	BL-d	
2WR	1941	15,000/2/43 LR	-		N	P	5	C	BL-d	
2WR	1941	644/Ch	1942		N	P	5	Ow	BL-d	‡
2WR	1941	25,000/8/44 Ch	-		N	P	5	Cb	BL-d	

See also supplement 3. 1. See supplement 8. 2. Adjoining sheet numbers 93-95 are erroneously printed as 104-106, and the 500 easting as 600. The Og copy was an OS file copy printed on 18 February 1942, one of 30,712 copies. The error is corrected by an overprint: 3. in red; 4. in black; 5. in blue.

Sheet 84 *Bedford* — 27 by 18 miles

1	2	4	6	7	10	11	12	13	14	15
BS	-	WO 2.25	1919	1924	P	P	P	C	PC	
MBS	1932	WO 3600/32	2500/30+	1930	P	P	P	Co	BL-d	
MBS		?WO 3600/32. 1000/37			P	P	P	C		
MBS	1931	WO 3600/32. 1000/37. 1000/38	2500/30+	1930	P	P	P	C	BL-d	
MBS	1931	WO 10,000/39			P	P	P	C	dealer	
MBS	1931	WO 6000/40	1919	pcr	P	P	P	C	Wc	
MBS	1931	WO 6000/40. 16,000/40/R	1919	pcr	P	P	P	C	BL-d	
MBS	1931	WO 6000/40. 40,000/7/40 Mc	1919	pcr	Po	P	P	C	PC	
WR	1931	no code	1919	pcr	P	P	P	C	BL-d	
2WR	1941	50,000/6/41	1941		5	P	5	C	BL-d	
2WR	1941	20,000/9/41 LR	1941		5	P	5	C	BL-d	
2WR	1941	30,000/3/42 LR	1942		N	P	5	C	BL-d	
2WR	1941	36,250/1/43 CK	1942		N	P	5	C	NLS	
2WR	1941	10,000/2/43 LR	-		N	P	5	C	BL-d	
2WR	1941	20,000/8/43/M	-		N	P	5	C	BL-d	
2WR	1941	644/Ch	1942		N	P	5	Ow	NLS	‡

1	2	4	6	7	8	9	10	11	12	13	14	15

Sheet 85 *Cambridge* — 27 by 18 miles

1	2	4	6	7	10	11	12	13	14	15
BS	-	WO 3.26	1923	1926	P	P	P	C	PC	
MBS	1932	WO 2650/32	1923	1929	P	P	P	Co	BL-d	
MBS		?1000/36+			P	P	P	C		
MBS		?1000/37++			P	P	P	C		
MBS	1932	1000/39+++	1923	1929	P	P	P	C	BL-d	
MBS	1932	10,000/39	none		P	P	P	C	RGS	
MBS	1932	6000/40 M	1923	pcr	P	P	P	C	Cu-m	
WR	1932	no code	1923	pcr	P	P	P	C	BL-d	
WR	1932	WO 20,000/41	1923	pcr	P	P	P	Cr	BL-d	
WR	1932	WO 10,000/5/41	none		P	P	P	Cr	Cu	
2WR	1941	WO 50,000/7/41	1941		5	P	5	C	BL-d	
2WR	1941	30,000/2/42 LR. 30,000/3/42 A	1942		N	P	5	C	BL-d	
2WR	1941	30,000/5/42 LR	-		N	P	5	C	BL-d	
2WR	1941	35,000/10/42/M	-		N	P	5	C	RGS	
2WR	1941	10,000/2/43 LR	-		N	P	5	C	BL-d	
2WR	1941	20,000/8/43/M	-		N	P	5	C	BL-d	
2WR	1941	600/11/43 Ch	-		N	P	5	Ow	NLS	‡
2WR	1941	15,000/3/44 Ch	-		N	P	5	C	BL-d	

Sheet 86 *Bury St. Edmunds & Sudbury* — 27 by 18 miles

1	2	4	6	7	10	11	12	13	14	15
BS	-				P	P	P	C		
MBS	1932	WO 1600/32	1921	1928	P	P	P	Co	PC	
MBS	1932	WO 1600/32. 400/34	1921	1933	P	P	P	C	BL-d	
MBS	1932	3000/36	1921	pcr	P	P	P	C	book	1
MBS		?3000/36. 1000/37			P	P	P	C		
MBS	1932	3000/36. 1000/37. 1000/39	1921	pcr	P	P	P	C	BL-d	
MBS	1932	WO 8000/40	1921	pcr	P	P	P	C	Cu-m	
MBS	1932	WO 13,000/40 C	1921	pcr	P	P	P	C	Wc	2
MBS	1932	WO 13,000/40 C. 40,000/40 M	1921	pcr	P	P	P	C	Bg	
WR	1932	20,000/41	1921	pcr	P	P	P	Cr	BL-d	
2WR	1941	WO 50,000/7/41	1941		5	P	5	C	BL-d	
2WR	1941	30,000/2/42/J	1942		N	P	5	C	BL-d	
2WR	1941	30,000/5/42 A	-		N	P	5	C	BL-d	
2WR	1941	40,000/10/42 A	-		N	P	5	C	RGS	
2WR	1941	26,200/12/43 Wa	-		N	P	5	C	BL-d	

1. See supplement 8. 2. The "1" of 13,000 has obviously been added to a "3000", which may imply an earlier printing, or a late reassessment of the printing requirement of this one.

Sheet 87 *Ipswich* — 27 by 18 miles

1	2	4	6	7	10	11	12	13	14	15
BS	-				P	P	P	C		
MBS	1932	WO 1650/32	1921	1928	P	P	P	Co	BL-d	
MBS		?WO 500/37			P	P	P	C		
MBS	1932	WO 500/37. 1000/39	1921	pcr	P	P	P	C	Cu	
MBS	1932	WO 6500/40	1921	pcr	P	P	P	C	PC	
MBS	1932	WO 6500/40 Mc	1921	pcr	P	P	P	C	Ag	
WR	1932	40,000/40 M	1921	pcr	P	P	P	C	Og	
WR	1932	20,000/41	1921	pcr	P	P	P	Cr	BL-d	
2WR	1941	50,000/7/41 A	1941		5	P	5	C	BL-d	1
2WR	1941	50,000/7/41 A	1941		5	P	5	C	Wc	2
2WR	1941	30,000/2/42/J	1942		N	P	5	C	BL-d	3
2WR	1941	30,000/2/42 J. 30,000/6/42 R	-		N	P	5	C	BL-d	
2WR	1941	30,000.10.42 H	-		N	P	5	C	BL-d	
2WR	1941	25,000/12/43 Wa	-		N	P	5	C	BL-d	

1. The print code figures are large (extending to Minist…). 2. The print code figures are small. 3. See also supplement 3.

1	2	4	6	7	8	9	10	11	12	13	14	15

Sheet 88 *St. David's & Cardigan* — 33 by 19½ miles

1	2	4	6	7	8	9	10	11	12	13	14	15
BS	-						P	P	P	C		
MBS	1931	no code	1923	1925			P	P	P	Co	BL-d	
MBS	1931	WO 1000/36	1923	1925			P	P	P	C	PC	
MBS	1931	5000/39 C	1535	pcr			P	P	P	C	BL-d	
MBS		WO 13,000/40 C					P	P	P	C		
WR	1932	WO 16,000/40	1923	pcr			P	P	P	C	BL-d	
WR	1932	WO 16,000/40. 20,000/40	1923	pcr			P	P	P	Cr	BL-d	
WR	1932	WO 16,000/40. 10,000/7/41	none				Pw	P	P	Cr	BL-d	
WR	1932	30,000/7/42 LR (blue)	none				Pw	P	P	Cr	BL-d	

2WR was not published.

Sheet 89 *Carmarthen* — 27 by 18 miles

1	2	4	6	7	8	9	10	11	12	13	14	15
BS	-						P	P	P	C		
MBS	1931	WO 500/31	1923	1926			P	P	P	Co	BL-d	
MBS	1931	WO 5000/39 C	1923	pcr			P	P	P	C	BL-d	
WR	1931	WO 6000/40	1923	pcr			P	P	P	C	BL-d	
WR	1931	WO 20,000/40	1923	pcr			P	P	P	C	BL-d	
WR	1931	24,000/40 W	1923	pcr			P	P	P	C	BL-d	
WR	1931	30,000/7/42 LR (blue)	none				P	P	P	Cr	BL-d	

2WR was not published.

Sheet 90 *Brecon & Llandovery* — 27 by 18 miles

1	2	4	6	7	8	9	10	11	12	13	14	15
BS	-						P	P	P	C		
BS	-	WO 3500/31	1923				P	P	P	Co	book	1
MBS	1931	WO 600/31	1925	1931	8/31		P	P	P	Co	BL-d	
MBS		?WO 600/31. 1000/35					P	P	P	C		
MBS	1931	WO 600/31. 1000/35. 1000/38	1925	1931	8/31		P	P	P	C	BL-d	
MBS	1931	WO 5000/39	1925	pcr			P	P	P	C	PC	
WR	1931	?WO 7000/40					P	P	P	C		
WR	1931	WO 7000/40. 17,000 C	1925	pcr			P	P	P	C	Wc	
WR	1931	WO 7000/40. 17,000 C. 4000/C40	1925	pcr			P	P	P	C	Cu	
WR	1931	20,000/40 M	1925	pcr			P	P	P	C	BL-d	
WR	1931	WO 7000/40. 10,000/6/41/F	1925	pcr			Pv	P	P	Cr	BL-d	
WR	1931	20,000/6/42 LR (blue)	-				Nv	P	P	Cr	BL-d	2
WR	1931	11,050/1/43 W	-				Nv	P	P	Cr	PC	
WR	1931	11,050/1/43 W	-				No	P	P	Cr	BL-d	†
2WR	1943	10,000/12/43 Wa	-				Nx	P	P	C	BL-d	3

1. See supplement 8. 2. One of only four England and Wales War Revision sheets recorded with the new style marginalia. 3. The Second War Revision was issued very late.

Sheet 91 *Abergavenny* — 27 by 18 miles

1	2	4	6	7	8	9	10	11	12	13	14	15
BS	-						P	P	P	C		
MBS	1932	WO 1100/32	1919	1931			P	P	P	Co	BL-d	
MBS	1932	1000/36+	1919	1931			P	P	P	C	BL-d	
MBS		?1500/37++					P	P	P	C		
MBS	1932	5000/39+++	1919	1931			P	P	P	C	BL-d	
WR	1932	20,000/40 M	1919	pcr			P	P	P	C	BL-d	
WR	1932	WO 20,000/40	1919	pcr			P	P	P	C	Wc	
WR	1932	WO 20,000/40. C/4000/40	1919	pcr			P	P	P	C	PC	
WR	1932	WO 10,000/4/41	none				P	P	P	Cr	Cu	
WR	1933	10,000/9/41 LR	none				P	P	P	Cr	BL-d	
2WR	1942	70,000/5/42 W	1942				N	P	P	C	BL-d	
2WR	1942	10,000/8/43 Wa	-				N	P	P	C	BL-d	
2WR	1942	644 Ch	1942				N	P	P	Ow	BL-d	‡

Sheet 92 *Gloucester & Forest of Dean*   27 by 18 miles

1	2	4	6	7	8	9	10	11	12	13	14	15
BS	-	WO 10.25	1919	1924			P	P	P	C	PC	
MBS	1931	WO 2800/31	3500/28	24-8	5/26		P	P	P	Co	BL-d	
MBS	1931	1500/37+	3500/28	24-8	-		P	P	P	C	PC	
MBS		?2000/39++					P	P	P	C		
MBS	1931	8000/39+++	3500/28	24-8			P	P	P	C	PC	
MBS	1932	WO 7500/40	1919	pcr			P	P	P	C	BL-d	
WR	1932	no code	2539 M39 R38	pcr			P	P	P	C	Lk	
WR	1932	20,000/8/40/H	2539 M39 R38	pcr			P	P	P	C	BL-d	
WR	1932	30,000/4/41/H	2539 M39 R38	pcr			P	P	P	Cr	BL-d	1
WR	1932	20,000/11/41 LR (blue)	none				P	P	P	C	BL-d	2
WR	1932	41,650/1/43 R	2539 M39 R38	pcr			P	P	P	Cr	BL-d	
WR	nd	41,650/1/43 R	2539 M39 R38	pcr			Po	P	P	Cr	Wc	†
2WR	1942	600/11/43 Ch	-				N	P	P	Ow	NLS	‡
2WR	1942	644 Ch	-				N	P	P	Ow	BL-d	

1. See also supplement 3. 2. With sienna main roads.

Sheet 93 *Stow on the Wold*   27 by 18 miles

1	2	4	6	7	8	9	10	11	12	13	14	15
BS	-	?WO 12.26. 1000/27					P	P	P	C		
BS	-	WO 12.26. 1000/27. 1000/28	1919	1926	6/26		P	P	P	C	PC	
BS	-	?WO 900/28					P	P	P	C		
BS	-	WO 900/28. 2275/29	1919	1926	6/26		P	P	P	C	book	1
BS	-	?WO 1000/30					P	P	P	C		
BS	-	WO 1000/30. 2150/31	3000/30	1926			P	P	P	C	book	1
MBS	1931	WO 2300/31	3000/30	1928			P	P	P	Co	BL-d	
MBS	1931	8500/37	3000/30	1928			P	P	P	C	BL-d	
MBS		?WO 600/38					P	P	P	C		
MBS	1931	WO 600/38. 6000/39	1919	pcr			P	P	P	C	BL-d	
MBS	1931	WO 600/38. 10,000/39 C	1919	pcr			P	P	P	C	BL-d	
WR	1932	WO 23,000/40	1919	pcr			P	P	P	C	BL-d	
WR	1932	WO 23,000/40. 20,000/12/40/F	1919	pcr			P	P	P	Cr	BL-d	
WR	1932	WO 23,000/40. 20,000/6/41	none				P	P	P	Cr	BL-d	
WR	1932	20,000/2/42 LR (blue)	1942				N	P	P	Cr	BL-d	2
WR	1932	45,000/1/43/BJ	-				N	P	P	Cr	BL-d	
WR	1932	2050/1/43 BJ	-				No	P	P	Cr	Rg	†
WR	1932	10,000/2/43 LR (blue)	-				N	P	P	Cr	BL-d	3
2WR	1941	600/11/43 Ch	-				N	P	5	Ow	NLS	‡
2WR	1941	20,000/8/44 Wa	-				N	P	5	Cb	BL-d	4

See also supplement 3. 1. See supplement 8. 2. One of only four England and Wales War Revision sheets recorded with the new style marginalia. 3. This is the last recorded printing of a War Revision sheet in England and Wales. 4. This was the last Second War Revision to be published in colour. Some mapping along the northern and western edges of this sheet remains in Popular Edition style.

Sheet 94 *Bicester*   27 by 18 miles

1	2	4	6	7	8	9	10	11	12	13	14	15
BS	-	WO 4.26	1919	1925			P	P	P	C	PC	
MBS	1931	WO 2150/31	2500/30+	1930			P	P	P	Co	BL-d	
MBS	1931	WO 2500/37	3500/32++	1932			P	P	P	C	BL-d	
MBS		?WO 2500/37 600/38					P	P	P	C		
MBS	1931	WO 2500/37. 600/38. 8000/39 C	3500/32++	1932			P	P	P	C	BL-d	
MBS	1931	WO 6000/40	1919	pcr			P	P	P	C	Bg	
WR	1931	WO 20,000/40	1919	pcr			P	P	P	C	BL-d	
WR	1931	26,000/7/40/F	1919	pcr			P	P	P	C	Wc	
WR	?1931	WO 20,000/4/41	none				P	P	P	Cr	PC	1

1	2	4	6	7	8	9	10	11	12	13	14	15
2WR	1941	50,000/8/41/F	1941				5	P	5	C	BL-d	2
2WR	1941	30,000/1/42 LR. 30,000/1/42 F	1941				N	P	5	C	BL-d	
2WR	1941	50,000/6/42 W	-				N	P	5	C	BL-d	
2WR	1941	10,000/1/43 LR	-				N	P	5	C	BL-d	
2WR	1941	600/11/43 Ch	1941				N	P	5	Ow	NLS	‡
2WR	1941	15,000/1/44 Wa	-				N	P	5	C	BL-d	
2WR	1941	25,000/8/44/Ch	-				N	P	5	Cb	BL-d	

On some Second War Revision printings the grid northing values 36 and 37 situated next to the 510 easting were printed transposed. They may be corrected, overprinted in purple. There is a note on a Military Survey catalogue card that "Base map in hand (preparation only at O.S.) 8.10.46". It is unclear what the post-war need for this sheet was. 1. Publication date uncertain: the War Office imprint is trimmed from the only copy recorded. 2. See also supplement 3.

Sheet 95 *Luton*   27 by 18 miles

1	2	4	6	7	8	9	10	11	12	13	14	15
BS	-						P	P	P	C		
MBS	1931	WO 3650/31	3000/29+	25-8		1924	P	P	P	Co	BL-d	
MBS	1931	WO 3650/31. 3100/38	3000/29+	25-8		1924	P	P	P	C	Cu	
MBS	1931	WO 3650/31. 3100/38. 5000/39 C	3000/29+	25-8		1924	P	P	P	C	BL-d	
MBS	1931	WO 6000/40	1923	pcr			P	P	P	C	IWM	
MBS	1931	WO 6000/40. 15,000/40/R	1923	pcr			P	P	P	C	BL-d	
MBS	1931	40,000/7/40/H	1923	pcr			P	P	P	C	BL-d	
WR	1931	no code	1921	pcr			P	P	P	C	Rg	1
WR	1931	WO 20,000/4/41	none				P	P	P	Cr	BL-d	
WR	1931	20,000/8/41 LR	none				P	P	P	Cr	BL-d	
WR	1931	10,000/10/41 LR (blue)	nd	pcr			P	P	P	Cr	BL-d	
WR	1931	10,000/1/42 LR (blue)	nd	pcr			P	P	P	Cr	BL-d	
2WR	1942	70,000/2/42 LR	1942				N	P	5	C	BL-d	
2WR	1942	50,000/8/42 LR	-				N	P	5	C	BL-d	
2WR	1942	10,000/1/43 LR	-				N	P	5	C	BL-d	
2WR	1942	10,000/2/43 LR	-				N	P	5	C	BL-d	
2WR	1942	20,000/8/43 Mc	-				N	P	5	C	Bg	
2WR	1942	644 Ch	1942				N	P	5	Ow	NLS	‡
2WR	1942	20,000/8/44 Ch	-				N	P	5	Cb	BL-d	

1. It is unclear how this printing, originally published in 1923, came to have a 1921 civilian imprint date.

Sheet 96 a. *Hertford & Bishop's Stortford* b. *Hertford and Bishop's Stortford*   27 by 18 miles

1	2	4	6	7	8	9	10	11	12	13	14	15
BS	-	WO 4.25	1919	1925			Pa	P	P	C	PC	
MBS	1931	WO 2600/31	3000/30+	1928			Pa	P	P	Co	BL-d	1
MBS	1931	WO 2600/31. 1000/36	3000/30+	1928			Pa	P	P	C	IWM	2
MBS	1931	1500/38	1919	pcr			Pa	P	P	C	IWM	
MBS	1931	1500/38. 2000/39	1919	pcr			Pa	P	P	C	PC	
MBS	1931	1500/38. 2000/39. 12,000/39	1919	pcr			Pa	P	P	C	BL-d	
MBS	1931	WO 6000/40	1919	pcr			Pa	P	P	C	Cu-m	
MBS	1931	WO 6000/40. 10,000/40/R	1919	pcr			Pa	P	P	C	RGS	
MBS	1931	40,000/40 W	1919	pcr			Pa	P	P	C	Lk	
WR	1931	WO 20,000/3/41	1919	pcr			Pa	P	P	Cr	BL-d	
WR	1932	WO 10,000/7/41	none				Pa	P	P	Cr	BL-d	3
2WR	1941	50,000/9/41 LR	none				5b	P	5	C	BL-d	4
2WR	1941	30,000/3/42 R	1942				Na	P	5	C	BL-d	
2WR	1941	30,000/6/42 LR	-				Na	P	5	C	BL-d	
2WR	1941	35,000/10/42 A	-				Na	P	5	C	Lk	
2WR	1941	11,850/5/43/C	-				Na	P	5	C	BL-d	
2WR	1941	25,000/10/43 Ch	-				Na	P	5	C	BL-d	
2WR	1941	20,000/8/44 Ch	-				Na	P	5	Cb	BL-d	

1. The GSGS imprint is unusually small. 2. See also supplement 8. 3. The GSGS imprint is reset in standard size lettering. 4. Some mapping along the eastern edge of this sheet remains in Popular Edition style on 2WR printings.

1	2	4	6	7	8	9	10	11	12	13	14	15

Sheet 97 *Colchester*   27 by 18 miles

1	2	4	6	7	8	9	10	11	12	13	14	15
BS	-						P	P	P	C		
BS	-	WO 3000/29	1921	1929	8/28		P	P	P	C	PC	
MBS	1931	WO 5100/31	1921	1925			P	P	P	Co	BL-d	
MBS		?500/34+					P	P	P	C		
MBS	1931	1000/35++	1921	1925			P	P	P	C	BL-d	
MBS	1931	1000/36+++	1921	1925			P	P	P	C	PC	
MBS	1931	1000/37	1921	pcr			P	P	P	C	Bc	
MBS	1931	1000/37. 750/39	1921	pcr			P	P	P	C	BL-d	
WR	1931	WO 11,000/40	1921	pcr			P	P	P	C	Bg	
WR	1931	WO 11,000/40. 21,000.C	1921	pcr			P	P	P	C	NTg	
WR	1931	WO 20,000/3/41	1921	pcr			P	P	P	Cr	Cu	
WR	1931	WO 20,000/5/41	none				P	P	P	Cr	BL-d	
2WR	1941	WO 50,000/7/41	1941				5	P	5	C	BL-d	
2WR	1941	20,000/2/42 R	1941				5	P	5	C	BL-d	
2WR	1941	30,000/6/42 A	-				N	P	5	C	BL-d	
2WR	1941	30,000/10/42 F	-				N	P	5	C	BL-d	
2WR	1941	600/11/43 Ch	-				N	P	5	Ow	BL-d	‡
2WR	1941	21,250,12/43 C&R	-				N	P	5	C	BL-d	

For GSGS 3907A Colchester Training Areas see supplement 4.

Sheet 98 *Clacton on Sea & Harwich*   27 by 18 miles

1	2	4	6	7	8	9	10	11	12	13	14	15
BS	-						P	P	P	C		
MBS	1931	WO 5150/31	3000/29	1928			P	P	P	Co	BL-d	
MBS	1931	1000/37					P	P	P	C	BSg	
MBS	1931	1000/38	1921	pcr			P	P	P	C	BL-d	
MBS		?1000/38. 3000/39					P	P	P	C		
MBS	1931	1000/38. 3000/39. 5000/39	1921	pcr			P	P	P	C	Cu	
MBS	1932	WO 6500/40	1921	pcr			P	P	P	C	Bg	
MBS	1932	WO 6500/40. 15,000/40	1921	pcr			P	P	P	C	Wc	
WR	1932	no code	1921	pcr			P	P	P	C	BL-d	
WR	1932	WO 30,000/3/41	1921	pcr			P	P	P	Cr	BL-d	
2WR	1941	50,000/7/41	1941				5	P	5	C	BL-d	
2WR	1940	30,000/2/42 H	1942				N	P	5	C	BL-d	
2WR	1940	40,000/7/42 LR	-				N	P	5	C	BL-d	
2WR	1940	21,050/12/42 Wa	-				N	P	5	C	BL-d	1
2WR	1940	21,050/12/42 Wa	-				N	P	5	C	IWM	2

See supplement 8. 1. The print code ends over the "i" of "Geographical". 2. The print code ends over the second "a" of "Geographical".

Sheet 99 *Pembroke & Tenby*   33 by 19½ miles

1	2	4	6	7	8	9	10	11	12	13	14	15
BS	-	WO 12.23	1922	1923			P	P	P	C	PC	
MBS	1932	WO 1100/32	2750/30	1924			P	P	P	Co	BL-d	
MBS	1932	1000/37	1922	pcr			P	P	P	C	PC	
MBS		?WO 4000/38					P	P	P	C		
MBS		?WO 4000/38. 1000/39					P	P	P	C		
MBS	1932	WO 4000/38. 1000/39. 4000/39	1922	pcr			P	P	P	C	BL-d	
MBS	1932	WO 17,500/40	1922	pcr			P	P	P	C	Bg	
WR	1932	20,000/40 M	1922	pcr			P	P	P	C	BL-d	
WR	1932	10,000/6/41	none				P	P	P	Cr	Cu	
WR	1932	30,000/11/41 A	1922	pcr			P	P	P	Cr	BL-d	
WR	1932	16,250/1/43 W	none				P	P	P	Cr	BL-d	
WR	nd	16,250/1/43 W	none				Po	P	P	Cr	Wc	†
2WR	1943	10,000/1/44 Wa	-				N	P	P	C	BL-d	1

1. This was the penultimate sheet to be issued in Second War Revision, in colour.

1	2	4	6	7	8	9	10	11	12	13	14	15

Sheet 100 *Llanelly*   27 by 18 miles

1	2	4	6	7	8	9	10	11	12	13	14	15
BS	-						P	P	P	C		
MBS	1931	WO 800/31	1923	1925			P	P	P	Co	BL-d	
MBS		?1000/35+					P	P	P	C		
MBS		?1000/36++					P	P	P	C		
MBS		?1000/36+++					P	P	P	C		
MBS	1931	7500/39++++	1923	1925			P	P	P	C	BL-d	
MBS	1931	WO 6000/40	1923	pcr			P	P	P	C	BL-d	
WR	1931	WO 20,000/40	1923	pcr			P	P	P	C	BL	
WR	1931	24,000/40/R	1923	pcr			P	P	P	C	RGS	1
WR	1931	20,000/11/41 LR (blue)	nd	pcr			P	P	P	Cr	BL-d	
WR	1931	21,050/1/43 W	none				P	P	P	Cr	BL-d	
WR	nd	21,050/1/43 W	none				Po	P	P	Cr	NLS	†
2WR	1943	600/11/43 Ch	-				N	P	P	Ow	NLS	‡

1. The *relation of grid letters and sheet numbers* diagram lacks sheet lines. Unusually for a War Revision printing, the water tint is still solid blue rather than screened.

Sheet 101 *Swansea & Aberdare*   27 by 18 miles

1	2	4	6	7	8	9	10	11	12	13	14	15
BS	-						P	P	P	C		
MBS	1932	WO 800/32	3250/31++	1931			P	P	P	Co	BL-d	
MBS	1932	WO 800/32. 1000/36	3250/31++	1931			P	P	P	C	BL-d	
MBS		?WO 800/32. 1000/36. 1750/38					P	P	P	C		
MBS	1932	8750/39+	3250/31++	1931			P	P	P	C	PC	
MBS	1932	8750/39 Mc_+	3250/31++	1931			P	P	P	C	Pg	
WR	1932	WO 3000/40	1923	pcr			P	P	P	C	Og	
WR	1932	20,000/8/40/H	1923	pcr			P	P	P	C	BL-d	
WR	1933	10,000/8/41 LR	none				P	P	P	Cr	BL-d	
WR	1933	30,000/5/42 LR (blue)	none				P	P	P	Cr	BL-d	
2WR	1943	15,000/12/43 Wa	-				N	P	P	C	BL-d	1

1. The Second War Revision was issued very late.

Sheet 102 *Newport*   27 by 18 miles

1	2	4	6	7	8	9	10	11	12	13	14	15
BS	-						P	P	P	C		
MBS	1932	WO 1100/32	3000/30+	1930	5/26	1928	P	P	P	Co	BL-d	1
MBS		?500/34+					P	P	P	C		
MBS		?1000/36++					P	P	P	C		
MBS		?1000/38+++					P	P	P	C		
MBS	1932	2000/39++++	3000/30+	1930	5/26	1928	P	P	P	C	BL-d	1
MBS	1932	8000/39+++++	3000/30+	1930	5/26	1928	P	P	P	C	PC	1
MBS	1932	WO 5000/40	1919	pcr			P	P	P	C	Wc	
WR	1932	WO 5000/40. 20,000/8/40/H	1919	pcr			P	P	P	C	BL-d	
WR	1932	WO 5000/40. 20,000/5/41/F	1919	pcr			P	P	P	Cr	Cu	
2WR	1942	70,000/5/42/M	-				N	P	P	C	BL-d	
2WR	1942	16,250/2/43 E	-				N	P	P	C	BL-d	
2WR	1942	644 Ch	-				N	P	P	Ow	NLS	‡

1. The OS print code string 1000/24. 3000/30 is not recorded on a civilian map, and was probably replaced in the event by 3000/31.

Sheet 103 *Stroud & Chepstow*   27 by 18 miles

1	2	4	6	7	8	9	10	11	12	13	14	15
BS	-						P	P	P	C		
MBS	1931	WO 1800/31	500/30++	1929	5.26	1928	P	P	P	Co	BL-d	1
MBS	1931	2000/35+	500/30++	1929	-	1928	P	P	P	C	BL-d	1
MBS		?1000/37++					P	P	P	C		
MBS		?600/38+++					P	P	P	C		
MBS	1931	4000/39++++	500/30++	1929	-	1928	P	P	P	C	BL-d	1
MBS		?6500/40+++++					P	P	P	C		
MBS	1931	16,000/40/R++++++	500/30++	1929	-	1928	P	P	P	C	Wc	1
WR	1931	10,000/7/40/F	1919	pcr			P	P	P	C	PC	2
WR	1931	20,000/8/40/F	1919	pcr			P	P	P	C	PC	3
WR	1931	20,000/5/41	1919	pcr			P	P	P	Cr	BL-d	

1	2	4	6	7	8	9	10	11	12	13	14	15
2WR	1942	70,000/3/42 W	1942				N	P	5	C	BL-d	4,5
2WR	1942	41,450/1/43 BJ	1942				N	P	5	C	BL-d	
2WR	1942	10,000/3/43 LR	-				N	P	5	C	BL-d	
2WR	1942	644 Ch	1942				N	P	5	Ow	BL-d	‡

1. The OS print code string is 500/28. 3000/29. 500/30, according to Hodson (1999) not seen on a civilian map. 2. The *relation of grid letters and sheet numbers* diagram lacks sheet lines and numbers. 3. The diagram is missing altogether. 4. Some mapping along the northern edge of this sheet remains in Popular Edition style on 2WR printings. 5. Several additional pulls from the plates for this printing are recorded, none with print code: black plate only, green woods only, blue water and grid figures only, black with orange roads and contours, black with orange and blue, black with orange, blue and green (copies Bg).

Sheet 104 a. *Swindon & Cirencester* b. *Swindon and Cirencester*   27 by 18 miles

1	2	4	6	7	8	9	10	11	12	13	14	15
BS	-						Pa	P	P	C		
BS	-	WO 1200/30	3000/29	24-8	6.26		Pa	P	P	C	BL-d	
MBS	1932	WO 1150/32	3000/29	24-8			Pa	P	P	Co	PC	
MBS	1932	WO 1150/32. 1750/33	3000/29	24-8			Pa	P	P	Co	PC	
MBS	1932	WO 1150/32. 1750/33. 500/34	3000/29	24-8			Pa	P	P	C	BL-d	
MBS	1932	WO 2000/35	1919	1932	1932	1932	Pa	P	P	C	PC	
MBS	1932	WO 600/38	1919	pcr			Pa	P	P	C	BL-d	
MBS	1932	WO 600/38. 15,500/39 C	1919	pcr			Pa	P	P	C	BL-d	
MBS	1932	WO 600/38. 15,500/39 C. 29,500/40	1919	pcr			Pa	P	P	C	BL-d	
WR	1932	20,000 40/J	1919	pcr			Pa	P	P	C	BL-d	
WR	1932	20,000/41	1919	pcr			Pa	P	P	Cr	BL-d	
2WR	1941	50,000/8/41 LR	none				5b	P	5	C	BL-d	
2WR	1941	30,000/1/42 LR	1942				Na	P	5	C	BL-d	
2WR	1941	25,000.10.42 H	-				Na	P	5	C	Ob	
2WR	1941	20,000/1/43 LR	-				Na	P	5	C	BL-d	
2WR	1941	35,000/5/44 Ch	-				Na	P	5	Cb	Ag	
2WR	1941	35,000/6/44 Ch	-				Na	P	5	Cb	BL-d	1

1. The "5" of the previous is apparently altered to a "6"; this is the continuation of the same print run. See also supplement 1.

Sheet 105 a. *Oxford & Henley on Thames* b. *Oxford and Henley on Thames* c. *Oxford & Henley-on-Thames*
27 by 18 miles

1	2	4	6	7	8	9	10	11	12	13	14	15
BS	-	?WO 3.25					Pa	P	P	C		
BS	-	WO 3.25. Reprint 1000/27	2500/26+	24-6	5-26		Pa	P	P	C	BL-d	
BS	-	WO 1350/29	3500/28++	24-6	5-26		Pa	P	P	C	BL-d	
MBS	1931	WO 2800/31	3500/28++	24-6	-		Pa	P	P	Co	BL-d	
MBS		?600/38					Pa	P	P	C		
MBS	1931	600/38. 2500/39	1919	pcr			Pa	P	P	C	PC	
MBS	1931	WO 28,500/40	1919	pcr			Pa	P	P	C	BL-d	
WR	1931	20,000/9/40/F	1919	pcr			Pa	P	P	C	BL-d	
WR	1931	WO 3000/41	1919	pcr			Pa	P	P	Cr	BL-d	1
WR	1931	WO 20,000/7/41	none				Pa	P	P	Cr	BL-d	
WR		WO 20,000/9/41 LR	none				Pa	P	P	C	card	2
2WR	1941	70,000/11/41 LR	none				5b	P	5	C	BL-d	
2WR	1941	50,000/6/42 LR	-				Nc	P	5	C	BL-d	
2WR	1941	10,000/1/43 LR	-				Nc	P	5	C	BL-d	
2WR	1941	15,000/1/43 LR	-				Nc	P	5	C	RGS	
2WR	1941	20,000/7/43/13S/38	-				Nc	P	5	C	PC	
2WR	1941	600/11/43 Ch	-				Nc	P	5	Ow	NLS	‡
2WR	1941	10,000/12/43/16MRS/95	-				Nc	P	5	C	BL-d	
2WR	1941	644 Ch	-				Nc	P	5	Ow	OS	
2WR	1941	15,000/1/44/16MRS/104	-				Nc	P	5	C	BSg	3
2WR	1941	20,000/8/44 B	-				Nc	P	5	Cb	BL-d	

1. In the *relation of grid letters and sheet numbers* diagram the sheet lines and numbers are blue, the Cassini Grid purple. 2. This printing was also used as the base for the civilian outline and water edition (copy PC). 3. See also supplement 1.

Sheet 106 *Watford* — 27 by 18 miles

1	2	4	6	7	8	9	10	11	12	13	14	15
BS	-						P	P	P	C		
MBS	-	WO 5550/31	5000/28++	1929		1927	P	P	P	Co	RGS	1
MBS		?300/34+					P	P	P	C		
MBS		?1500/36++					P	P	P	C		
MBS		?3500/38+++					P	P	P	C		
MBS	1931	3150/39++++	5000/28++	1929		1927	P	P	P	C	Cu	1
MBS	1931	12,000/39+++++	5000/28++	1929		1927	P	P	P	C		1,2
MBS	1931	6000/40++++++	5000/28++	1929		1927	P	P	P	C	PC	1
MBS	1931	40,000/8/40/A+++++++	5000/28++	1929		1927	P	P	P	C	Bg	1

WR was almost certainly not published.

1	2	4	6	7	8	9	10	11	12	13	14	15
2WR	1940	WO 20,000/40	1940.s				5	P	5	C	Wc	
2WR	1940	WO 20,000/40. 30,000/41	1940.s				5	P	5	C	BL-d	
2WR	1941	20,000/6/41	none				5	P	5	C	Cu	
2WR	1940	20,000/8/41 LR	none				5	P	5	C	BL-d	
2WR	1940	30,000/10/41 LR	none				5	P	5	C	BL-d	
2WR	1940	30,000/6/42 LR	-				N	P	5	C	BL-d	
2WR	1940	30,000/1/43 LR	-				N	P	5	C	BL-d	
2WR	1940	10,000/3/43 LR	-				N	P	5	C	BL-d	
2WR	1940	20,000/5/43/C	-				N	P	5	C	BL-d	
2WR	1940	2000/10/43 Ch	-				N	P	5	C	PC	
2WR	1940	20,000/11/43 Ch	-				N	P	5	C	BL-d	
2WR	1940	10/44 Ch	-				N	P	5	Ox	NLS	‡
2WR	1940	30,000/6/44 HAY	-				N	P	5	Cb	BL-d	

GSGS 3907 current edition lists note only Popular Edition and Second War Revision, making it highly probable that this sheet was not published in War Revision (see appendix 1). 1. The minor correction date is updated from that listed in Hodson (1999). 2. See also London special mapping in section 3.

Sheet 107 *N.E. London & Epping Forest* — 27 by 18 miles

1	2	4	6	7	8	9	10	11	12	13	14	15
BS	-	WO 3.23	1920				P	P	P	C	PC	
MBS	-	WO 4550/31	500/30+++++	1930			P	P	P	Co	PC	1
MBS	1931	WO 300/34	1920	1934	1932		P	P	P	C	BL-d	
MBS	1931	WO 3500/38	1938.s				5	P	5	C	IWM	2
MBS		?2650/39					5	P	5	C		
MBS	1931	2650/39. 10,000/39	1938.s				5	P	5	C	BL-d	
MBS	1931	WO 10,000/39	1938.s				5	P	5	C	Lk	
MBS	1931	7000/40 M	1938.s				5	P	5	C	Wc	
MBS	1931	10,000/40 M	1938.s				5	P	5	C	BL-d	
MBS	1931	5000/7/40/F	1938.s				5	P	5	C	Bc	
MBS	1931	40,000/8/40/A	1938.s				5	P	5	C	Rg	
WR	1931	WO 20,000/4/41	none				5	P	5	Cr	BL-d	3
WR	1931	20,000/7/41	none				5	P	5	Cr	BL-d	
WR	1931	20,000/11/41 LR (blue)	none				5	P	5	Cr	BL-d	
2WR	1942	70,000/2/42 A	1942				N	P	5	C	BL-d	4
2WR	1942	40,000/7/42 LR	-				N	P	5	C	BL-d	
2WR	1942	22,250/1/43 CK	1942				N	P	5	C	Wc	
2WR	1942	10,000/3/43 LR	-				N	P	5	C	BL-d	
2WR	1942	25,000/11/43 Ch	-				N	P	5	C	Bg	5
2WR	1942	25,000/11/43 Ch	-				N	P	5	C	BL-d	6
2WR	1942	644/Ch	-				N	P	5	Ox	NLS	‡
2WR	1942	22,050/8/44 B	-				N	P	5	Cb	BL-d	

See figures 2 and 3; also London special mapping in section 3. 1. The full OS print code string is Reprint 6000/21. 6000/21. 500/25. 5000/26. 5000/29. 500/30, according to Hodson (1999) not seen on a civilian printing. 2. Noted in GSGS documents as "Special Popular Edition", but now with Fifth Edition mapping and marginalia on Popular Edition sheet lines. The heading is Ordnance Survey of Great Britain. 3. Curiously War Revision did not appear on a *GSGS 3907 current edition* statement until 31 October 1941 (see appendix 1). Even then the "Special Popular Edition" continued to be offered as an alternative in spite of the massive amount of ARP revision added to the War Revision. 4. See also supplement 3. 5. The print code is printed above "Section". 6. The print code is scribed above "Geographical".

1	2	4	6	7	8	9	10	11	12	13	14	15

Sheet 108 *Southend & District* — 27 by 18 miles

1	2	4	6	7	8	9	10	11	12	13	14	15
BS	-	WO 1.24	1921				P	P	P	C	PC	
MBS	1931	WO 2650/31	500/30++	24-9			P	P	P	Co	PC	1
MBS		?WO 1000/35					P	P	P	C		
MBS		?1000/36+					P	P	P	C		
MBS		?1000/37++					P	P	P	C		
MBS		?1000/37+++					P	P	P	C		
MBS	1931	2000/39 C++++	1921	1922			P	P	P	C	Cu	
MBS	1931	WO 6000/40	1921	1922			P	P	P	C	PC	
MBS	1931	WO 6000/40. 15,000/40/R	1921	1922			P	P	P	C	BL-d	
MBS	1931	40,000/7/40/H	1921	1922			P	P	P	C	Bg	

WR was probably not published.

1	2	4	6	7	8	9	10	11	12	13	14	15
2WR	1940	WO 45,000/3/41	1940.s				5	P	5	C	BL-d	
2WR	1940	WO 20,000/8/41	none				5	P	5	C	PC	
2WR	1940	WO 20,000/8/41 LR	none				5	P	5	C	BL-d	
2WR	1940	30,000/3/42 A	1942				N	P	5	C	BL-d	
2WR	1940	30,000/8/42 F	-				N	P	5	C	BL-d	
2WR	1940	12,000/1/44 HAY	-				N	P	5	C	BL-d	
2WR	1940	20,000/8/44 B	1942				N	P	5	Cb	BL-d	

War Revision never appears on a *GSGS 3907 current edition* statement (see appendix 1), strong evidence that it was not issued (but see sheet 134). 1. The full OS print code string is 3500/30. 200/30. 500/30, according to Hodson (1999) not seen on a civilian printing.

Sheet 109 *Pontypridd & Barry* — 34 by 18 miles

1	2	4	6	7	8	9	10	11	12	13	14	15
BS	-	WO 12.23	1922			1922	P	P	P	C	PC	
MBS							P	P	P	Co		
MBS	1932	WO 1000/39	1922	pcr			P	P	P	C	BL-d	
MBS	1932	WO 1000/39. 1500/39	1922	pcr			P	P	P	C		
MBS	1932	WO 6000/40	1922	pcr			P	P	P	C	Bg	
WR	1932	20,000/8/40/F	1922	pcr			P	P	P	C	BL-d	
WR	1932	10,000/6/41	none				P	P	P	Cr	BL-d	
WR	1932	10,000/2/42 A	1922	pcr			P	P	P	Cr	RGS	
WR	1932	20,000/5/42 LR (blue)	none				P	P	P	Cr	BL-d	
WR	1932	20,000/1/43 LR (blue)	none				P	P	P	Cr	BL-d	
WR	nd	20,000/1/43 LR (blue)	none				Po	P	P	Cr	NLS	†
2WR		proofs					P	P	P	C		1
2WR	1943	644/Ch	-				P	P	P	Ow	NLS	‡

1. 2WR was not published in colour. Two colour proof copies were received from the Ordnance Survey by Military Survey on 25 October 1943 and submitted for action to AD Survey, Home Forces on 12 November with instructions to pass on to the Ordnance Survey at Chessington; any further work on them is improbable. A comment written on 19 November 1943 on a Military Survey catalogue card refers to "No WOPD at present". See also supplement 8.

Sheet 110 a. *Cardiff & Mouth of the Severn* b. *Cardiff and Mouth of the Severn* — 27 by 18 miles

1	2	4	6	7	8	9	10	11	12	13	14	15
BS	-						Pa	P	P	C		
MBS	1931	WO 1100/31	1000/24	1926		1922	Pa	P	P	Co	BL-d	
MBS		?WO 1000/35					Pa	P	P	C		
MBS		?1000/38+					Pa	P	P	C		
MBS	1931	600/38++	2000/32+	1932	4/32p	1922	Pa	P	P	C	BL-d	
MBS	1931	5000/39+++	2000/32+	1932	4/32p	1922	Pa	P	P	C	BL-d	
WR	1931	WO 11,000/40					Pa	P	P	C	card	
WR	1931	WO 11,000/40. 21,000 C	1919	pcr			Pa	P	P	C	BL-d	
WR	1931	WO 11,000/40. 20,000/8/40/F	1919	pcr			Pa	P	P	C	BL-d	
2WR	1941	50,000/11/41 F	none				5b	P	5	C	BL-d	
2WR	1941	20,000/5/42 LR	-				Nb	P	5	C	BL-d	
2WR	1941	20,000/7/42/C	-				Nb	P	5	C	BL-d	
2WR	1941	20,000/7/42/C. 30,000/7/42/C	-				Nb	P	5	C	BL-d	
2WR	1941	644/Ch	-				Nb	P	5	Ox	NLS	‡

Sheet 111 *Bath & Bristol*   27 by 18 miles

1	2	4	6	7	8	9	10	11	12	13	14	15
BS	-						P	P	P	C		
MBS	1931	2600/31	3500/29+++	23-9		1927	P	P	P	Co	PC	
MBS	1931	WO 2000/34	3500/29+++	23-9		1927	P	P	P	C	BL-d	
MBS	1931	WO 2000/34. 2000/35	3500/29+++	23-9		1927	P	P	P	C	dealer	
MBS	1931	WO 3100/38	1919	pcr			P	P	P	C	PC	
MBS	1931	WO 1000/39	1919	pcr			P	P	P	C	BL-d	
MBS	1931	WO 1000/39. 4000/39	1919	pcr			P	P	P	C	BL-d	
MBS	1931	?WO 20,500/40					P	P	P	C		
MBS	1931	WO 20,500/40. 10,000/40	1919	pcr			P	P	P	C	Bc	
WR	1931	20,000/8/40/F	1919	pcr			P	P	P	C	BL-d	
WR	1931	WO 20,000/41	1919	pcr			P	P	P	Cr	BL-d	
WR	1931	WO 20,000/8/41 LR	none				P	P	P	Cr	BL-d	
2WR	1941	70,000/2/42 LR	1942				N	P	5	C	BL-d	
2WR	1941	50,000/6/42 LR	-				N	P	5	C	BL-d	
2WR	1941	10,000/3/43 LR	-				N	P	5	C	BL-d	
2WR	1941	600/9/43 Ch	1942				N	P	5	Ow	BL-d	‡
2WR	1941	2000/10/43 Wa	1942				N	P	5	C	BL-d	
2WR	1941	25,000/3/44 Ch	-				N	P	5	C	BL-d	
2WR	1941	100/8/47	-				N	P	5	C	BL-d	1

1. Printed on wet strength paper.

Sheet 112 *Marlborough*   27 by 18 miles

1	2	4	6	7	8	9	10	11	12	13	14	15
BS	-	WO 12.25	1919	1925			P	P	P	C	PC	1
BS	-	?WO 700/26					P	P	P	C		
BS	-	WO 700/26. 1000/27	1919	1926			P	P	P	C	PC	
BS	-	WO 700/26. 1000/27. 2450/27	1919	1926			P	P	P	C	book	2
BS	-	WO 1350.29	4500/29++	26-9		4.26	P	P	P	C	PC	
BS	-	WO 3000/30	4500/29++	1929		4.26	P	P	P	C	BL-d	
BS	-	WO 1000/30. 2150/31	4500/29++	26-9		4.26	P	P	P	C	book	2
MBS	1931	WO 3780/31	4500/29++	1929			P	P	P	Co	PC	
MBS		?7000/32+					P	P	P	Co		
MBS		?3000/33++					P	P	P	Co		
MBS	1931	2000/33+++	4500/29++	1929			P	P	P	Co	PC	
MBS	1931	1700/34++++	4500/29++	1929			P	P	P	C	PC	
MBS	1931	WO 12,000/39	1919	pcr			P	P	P	C	BL-d	
WR	1931	no code	1919	pcr			P	P	P	C	Bg	
WR	1931	WO 20,000/40	1919	pcr			P	P	P	C	Og	
WR	1931	WO 20,000/41	1919	pcr			P	P	P	Cr	BL-d	
WR	1931	20,000/4/41/A	1919	pcr			P	P	P	Cr	Cu	
WR	1931	10,000/10/41 LR (blue)	none				P	P	P	Cr	BL-d	
WR	1931	20,000/1/42 LR	1942				N	P	P	Cr	BL-d	3
2WR	1942	70,000/6/42 LR	-				N	P	5	C	BL-d	
2WR	1942	35,000/9/42 F	-				N	P	5	C	BL-d	
2WR	1942	25,000/1/43 LR	-				N	P	5	C	BL-d	
2WR	1942	10,000/3/43 LR	-				N	P	5	C	BL-d	
2WR	1942	400/11/43 Ch	-				N	P	5	Ow	NLS	‡
2WR	1942	40,000/1/44/16MRS/102	-				N	P	5	C	BL-d	4,5
2WR		10,000					N	P	5	C		4
2WR	1942	100/8/47	-				N	P	5	C	BL-d	6

1. A copy of this sheet is recorded on waterproof paper – presumably some other method than that developed by Colonel C.O. Place, which came into widespread use by GSGS and Ordnance Survey in 1928. 2. See supplement 8. 3. One of only four England and Wales War Revision sheets recorded with the new style marginalia. 4. The print order was for 50,000 sheets. It would be consistent with similar orders for other sheets were a supplementary printing of 10,000 to be recorded (e.g. see sheets 113, 131). 5. For further use see supplement 1. 6. Printed on wet strength paper.

Sheet 113 a. *Reading & Newbury* b. *Reading and Newbury* 27 by 18 miles

1	2	4	6	7	8	9	10	11	12	13	14	15
BS	-	WO 11.23	1919				Pa	P	P	C	BL-d	
MBS	1931	WO 2980/31	4000/29++	1928			Pa	P	P	Co	PC	
MBS	1931	1750/33+	4000/29++	1928			Pa	P	P	Co	BL-d	
MBS	1931	5000/33++	4000/29++	1928			Pa	P	P	Co	PC	
MBS	1931	2000/35+++	4000/29++	1928			Pa	P	P	C	PC	
MBS		?300/36					Pa	P	P	C		
MBS		?300/36. 250/36					Pa	P	P	C		
MBS	1931	300/36. 250/36. 1000/37					Pa	P	P	C		
MBS	1931	WO 1500/39	3200/34	1933	1931		Pa	P	P	C	PC	
MBS	1931	WO 1500/39. 8000/39	3200/34	1933	1931		Pa	P	P	C	IWM	
MBS	1931	WO 35,000/40	3200/34	1933	1931		Pa	P	P	C	BLd	
WR	1931	20,000/40/A	3200/34	1933	1931		Pa	P	P	C	Cu-m	
WR	1931	30,000/12/40/A	3200/34	1933	1931		Pa	P	P	Cr	Cu	
WR	1931	20,000/4/41/H	3200/34	1933	1931		Pa	P	P	Cr	Dtc	
WR	1931	WO 10,000/6/41	none				Pa	P	P	Cr	BL-d	
2WR	1941	50,000/8/41	none				5b	P	5	C	BL-d	
2WR	1941	WO 30,000/11/41 LR	none				5b	P	5	C	BL-d	
2WR	1941	30,000/3/42 LR	1942				Na	P	5	C	BL-d	
2WR	1941	50,000/7/42 LR	-				Na	P	5	C	BL-d	
2WR	1941	20,000/1/43 LR	-				Na	P	5	C	BL-d	
2WR	1941	10,000/3/43 LR	-				Na	P	5	C	BL-d	
2WR	1941	25,000/10/43/14MRS/5	1942				Na	P	5	C	Sg	
2WR	1941	400/11/43 Ch	-				Na	P	5	Ow	NLS	‡
2WR	1941	10,000/12/43/16MRS/93	1942				Na	P	5	C	BL-d	
2WR	1941	50,000/1/44/16MRS/101	1942				Na	P	5	C	BL-d	1

For further use see supplement 8. 1. For further use see supplement 1.

Sheet 114 *Windsor* 27 by 18 miles

1	2	4	6	7	8	9	10	11	12	13	14	15
BS	-	WO 3.23	7.21,12.21				P	P	P	C	BL-d	
MBS							P	P	P	Co		
MBS	1931	WO 2700/34	1920	1933	1931		P	P	P	C	BL-d	
MBS	1931	2000/35+	1920	1933	1931		P	P	P	C	PC	
MBS		?4000/37++					P	P	P	C		
MBS		?2500/38+++					P	P	P	C		
MBS	1931	4150/39 I I I I	1920	1933	1931		P	P	P	C	IWM	
MBS	1931	16,000/39+++++	1920	1933	1931		P	P	P	C	Cu	1
MBS	1931	7000/40++++++	1920	1933	1931		P	P	P	C	BL-d	
MBS	1940	WO 40,000/40	1940.s				P	P	5	C	PC	2

WR was not published.

1	2	4	6	7	8	9	10	11	12	13	14	15
2WR	1940	WO 20,000/40	1940.s				5	P	5	C	Wc	3
2WR	1941	WO 20,000/4/41	none				5	P	5	C	Cu-m	
2WR	1940	20,000/8/41 LR	none				5	P	5	C	LVg	
2WR	1940	40,000/10/41 LR	1940.s				5	P	5	C	BL-d	
2WR	1940	30,000/4/42 LR	-				N	P	5	C	Cu	
2WR	1940	45,000/8/42 LR	-				N	P	5	C	BL-d	
2WR	1940	15,000/1/43 LR	-				N	P	5	C	NLS	
2WR		10,000/3/43 LR					N	P	5	C	card	
2WR	1940	20,000/7/43/13.S/39	1942				N	P	5	C	PC	
2WR	1940	50,000/1/44 Ch	-				N	P	5	C	BL-d	
2WR	1940	10,000/8/48	-				N	P	5	C	BL-d	

1. See also London special mapping in section 3. 2. This "Special Popular" Edition, uniquely with Fifth Edition mapping inside a Popular Edition border, was apparently issued between 10 and 21 August 1940. It was to be printed in the Second War Revision four-colour scheme, but in the event it was printed in five, the grid remaining purple, the roads being combined with contours. It remained valid until the stock ran out in February 1942. See figure 19. 3. This was the first Second War Revision sheet to be published, at the end of October 1940. Some copies have colour blocks top right. Both Special Popular and Second War Revision were announced in *GSGS 3907 current edition,* 31 October 1940 (see appendix 1), effectively removing all possibility of War Revision.

1	2	4	6	7	8	9	10	11	12	13	14	15

Sheet 115 a. *S.E. London & Sevenoaks* b. *S.E. London and Sevenoaks* 27 by 18 miles

1	2	4	6	7	8	9	10	11	12	13	14	15
BS	-	?WO 1.23					Pa	P	P	C		
BS	-	WO 1.23. 1000/28	5000/28++				Pa	P	P	C	PC	
BS	-	WO 1500/30					Pa	P	P	C		
MBS	-	WO 4980/31	5000/30++++	1929			Pa	P	P	Co	Lk	
MBS	1931	WO 4500/34	1920	1932	1932	1932	Pa	P	P	C	Ob	
MBS	1931	WO 4500/34. 2000/34	1920	1932	1932	1932	Pa	P	P	C	PC	
MBS		?WO 1000/35					Pa	P	P	C		
MBS		?3000/36+					Pa	P	P	C		
MBS	1931	6000/38++	1920	pcr			Pa	P	P	C	PC	
MBS	1931	4150/39+++	1920	pcr			Pa	P	P	C	IWM	
MBS	1931	16,000/39++++	1920	pcr			Pa	P	P	C	Cu	1
MBS	1932	WO 6000/40	10,000/33++++++	1933			Pa	P	P	C	PC	
MBS	1932	WO 6000/40. 10,000/40/R	10,000/33++++++	1933			Pa	P	P	C	PC	
MBS	1932	WO 6000/40. 40,000/7/40/F	10,000/33++++++	1933			Pa	P	P	C	Bg	

WR was probably not published.

1	2	4	6	7	8	9	10	11	12	13	14	15
2WR	1940	WO 45,000/41	1940.s	pcr			5b	P	5	C	BL-d	
2WR	1941	WO 25,000/4/41	none				5b	P	5	C	BL-d	
2WR	1941	20,000/8/41 LR	none				5b	P	5	C	BL-d	
2WR	1941	30,000/12/41 LR	nd	pcr			5b	P	5	C	BL-d	
2WR	1941	30,000/6/42 A	-				Na	P	5	C	BL-d	
2WR	1941	35,000/10/42 A	-				Na	P	5	C	PC	
2WR	1941	15,000/1/43 LR	-				Na	P	5	C	BL-d	
2WR	1941	644/Ch	1941				Na	P	5	Ow	NLS	‡
2WR	1941	50,000/1/44 Wa	-				Na	P	5	C	BL-d	

War Revision never appears on a *GSGS 3907 current edition* statement (see appendix 1), strong evidence that it was not issued (but see sheet 134). 1. See also London special mapping in section 3.

Sheet 116 *Chatham & Maidstone* 27 by 18 miles

1	2	4	6	7	8	9	10	11	12	13	14	15
BS	-	WO 1.24	1921			1922	P	P	P	C	Mg-d	
MBS	1931	WO 5000/31	5000/29+	1928		1922	P	P	P	Co	BL-d	
MBS	1931	WO 5000/31. 700/34	5000/29+	1928		1922	P	P	P	C	BL-d	
MBS		?WO 1500/35					P	P	P	C		
MBS	1931	WO 1500/35. 1000/36	1921	pcr			P	P	P	C	Mg	
MBS	1931	7000/37	2035	pcr			P	P	P	C	PC	
MBS		?WO 1000/37					P	P	P	C		
MBS	1931	WO 1000/37. 2500/38	1921	pcr			P	P	P	C	RGS	
MBS	1931	WO 1000/37. 2500/38. 7500/39	1921	pcr			P	P	P	C	PC	
MBS	1931	WO 8000/40	1921	pcr			P	P	P	C	BL-d	
MBS	1931	WO 8000/40. 18,000/40/R	1921	pcr			P	P	P	C	Mg-d	1
MBS	1931	WO 8000/40. 40,000/7/40/F	1921	pcr			P	P	P	C	Bg	
WR	1931	10,000/41	1921	pcr			P	P	P	Cr	BL-d	2
2WR	1941	WO 45,000/4/41	1941				5	P	5	C	BL-d	
2WR	1941	WO 20,000/7/41	1941				5	P	5	C	BL-d	
2WR	1941	20,000/11/41 LR	1941				5	P	5	C	BL-d	
2WR	1941	30,000/3/42 A	1942				N	P	5	C	BL-d	
2WR	1941	25,000/10/42 A	-				N	P	5	C	BL-d	
2WR	1941	22,050/5/43/C	-				N	P	5	C	BL-d	
2WR	1941	40,000/9/43 F	1942				N	P	5	C	BL-d	
2WR	1941	600/11/43 Ch	-				N	P	5	Ow	NLS	‡
2WR	1941	20,000/3/44 Ch	-				N	P	5	C	BL-d	

War Department lands at Chatham were overprinted by MO1, dated 2 February 1925, on outline Popular Edition sheet 116 (with no military grid) (copy Ob). Land required is infilled purple, and that not required yellow. Filed as MRLG Misc.166. For a note on an experimental Ansell fold printing of a Second War Revision, see sheet 126. 1. The print code "18,000" or possibly "13,000" – the only copy recorded had a crease at the critical point. 2. One of two recorded copies of this War Revision is in BL-d; it never appears on a *GSGS 3907 current edition* statement so was probably never issued (see appendix 1). A 1941 sheet, it was superseded by Second War Revision in April 1941, and, as was the policy of the time for issues deemed not to be current, any stock was probably turned to salvage. The other copy is in the Library of Congress, Washington, D.C. (ex US War Department map collection).

1	2	4	6	7	8	9	10	11	12	13	14	15

Sheet 117 *East Kent* — 18 by 27 miles

1	2	4	6	7	8	9	10	11	12	13	14	15
BS	-	?WO 11.23					P	P	P	C		
BS	-	?Reprint 400/25+					P	P	P	C		
BS	-	1000/27++	3500/26	23-6	7/26	1926	P	P	P	C	Lk	
BS	-	WO 3.28	3500/26	23-7	7/26	1927	P	P	P	C	PC	
BS	-	?WO 500/29					P	P	P	C		
BS	-	WO 500/29. 3200/29	5500/29	1928	9.26	1926	P	P	P	C	PC	
BS	-	WO 1300/31	5500/29	1928	9.26	1926	P	P	P	C+	Mg-d	
MBS	1931	WO 11,050/31	5500/29	1928	-	1926	P	P	P	Co	PC	
MBS	1931	WO 7000/34	1921	1933	1928	-	P	P	P	C	PC	
MBS	1931	WO 3500/35	2500/33	1933	1928		P	P	P	C	PC	1
MBS	1931	3000/36+	2500/33	1933	1928		P	P	P	C	BL-d	1
MBS	1931	1500/38++	1921	1933	1928		P	P	P	C	IWM	
MBS		?6000/39 C+++					P	P	P	C		
MBS	1931	40,000/40 W++++	1921	1933	1928		P	P	P	C	PC	2
MBS	1931	WO 6000/40	1920	pcr			P	P	P	C	Wc	
MBS	1931	WO 18,000/40	1920	pcr			P	P	P	C	Mg-d	3
WR	1931	WO 10,000/41	1920	pcr			P	P	P	Cr	BL-d	4

2WR see sheet 117A.

1. This OS print code is not recorded on a civilian printing. 2. The water infill plate is lacking. 3. The print code looks like "18000", altered from "6000". 4. The only recorded copy of this War Revision is in DGC Superseded; it never appears on a *GSGS 3907 current edition* statement so was probably never issued (see appendix 1). A 1941 sheet, it was superseded by Second War Revision sheet 117A in April 1941, and, as was the policy of the time for issues deemed not to be current, any stock was probably turned to salvage.

East Kent Special Sheet. Parts of sheets 116, 117, 126. — 42 by 42 km

1	2	4	6	7	8	9	10	11	12	13	14	15
MBS	1935	WO 7000/35	-				P	-	P	C	PC	
MBS	1935	WO 7000/35. 8000/37	-				P	-	P	C	PC	1
MBS	1935	WO 7000/35. 8000/37. 8000/39 C	-				P	-	P	C	Lk	

Sheet 117A *East Kent Special Sheet.* Parts of sheets 116, 117, 126. — Second War Revision 1941

1	2	4	6	7	8	9	10	11	12	13	14	15
2WR	1941	WO 45,000/4/41	1941				5	-	5	C	Cu	
2WR	1941	WO 45,000/4/41. 20,000/7/41	none				5	-	5	C	PC	
2WR	1941	20,000/11/41 A	1941.s				5	-	5	C	RGS	
2WR	1941	30,000/3/42 LR	1942				N	-	5	C	RGS	
2WR	1941	40,000/10/42 A	-				N	-	5	C	BL-d	
2WR	1941	50,000/10/43 Wa	-				N	-	5	C	BL-d	
2WR	1941	20,000/6/44 Ch	-				N	-	5	Cb	BL-d	

On grid sheet lines (643-685, 148-190). See also supplement 4. 1. See Kent Manoeuvres in supplement 7 for another issue, with red overprint.

Sheet 118 a. *Barnstaple & Exmoor* — 27 by 18 miles

1	2	4	6	7	8	9	10	11	12	13	14	15
BS	-	WO 5.26	2500/23	1925	5.25		Pa	P	P	C	PC	
MBS	1931	WO 1100/31	3500/27+	1926			Pa	P	P	Co	BL-d	
MBS		?4000/37					Pa	P	P	C		1
MBS	1931	4000/37. 1500/38	3500/34++++	1930			Pa	P	P	C	BL-d	1
MBS	1931	4000/37. 1500/38. 2000/39	3500/34++++	1930			Pa	P	P	C	PC	1

Sheet 118 b. *Barnstaple* — 50,000 by 35,000 yards

1	2	4	6	7	8	9	10	11	12	13	14	15
MBS	1940	WO 6000/40	1933.s	pcr	1936		5b	5	5	C	BL-d	2,3
WR	1940	WO 20,000/40	1933.s	pcr	1936		5b	5	5	C	BL-d	4
WR	1940	WO 20,000/8/41 LR	none		1936		5b	5	5	Cr	BL-d	
WR	1941	40,000/7/42 LR (blue)	-				Nb	5	5	Cr	BL-d	
WR	1941	644/Ch (blue)	-				Nbp	5	5	Ox	BL-d	‡

2WR was not published.

1. The 1500/38 and 2000/39 printings carry the OS Central Registry number 7959, possibly retained from the 4000/37 printing which may have been for examination purposes. See supplement 8. 2. Issued before 10 August 1940. 3. *Braunton Burrows Training Areas* appears in manuscript detail on a copy in BL-d. See supplement 4. 4. An unusual case of the yard grid remaining in place on War Revision.

1	2	4	6	7	8	9	10	11	12	13	14	15

Sheet 119 *Exmoor* — 27 by 18 miles

1	2	4	6	7	8	9	10	11	12	13	14	15
BS	-	?WO 6.25. 1000.26					P	P	P	C		
MBS	1931	1100.31+	3500/28+	25-6-9			P	P	P	Co	BL-d	1
MBS		?1000/36++					P	P	P	C		
MBS	1931	1500/38+++	3500/28+	25-6-9			P	P	P	C	PC	1
MBS	1931	7500/39++++	3500/28+	25-6-9			P	P	P	C	BL-d	1

Sheet 119 *Exmoor* — 52,000 by 35,000 yards

1	2	4	6	7	8	9	10	11	12	13	14	15
MBS	1940	WO 6000/40	none			1937	5	5	5	C	RGS	2
MBS	1940	WO 26,000/40	none			1937	5	5	5	C	BL-d	3
WR	1940	WO 20,000/40	none			1937	5	5	5	C	Cu	
WR	1931	WO 10,000/41	none			1937	5	5	5	Cr	BL-d	4
WR	1941	20,000/11/41 LR (blue)	1941				N	5	5	Cr	BL-d	
WR	1941	20,000/6/42 LR (blue)	-				N	5	5	Cr	BL-d	
WR	1941	644/Ch (blue)	-				Np	5	5	Ox	NLS	‡

2WR was not published.

1. Minor correction date is updated from that shown in Hodson (1999), and can variously be read as 23-6-9 or 25-6-9. 2. Issued before 10 August 1940. 3. This print code seems to have been accomplished by the addition of a "2" within the previous. 4. Note the reversion to the original imprint date of the Popular Edition sheet.

Sheet 120 *Bridgwater & Quantock Hills* — 27 by 18 miles

1	2	4	6	7	8	9	10	11	12	13	14	15
BS	-						P	P	P	C		
MBS	1931	WO 2400/31	3000/29	1929			P	P	P	Co	BL-d	
MBS		?WO 1000/33					P	P	P	C		
MBS		?1000/35+					P	P	P	C		
MBS		?3000/37++					P	P	P	C		
MBS		?5000/37+++					P	P	P	C		
MBS		?3250/39++++					P	P	P	C		
MBS	1931	5000/39+++++	1918	1930			P	P	P	C	BL-d	
WR	1931	20,000/8/40/H	1918	pcr			P	P	P	C	Bg	
WR	1931	WO 20,000/40	1918	pcr			P	P	P	C	PC	
WR	1931	20,000/4/41/F	1918	pcr			P	P	P	Cr	BL-d	
WR	1931	10,000/11/41 LR	nd	pcr			P	P	P	Cr	BL-d	
2WR	1941	70,000/12/41 LR	1941				N	P	5	C	BL-d	
2WR	1941	40,000/7/42 LR	-				N	P	5	C	BL-d	
2WR	1941	600/11/43 Ch	-				N	P	5	Ow	NLS	‡

See supplement 8.

Sheet 121 a. *Wells & Frome* b. *Wells and Frome* — 27 by 18 miles

1	2	4	6	7	8	9	10	11	12	13	14	15
BS	-	WO 1.24	1919				Pa	P	P	C	BL-d	1
BS	-	?WO 1.24. 800/27					Pa	P	P	C		
BS	-	WO 1.24. 800/27. 2200/28	1919	1925			Pa	P	P	C	book	1
MBS	1931	WO 1600/31	7.21	1929			Pa	P	P	Co	PC	2
MBS		?WO 1600/31. 150/32					Pa	P	P	Co		
MBS	1932	WO 1600/31. 150/32. 500/32	7.21	1929			Pa	P	P	Co	Lu	2
MBS	1932	WO 2500/34	1919	1929		1926	Pa	P	P	C	IWM	
MBS	1932	WO 1500/35	2000/34	1933	1932		Pa	P	P	C	PC	
MBS	1932	WO 5436	1919	1929		1926	Pa	P	P	C	Ob	
MBS		?WO 500/38					Pa	P	P	C		
MBS	1932	2500/38+	1919	pcr			Pa	P	P	C	BL-d	
MBS	1932	400/39++	1919	pcr			Pa	P	P	C	Mg-d	
MBS	1932	10,000/39/C+++	1919	pcr			Pa	P	P	C	PC	
WR	1932	WO 23,000/40	1919	pcr			Pa	P	P	C	BL-d	
WR	1932	20,000/40/M	1919	pcr			Pa	P	P	C	PC	
WR		10,000/41					Pa	P	P	C	card	

1	2	4	6	7	8	9	10	11	12	13	14	15
2WR	1941	50,000/5/41	none				5b	P	5	C	BL-d	
2WR	1941	20,000/9/41 LR	none				5b	P	5	C	BL-d	
2WR	1941	30,000/3/42 LR	1942				Na	P	5	C	BL-d	
2WR	1941	25,000/8/42 A	-				Na	P	5	C	BL-d	
2WR	1941	20,000/1/43 LR	-				Na	P	5	C	BL-d	
2WR	1941	10,000/12/43/16MRS/98	1942				Na	P	5	C	Bg	
2WR	1941	15,000/1/44/16MRS/107	1942				Na	P	5	C	PC	3
2WR	1941	22,050/8/44 B	-				Na	P	5	Cb	BL-d	
2WR	1941	100/8/47	1942				Na	P	5	C	BL-d	4

For GSGS Misc.363 see supplement 7. 1. See supplement 8. 2. The minor correction date is updated from that listed in Hodson (1999). 3. The 12/43 print code is still visible. 4. Printed on wet strength paper.

Sheet 122 *Salisbury & Bulford*   27 by 18 miles

1	2	4	6	7	8	9	10	11	12	13	14	15
BS	-	WO 3.23	12.21				P	P	P	C	BL-d	
BS	-	WO 3.23	5000/24				P	P	P	C	PC	1
MBS	1931	WO 2680/31	3500/27	1925			P	P	P	Co	BL-d	
MBS	1931	WO 3200/34	1919	1931	1931		P	P	P	C	BL-d	
MBS		?WO 2000/37					P	P	P	C		
MBS	1931	WO 2000/37. 2000/39	1919		pcr		P	P	P	C	BL-d	
MBS	1932	WO 6000/39 C	1919		pcr		P	P	P	C	BL-d	
WR	1932	WO 25,000/40	1919		pcr		P	P	P	C	Og	
WR	1932	WO 20,000/40	1919		pcr		P	P	P	C	BL-d	
WR	1932	20,000/7/40/H (blue)	1919		pcr		P	P	P	C	PC	
WR	1932	29,000/7/40/H (black)	1919		pcr		P	P	P	C	Bg	2
WR	1932	WO 20,000/6/41	none				P	P	P	Cr	Cu	
WR	1932	10,000/11/41 LR (blue)	none				P	P	P	Cr	BL-d	
WR	1932	20,000/2/42 A	1919		pcr		P	P	P	Cr	BSg	
2WR	1942	70,000/7/42 LR	-				N	P	5	C	BL-d	
2WR	1942	45,000/9/42 A	-				N	P	5	C	BL-d	
2WR	1942	20,000/1/43 LR	-				N	P	5	C	BL-d	
2WR	1942	10,000/3/43 LR	-				N	P	5	C	BL-d	
2WR	1942	30,000/8/43/13S/245	-				N	P	5	C	Cu-m	
2WR	1942	25,000/2/44 Mc	-				N	P	5	C	BL-d	
2WR	1942	21,550/8/44 B	-				N	P	5	Cb	BL-d	3
2WR	1942	100/8/47	-				N	P	5	C	BL-d	4
2WR	1942	10,000/10/48	-				N	P	5	C	BL-d	

For GSGS Misc.302 and GSGS Misc.364 see supplement 7. 1. The OS print code is not recorded on a civilian printing. 2. The "9" is written over the "0", the print code is black. 3. For further use see supplement 1. A copy of this printing has a Gee Lattice in manuscript (copy BL-d). See also supplement 3. 4. Printed on wet strength paper.

Sheet 123 *Winchester*   27 by 18 miles

1	2	4	6	7	8	9	10	11	12	13	14	15
BS	-	WO 3.23	12.21				P	P	P	C	PC	
BS	-	WO 3.23. Reprint 2250/25	1919				P	P	P	C	PC	
BS	-	WO 900/28	2000/23++	25-7	10/25		P	P	P	C	IWM	1
BS	-	WO 1200/30	3500/29+++	25-9	10/25		P	P	P	C	BL-d	
MBS		?WO 3030/31					P	P	P	Co		
MBS		?WO 3030/31. 2000/32					P	P	P	Co		
MBS	1931	WO 3030/31. 2000/32. 3025/33	3500/32++++	25-9			P	P	P	Co	book	2
MBS	1931	WO 3500/35	3500/32++++	1931			P	P	P	C	PC	
MBS		?WO 3500/35. 2500/35					P	P	P	C		
MBS	1931	WO 3500/35. 2500/35. 550/36	3500/32++++	1931			P	P	P	C	PC	
MBS		?WO 4000/37					P	P	P	C		
MBS	1931	1500/38+	3500/32++++	1931			P	P	P	C	PC	
MBS	1931	2000/39++	3500/32++++	1931			P	P	P	C	PC	
MBS	1931	10,000/39+++	3500/32++++	1931			P	P	P	C	Bg	
WR	1932	WO 14,000/40	3500/32++++	1931			P	P	P	C	BL-d	
WR	1932	20,000/7/40/H (blue)	3500/32++++	1931			P	P	P	C	Cu-m	3
WR	1932	WO 29,000/40	3500/32++++	1931			P	P	P	C	Ag	
WR	1932	WO 20,000/3/41	3500/32++++	1931			P	P	P	C	PC	
WR	1932	WO 20,000/5/41	3500/32++++	1931			P	P	P	C	BL-d	

1	2	4	6	7	8	9	10	11	12	13	14	15
2WR	1941	50,000/8/41 LR	none				5	P	5	C	BL-d	
2WR	1941	30,000/12/41 LR	none				5	P	5	C	BL-d	
2WR	1941	30,000/3/42 LR	1942				N	P	5	C	BL-d	
2WR	1941	40,000/7/42 LR	-				N	P	5	C	BL-d	
2WR	1941	45,000/10/42 A	-				N	P	5	C	Bg	
2WR	1941	30,000/7/43/13S/37	1941				N	P	5	C	BL-d	
2WR	1941	60,000/12/43 HAY	-				N	P	5	C	BL-d	4

1. The OS print code string is 1000/21. 1600/21. 2000/23, not recorded on a civilian printing. 2. See supplement 8.
3. There is a grid error, 96-98 corrected to 97-99 by overprint in red. 4. For further use see supplement 1.

Sheet 124 *Guildford & Horsham* 27 by 18 miles

1	2	4	6	7	8	9	10	11	12	13	14	15
BS	-	WO 1.24	1920				P	P	P	C	PC	
BS	-	no code	3000/27++	1925	11.25		P	P	P	C		1
MBS	1931	WO 3330/31	6000/29+++	1925			P	P	P	Co	BL-d	
MBS	1931	1000/34+	6000/29+++	1925			P	P	P	C	PC	
MBS	1931	1000/35++	6000/29+++	1925			P	P	P	C	PC	
MBS	1931	1000/35+++	1920	1925			P	P	P	C	PC	
MBS	1931	2000/36++++	1920	1925			P	P	P	C	PC	
MBS	1931	1500/38+++++	1920	1925			P	P	P	C	Lk	
MBS	1931	2500/39++++++	1920	1925			P	P	P	C	Cu	
MBS		?12,000/40+++++++					P	P	P	C		
MBS	1931	10,000/40/R++++++++	1920	1925			P	P	P	C	PC	
WR	1931	no code	8000/32+++++	1929	8.29		P	P	P	C	Bg	2
WR	1931	no code	8000/32+++++	1929	-		P	P	P	C	Bg	2
WR	1931	25,000/12/40/F	8000/32+++++	1929			P	P	P	Cr	Wc	3
WR		WO 10,000/4/41					P	P	P	C	card	
WR	1931	WO 20,000/5/41	none				P	P	P	Cr	BL-d	
WR	1931	20,000/7/41	none				P	P	P	Cr	BL-d	
2WR	1941	70,000/11/41 LR	1941				N	P	5	C	BL-d	4
2WR	1941	30,000/5/42 LR	-				N	P	5	C	Rg	
2WR	1941	25,000/7/42/C	-				N	P	5	C	Wc	
2WR	1941	25,000/7/42/C. 30,000/7/42/C	-				N	P	5	C	PC	
2WR	1941	20,000/1/43 LR	-				N	P	5	C	BL-d	
2WR	1941	30,000/8/43/13S/246	1941				N	P	5	C	IWM	
2WR	1941	50,000/12/43 Ch	-				N	P	5	C	BL-d	
2WR	1941	22,050/8/44 B	-				N	P	5	Cb	RGS	

1. So far recorded only for the Sussex Manoeuvres, 1928. See supplement 7. 2. In the *relation of grid letters and sheet numbers* diagram, the Cassini Grid is purple, the remainder blue. States both with and without the road revision date have been recorded. 3. The *relation of grid letters and sheet numbers* diagram lacks sheet lines and numbers. 4. Some copies of this printing erroneously have the label East Grinstead Sta., rather than West Grinstead Sta. in square 6241. Instructions were issued to troops in possession of this sheet to cross out the offending word in ink, and replace with the correct one in the margin, adding a short line to indicate where it belongs. Stock still in Survey Depots were to be overprinted with a correction.

Sheet 125 *Tunbridge Wells* 27 by 18 miles

1	2	4	6	7	8	9	10	11	12	13	14	15
BS	-	WO 1.24	1920				P	P	P	C	PC	
BS	-	no code	5000/27	24-5			P	P	P	C		1
BS	-	WO 3750/30	2000/29+	24-9	8/29		P	P	P	C	IWM	2
MBS	1931	WO 3150/31	2000/29+	24-7			P	P	P	Co	BL-d	
MBS	1931	WO 1500/34	1920	1934	1929		P	P	P	C	Lk	
MBS	1931	1000/36+	1920	1934	1929		P	P	P	C	Cu	
MBS		?500/37++					P	P	P	C		
MBS		?1000/38+++					P	P	P	C		
MBS	1931	2500/39 C++++	1920	1934	1929		P	P	P	C	BL-d	
MBS	1931	WO 19,000/40	1920	pcr			P	P	P	C	Bg	
MBS	1931	40,000/40/R	1920	pcr			P	P	P	C	BL-d	
WR	1931	20,000/41	1920	pcr			P	P	P	Cr	BL-d	
WR		WO 20,000/5/41					P	P	P	C	card	

1	2	4	6	7	8	9	10	11	12	13	14	15
2WR	1941	50,000/8/41	none				5	P	5	C	BL-d	
2WR	1941	30,000/12/41 LR	1941				N	P	5	C	BL-d	
2WR	1941	50,000/6/42 LR	-				N	P	5	C	BL-d	
2WR	1941	20,000/11/42 LR	-				N	P	5	C	BL-d	
2WR	1941	20,000/11/42 LR. 5000/12/42 LR	-				N	P	5	C	BL-d	3
2WR	1941	20,000/1/43 LR	-				N	P	5	C	BL-d	
2WR	1941	30,000/11/43/14MRS/18	-				N	P	5	C	BL-d	
2WR	1941	644/Ch	-				N	P	5	Ox	NLS	‡
2WR	1941	25,000/2/44 HAY	-				N	P	5	C	BL-d	

1. So far recorded only for the Sussex Manoeuvres, 1928. See supplement 7. 2. See also supplement 7. 3. These print codes are in "{ }" brackets.

Sheet 126 *Weald of Kent* 27 by 18 miles

1	2	4	6	7	8	9	10	11	12	13	14	15
BS	-	WO 12.25	1921	1925			P	P	P	C	PC	
MBS	1931	WO 4650/31	3500/27	1928		1927	P	P	P	Co	BL-d	1
MBS	1931	1000/34+	3500/27	1928		1927	P	P	P	C	BL-d	
MBS		?1500/35++					P	P	P	C		
MBS	1931	3000/36+++	3500/27	1928		1927	P	P	P	C		2
MBS	1931	2000/38++++	3500/27	1928		1927	P	P	P	C	BL-d	
MBS	1931	5000/39+++++	3500/27	1928		1927	P	P	P	C	BL-d	
MBS	1931	WO 13,500/40	1921	pcr			P	P	P	C	Mg-d	
WR	1931	25,000/40/R	1921	pcr			P	P	P	C	PC	
WR	1931	40,000/7/40 Mc	1921	pcr			P	P	P	C	BL-d	
2WR	1941	WO 45,000/4/41	1941				5	P	5	C	BL-d	
2WR	1941	WO 45,000/4/41. 20,000/7/41	1941				5	P	5	C	BL-d	
2WR	1941	20,000/9/41 LR	1941				5	P	5	C	BL-d	
2WR	1940	30,000/3/42 LR	1942				N	P	5	C	BL-d	
2WR	1940	30,000/8/42 A	-				N	P	5	C	BL-d	
2WR	1940	17,050/5/43/C	-				N	P	5	C	BL-d	
2WR	1940	50,000/9/43 Г	-				N	P	5	C	BL-d	
2WR	1940	25,000/6/44 Mc	-				N	P	5	Cb	BL-d	

1. The minor correction date is updated from that listed in Hodson (1999). 2. So far only recorded overprinted in red for East Kent Manoeuvres. See supplement 7.

Also recorded are experimental Ansell fold Second War Revision printings, without print codes, made in 1941 of sheets 116 and 126, printed back to back and head to foot, with the instructions *To join sheet 126 to sheet 116 fold "A" to "A" and "B" to "B"*. Three versions are recorded: in black outline (copy BL-d (OSD&R stamp 19.6.41)), in blue outline (copy Og (OSD&R stamp 16.12.41)), in four colours (copy Og (OSD&R stamp 16.12.41)). It was an Ordnance Survey experiment in saving paper, but its disadvantages were enough to persuade the General Staff ultimately to reject it. See *Report on the work of Home Forces Survey Service during the year 1941* (PRO WO 252/1412).

Sheet 127 a. *River Torridge* 28½ by 18 miles

1	2	4	6	7	8	9	10	11	12	13	14	15
BS	-	WO 9.24	1919	1924			Pa	P	P	C	BL-d	
MBS		?WO 1100/31					Pa	P	P	Co		
MBS		?WO 1100/31. 1000/36					Pa	P	P	C		
MBS	1931	WO 1100/31. 1000/36. 6000/39	500/30+	24-6		1926	Pa	P	P	C	BL-d	

Sheet 127 b. *Bideford and Bude* c. *Bideford & Bude* 52,000 by 30,000 yards

1	2	4	6	7	8	9	10	11	12	13	14	15
MBS	1940	WO 20,000/40	none		1939		5b	5	5	C	BL-d	1
MBS	1940	12,000/40 M	none		1939		5b	5	5	C	BL-d	
MBS	1940	WO 4000/40. 20,000/40/R+	none		1939		5b	5	5	C	PC	
WR	1940	20,000/11/41 LR (blue)	1941				Nc	5	5	Cr	BL-d	2
WR	1940	30,000/8/42 C (blue)	1941				Nc	5	5	Cr	BL-d	

2WR was not published.

1. Issued before 10 August 1940. 2. War Revision was already listed in *GSGS 3907 current edition*, 31 October 1940 (see appendix 1).

1	2	4	6	7	8	9	10	11	12	13	14	15
Sheet 128 *Tiverton*							27 by 18 miles					
BS	-						P	P	P	C		
MBS	1931	WO 1100/31	1918	1926			P	P	P	Co	BL-d	
MBS	1931	WO 3000/39	1918	pcr			P	P	P	C	BL-d	
Sheet 128 *Tiverton*							52,000 by 30,000 yards					
MBS	1940	WO 20,000/40	none				5	5	5	C	Lk	1
MBS	1940	20,000/40	none				5	5	5	C	BL-d	1
MBS	1940	13,000/40 M. WO 13,000/40	none				5	5	5	C	PC	
MBS	1940	20,000/40/R+	none				5	5	5	C	IWM	2
WR	1940	20,000/12/41 C	1941				N	5	5	Cr	RGS	3
WR	1940	40,000/7/42 C (blue)	-				N	5	5	Cr	BL-d	

2WR was not published.

1. The earlier of these printings was issued before 10 August 1940. 2. The print code sequence is reordered to WO 13000/40. 20000/40/R. 13000/40 M. 3. War Revision was already listed in *GSGS 3907 current edition*, 31 October 1940 (see appendix 1).

1	2	4	6	7	8	9	10	11	12	13	14	15
Sheet 129 *Chard & Axminster*							27 by 18 miles					
BS	-						P	P	P	C		
MBS	1931	WO 1400/31	2300/31+	24-8	7/26		P	P	P	Co	BL-d	
MBS	nd	WO 1500/38	1919	pcr			P	P	P	C	BL-d	1
MBS	nd	WO 1400/31. 10,000/39 C	1919	pcr			P	P	P	C	BL-d	1
WR	1932	WO 20,000/40	1919	pcr			P	P	P	C	Cu	
WR	1932	WO 14,000/40	1919	pcr			P	P	P	C	Wc	
WR	1932	WO 14,000/40. 20,000/7/40 AS	1919	pcr			P	P	P	C	PC	
WR	1932	WO 20,000/5/41	none				P	P	P	C	BL-d	2
2WR	1941	50,000/10/41 LR	1941				N	P	5	C	BL-d	
2WR	1941	30,000/12/41 LR	1941				N	P	5	C	BL-d	
2WR	1941	50,000/6/42 LR	-				N	P	5	C	BL-d	

1. The War Office imprint is lacking. 2. The roads colour is unchanged.

1	2	4	6	7	8	9	10	11	12	13	14	15
Sheet 130 a. *Yeovil & Blandford* b. *Yeovil and Blandford*							27 by 18 miles					
BS	-	?WO 9.24					Pa	P	P	C		
BS	-	? WO 9.24. 700/26					Pa	P	P	C		
BS	-	WO 9.24. 700/26. 2450/27	1919				Pa	P	P	C	book	1
MBS		?WO 1600/31					Pa	P	P	Co		
MBS		?150/32+					Pa	P	P	Co		
MBS	1932	500/32++	2800/30+	1928			Pa	P	P	Co	Lu	2
MBS	1932	1600/34+++	2800/30+	1928			Pa	P	P	C	PC	
MBS		?250/34++++					Pa	P	P	C		
MBS		?1500/35+++++					Pa	P	P	C		
MBS		?500/36++++++					Pa	P	P	C		
MBS		?500/37+++++++					Pa	P	P	C		
MBS	1932	500/37++++++++	2800/30+	1928			Pa	P	P	C	IWM	
MBS	1932	WO 1000/38					Pa	P	P	C	dealer	
MBS	1932	2000/38+	1919	pcr			Pa	P	P	C	Mg-d	
MBS	1932	400/39++	1919	pcr			Pa	P	P	C	BL-d	
MBS	1932	11,000/39 C+++	1919	pcr			Pa	P	P	C	BL-d	
WR	1932	WO 24,500/40	1919	pcr			Pa	P	P	C	IWM	
WR	1932	WO 24,500/40. 20,000/7/40 AS	1919	pcr			Pa	P	P	C	Cu	
WR	1932	WO 24,500/40. 10,000/41	1919	pcr			Pa	P	P	Cr	PC	
WR	1932	WO 24,500/40. 10,000/6/41 A	1919	pcr			Pa	P	P	Cr	BL-d	
2WR	1941	50,000/7/41	none				5b	P	5	C	BL-d	
2WR	1941	30,000/12/41 LR	none				5b	P	5	C	BL-d	
2WR	1941	50,000/6/42 LR	-				Na	P	5	C	BL-d	
2WR	1941	15,000/1/43 LR	-				Na	P	5	C	BL-d	
2WR	1941	20,000/2/44 Mc	-				Na	P	5	C	BL-d	

1. See supplement 8. 2. The OS print code string is 500/28. 2800/30, not recorded on a civilian printing, and probably replaced in the event by 2800/31.

Sheet 131 a. *Wimborne & Ringwood* b. *Wimborne and Ringwood* 27 by 18 miles

1	2	4	6	7	8	9	10	11	12	13	14	15
BS	-	WO 7.24	1919				Pa	P	P	C	Cu-m	
BS	-	?WO 7.24. 300/26					Pa	P	P	C		
BS	-	WO 7.24. 300/26. 1000/27	1919	1925	10.25	1925	Pa	P	P	C	PC	
MBS	1931	WO 1430/31	2000/29+	1929		1925	Pa	P	P	Co	BL-d	
MBS		?WO 2000/33					Pa	P	P	C		
MBS	1931	1000/35+	1919	1929		1925	Pa	P	P	C	.PC	
MBS	1931	3000/36++	1919	1929		1925	Pa	P	P	C	PC	
MBS	1931	1000/39+++	1919	1929		1925	Pa	P	P	C	PC	
MBS	1931	6000/39 C++++	1919	1929		1925	Pa	P	P	C	Cu-m	
MBS	1931	WO 2500/38	1919	pcr			Pa	P	P	C	BL-d	
WR		?WO 14,000/40					Pa	P	P	C		
WR	1931	WO 14,000/40. 20,000/40/R	6500/32++	19--		1925	Pa	P	P	C	IWM	
WR	1931	WO 14,000/40. 20,000/9/40/F	6500/32++	19--		1925	Pa	P	P	C	BL-d	
2WR	1940	WO 20,000/41	1940.s				5b	P	5	C	Cu	
2WR	1940	WO 25,000/41	1940.s				5b	P	5	C	PC	
2WR	1940	WO 25,000/3/41	1940.s				5b	P	5	C	BL-d	1
2WR	1940	WO 25,000/3/41. 20,000/6/41/F	1940.s				5b	P	5	C	BL-d	
2WR	1940	WO 25,000/3/41. 20,000/9/41 LR	none				5b	P	5	C	BL-d	
2WR	1940	30,000/3/42 LR	1942				Na	P	5	C	BL-d	
2WR	1940	30,000/12/42 LR	1942				Na	P	5	C	BL-d	
2WR	1940	10,000/1/43 LR	-				Na	P	5	C	BL-d	
2WR	1940	16,500/2/43 E	-				Na	P	5	C	PC	
2WR	1920	10,000/12/43/16MRS/96	-				Na	P	5	C	Lu	
2WR	1940	30,000/1/44/16MRS/105	-				Na	P	5	C	BL-d	

1. This print code has been crudely printed over the WO 20,000/41 code..

Sheet 132 a. *Portsmouth & Southampton* b. *Portsmouth and Southampton* 27 by 18 miles

1	2	4	6	7	8	9	10	11	12	13	14	15
BS	-	?WO 12.23					Pa	P	P	C		
BS	-	WO 12.23. 300/26	2000/25	1925	5.25	1925	Pa	P	P	C	PC	
MBS	-	WO 2680/31	5000/29++	1929		1925	Pa	P	P	Co	PC	
MBS	1931	WO 2680/31. 3500/32	5000/29++	1929		1925	Pa	P	P	Co	BL-d	
MBS	1931	WO 2500/35	1919	1929	1925		Pa	P	P	C	BL-d	
MBS	1931	3000/36+	1919	1929	1925		Pa	P	P	C	Rg	
MBS		?1000/37++					Pa	P	P	C		
MBS		?2500/38+++					Pa	P	P	C		
MBS	1931	1500/39++++	1919	1929	1925		Pa	P	P	C	Bg	
MBS	1931	WO 19,000/40 C					Pa	P	P	C		
WR	1931	no code	1919	pcr			Pa	P	P	C	Bg	
WR	1931	WO 30,000/40	1919	pcr			Pa	P	P	C	RGS	
2WR	1940	no code	1940.s				5b	P	5	C	PC	1
WR	1931	WO 20,000/3/41	1919	pcr			Pa	P	P	Cr	BL-d	
2WR	1941	WO 50,000/5/41	1941				5b	P	5	C	BL-d	
2WR	1941	20,000/8/41	1941				5b	P	5	C	BL-d	
2WR	1941	30,000/11/41 LR	1941				5b	P	5	C	BL-d	
2WR	1941	30,000/4/42 LR	-				Na	P	5	C	BL-d	
2WR	1941	45,000/8/42 F	-				Na	P	5	C	BL-d	
2WR	1941	60,000/1/43/16MRS/100	1942				Na	P	5	C	Sg	
2WR	1941	10,000/3/43 LR	-				Na	P	5	C	BL-d	
2WR	1941	20,000/7/43/13S/40	1942				Na	P	5	C	RGS	
2WR	1941	10,000/12/43/16MRS/94	1942				Na	P	5	C	BL-d	
2WR	1941	60,000/1/44/16MRS/100	1942				Na	P	5	C	BL-d	

War Department lands in the Portsmouth area were overprinted by MO1, dated 2 February 1925, on outline Popular Edition sheet 132 (with no military grid) (copy Ob). Lands required are infilled purple, and that not required in yellow. Filed as MRLG Misc.173. 1. A prototype Second War Revision printing carrying a different heading, top right: *Military Edition (1940) / Second War Revision Sheet 132.* On the May 1941 printing the words "Second War Revision" were noticeably redrawn in order to permit the addition of the 1940 date (see figure 23). The sheet was still listed as War Revision in *GSGS 3907 current edition,* 1 February 1941 (see appendix 1), and there was a March 1941 War Revision printing.

Sheet 133 a. *Chichester & Worthing* b. *Chichester and Worthing*   27 by 18 miles

1	2	4	6	7	8	9	10	11	12	13	14	15
BS	-	WO 1.24	1920	1924			Pa	P	P	C	Lk	
BS	-	no code	3500/28+++	24-7	3.26		Pa	P	P	C		1
BS	-	WO 2750/30	6000/29++++	1929	3.26		Pa	P	P	C	PC	
MBS	1931	WO 8050/31	500/30+++++	1930			Pa	P	P	Co	Mg-d	2
MBS	1931	WO 300/34	5000/33	1933	1929	1933	Pa	P	P	C	BL-d	
MBS		?WO 1000/37					Pa	P	P	C		
MBS	1931	WO 1000/37. 2000/38	5000/33	1933	1935	1933	Pa	P	P	C	IWM	
MBS	1931	WO 1000/37. 2000/38. 8000/39	5000/33	1933	1935	1933	Pa	P	P	C	BL-d	
MBS	1931	WO 10,000/40 M	1920	pcr			Pa	P	P	C	Cu-m	
MBS	1931	WO 14,500/40 M	1920	pcr			Pa	P	P	C	BL-d	
MBS	1931	40,000/7/40/H	1920	pcr			Pa	P	P	C	RGS	
WR	1931	20,000/41	1920	pcr			Pa	P	P	Cr	BL-d	
WR	1931	WO 20,000/5/41	none				Pa	P	P	Cr	BL-d	
2WR	1941	50,000/7/41	none				5b	P	5	C	BL-d	
2WR	1941	30,000/12/41 LR	none				5b	P	5	C	BL-d	
2WR	1941	30,000/5/42 LR	-				Na	P	5	C	BL-d	
2WR	1941	20,000/7/42 C	-				Na	P	5	C	BL-d	
2WR	1941	20,000/7/42 C. 30,000/7/42 C	-				Na	P	5	C	Mg-d	
2WR	1941	10,000/1/43 LR	-				Na	P	5	C	BL-d	
2WR	1941	10,000/3/43 LR	-				Na	P	5	C	BL-d	
2WR	1941	20,000/8/43/13S/209	1941				Na	P	5	C	IWM	
2WR	1941	10,000/12/43/16MRS/91	1941				Na	P	5	C	PC	
2WR	1941	35,000/1/44/16MRS/103	1941				Na	P	5	C	BL-d	
2WR	1941	20,000/6/44 Ch	-				Na	P	5	Cb	RGS	

For *South Downs Training Area (West)* see supplement 4. 1. So far recorded only for the Sussex Manoeuvres, 1928. See supplement 7. 2. The OS print code string is Reprint 2500/23. 3000/24. 3500/26. 3500/28. 6000/29. 500/30, according to Hodson (1999) not seen on a civilian printing.

Sheet 134 *Brighton & Eastbourne*   27 by 18 miles

1	2	4	6	7	8	9	10	11	12	13	14	15
BS	-	WO 1.24	1920	1923			P	P	P	C	PC	1
MBS	1931	WO 6980/31	5500/30++++	1930	8.29		P	P	P	Co	Lk	
MBS		?WO 1500/35					P	P	P	C		
MBS		?2000/36+					P	P	P	C		
MBS		?2000/37++					P	P	P	C		
MBS	1931	1000/37+++	5500/33	1933	1929	1933	P	P	P	C	Mg-d	
MBS		?1000/38++++					P	P	P	C		
MBS	1931	4000/39+++++	5500/33	1933	1929	1933	P	P	P	C	Wc	
MBS	1932	WO 20,000/40	1920	pcr			P	P	P	C	Cu-m	
MBS	1932	WO 20,000/40. 40,000/7/40/F	1920	pcr			P	P	P	C	Bg	
WR	1932	WO 20,000/41	1920	pcr			P	P	P	Cr	BL-d	2
2WR	1941	no code	1941.s				5	P	5	C	BL-d	
2WR	1941	WO 45,000/4/41	1941.s				5	P	5	C	PC	
2WR	1941	WO 45,000/4/41. 20,000/7/41	none				5	P	5	C	PC	
2WR	1941	20,000/9/41 LR	none				5	P	5	C	BL-d	
2WR	1941	30,000/4/42 LR	-				N	P	5	C	BL-d	
2WR	1941	45,000/10/42 A	-				N	P	5	C	PC	
2WR	1941	22,050/5/43/C	-				N	P	5	C	BL-d	
2WR	1941	35,000/11/43/14MRS/19	1942				N	P	5	C	BL-d	
2WR	1941	25,000/2/44 Ch	-				N	P	5	C	BL-d	
2WR	1941	30,000/7/44 Ch	-				N	P	5	Cb	LDg	

For *South Downs Training Area (East)* see supplement 4. 1. Also recorded for the Sussex Manoeuvres, 1928. See supplement 7. 2. This War Revision never appears on a *GSGS 3907 current edition* statement (see appendix 1), but some copies were nonetheless issued. It must have been replaced within weeks by the Second War Revision, and, as was the policy of the time for issues deemed not to be current, any remaining stock was probably turned to salvage.

1	2	4		6	7	8	9	10	11	12	13	14	15

Sheet 135 *Hastings* — 27 by 18 miles

1	2	4	6	7	8	9	10	11	12	13	14	15
BS	-	WO 12.25	1921	24-5	8.25		P	P	P	C	Ag	
MBS	1931	WO 2680/31	5000/28+	24-8		1927	P	P	P	Co	BL-d	
MBS	1931	5000/39 C	1921	pcr			P	P	P	C	Mg-d	
MBS	1931	WO 12,000/40	1921	pcr			P	P	P	C	BL-d	
MBS	1931	WO 12,000/40 Mc	1921	pcr			P	P	P	C	Mg-d	
WR	1931	no code	1921	pcr			P	P	P	C	RGS	
WR	1931	20,000/40/R. WO 12,000/40	1921	pcr			P	P	P	C	PC	
WR	1931	WO 10,000/41	1921	pcr			P	P	P	Cr	BL-d	
2WR	1941	WO 45,000/4/41	1941				5	P	5	C	Cu	1
2WR	1941	WO 45,000/4/41. 20,000/7/41	none				5	P	5	C	BL-d	
2WR	1941	20,000/9/41 LR	none				5	P	5	C	BL-d	
2WR	1941	30,000/5/42 LR	-				N	P	5	C	BL-d	
2WR	1941	11,800/12/42 LR	-				N	P	5	C	BL-d	
2WR	1941	30,000/1/43 LR	-				N	P	5	C	BL-d	
2WR	1941	30,000/1/44 Wa	-				N	P	5	C	BL-d	
2WR	1941	20,000/8/44 B	-				N	P	5	Cb	BL-d	

See supplement 8. 1. There is a gap in the imprint after *Ordnance Survey Office*, where *Southampton* has been deleted.

Sheet 136 a. *Boscastle & Padstow* — 24 by 21 miles

1	2	4	6	7	8	9	10	11	12	13	14	15
BS	-						Pa	P	P	C		
MBS		?WO 1100/31					Pa	P	P	Co		
MBS		?WO 1100/31. 1000/36					Pa	P	P	C		
MBS	1931	WO 1100/31. 1000/36. 4000/39	3000/28	1927			Pa	P	P	C	BL-d	

Sheet 136 b. *Bodmin* — 50,000 by 40,000 yards

1	2	4	6	7	8	9	10	11	12	13	14	15
MBS	1940	WO 4000/40. 13,000/40/R	1933.s	pcr	1938		5b	5	5	C	IWM	1
MBS	1940	20,000/40/R	1933.s	pcr	1938		5b	5	5	C	Cu	
WR	1940	WO 4000/40. WO 20,000/40	1933.s	pcr	1938		5b	5	5	C	BL-d	
WR	1941	20,000/11/41 LR. 20,000/12/41 C	1941				Nb	5	5	Cr	BL-d	2
WR	1941	30,000/8/42 C (blue)	1941				Nb	5	5	Cr	BL-d	

2WR was not published.
1. Issued before 10 August 1940. 2. Both print codes are blue.

Sheet 137 a. *Dartmoor, Tavistock & Launceston* — 27 by 18 miles

1	2	4	6	7	8	9	10	11	12	13	14	15
BS	-	WO 9.24					Pa	P	P	C	PC	
BS	-	?WO 9.24. 1400/28					Pa	P	P	C		
BS	-	WO 9/24. 1400/28. 500/28	3500/28	27-8			Pa	P	P	C	BL-d	
MBS		?WO 1810/31					Pa	P	P	Co		
MBS		?1500/32+					Pa	P	P	Co		
MBS	1931	1600/34++	3500/28	1930			Pa	P	P	C	PC	1
MBS	1931	2500/35+++	3500/28	1930			Pa	P	P	C	PC	
MBS	1931	WO 17,500/40	3500/28	1930			Pa	P	P	C	Wc	

Sheet 137 b. *Tavistock and Okehampton* c. *Tavistock & Okehampton* — 52,000 by 42,000 yards

1	2	4	6	7	8	9	10	11	12	13	14	15
MBS	1940	WO 20,000/40	none				5b	5	5	Cr	Cu	2
MBS	1940	WO 16,000/40. 20,000/40	none				5b	5	5	Cr	PC	
MBS		?WO 16,000/40. 15,000/40/R					5b	5	5	C		
MBS	1940	15,000/40/R+	none				5b	5	5	C	BL-d	
MBS	1940	20,000/40/R_+	none				5b	5	5	C	Cu	
WR	1941	20,000/1/42 LR (blue)	1941				Nc	5	5	Cr	BL-d	3,4
WR	1941	30,000/8/42 C (blue)	1941				Nc	5	5	Cr	BL-d	4

2WR was not published.
1. The minor correction date has been updated from that listed in Hodson (1999). 2. Issued before 10 August 1940. 3. War Revision was already listed in *GSGS 3907 current edition*, 31 October 1940 (see appendix 1). 4. *Administrative Map No.4, Sheet No 137 April 10 1944*, was drawn on one of these base maps (copy BL-d, trimmed). See supplement 2.

Sheet 138 a. *Dartmoor & Exeter* — 27 by 18 miles

1	2	4	6	7	8	10	11	12	13	14
BS	-					Pa	P	P	C	
MBS	1931	WO 1100/31 [cropped]				Pa	P	P	Co	RGS
MBS	1931	1500/32+	3300/31+	1930		Pa	P	P	Co	dealer
MBS	1931	1400/34++	3300/31+	1930		Pa	P	P	C	PC
MBS	1931	2500/35+++	3300/31+	1930		Pa	P	P	C	BL-d

Sheet 138 b. *Exeter* — 52,000 by 42,000 yards

1	2	4	6	7	8	10	11	12	13	14	15
MBS	1940	20,000/40	5039.M38.R37	pcr	1938	5b	5	5	C	RGS	1
MBS	1940	WO 3000/40. 20,000/40	1933.s	pcr	1938	5b	5	5	C	PC	
MBS	1940	WO 3000/40. 20,000/40/R	1933.s	pcr	1938	5b	5	5	C	RGS	
MBS	1940	WO 3000/40. 15,000/40 M	1933.s	pcr	1938	5b	5	5	C	BL-d	
WR	1940	WO 20,000/8/41 LR	none		1938	5b	5	5	Cr	Cu	2
WR	1941	20,000/4/42 LR (blue)	1941			Nb	5	5	Cr	BL-d	3
WR	1941	30,000/8/42 C (blue)	1941			Nb	5	5	Cr	BL-d	
WR	1941	644/Ch (blue)	-			Nbp	5	5	Ox	NLS	‡

2WR was not published.

1. Issued before 10 August 1940. 2. War Revision was already listed in *GSGS 3907 current edition*, 31 October 1940 (see appendix 1). 3. Also used as *Top Secret Administrative Map No.2, 10 April 1944* (copy BL-d). See supplement 2.

Sheet 139 a. *Sidmouth & Bridport* b. *Sidmouth and Bridport* — 27 by 18 miles

1	2	4	6	7	8	10	11	12	13	14
BS	-	WO 2.25	1919	23-4	10.24	Pa	P	P	C	BL-d
MBS		WO 1100/31				Pa	P	P	Co	
MBS		?WO 1100/31. 1500/35				Pa	P	P	C	
MBS	1931	WO 1100/31. 1500/35. 2000/38	3500/28+	23-5		Pa	P	P	C	PC
WR	1931	WO 24,000/40	1919	pcr		Pa	P	P	C	BL-d
WR	1931	20,000/7/40/H	1919	pcr		Pa	P	P	C	Cu
WR	1931	WO 24,000/40. 20,000/41	1919	pcr		Pa	P	P	Cr	BL-d
WR	1931	WO 10,000/6/41	none			Pa	P	P	Cr	BL-d
2WR	1941	50,000/9/41 LR	1941			5b	P	5	C	BL-d
2WR	1941	30,000/12/41 LR	1941			5b	P	5	C	BL-d
2WR	1941	50,000/6/42 LR	-			Na	P	5	C	BL-d

Sheet 140 *Weymouth & Dorchester* — 18 by 27 miles

1	2	4	6	7	8	10	11	12	13	14
BS	-					P	P	P	C	
MBS		?WO 2240/31				P	P	P	Co	
MBS	1932	WO 2240/31. 400/34	3000/30+	1929	9.24	P	P	P	C	BL-d
MBS	1932	WO 2240/31. 400/34. 1000/35	3000/30+	1929	9.24	P	P	P	C	PC
MBS		?WO 1000/38				P	P	P	C	
MBS	1932	WO 1000/38. 2000/39	1919	pcr		P	P	P	C	BL-d
MBS	1932	WO 29,000/40 C	1919	pcr		P	P	P	C	Bg
WR	1932	20,000/40 M	1919	pcr		P	P	P	C	PC
WR	1932	WO 30,000/3/41	1919	pcr		P	P	P	Cr	BL-d
WR	1932	10,000/7/41	none			P	P	P	Cr	BL-d
2WR	1941	50,000/11/41 LR	1941			N	P	5	C	BL-d
2WR	1941	30,000/2/42 LR	1941			N	P	5	C	BL-d
2WR	1941	20,000/7/42/C	-			N	P	5	C	BL-d
2WR	1941	30,000/7/42/C+	-			N	P	5	C	BL-d
2WR	1941	20,000/3/44 Ch	-			N	P	5	C	BL-d

Sheet 141 a. *Bournemouth & Swanage* b. *Bournemouth and Swanage* — 27 by 18 miles

1	2	4	6	7	8	9	10	11	12	13	14	15
BS	-						Pa	P	P	C		
MBS	1931	WO 1380/31	5000/28++	1926		1922	Pa	P	P	Co	PC	
MBS	1931	WO 1500/34	1919	1933	1932	1933	Pa	P	P	C	BL-d	
MBS	1931	WO 1500/34. 1000/35	1919	1933	1932	1933	Pa	P	P	C	PC	
MBS		?WO 1000/38					Pa	P	P	C		
MBS	1931	WO 1000/38. 1500/38	1919	pcr			Pa	P	P	C	PC	
MBS	1931	WO 1000/38. 1500/38. 11,000/39	1919	pcr			Pa	P	P	C	RGS	
WR	1931	WO 3000/40	1919	pcr			Pa	P	P	C	Wc	1
WR	1931	WO 3000/40. 20,000/40/A	1919	pcr			Pa	P	P	C	Cu	
WR	1931	WO 3000/40. 20,000/40 B	1919	pcr			Pa	P	P	C	BL-d	
WR	1931	WO 10,000/41	1919	pcr			Pa	P	P	Cr	BL-d	
2WR	1941	50,000/7/41	none				5b	P	5	C	BL-d	
2WR	1941	30,000/12/41 LR	1941				5b	P	5	C	Og	
2WR	1941	50,000/6/42 W	-				Na	P	5	C	BL-d	
2WR	1941	10,000/2/43 LR	-				Na	P	5	C	BL-d	
2WR	1941	10,000/12/43/16MRS/97	1941				Na	P	5	C	RGS	
2WR	1941	25,000/1/44/16MRS/106	1941				Na	P	5	C	BL-d	

See supplement 8. 1. A Military Survey catalogue card has the print code WO 3000/40 B, but all copies seen so far have no "B".

Sheet 142 *Isle of Wight* — 27 by 18 miles

1	2	4	6	7	8	9	10	11	12	13	14
BS	-						P	P	P	C	
MBS		?WO 1280/31					P	P	P	Co	
MBS		?1000/33+					P	P	P	C?	
MBS	1931	2000/34++	6500/30++	1930			P	P	P	C	BL-d
MBS	1931	1500/35+++	6500/30++	1930			P	P	P	C	PC
MBS		?1500/38					P	P	P	C	
MBS		? 1500/38. 3400/39					P	P	P	C	
MBS	1931	1500/38. 3400/39. 6000/39 C	1919	pcr			P	P	P	C	BL-d
WR	1931	WO 6000/40	1919	pcr			P	P	P	C	Wc
WR	1931	WO 6000/40. 20,000/40 B	1919	pcr			P	P	P	C	BL-d
WR	1931	WO 6000/40. 20,000/9/40/F	1919	pcr			P	P	P	C	Cu
WR	1931	WO 6000/40. 20,000/4/41/F		pcr			P	P	P	Cr	BL-d
2WR	1941	50,000/11/41 LR	none				5	P	5	C	BL-d
2WR	1941	30,000/3/42 LR	1942				N	P	5	C	BL-d
2WR	1941	30,000/8/42/M	-				N	P	5	C	BL-d
2WR	1941	10,000/1/43 LR	-				N	P	5	C	BL-d
2WR	1941	10,000/12/43/16MRS/99	1942				N	P	5	C	BL-d
2WR	1941	20,000/1/44/16MRS/108	1942				N	P	5	C	Rg

See supplement 8.

Sheet 143 a. *Truro* b. *Truro & St. Austell* — 33 by 21 miles

1	2	4	6	7	10	11	12	13	14	15
BS	-				Pa	P	P	C		
MBS	1931	WO 1100/31	4000/29+++	1929	Pb	P	P	Co	BL-d	1
MBS	1931	no code	2000/36+++++	1930	Pb	P	P	C	PC	2
MBS	1931	WO 6000/39	2000/36+++++	1930	Pb	P	P	C	Bg	2

Sheet 143 c. *Truro and St. Austell* — 62,000 by 42,000 yards

1	2	4	6	7	8	10	11	12	13	14	15
MBS	1940	WO 20,000/40	1934.s	pcr	1939	5c	5	5	C	BL-d	3
MBS	1940	WO 6000/40. 11,000/40/R	1934.s	pcr	1939	5c	5	5	C	Lk	
MBS	1940	20,000/40/R+	1934.s	pcr	1939	5c	5	5	C	PC	4
WR	1941	20,000/12/41 LR (blue)	1941			Nb	5	5	Cr	BL-d	
WR	1941	25,000/12/42/M (purple)	1941			Nb	5	5	Cr	BL-d	5
WR	1941	2050/12/42/M	1941			Nbo	5	5	Cr	NLS	†
WR	1941	15,000/4/47	1941			Nbp	5	5	C	BL-d	

2WR was not published.

1. The OS print code string is 3500/19. 1000/24. 3500/27. 4000/29, not recorded on a civilian printing. 2. The OS print code string is 3500/19. 1000/24. 3500/27. 4000/29. 5500/31. 2000/36, not recorded on a civilian printing. 3. Issued before 10 August 1940. 4. The 11,000/40/R print code is blue in this state, the others black, and has been moved from below the left corner of the map frame to third in the string under the legend. 5. Also used for *Top Secret Administrative Map No.5, 10 April 1944* (copy BL-d). See supplement 2.

1	2	4	6	7	8	9	10	11	12	13	14	15

Sheet 144 *Plymouth* — 27 by 18 miles

1	2	4	6	7	8	9	10	11	12	13	14	15
BS	-	WO 11.23	1919				P	P	P	C	BL-d	
BS	-	WO 11.23. 250.12.25					P	P	P	C	PC	1
MBS	1931	WO 2150/31	5000/27		1930		P	P	P	Co	BL-d	
MBS		? [cropped]					P	P	P	Co	RGS	2
MBS		?WO 3000/34					P	P	P	C		
MBS	1931	1500/35+	1919		1933	1929	P	P	P	C	Mg-d	
MBS		?1000/38++					P	P	P	C		
MBS	1931	2000/39+++	1919		1933	1929	P	P	P	C	PC	
MBS	1931	8000/39++++	1919		1933	1929	P	P	P	C	PC	

Sheet 144 *Plymouth* — 52,000 by 30,000 yards

1	2	4	6	7	8	9	10	11	12	13	14	15
MBS	1940	WO 20,000/40	1931.s	pcr		1939	5	5	5	C	BL-d	3
MBS	1940	WO 7000/40. 19,000/40/R	1931.s	pcr		1939	5	5	5	C	Cu	
MBS	1940	20,000/40/R+	1931.s	pcr		1939	5	5	5	C	Cu	
WR	1941	20,000/12/41 LR (blue)	1941				N	5	5	Cr	NLS	
WR	1941	20,000/1/43 LR (blue)	-				N	5	5	Cr	BL-d	4
WR	1941	20,000/1/43 LR (blue)	-				No	5	5	Cr	Rg	†

2WR was not published.

1. A copy of this sheet is recorded on waterproof paper – presumably some other method than that developed by Colonel C.O. Place, which came into widespread use by GSGS and Ordnance Survey in 1928. 2. This printing has no road fill. 3. Issued before 10 August 1940. 4. Also used for *Top Secret Administrative Map No.3, Sheet No 144, April 10 1944* (copy BL-d). See supplement 2.

Sheet 145 a. *Torquay & Dartmouth* — 21 by 21 miles

1	2	4	6	7	8	9	10	11	12	13	14	15
BS	-	WO 4.25	2000/25	24-5	4.25		Pa	P	P	C	PC	
MBS		?WO 1100/31					Pa	P	P	Co		
MBS	1931	WO 1100/31. 1500/33	4000/29++		1930		Pa	P	P	Co	BL-d	
MBS		?WO 4500/38					Pa	P	P	C		
MBS	1931	WO 4500/38. 15,000/39	3500/34++++		1931		Pa	P	P	C	BL-d	

Sheet 145 b. *Torquay* — 40,000 by 50,000 yards

1	2	4	6	7	8	9	10	11	12	13	14	15
MBS	1940	WO 6000/40	none				5b	5	5	C	BL-d	1,2
MBS	1940	17,000/40/R+	none				5b	5	5	C	Bg	2
MBS	1940	20,000/40/R++	none				5b	5	5	C	BL-d	2
WR	1933	20,000/12/41/LR (blue)	1941				Nb	5	5	Cr	BL-d	3,4
WR	1933	40,000/7/42 LR (blue)	-				Nb	5	5	Cr	BL-d	4
WR	1933	no code	-				Nbp	5	5	Ow	NLS	‡

2WR was not published.

1. Issued before 10 August 1940. 2. The *relation of grid letters and sheet numbers* diagram lacks sheet lines and numbers. 3. War Revision was already listed in *GSGS 3907 current edition*, 31 October 1940 (see appendix 1). 4. One of these base maps was used for *Top Secret Administrative Map No.1, 10 April 1944* (copy BL-d, trimmed). See supplement 2.

Sheet 146 a. *Land's End & Lizard* — 33 by 24 miles

1	2	4	6	7	8	9	10	11	12	13	14	15
BS	-	WO 12.26. 1000/27	3000/26+	24-6	11.24		Pa	P	P	C	BL-d	
MBS	1931	WO 1100/31	5000/28++		1928		Pa	P	P	Co	PC	

Sheet 146 b. *Land's End and Lizard* — 60,000 by 50,000 yards

1	2	4	6	7	8	9	10	11	12	13	14	15
MBS	1940	WO 20,000/40	1934.s	pcr		1939	5b	5	5	Cr	Mg-d	1
MBS	1940	WO 6000/40. 12,000/40/R	1934.s	pcr		1939	5b	5	5	C	BL-d	
MBS	1940	20,000/40/R+	1934.s	pcr		1939	5b	5	5	C	Cu	
WR	1941	20,000/12/41 LR (blue)	1941				Na	5	5	Cr	BL-d	2,3
WR	1941	25,000/12/42/M (purple)	1941				Na	5	5	Cr	RGS	3
WR	1941	2050/12/42/M	1941				Nao	5	5	Cr	NLS	3†

2WR was not published.

One of the gridded War Revision printings was used for *Top Secret Administrative Map No.5A, 10 April 1944* (copy BL-d, trimmed). See supplement 2. 1. Issued before 10 August 1940. 2. War Revision was already listed in *GSGS 3907 current edition*, 31 October 1940 (see appendix 1). 3. The grid letters in the *relation of grid letters and sheet numbers* diagram are misplaced 100 km too far south.

Supplements to sections 1 and 2

Supplement 1. *GSGS 3907 Second War Revision, layered editions*

The Survey Production Centre, Royal Engineers (SPC RE) was ordered to prepare a layered edition for the Staff College of six sheets, 104, 105, 112, 113, 122 and 123, to be ready by 12 December 1947. They were completed by 16 December (WOPD 1255/R, 14 November 1947).

Sheet 104 *Swindon & Cirencester*   27 by 18 miles
2WR   1941   35,000/6/44 Ch   -   700 copies   N   P   5   CLb PC

Sheet 105 *Oxford & Henley-on-Thames*   27 by 18 miles
2WR   1941   15,000/1/44/16MRS/104   -   700 copies   N   P   5   CL PC

Sheet 112 *Marlborough*   27 by 18 miles
2WR   1942   40,000/1/44/16MRS/102   -   800 copies   N   P   5   CL PC

Sheet 113 *Reading & Newbury*   27 by 18 miles
2WR   1941   50,000/1/44/16MRS/101   1942   900 copies   N   P   5   CL PC

Sheet 122 *Salisbury & Bulford*   27 by 18 miles
2WR   1942   21,550/8/44 B   -   500 copies   N   P   5   CLb PC
See figure 11.

Sheet 123 *Winchester*   27 by 18 miles
2WR   1941   60,000/12/43 HAY   -   800 copies   N   P   5   CL PC

There was a further demand the day before for two composite sheets to be prepared for the Staff College by SPC RE, each in 500 copies, again to be ready by 12 December.
> A composite from sheets 105, 113. Completed on 5 December 1947. Not found.
> A composite from sheets 113, 114. Completed on 16 December 1947. Not found.

Both were designated GSGS 3907, and would have utilised Second War Revision material (WOPD 1246/R, 13 November 1947). The composite from sheets 113 and 114 was mentioned again with regard to a layered composite National Grid map in GSGS 4620A (see page 244).

(Information from Military Survey catalogue cards).

Supplement 2. *Top secret administrative maps*

Administrative maps 1 (sheet 145), 2 (sheet 138), 3 (sheet 144), 4 (sheet 137), 5 (sheet 143), 5A (sheet 146) all classified *top secret*. The maps were annotated by hand to 10 April 1944. There is no indication of their purpose, though the date is obviously suggestive of a connection with the forthcoming events in June. Copies of all six are in DGC Superseded, now in the British Library (BL-d).

Also recorded is a map overprinted in black with secret information, filed as MRLG Misc.331. It is a 22 by 14 km section (647-669, 151-165) of Second War Revision sheet 117A entitled **South Eastern Command "Overlord"**. The print code is 150/2/44/14MRS/62A. Copy No 154 is in BL-d.

Supplement 3. *Navigation charts*

1. *Trigonometric station data map*   27 by 18 miles

WR	1932	sheet 92. 30,000/4/41/H	2539 M39 R38 pcr		P	P P P O	Wc
WR	1932	sheet 93. nc ?23,000/40	1919	pcr		P	P P P O	Wc
2WR	1941	sheet 94. 50,000/8/41/F	-			5	P 5 O	Wc

With overprint in red, on grey outline printings. The marginalia on sheet 94 provides most information: it was *Reproduced by 660th Engineers, US Army / Overprint data compiled by HQ SOS OCE, US Army, March 1943 from information furnished by Survey Directorate GHQ Home Forces. / Note: five color map reproduced in one color.* On the overprint plate is added *For use of war and navy departments only. / Note: descriptions of trig. points on printed sheets are in numerical and alphabetical order.* All the locations marked are between 410 and 500 km E, marked by an open triangle symbol, and mostly comprise church towers and steeples, also some more particular sites such as Blenheim Palace, Blenheim Park Pillar, High Lodge Tower and Sturdys Castle. All the original lower marginalia is deleted except the scale bars.

2. Correspondence to the Directorate of Military Survey from the RAF at Bentley Priory, Stanmore, concerning reductions and enlargements of GSGS 3907 mapping (documents from GSGS 3907 series file)

6 November 1945: request for 6 copies of sheets 115, 116, 117, 125, 126, 134, 135, reduced to 1:100,000.
7 January 1946: request for 6 copies of sheets 110, 111, enlarged to 1:50,000.
12 March 1946: request for portion of 111, 112, 121, 122, enlarged to 1:50,000.

Correspondence to the Directorate of Military Survey from Command Navigation Office, HQ Fighter Command, concerning enlargements of GSGS 3907 mapping (documents from GSGS 3907 series file)

16 April 1946: request for portion of 56, 57, 65, 66, enlarged to 1:50,000, required by a Radar Research Unit.
26 April 1946: request for portion of 56, 57, 65, 66, 74, 75, enlarged to 1:50,000.

3. GSGS Misc.516 *S.A.D.E. Decca chart*   27 by 18 miles

2WR	1941	sheet 87. 150/46	1942		N	P 5	C	DGC
2WR	1942	sheet 107. 150/46	1942		N	P 5	C	DGC

The lattice curves were computed by the War Office and drawn by GSGS (AM) in July 1946. Drawings, each on four enamels, were despatched from Military Survey to Ordnance Survey on 22 July. Four proof versions of each map were printed on 10 August (copies NLS), each with a lattice overprint in green and red cumulatively using base maps in one, two, three or four colours (outline, blue sea, brown, green). The base is grey for the last two. After corrections to the proofs, 150 copies of each sheet were ordered from the Ordnance Survey for delivery by 17 October 1946; 100 copies to S.A.D.E., Flat 78, 3 Whitehall Court, London, SW1, three to Survey 2(a), and the remainder to Survey 3(b). Sheet 87 is on the 30,000/2/42/J, sheet 107 probably on the 70,000/2/42 A printing.

4. GSGS Misc.519 *Special Gee chart (London Airport-Northolt) : eastern chain*

2WR		3000/3/47	1946		-	- 5	C	NLS

Compiled from parts of GSGS 3907, Second War Revision, sheets 106, 107, 114, 115, covering an area from Maidenhead to Regent's Park, from Leatherhead to Bovingdon. Photolithographed by the Ordnance Survey in 1946. Overprinted with a lattice in red and green, and a graticule in purple.

5. *Experimental Gee chart : eastern chain*   27 by 18 miles

2WR	1942	sheet 122. 100/8/47	-		N	P 5	C	BL-d

On 16 July 1947 a special printing of 100 copies each of sheets 111, 112, 121, 122 was ordered from the Ordnance Survey, to be printed on Wet Strength Paper (WOPD 4156/OS. Information from Military Survey catalogue cards). They were completed on 27 August 1947, and perhaps intended specifically for this purpose. Overprinted with a lattice in purple and green. The three other sheets have not been recorded with overprints. A copy of sheet 122 with a Gee Lattice in manuscript is in BL-d.

6. Untitled   29 by 24 miles
2WR   1932   sheet 41   -   N   P   P   O   book
In *Plan from radar fixed air photo's,* 1947, in Major C.A. Hart *Mapping by remote control with the aid of radar* (Directorate of Military Survey, Air Research Paper 19). London: War Office, 1946.

7. GSGS Misc.332 *Experimental Decca chart*   40 by 45 km
              sheet 167. 60/11/48   -   6   6   5   O   DGC
New Popular Edition sheet 167 in grey with green woods, overprinted with a lattice in purple and green, and with the War Office Cassini Grid in brown.

8. A reference appears on a Military Survey catalogue card to:
"Sheet 83: Survey of Gee Stn site – Bigg Hill arranged by ?ltr [?letter] Svy 2/6215, dated 28 October 1947."

Supplement 4. *Training area maps*

Aldershot and district   20 by 20 km
BS   1926p   no code   1926   P   -   P   C   PC
With the heading *1 Inch Training Map.* On grid sheet lines (520-540, 167-187).

Aldershot area (north)
BS   -
Not recorded, and its existence is not confirmed. But see the next. There was a continuing requirement for coverage of the Command area divided between north and south sheets, filled by a sequence of maps published in 1905, 1914, 1919 and 1932. North and south sheet limits may have been those of Popular Edition sheets 113 and 114, but it is more probable that the northern sheet limit would have coincided with that of *Map of the Aldershot Command,* so providing an overlap between north and south sheets of four miles in order to avoid the inconvenient divide through the Aldershot camp area itself.

Aldershot area (south)   c.31¾ by 18 miles
BS   -   P   -   P   C
BS   -   ?Reprint 700/25   P   -   P   C
BS   -   Reprint 700/25. 2500/26   1924p   P   -   P   C   PC
With a simple unmeasured border. The north and south sheet limits are those of Popular Edition sheets 123 and 124, with the extrusions at Basingstoke and Aldershot also present. The south sheet limit also coincides with that of *Map of the Aldershot Command.* The map extends from Whitchurch in the west to the outskirts of Godalming in the east, and is thus set further west than conventional maps of the Aldershot area.

Map of the Aldershot Command   Revised 1912-14   24 by 32 miles

The full print code string, not used on any single issue (some are alternatives), appears to be: 1. WO 8.23. 2. Reprint 2000/24. 3. 5000/24. 4. 5000/25 OR 5. 5000/26. 6. 1500/27. 7. 7500/27. 8. 1100/28 OR 9. 1000/28. 10. 5000/28. 11. 3400/29. 12. 5500/29. 13. 1100/29. 14. 1100/30 OR 15. 1000/30. 16. 1500/30 OR 17. 1500/31. 18. 17,900/31. 19. 2000/31. 20. 1000/31. 21. 1000/32. 22. 500/32. 23. 200/33.

1	2	4	6	7	8	9	10	11	12	13	14	15
BS	-	1	1920p				P		D	P	C	PC
BS	-	1-2	1920p				P		D	P	C	PC
BS	-	?1-3	1920p				P		D	P	C	
BS	-	1-4	1920p				P		D	P	C	PC
BS	-	1-3, 5-6	1920p				P		D	P	C	PC
BS	-	1-3, 5-7	1920p				P		D	P	C	PC
BS	-	1-3, 5, 7-8	1920p				P		D	P	C	PC
BS	-	1-3, 5, 7-8, 10	1920p				P		D	P	C	RGS
BS	-	1-3, 5, 7,11	1920p				P		D	P	C	PC	1
BS	-	1-3, 5, 7, 11-12	1920p				P		D	P	C	PC
BS	-	1-3, 5, 7-8, 11-12, 14	1920p				P		D	P	C	book	2
BS	-	?, 16 or 17	1920p				P		D	P	C?o	
MBS	1931	1-3, 5, 7, 18	1920p				P		D	P	Co	PC
MBS	1931	1-3, 5, 7, 15-16, 19	1920p				P		D	P	Co	book	3
MBS	1931	?, 20	1920p				P		D	P	Co	
MBS	1931	?, 21	1920p				P		D	P	Co	
MBS	1931	?, 22	1920p				P		D	P	Co	
MBS	1931	1-3, 5, 7, 9-13, 15, 17-23	1920p				P		D	P	Co	PC

Aldershot Command   Revised 1930-2   50,000 by 60,000 yards

1	2	4	6	7	8	9	10	11	12	13	14	15
MBS	1934	WO 13,000/35	1932.s				5	-	5	C		4
MBS	1934	WO 13,000/35. 600/35	1932.s				5	-	5	C	PC
MBS	1934	WO 17,036	1932.s				5	-	5	C	PC
MBS	1934	WO 10,000/37	1932.s				5	-	5	C	BL-d
MBS	1934	WO 10,000/37. 10,500/39	1932.s				5	-	5	C	PC
MBS	1934	WO 40,000/39	1932.s				5	-	5	C	BL-d
MBS	1934	WO 75,000/40/R	1932.s				5	-	5	C	BL-d	5
MBS	1934	WO 500/40	1932.s				5	-	5	O	BL-d	6

Aldershot   Revised 1946   40 by 45 km

1	2	4	6	7	8	9	10	11	12	13	14	15
MBS	1946	10,000/10/46	1946				Np	6	5	Cb	BL-d	7
MBS	1946	6000/5/47	1946				Np	6	5	Cb	BL-d
-	1946	300/3/48	1946				N	6	5	O	BL-d	8
MBS	1946	2000/4/49	1946				Np	6	5	Cb	PC

GSGS 3907 from 1931 until 1940. The boundary of the Aldershot Command is overprinted in red until 1940. For the printing prepared as the southern sheet for *Manoeuvre area, 1939,* see supplement 7. 1. In *Report on War Office Exercise No.1 (1929). Aldershot 10th-12th April* (PRO WO 279/66). 2. In A.H.C. Kearsey, *Tactical schemes from platoons to brigades with solutions and notes,* third edition. Aldershot: Gale & Polden, 1930. 3. In A.H.C. Kearsey, *Tactical schemes from platoons to brigades with solutions and notes,* fourth and fifth editions. Aldershot: Gale & Polden, 1932 and 1934. 4. In 1934 the Popular Edition district map was replaced by a Fifth Edition map covering the same area as the Fifth Edition Special District (Relief) maps *Aldershot North* and *South* combined, without relief. This printing (listed in Nicholson (1992)) has not been verified. 5. With contours in orange. 6. In grey outline (including grid and military imprint). Without the overprint of the command boundary. 7. Redesignated GSGS 4620 and headed *6th Edition style.* Without overprint. This was one of three sheets made after the war on National Grid sheet lines to which the War Office Cassini Grid continued to be applied prior to the implementation of the National Grid by the War Office in 1950. The others are *Salisbury Plain* and *Catterick area.* On the sheet lines of New Popular Edition sheet 169 [unnumbered] (463-503, 128-173). 8. A printing in grey outline, with grid figures, but no grid.

Barden Moor   32 by 25 km
MBS   -   5000/33   1933   Pp - P Oy BL-d

CR 4521. On grid sheet lines (447-479, 505-527). An extract map covering the centre of the Catterick Camp training area. With an overprint of the training area boundary and War Department land in red. Filed as MRLG Misc.275, artillery ranges.

Blandford   Revised 1913-4   26 by 28 miles
BS   -   WO 2.24   1924p   P   - P C   PC
MBS   1931   1100/31+   1924p   P   - P Co BL-d
MBS   1931   ?2000/33++   1924p   P   - P C?o
MBS   1931   ?400/33+++   1924p   P   - P C?o
MBS   1931   ?2000/36++++   1924p   P   - P C
MBS   1931   ?5000/37+++++   1924p   P   - P C
MBS   1931   5000/39 C++++++   1924p   P   - P C   NLS
GSGS 3907 from 1931.

Bordon   27 by 21 km
BS   -   1929   - P
MBS   -   1000/34   1934   5   - 5 Oy BL-d

CR 4275. On grid sheet lines (515-542, 147-168). One of two overlapping extract maps, slightly offset, covering the centre of the Aldershot Command area. The other is *Farnborough*. The 5000 yard grid lines of the base map are still in place. Filed as MRLG Misc.276, army camps. There is reference to a 1929 issue, therefore Popular Edition based, on a MRLG index, but nothing is known of its sheet dimensions or further specification.

Braunton Burrows training areas   50,000 by 35,000 yards
MBS   1940   sheet 118. WO 6000/40   1933.s   pcr   1936   5   5 5 C   BL-d

GSGS 3907. Training area detail appears in manuscript on an ex-Military Survey copy of War Revision sheet 118 (see above), showing in blue "manoevre rights req'd" and in red "danger area". Four areas around Appledore are marked in blue, in addition to Braunton Burrows itself. The map title is also manuscript. No overprinted version has been recorded. A map of the training area is marked up on a MRLG index.

Builth Wells. (Parts of) England sheets 79 & 90.   22 by 18 km
MBS   1939   10,000/39   1939   P   - P C   BL-d 1
MBS   1939   10,000/39   1939   P   - P C   PC   2

GSGS 3907. WE 321. On grid sheet lines (328-350, 253-271). The Builth Wells sheet area is not shown on the adjoining sheet diagram. 2. The Builth Wells sheet area is shaded on the adjoining sheet diagram. Presumably superseded in 1943 by *Sennybridge Artillery Ranges*.

Castle Howard training area   29 by 31 km
BS   -   no code   1926   P   - P C   BL-d

On grid sheet lines (503-532, 474-505). Filed as MRLG Misc.280. Without overprint.

Catterick area. Parts of sheets 13, 14, 20, 21.   Revised 1920-2   48 by 37 km
BS   -   WO 12.25   1925p   P   - P C   PC   1
BS   -   ?Reprint 1000/28+   1925p   P   - P C
BS   -   ?1400/28++   1925p   P   - P C
BS   -   ?1000/29+++   1925p   P   - P C
BS   -   ?3000/30++++   1925p   P   - P C
BS   -   3000/31+++++   1925p   P   - P Co PC
MBS   1932   WO 12.25. 16,125/32   1925p   P   - P Co BL-d
MBS   1932   WO 12.25. 10,000/39 C   1925p   P   - P C   PC
MBS   1932   WO 27,000/40   1925p   P   - P C   PC
Catterick area. Parts of New Popular sheets 84, 85, 90, 91.   Revised 1920   50 by 38 km
MBS   1948   3000/9/48   1948   6   - P C   BL-d 2

GSGS 3907 from 1932. With an overprint in red showing the boundary of the training area and War Department land. 1. On Cassini Grid sheet lines (440-488, 502-539). 2. On National Grid sheet lines (391-441, 481-519). One of three sheets made after the Second World War to which War Office Cassini Grid was temporarily applied, prior to the implementation by the War Office of the National Grid in 1950. The other sheets are *Aldershot* and *Salisbury Plain*. The GSGS imprint reads *G.S.G.S., No.3907 / Published by War Office 1932. / 2nd. Edition, 1948*. At the same time a *War Office Edition* printing with National Grid (Military System) was issued (4000/9/48): see page 245.

1	2	4	6	7	8	9	10	11	12	13	14	15

Colchester area
Revised 1914-19 — 40 by 42½ km

1	2	4	6	7	8	9	10	11	12	13	14	15
MBS	1933	8000/34	1933	1932	1932		P	-	P	C	BL-d	
MBS	1933	?100/35+	1933	1932	1932		P	-	P	C		
MBS	1933	?1000/35++	1933	1932	1932		P	-	P	C		
MBS	1933	10,000/39 C+++	1933	1932	1932		P	-	P	C	NLS	

GSGS 3907. On grid sheet lines (625-665, 227.5-270).

Colchester training areas
27 by 18 miles

GSGS 3907A. Not found. A Military Survey catalogue card for sheet 97 notes the request for: "GSGS 3907A. Overprint of Colchester Training Areas : 2nd War Revision 1940 with an overlay shewing training areas". The order (PD/1439R) for 200 copies from SPC RE was made on 20 December 1948, and completed by 7 January 1949. Evidently no new printing of sheet 97 was required.

Dartmoor
40,000 by 50,000 yards

1	2	4	6	7	8	9	10	11	12	13	14	15
MBS	-	237	1936.s	pcr			5	D	5	C	BL-d	

The Fifth Edition Special District (Relief) Map was used, without the relief colouring, and without the word *Relief* in the heading. Presumably printed in 1937. Filed as MRLG Misc.277.

East Kent. (Part of) sheet 117.
see note for dimensions

1	2	4	6	7	8	9	10	11	12	13	14	15
BS	-	?WO 750/30					P	-	P	C		
BS	-	WO 750/30. 2750/30	1930				P	-	P	C	book	1
MBS	1931	WO 23,000/31	1930				P	-	P	Co	BL-d	
MBS		?WO 750/30. 2750/30. 5000/33					P	-	P	C		
MBS	-	2000/34+	1930				P	-	P	C	book	2
MBS		?1500/35++					P	-	P	C		
MBS	1931	2100/39+++	1930				P	-	P	C	book	3

GSGS 3907 from 1931. On mixed grid and Popular Edition sheet lines, from the SW corner of sheet 117 to 673 km E, 170 km N. Entered here in preference to supplement 9 in view of the military rather than didactic use of the map in 1931. 1. Accompanied by a tracing of the modified grid system. In Captain C.A. Wilson *The map reading "instructor"*. London: Sifton, Praed & Co., Ltd, 1931. 2. In Major C.A. Wilson *The map reading "instructor"*, second edition. London: Sifton, Praed & Co., Ltd, 1934. 3. In Major C.A. Wilson *The map reading "instructor"*, third edition. London: Sifton Praed & Co., Ltd, 1939.

East Kent special sheet. Parts of sheets 116, 117, 126.
42 by 42 km

1	2	4	6	7	8	9	10	11	12	13	14	15
MBS	1935	WO 7000/35	-				P	-	P	C	PC	
MBS	1935	WO 7000/35. 8000/37	-				P	-	P	C	PC	1
MBS	1935	WO 7000/35. 8000/37. 8000/39 C -					P	-	P	C	Lk	

GSGS 3907. On grid sheet lines (643-685, 148-190). The same sheet lines were used for Second War Revision sheet 117A, using Fifth Edition mapping (see page 145). 1. See East Kent manoeuvres in supplement 7 for a version with red overprint.

Farnborough
28 by 23 km

1	2	4	6	7	8	9	10	11	12	13	14	15
BS	-	1929					-		P			
MBS	-	5000/34	1933				5	-	5	Oy	BL-d	
MBS	-	?10,000/34	1933				5	-	5	Oy		
MBS	-	?1000/35+	1933				5	-	5	Oy		
MBS	-	?3000/36++	1933				5	-	5	Oy		
MBS	-	?10,000/38+++	1933				5	-	5	Oy		
MBS	-	10,000/39++++	1933				5	-	5	Oy	PC	

CR 4275. On grid sheet lines (517-545, 166-189). One of two overlapping extract maps, slightly offset, covering the centre of the Aldershot Command area. The other is *Bordon*. The 5000 yard grid lines of the base map are still in place. Filed as MRLG Misc.276, army camps. There is reference to a 1929 issue, therefore Popular Edition based, on a MRLG index, but nothing is known of its sheet dimensions or further specification. See figure 17.

Inveraray. Parts of sheets 61, 62, 65 and 66.
37 by 22 km

1	2	4	6	7	8	9	10	11	12	13	14	15
MBS	1941	no code	1941				Pp	-	P	C	BL-d	1
MBS	1941	2000/12/42 519 RE (301) (blue)	1941				Pp	-	P	C	PC	2

GSGS 3908. WE 4269. On grid sheet lines (248-285, 716-738). The meaning of the tiny figures "736", inside the border in the bottom left hand corner, is unclear. 1. With an erroneous magnetic variation diagram, which was cancelled and replaced by a corrected one by overprinting in purple. 2. With the correct magnetic variation diagram in blue.

Llandrindod Wells. Parts of sheets 69, 70, 79, 80, 90, 91. 30 by 50 km
MBS - WO 6000/40 - P - P C BL-d
Without GSGS number or imprint. On grid sheet lines (340-370, 260-310). Filed as MRLG Misc.278.

Netheravon 30 by 23 km
MBS - ?10,000/33 1933 Pp - P Oy
MBS - 10,000/33. 1500/35 1933 Pp - P Oy BL-d
On grid sheet lines (442-472, 154-177). One of two overlapping extract maps covering the centre of the Salisbury Plain training area. The other is *Tilshead*. The 1935 issue has an overprint in red showing the boundary of War Department lands, out of bounds areas, aerodromes, cultivated areas, rifle range danger and RAF danger and bombing areas, revised to April 1935. No copy of the 1933 issue has yet been located. Filed as MRLG Misc.275, artillery ranges.

New Forest Revised 1913 26 by 22 miles
- - WO 1.24 1924p 1923 Po T P C PC 1
BS - Reprint 3000/24+ 1924p 1923 P T P C PC
BS - ?1000.24++ P T P C
MBS 1931 ?2200/31+++ 1924p 1923 P T P Co 2
MBS 1931 ?3000/36++++ 1924p 1923 P T P C 2
MBS 1931 15,000.39 C__+++ 1924p 1923 P T P C NLS 3

New Forest 41 by 46 km
MBS nd 10,000/40 M 1939.s 5 T 5 C BL-d 4

New Forest training map, 1941
MBS nd WO 1000/3/41 1939.s 5 T 5 C BL-d 5

New Forest training area map, 1943
MBS nd 10,000/7/43 Ch 1939.s 5 T 5 C PC 6
GSGS 3907 from 1931. The Popular Edition map is based on the civilian Tourist Map, without layers. It was replaced by one based on the Fifth Edition Yard Grid Tourist Map, without hill shading. 1. This issue has no overprint, so no grid. 2. This printing (listed in Nicholson (1992)) has not been verified. 3. The full print code string is WO 1.24. Reprint 3000/24. 1000/24. 15,000.39 C. 4. With contours in orange. 5. With an overprint in red showing the forest boundary, and various categories of out of bounds areas. Classified roads and railway stations are also on the red plate. 6. With road and railway station infill in red. With matters related to the forest overprinted in red, the training area boundary and RAF areas in blue, and field firing areas in yellow.

Redesdale & Otterburn ranges 27 by 18 miles
2WR 1942 sheet 3/86. 72,000/7/42 LR - N P P C DRg
GSGS 3907 sheet 3 / GSGS 3908 sheet 86. With an overprint in red added to some copies from the 72,000/7/42 LR printing. There was another printing of 300, completed by 8 June 1948 (not found). There is a note on a Military Survey catalogue card of a "Request for Completion by Nov 5th 1949 of Target Area overprints".

Ripon special one-inch sheet 33 by 44 km
MBS - ?AD 192. 100 12/40 - - - P C
MBS - ?1500 1/41+ - - - P C
MBS - Y51 1200 10/41++ - - - P C PC
With no GSGS number or imprint. On grid sheet lines (459-492, 471-515). *Made-Up from 1" Sheets of Ord. Svy. / Printed by 13 Corps Fd. Svy. Coy. R.E.*

Salisbury Plain

			Revised 1913				32⅞ by 22 miles					

The full print code string, not used on any single issue, appears to be: 1. WO Reprint 1500/25. 2. 5000/25. 3. 5000/27. 4. 1650/29. 5. 5200/29. 6. 8500/31. 7. 5000/32. 8. 17,000/33. 9. 5500/33. 10. 11,000/34. 11. 2500/35. 12. 5000/36. 13. 5000/38. 14. 6000/39. 15. 62,500/40/R.

1	2	4	6	7	8	9	10	11	12	13	14	15
BS	-	1	1920p				P	D	P	C	PC	1
BS	-	1-2	1920p	1925			P	D	P	C	PC	2
BS	-	1-3	1920p	1926	5.26		P	D	P	C	PC	
BS	-	?1-4	1920p	1926			P	D	P	C		
BS	-	?1-5	1920p	1926			P	D	P	C		
MBS	1931	1-6	1920p	1926	-		P	D	P	Co	Lk	3
MBS	1931	1-7	1920p	1926	5.26		P	D	P	Co	PC	
MBS	1931	1-6, 8	1920p	1926	5.26		P	D	P	Co		4
MBS	1931	1-6, 8-9	1920p	1926	-		P	D	P	C+	Ob	
MBS	1931	1-6, 8-10	1920p	1926		4.34	P	D	P	C	PC	5
MBS	1931	1-6, 8-11	1920p	1926		4.35	P	D	P	C	PC	6
MBS	1931	?1-5, 12	1920p	1926			P	D	P	C		
MBS	1931	1-5, 12-13	1920p	1926		10.37	P	D	P	C	BL-d	
MBS	1931	1-5, 14	1920p	1926		4.39	P	D	P	C	BL-d	7
MBS	1940	1-5, 15	1919	pcr		4.39	P	D	P	C	PC	

Salisbury Plain

			Revised 1946				40 by 45 km					
MBS	1946	12,000/5/46 Wa	1946			3.46	Np	6	5	Cb	BL-d	8
MBS	1946	6000/7/47	1946			3.47	Np	6	5	Cb	BL-d	
MBS	1946	3000/7/49	1946			3.47	Np	6	5	Cb	card	

NB in column 9 is listed the date of revision of War Department information.

GSGS 3907 from 1931 until 1940. The base of the original map is a civilian Popular Edition district map first published in 1920, which was in effect sheet 122 extended west and north to include coverage of the entire plain. 1. Without overprint. 2. With overprint in red showing War Department boundary and cultivated areas. 3. The overprint detail shown is now listed, and includes the War Department boundary, out of bounds, cultivated, rifle range danger and RAF danger and bombing areas, and aerodromes. 4. So far recorded only as a printing covering a special event *Training area Aug.-Sept. 1933.* See supplement 7. 5. Also recorded for a special printing *Southern Command manoeuvre area, 1934 (southern section).* See supplement 7. 6. The title is relettered in Withycombe's alphabet. 7. The title reverts to Popular Edition lettering. 8. Redesignated GSGS 4620 and headed *6th Edition style.* This was one of three sheets remade after the war on National Grid sheet lines to which the War Office Cassini Grid continued to be applied prior to the implementation of the National Grid by the War Office in 1950. The others are *Aldershot* and *Catterick area.* On the sheet lines of New Popular Edition sheet 167 [unnumbered] (388-428, 120-165, with the addition of an extrusion between Westbury and Warminster to complete coverage of the War Department property). See figure 14. Once with National Grid (military system), the overprinted version of sheet 167 was allocated the number GSGS Misc.433.

Sennybridge artillery ranges. (Parts of) England sheets 79 & 90.

							25 by 27 km					
MBS	-	6450/3/43 LR	-			9.42	P	-	P	C	BL-d	
MBS	-	2000/8/47	-			9.42	P	-	P	C	BL-d	

NB in column 9 is listed the date of revision of the range area.

Without GSGS number or imprint, though there was an instruction to add 3907 on future reprints. Presumably superseding *Builth Wells.* On grid sheet lines (327-352, 248-275). With a graduated border. With overprint in red (boundary of range area, metalled roads), yellow (training areas and for deployment only) and purple hatching (safety area, not for deployment). With the addition of some newly built roads, some metalled, apparently for military purposes. Some have military names or nicknames, such as Druids Way, Burma Road, Piccadilly Circus, Dixie's Corner, Ffynnon-Dafydd-Bevan. The range area was divided into zones, A, B, C ranges, "The Annexe" in the south, and "Common Target Area" in the centre, encompassing two special tank ranges, Pen Gawse and PDH. The map was filed as MRLG Misc.279; MRLG Misc.279A was a tracing of the target area.

South Downs training area (west) and (east)

							27 by 18 miles					
2WR	1941	sheet 133. 5000/4/42 LR	1941				N	P	5	C	BL-d	
2WR	1941	sheet 134. 5000/4/42 LR	1942				N	P	5	C	BL-d	
2WR	1941	sheet 134. 1510/8/43 Ch	-				N	P	5	C	BL-d	

GSGS 3907. Second War Revision sheets 133 and 134, with an overprint in red. An MRLG index dates this as issued in 1941; if so the earliest printings are not recorded.

Thames Valley. *See* Manoeuvre area, 1939 *in supplement 7.*

1	2	4	6	7	8	9	10	11	12	13	14	15

Tilshead   30 by 23 km

MBS	-	?10,000/33	1933				Pp	-	P	Oy		
MBS	-	10,000/33. 1000/35	1933				Pp	-	P	Oy	BL-d	

On grid sheet lines (430-460, 154-177). One of two overlapping extract maps covering the centre of the Salisbury Plain training area. The other is *Netheravon*. The 1935 issue has an overprint in red showing the boundary of War Department lands, out of bounds areas, aerodromes, cultivated areas, rifle range danger and RAF danger and bombing areas. No copy of the 1933 issue has yet been located. Filed as MRLG Misc.275, artillery ranges.

Supplement 5. *Artillery practice camp maps*

Lark Hill and West Down. Part of sheet 122.   13½ by 13½ km

MBS	-	4483-2000-10.32					-	-	P	Co	BL-d	

On grid sheet lines (445.5-459, 163-176.5). Filed as MRLG Misc.282.

Okehampton. Part of sheet 137.   see note for dimensions

MBS	-	4483-1000-10.32					-	-	P	Co	BL-d	

On mixed grid and Popular Edition sheet lines, from the NE corner of sheet 137 for eight miles west, south to 107 km N. Filed as MRLG Misc.282.

Redesdale. Part of sheet 3.   10 by 17 km

MBS	-	4483-1000-10.32					-	-	P	Co	BL-d	

On grid sheet lines (428-438, 616-633). Filed as MRLG Misc.282.

Trawsfynydd. Part of sheet 50.   12 by 10 km

MBS	-	4483-1000-10.32					-	-	P	Co	BL-d	

On grid sheet lines (315-327, 350-360). Filed as MRLG Misc.282.

Supplement 6. *Special pocket maps*

Christchurch   19 by 17 km

MBS	-	no code	1938				P	-	P	C	PC	

G.S.G.S. 3907, 1 inch to 1 mile New Forest Special Sheet (part of). This is still the Popular Edition version. On grid sheet lines (450-469, 110-127).

Dover   10 by 14 km

MBS	-	5000/37	1937				P	-	P	C	BL-d	

CR 4682. On grid sheet lines (670-680, 156-170). Filed as MRLG Misc.281.

Lympne   11 by 15 km

MBS	-	5000/37	1937				P	-	P	C	BL-d	
MBS	-	5000/37	1937				P	-	P	C	BL-d	1

CR 4682. On grid sheet lines (649-660, 148-163). Filed as MRLG Misc.281. 1. With an overprint in red.

Shorncliffe   13 by 10 km

MBS	-	5000/37	1937				P	-	P	C	BL-d	
MBS	-	WO 1100/38	1937				P	-	P	C	PC	

CR 4682. On grid sheet lines (656-669, 153-163). Filed as MRLG Misc.281.

Swanage   14 by 14 km

MBS	-	5000/37	1937				P	-	P	C	BL-d	

CR 4682. On grid sheet lines (435-449, 096-110). Filed as MRLG Misc.281.

Supplement 7. *Manoeuvre and exercise maps*

NB These maps are set in chronological sequence

Manœuvre map, 1925   43 by 59 km

BS	-	1. no code	1925p	P	-	P	C	PC
BS	-	1. 2000/25	1925p	P	-	P	C	book	1
BS	-	2. no code	1925p	P	-	P	C	PC
BS	-	2. 2000/25	1925p	P	-	P	C	book	1
BS	-	3. no code	1925p	P	-	P	C	PC
BS	-	3. 2000/25	1925p	P	-	P	C	book	1

With overprint in red showing the manoeuvre area boundary, out of bounds areas, gallops and the frontier. Sheet 1. Parts of sheets 111, 112, 121, 122, 130, 131. On grid sheet lines (427-470, 132-191). Sheet 2. Parts of sheets 112, 113, 122, 123, 131, 132. On grid sheet lines (460-503, 132-191). Sheet 3. Parts of sheets 113, 114, 123, 124, 132, 133. On grid sheet lines (493-536, 132-191). 1. In *Report on Army Manoeuvres 1925* (PRO WO 279/56).

Aldershot Command manœuvre area, 1927   45 by 52 km

| BS | - | WO 4.27. 5000/27 | 1927p | P | - | P | C | PC |

Parts of sheets 94, 95, 105, 106, 113, 114. On grid sheet lines (490-535, 188-240). With overprint in red showing the manoeuvre area boundary, out of bounds areas, gallops, restricted areas and the inter-divisional boundary.

Salisbury and Winchester : War Office staff exercise no.2, 1927   49 by 31 km

| BS | - | WO 7/27. 1250/27 | 1927p | P | - | P | C | book |

Parts of sheets 122, 123. On grid sheet lines (455-504, 142-173). Without overprint. In *Report on War Office Exercise No.2 (1927). Winchester, 9th-12th May* (PRO WO 279/59).

Manoeuvres in Kent, 1927 (*London Gazette* record of Orders in Council). Maps (no scale was mentioned) were issued, but not found.

Untitled [Sussex manoeuvres]   27 by 18 miles

BS	-	sheet 124. no code	3000/27++	1925	11.25	P	P	P	C	ALm
BS	-	sheet 125. no code	5000/27	24-5		P	P	P	C	ALm
BS	-	sheet 133. no code	3500/28+++	24-7	3.26	P	P	P	C	ALm
BS	-	sheet 134. WO 1.24	1920	1923		P	P	P	C	ALm

Popular Edition sheets 124, 125, 133, 134, with an overprint in red showing the 1928 manoeuvre area, divisional boundaries, restricted and out of bounds areas, and gallops. Other copies of sheets 124, 125, 133 are in Mg-d.

Map shewing situation 1ˢᵗ May on front of 1ˢᵗ Corps. Part of sheet 105.   33 by 19 km

| BS | - | no code | 1919p | P | - | P | C | book |

On grid sheet lines (492-525, 210-229). With overprint in red showing northland positions and blue showing British positions and divisional boundaries. Map No.2 in *Report on War Office Exercise No.4 (1928) Oxford 30th April-3rd May* (PRO WO 279/63). See figure 7.

Popular Edition sheet 26 *Harrogate*   27 by 18 miles

| note | - | WO Reprint 3750/28 | 3000/27 | P | P | P | C | book |

Employing an experimental form of what would, three years later, become the modified system of the War Office Cassini Grid. The origin of the grid was not Dunnose, as was traditional, but Delamere, calculated from a false origin near Atherton. Thus grid lines are parallel with and perpendicular to the sheet lines. The grid is black, with purple figures on the map face, and two-figure digits all round. With RE dumps overprinted in red, boundaries in purple, vital ground in both. In *Report on War Office Exercise No.5 (1928) Harrogate 15th-18th May* (PRO WO 279/64). See figure 18, and, for further information, Hellyer (1999b).

4th Division manoeuvre map, 1928   52 by 34 km
BS   -   WO 7.28. 2300/28   1928p   P   -   P   C   PC

Parts of sheets 86, 87, 97, 98. On grid sheet lines (620-672, 229-263). With an overprint of the manoeuvre area boundary in green and out of bounds areas in red. The manoeuvre area was divided into six zones, given letter references between A and F on a special index diagram.

Map of the Aldershot Command   24 by 32 miles
BS   -   3400/29   1920p   P   -   P   C   book

In *Report on War Office Exercise No.1 (1929). Aldershot 10th-12th April* (PRO WO 279/66). For the full print code string see the training area map in supplement 4.

Popular Edition sheet 45 *Buxton & Matlock*   27 by 18 miles
BS   -   WO 3750/30   3000/30   1928 2/28   P   P   P   C   book

Without overprint. In *Report on War Office Exercises Nos 1, 2, 4 (1930)* (PRO WO 279/71).

Popular Edition sheet 125 *Tunbridge Wells*   27 by 18 miles
BS   -   WO 3750/30   2000/29+   24-9 8/29   P   P   P   C   book

Without overprint. In *Report on War Office Exercise No.3 (1930) Crowborough 5th-8th May* (PRO WO 279/72).

[Norfolk and Suffolk manoeuvre area, 1930]   50 by 50 km
BS   -   no code   P   -   P   Co PC

Parts of sheets 76, 77, 86, 87. On grid sheet lines (650-700, 260-310). With an overprint in red showing the manoeuvre area boundary, boundaries of training sub areas and out of bounds areas. The only copy so far recorded is dissected and mounted back to back on cloth, without margins. It carries a magnetic variation diagram for January 1930. Whether the complete sheet had a title is so far unknown.

Salisbury Plain : training area Aug.-Sept. 1933   32⅞ by 22 miles
MBS 1931   17,000/33   1920p   1926 5.26   P   D   P   Co BL-d 1

GSGS 3907. The *Salisbury Plain* district map with a special overprint red, more in the nature of a manoeuvre map, showing the boundary of the training area, out of bounds, restricted and RAF danger and bombing areas. For the full print code string of *Salisbury Plain*, see the training area map in supplement 4.

Southern Command manœuvre area, 1934 : (northern section) and **(southern section)**
MBS -   16,700/34   1934   31-3 1932   P   -   P   C   BL-d
MBS 1931   11,000/34   1920p   1926 -   P   D   P   C   PC

GSGS 3907 imprint is on the southern sheet only. The northern sheet is on sheet lines parallel and perpendicular to those of the Popular Edition, and is contiguous with the *Salisbury Plain* district map used as the southern sheet, offset to the west. War Department, out of bounds, restricted, RAF danger and bombing areas, and training gallops are all overprinted in red, the manoeuvre area in purple. Classified *for official use only*. For the full print code string of *Salisbury Plain*, see the training area map in supplement 4.

Manoeuvres in Cambridgeshire, Essex and Hertfordshire, 1934 (*London Gazette* record of Orders in Council). Maps (no scale was mentioned) were issued, but not found.

Army manœuvres. 1935   50 by 59 km

| MBS | 1935 | 1. WO 4035 | ?1935 | Pq | - | P | C | book |
| MBS | 1935 | 2. WO 4035 | 1935 | Pq | - | P | C | book |

GSGS 3907. CR 4610. With manoeuvre area boundary, out of bounds areas and gallops overprinted in red. Sheet 1. Parts of sheets 112, 113, 122, 123, 131, 132. On grid sheet lines (445-495, 125-184). Sheet 2. Parts of sheets 113, 114, 123, 124, 132, 133. On grid sheet lines (484-534, 125-184, with a partial extension south to 124). In *Report on War Office Manoeuvres 1935* (PRO WO 279/76).

Manœuvre area, 1936   see note for dimensions

| MBS | 1936 | 1. WO 20,000/36 | 1936 | Pq | - | P | C | Lk |
| MBS | 1936 | 2. WO 20,000/36 | 1936 | Pq | - | P | C | BL-d |

GSGS 3907. With the manoeuvre area overprinted in red with a black border, out of bounds and restricted areas in red. Sheet 1. Parts of sheets 124, 125, 133, 134. On grid sheet lines (530-566, 120-169, with partial extensions west to 528 and south to 118). Sheet 2. Parts of sheets 124, 125, 133, 134. On grid sheet lines (563-598, 120-169).

East Anglia manœuvre area, 1937   see note for dimensions

| MBS | 1937 | 1. 23,500/37 | - | Pq | - | P | C | BL-d |
| MBS | 1937 | 2. 23,500/37 | - | Pq | - | P | C | BL-d |

GSGS 3907. With manoeuvre area boundaries, out of bounds and restricted areas and other detail overprinted in red. Sheet 1. Parts of sheets 74, 75, 84, 85, 95, 96, 106, 107. On grid sheet lines (560-610, 226-291). Sheet 2. Parts of sheets 75, 76, 85, 86, 96, 97, 107, 108. On grid sheet lines (598-649, 226-291).

Untitled [East Kent manoeuvres area (handwritten title)]   see note for dimensions

| MBS | 1935 | 8000/37+ | - | | P | - | P | C | PC |
| MBS | 1931 | sheet 126. 3000/36+++ | 3500/27 | 1928 | 1927 P | P | P | C | BL-d |

GSGS 3907. The northern sheet employs the *East Kent Special Sheet* (see the training area map in supplement 4, also sheet 117A); the southern is sheet 126 (q.v.). Both are overprinted with the manoeuvre area boundary, restricted and out of bounds areas in red. There is no overprint title or date, but copies were received into the GSGS map room on 29 June 1937. A small portion of the boundary would lie on sheet 116, but it is not known whether this sheet was overprinted.

Aldershot Command manœuvre area, 1938   58 by 39 km

| MBS | 1938 | 1. 22,500/28 | 1938.s | 5p | - | 5 | C | BL-d |
| MBS | 1938 | 2. 22,500/28 | 1938.s | 5p | - | 5 | C | BL-d |

GSGS 3907. The print codes are apparently errors for 22,500/38. With an overprint in purple showing manoeuvre area boundaries, restricted and out of bounds areas and gallops. Issues without overprint have not been recorded, but would be standard practice. Sheet 1. (Fifth Edition) parts of sheets 112, 113, 114, 123, 124, 131. On grid sheet lines (476-534, 153-192). Sheet 2. (Fifth Edition) parts of sheets 131, 132, 141, 142. On grid sheet lines (476-534, 124-163).

Southern Command manœuvre area   43 by 47 km

| MBS | 1938 | 11,950/38 | 1938.s | 5p | - | 5 | C | BL-d | 1 |
| MBS | 1938 | 11,950/38 | 1938.s | 5p | - | 5 | C | BL-d | 2 |

GSGS 3907. (Fifth Edition) parts of sheets 112, 113, 123, 131. On grid sheet lines (449-492, 137-184). 1. Without overprint. 2. With an overprint in purple showing the 1938 manoeuvre area boundary, restricted and out of bounds areas and gallops.

The Suffolk manœuvre area, 1938   see note for dimensions

MBS	1938	1. 5500/38	-	Pp	-	P	C	BL-d	1
MBS	1938	1. 5500/38	-	Pp	-	P	C	BL-d	2
MBS	1938	2. 5500/38	-	Pp	-	P	C	BL-d	1
MBS	1938	2. 5500/38	-	Pp	-	P	C	BL-d	2

GSGS 3907. Sheet 1. Parts of sheets 76, 77, 86, 87, 97, 98. On grid sheet lines (630-670, 250-301). Sheet 2. Parts of sheets 77, 87, 98. On grid sheet lines (659-702, 250-312). 1. Without overprint. 2. With an overprint in purple showing manoeuvre area boundaries, restricted and out of bounds areas.

Manœuvre area, 1939 : Thames Valley / Aldershot Command   see note for dimensions

MBS	1939	15,200/39	1939.s					5p	-	5	C	BL-d	1,3
MBS	1939	15,200/39	1939.s					5p	-	5	C	Lk	1,4
MBS	1934	WO 14,400/39	1932.s					5p	-	5	C	Lk	2,4

GSGS 3907. Also issued, certainly using *Aldershot Command* (copy PC), and perhaps also *Thames Valley*, was a *Traffic Map*, overprinted in red by 19 (Fd Svy) Coy RE, July 1939. 1. CR 4752. (Fifth Edition) parts of sheets 94, 113, St. Albans, London. On grid sheet lines (490-538, 175-229), probably made specifically as the northern sheet for these manoeuvres. 2. A special printing of the *Aldershot Command* map (see the training area map in supplement 4), with grid in black and GSGS imprint and grid values in blue. 3. Without overprint, so lacking the *Manoeuvre area, 1939* part of the title. 4. With an overprint in purple showing manoeuvre area boundaries, restricted and out of bounds areas, and areas allotted to H.Q. London District.

GSGS 3907Z ***Yorkshire manœuvre area***   27 by 18 miles

MBS	1932	sheet 16. 5000/39	1925	pcr				Pp	P	P	C	PC	
MBS	1932	sheet 22. WO 24,800/39	1924	pcr				Pp	P	P	C	PC	
MBS	1932	sheet 23. WO 24,800/39	1925	pcr				Pp	P	P	C	BL-d	
MBS	1932	sheet 27. 24,800/39	1924	pcr				Pp	P	P	C	Bg	
MBS	1932	sheet 28. 24,800/39	1924	pcr				Pp	P	P	C	BL-d	
MBS	1932	sheet 32. WO 19,800/39	1924	pcr				Pp	P	P	C	IWM	
MBS	1932	sheet 33. WO 19,800/39	1924	pcr				Pp	P	P	C	PC	1

Popular Edition sheets 16, 22, 23, 27, 28, 32, 33. With an overprint in purple showing out of bounds and restricted areas and bloodstock breeding establishments. 1. Without overprint, thus also lacking both the "Z" and the title, but recognisable as a 1939 printing with grid in black with blue figures.

Exercise Excelsior   33 by 45 km

| 2WR | 1943 | 200/11/43/13S/667 | - | | | | | 5 | - | 5 | C | BL-d | |

Parts of GSGS 3907 sheets 112, 113, 122, 123. On grid sheet lines (454-487, 155-190). An exercise map, classified *secret*, overprinted in red, green, blue and black, on a grey base.

GSGS Misc.302 ***Exercise Ubique II***   27 by 18 miles

| 2WR | - | sheet 122. 275/11/47 SPC | - | | | | | N | P | 5 | C | Ob | |

Sheet 122, 25,000/2/44 Mc printing. The date is supplied by the print code. The overprint is red.

Exercise Ubique IV

GSGS 3907. Composite sheets, parts of [Second War Revision] 112, 113, 122, 123 were required, 400 copies in each of two styles. The order was made on 27 July 1949, and supplied in October. Not found (WOPD 4380/OS. Information from a Military Survey catalogue card).

GSGS Misc.363 ***Exercise Viking***   27 by 18 miles

2WR	1949	sheet 121. 900/12/49	1942					N	P	5	C	DGC	1
2WR	1949	sheet 121. 900/12/49	1942					N	P	5	C	DGC	2
2WR	1949	sheet 121. no code	1942					N	P	5	C	DGC	3

Sheet 121, with three different overprints: 1. GSGS Misc.363/1 *23 Corps Plan*. 2. GSGS Misc.363/2 *8 Corps Plan*. 3. GSGS Misc.363/3, untitled.

GSGS Misc.364 ***Exercise Viking***   27 by 18 miles

| 2WR | 1949 | sheet 122. 900/12/49 | - | | | | | N | P | 5 | C | DGC | 1 |
| 2WR | 1949 | sheet 122. 900/12/49 | - | | | | | N | P | 5 | C | DGC | 2 |

Sheet 122, with two recorded overprints: 1. GSGS Misc.364/1 *23 Corps Plan*. 2. GSGS Misc.364/2 *8 Corps Plan*. Map colours are subdued, with an overprint in red and brown.

GSGS Misc.395 ***Exercise Black Tarquin***   54 by 35 km

| 2WR | 1950 | 250/1/50 | - | | | | | Np | P | 5 | C | DGC | 1 |
| 2WR | 1950 | 250/1/50 | - | | | | | Np | P | 5 | C | DGC | 2 |

Parts of sheet 111, 112, 121, 122, 130, 131. On grid sheet lines (398-452, 144-179). There are two versions each with a different situation overprint: 1. GSGS Misc.395/1 *Saturnian Situation Five Days After Contact*. 2. GSGS Misc.395/2 *44 Brit Inf Div Dispositions Before Contact*.

Supplement 8. *Examination papers*

See the bibliography for the titles of the reports that contain most of the Staff College papers.

Staff College entrance examinations: training for war papers

Sheet 121, a pre-military grid printing was used in February-March 1923
Sheet 121, WO 1.24, February-March 1925
Sheet 112, WO 700/26. 1000/27. 2450/27, February-March 1927
Sheet 130, WO 9.24. 700/26. 2450/27, February-March 1927

Staff College entrance examinations: strategy and tactics papers

Sheet 121, WO 1.24. 800/27. 2200/28, February-March 1928
Sheet 83, WO 900/28. 2275/29, February-March 1929
Sheet 93, WO 900/28. 2275/29, February-March 1929
Sheet 61, WO 1000/29. 2275/30, February-March 1930
Sheet 93, WO 1000/30. 2150/31, February-March 1931
Sheet 112, WO 1000/30. 2150/31, February-March 1931
Sheet 46, WO 3500/31, February-March 1932
Sheet 90, WO 3500/31, February-March 1932
GSGS 3907 sheet 123, WO 3030/31. 2000/32. 3025/33, February-March 1934
GSGS 3907 sheet 113, WO 2980/31. 1750/33. 5000/33. 2000/35, February-March 1936
GSGS 3907 sheet 86, 3000/36, February-March 1937

Staff College entrance examinations: administration and morale paper

GSGS Misc.387 sheet 130, 1500/6/50. Copy DGC

Staff College examinations for promotion

GSGS 3907 sheet 96, WO 2600/31. 1000/36, October 1936
GSGS 3907 sheet 121, WO 5436, March 1937
GSGS 3907 sheet 93, 8500/37, October 1937. Copy Ob
GSGS 3907 sheet 21, WO 3550/32. 1000/36. 1000/38, 4500/38, 1939

Maps carrying Ordnance Survey Central Registry number CR 7959
        This may relate to the use of these maps in officers' examination papers:

GSGS 3907 sheet 135, 1400/35, printed without legends, possibly for exam use
GSGS 3907 sheet 118, 4000/37 (not found). CR 7959 is present on the subsequent two printings
GSGS 3907 sheet 109, 4500/38, printed with red main roads, used in an officers' examination. Copy Ob

Other sheets without headings, but with unusual specifications, perhaps for educational purposes

GSGS 3907 sheet 7, WO 1400/33, without legends but with red main roads and WO imprint
Sheet 28, WO 1500/31, without legends, but with green woodland. With British System grid
GSGS 3907 sheet 98, WO 1750/32, with red roads and green woodland
GSGS 3907 sheet 120, WO 1750/32 with red roads and green woodland
GSGS 3907 sheet 141, 1400/34, without legends but with WO imprint
GSGS 3907 sheet 142, WO 1750/32, with red main roads and green woodland

Supplement 9. *Map extracts in books and examination papers*

GSGS Misc.268 Adderbury area   16 by 9 km

2WR	1946	200/10/47 SPC	1946	5	-	5	C	DGC	
2WR	1946	120/10/49	1949	5	-	5	C	DGC	1
2WR	1946	200/10/53 OS	1949	5	-	5	C	DGC	2

Used in Staff College entrance examinations. On grid sheet lines (484-500, 250-259). 1. GSGS Misc.268/1, with an overprint in red and blue. 2. GSGS Misc.268/2, Second Edition-GSGS, with the overprint colours reversed. NB a 1953 map, remarkably still using the Cassini Grid.

GSGS Misc.397 Bath to Chippenham area

MBS	10,000/1/50	1950	5	-	5	C	DGC
MBS	5200/12/50	1950	5	-	5	C	DGC

With heading *Applied Map Reading*, for use in March 1950 examinations.

GSGS Misc.337 Castle Howard area

2WR	1948	1200/9/49	1948	P	-	5	C	DGC

Used in the Staff College entrance examination, 1949. Photolithographed by OS 1948.

Chipping Norton area

MBS -	3000/34	1934	P	-	P	C	book

CR 4396. Parts of sheets 93, 94. North-south limits are those of the sheets, from west of Chipping Camden to east of Brackley. Used in strategy and tactics papers of the Staff College entrance examination in February-March 1935 (see bibliography for title of the report on the examination).

Corwen area   see note for dimensions

MBS	nc	1944	P	P	C	DGC

WE 715/18347. 4000 copies were required for a map reading exercise. On mixed grid and Popular Edition sheet lines, from the NE corner of sheet 50 to 340 km E, 362 km S. A proof copy dated 13 April 1944 is recorded. It was requested by the Directorate of Military Survey on 14 March 1944.

Dartford & Sittingbourne   26½ by 18 miles

MBS	1932	2000/32	nd:p	1930	P	-	P	Co	book

GSGS 3907. Parts of sheets 115, 116. In Lieut-Colonel R.P. Pakenham-Walsh and Major E.E. Dorman-Smith *Elementary tactics: an introduction to the art of war, British school*, second edition: volume 2, *Tactical studies*. London: Sifton, Praed & Co. Ltd, 1934.

For East Kent *in C.A. Wilson* The map reading "instructor" *see supplement 4.*

North west of Dover area

MBS	38,500/36		P

CR 4391. Used in a map reading examination in October 1936. Not seen. (Nicholson (1992) *Sheetlines* 34)

Guildford area

BS -	3000/30	1930	P	-	P	C	book	1
MBS -	2000/38	1938	P	-	5	C	book	2
MBS -	7000/40	1938	P	-	5	C	book	3
MBS -	7000/40. 4000/6/41	1938	P	-	5	C	book	4

1. Plate A in *The complete guide to military map reading,* ninth edition. Aldershot: Gale & Polden, 1930. 2. Plate A in *The complete guide to military map reading,* tenth edition. Aldershot: Gale & Polden, 1938. Sheet lines are slightly altered. 3. With code WE 299, in a reprint. 4. With code WE 5196, in a reprint.

Shrewsbury area   43 by 37 km

BS -	?WO 9.27. 800.27	1928						
BS -	2200.28+	1928	P	-	P	C	book	1
BS -	?1000.29++	192?						
BS -	2275.30+++	1927	P	-	P	C	book	1

On grid sheet lines (380-423, 310-347). 1. Used in strategy and tactics papers of the Staff College entrance examinations in February-March 1928 and 1930 (see bibliography for title of the report on the examination).

1	2	4		6		7	8	9	10	11	12	13	14	15

Thetford Forest area   see note for dimensions

BS	-	12,500/29		1929					P	-	P	C	PC	

The map reading paper in *Examination for army first class and special certificates of education, October, 1929.*
On mixed grid and Popular Edition sheet lines, from the SW corner of sheet 76 to 633 km E, 304 km N.

GSGS Misc.289 Uppingham area   32 by 16 km

2WR	1948	2000/8/48		1948					P	-	P	C	DGC	

Used in a Staff College entrance examination. On grid sheet lines (520-552, 315-331).

Warrington area

MBS	-	no code		1936					-	-	P	C	book	
MBS	-	193,000/40		1936					-	-	P	C	book	
MBS	-	?85,000/40		1936					-	-	P	C	book	
MBS	-	85,000/40. 300,000/41		1936					-	-	P	C	book	
MBS	-	12,800/10/48		1936					-	-	P	C	book	1

Plate XII, *Modified British System (medium scale) taken from 1:63360 (1 inch to 1 mile), sheet 36.* in *Manual of map reading, photo reading and field sketching,* and *Notes on map reading,* both *1929 (reprinted with amendments (nos.1 to 4) 1939).* London: HMSO, 1940. The south-west corner of sheet 36 is used. 1. OR 1426.

Watford, Hemel Hempstead and St Albans area

BS	-	no code		1925					P	-	P	C	book	

Parts of sheets 95 and 106, with Popular Edition marginalia. Plate X in *Notes on map reading, 1925.* London: HMSO, 1926.

Watford area

BS	-	no code		1929					-	-	P	C	book	1
BS	-	no code		1938					-	-	P	C	book	2
BS	-	?85,000/40		1938					-	-	P	C	book	2
BS	-	300,000/41		1938					-	-	P	C	book	2,3
BS	-	300,000/41		1938					-	-	P	C	book	2,4
BS	-	12,800/9/48		1939					-	-	P	C	book	2,5

As the previous, reduced by nearly three miles in the north. Without marginalia. Plate IX, *British System. Standard scale:* 1. in *Manual of map reading, photo reading and field sketching, 1929,* and *Notes on map reading, 1929.* both London: HMSO, 1929. 2. In *Manual of map reading, photo reading and field sketching,* and *Notes on map reading,* both *1929 (Reprinted with amendments (nos.1 to 4) 1939).* London: HMSO, 1940. 3. With round figures. 4. With tall figures. 5. OR 1423.

Unrecorded extract maps

The following have been identified from documentary sources, in GSGS 3907 series files.

Extract of sheet 51
'Job No OS/30, OR 1839 – part of sheet 51 required for map reading training. / 1. Attached is a mock-up of a section of GSGS 3907 sheet "Wrexham and Oswestry" required for map-reading training. / 2. Details of heading, scale and imprints are shown on the mock-up, and are similar for your DR 414. The difference being the OR Number which is shown in place of your DR Number. 4000 copies please.'
(Svy 2/6215 from D.Mil.Svy to DGOS, 18 November 1947)

Extract of sheet 51
'Job No OS/145, for GSOR 1934 – part of sheet 51. / Will you please prepare that part of GSGS 3907 sheet 51 in blue/black ink on the enclosed copy, in the style of OR 1839 a copy of which is sent herewith. Four proofs are required by 31st March.'
(Svy 2/6215 from D.Mil.Svy to DGOS, 1 March 1949)

3. *London*

The definitive cartobibliography of military mapping of London is for the present an unachievable ambition, thus what follows in this section is a summary of "work in progress". In several cases no copy of a map has been located; what has been recorded may be no more than a reference to one in a card catalogue or a document. Indeed in some cases it is quite possible that no copies of such maps survive at all.

For a explanation of the detail in each column see pages 86 to 89.

1. *London* – overprinted title: ***London (Tourist Map)***   Revised 1912-4   36 by 26 miles
note   -   WO 500/28   5000/27   23-6   P   T   P   C   PC

The base map is the civilian Tourist Map of London, in conventional Popular Edition style, without enhanced hill colouring but with woods in green. With the standard War Office Cassini Grid (British System), and, in the usually empty map frame, an additional co-ordinate system comprising the same sequence of two-digit values as would from 1931 be found on maps carrying the Modified British System. The additional "hundred kilometre" digit included in the modified system at 10 km intervals is not present. But the values, significantly, can be construed as part of a national system of co-ordinate values, not just a local system to satisfy the needs of this particular map of London. The same values also appear on GSGS 3786, the 1:20,000 *County of London* map published in 1926.[261] A marginal note links this system of reference on the one-inch map to the special Gazetteer of London prepared for the 1:20,000 map, and the usual marginal index showing 1:20,000 sheets also carries the sheet lines of the 1:20,000 London map.[262] See figure 6, and, for further information, Hellyer (1999b).

2. GSGS 3994

An untitled grey monochrome base map of London, first published by the War Office, 1937. The map is Fifth Edition, on Yard Grid sheet lines (1,115,000-1,170,000, 1,285,000-1,330,000) but with no grid. Four versions are recorded:

a. Outline edition, with print code 500/37. Not found.

b. *Territorial drill halls in and around London and zones of influence within the County of London,* 1937.
        Not found. Overprint colour unknown, print code unknown. As described in the *Register of GSGS maps.*

c. Outline edition, with print code 500/37. 500/38. Printed by the Ordnance Survey, 1938. Copy BL-d.

d. *Map showing Territorial Army and Auxiliary Air Force headquarters in the Greater London area : also zones of influence within the County of London,* 1939.
        Print code 1500/39. Overprinted in red, showing field force units, anti aircraft units, auxiliary air force squadrons and balloon squadrons. Copies BL-d, Ob.

3. GSGS 3907 Popular Edition sheets with overprints showing police divisions

MBS	1931	sheet 106. 12,000/39+++++	5000/28++	1929		1927	P	P	P	C	note
MBS	1931	sheet 107	1938.s				5	P	5	C	
MBS	1931	sheet 114. 16,000/39+++++	1920	1933	1931		P	P	P	C	note
MBS	1931	sheet 115. 16,000/39++++	1920	pcr			Pa	P	P	C	note

The legend is on sheet 114. Two variants of the overprint are recorded: a. Overprinted in purple with Metropolitan Police divisions. A copy of sheet 106 is recorded, in BL-d. b. Overprinted in purple with Metropolitan Police divisions and in red with the London area boundary. Copies of sheets 106, 114 and 115 are in a private collection.

---

[261] Christopher Board, 'The secret map of the County of London, 1926, and its sequels', *London Topographical Record* 27 (1995), 257-280; and 'The three-inch map of London, and its predecessors of 1926', *Sheetlines* 43 (1995), 48-50.
[262] Roger Hellyer, 'Some notes on the origin of the Modified British System of the War Office Cassini Grid', *Sheetlines* 55 (1999), 3-11.

4. A Military Survey catalogue card describes various applications made of a special sheet of London, designated as GSGS 3907. No base map has yet been found with a title, a date, or this GSGS number, though various overprinted versions with the GSGS (OR) [Office Reference] number 1527 are recorded or documented. The map is Fifth Edition based, and is a large sheet on grid sheet lines (536-600, 176-225). It was apparently made in 1941. Notes on the various overprinted versions so far recorded or reported are offered below. MRLG Misc.268 file reference *Map of London showing police and civil defence areas* may apply to either of the first two maps listed.

a. OR 1527 *London Region Civil Defence groups*
> The recorded copy is presumably a reprint by the OS in 1944 (print code 1000/1/44 Ch). It is in grey outline with water in blue. Grid references are at 10 km intervals. The London region border is overprinted in purple, groups in red, sub-groups in green. Copy BL-d.

b. Untitled, the boundaries of the London District and of Metropolitan Police divisions overprinted in purple.
> 1. Grey base, with blue grid references. No print code, published in 1941. Copy BL-d.
> 2. Another edition, in black, with water, woods and main roads coloured. With blue grid references. With OR 1527B added by hand. Print code WO 5000/8/41 LR. Copy BL-d.
> 3. OR 1527B, another edition, in the same colours. Print code 5000/5/44 Ch. Copy BL-d.

c. [OR 1527C] London District anti tank groups
> Print code 260/7/43 Ch (copy BL-d). There is no title, just a legend in the top margin, listing: boundaries of L.D. & sub-districts (purple lines), boundaries of sectors (pecked purple lines), general line of A/Tk. defences (green dots), roads (green lines). Classified *secret*. The base map is grey, with grid and water in purple. The OR number is lacking. MRLG Misc.155 file reference *General line of A/Tk Defences* may apply to this map. A secret document (HF/5724/Svy) to DGOS from GHQ HF DMA dated 2 October 1943 seems to refer to a reprint:
> "A reprint of the special 1" London sheet, overprinted with sub-districts, sectors and A/Tank defences is now necessary as an urgent operational requirement. Will you therefore please print a further 1000 copies of this sheet as per specimen attached and distribute as follows: G Maps HQ, London District – 700 copies; AD Survey, Eastern Command – 300 copies. Copies are not required to be numbered but the note "Copy Number" in top right hand corner is to be retained. Please treat this job as Priority 2 for delivery in three weeks time."

d. [OR 1527D] *London District training areas (first edition, September, 1943)*.
> Print code 400/12/43 Ch (copy BL-d). According to a Military Survey catalogue card, 1000 copies were ordered by 23 October 1943, and 400 were printed in December. The base map is grey, with grid and water in purple; with an overprint in green, yellow, red and black. Classified *secret*. Filed as MRLG Misc.156.

e. London District boundaries and defence zones
> Not found and date uncertain. Noted on a Military Survey catalogue card.

f. London District bridge classification
> Not found. Noted on a Military Survey catalogue card. Printed OS, 1943 (OS job card in CCS Archives).

5. OR 1826 **Map of London District**
> The base map was printed by the Ordnance Survey in 1947, in black with grey woods, without title or imprint (print code 3208/A, copies in copyright collections); a reprint followed in 1948 printed in grey throughout (print code 250/11/48, copy Bg). It was produced as a result of a request in 1946 from New Scotland Yard for a "general base map of London".[263] The British Library catalogue notes the map as "special sheets printed in matt for use as base maps". It carries the National Grid, and is on National Grid sheet lines, in two halves (497-529 and 527-559, W-E, 148-211, S-N), suggesting that at the time the OS had not the capacity to print so large a sheet in one (see also GSGS 4692 on page 260). In 1947, the Ordnance Survey heliozincographed and printed this grey base map for the War Office, as OR 1826 (print code 1500/12/47 (not found), another edition 1100/3/49 (copy BL-d)). There was still no title, and the National Grid remained in place. Both printings were overprinted as OR 1826AA in purple with the title as above, the War Office Cassini Grid, and the boundaries of the London District and of the Metropolitan Police divisions. The boundaries of garrisons are in red. Copies of both are in BL-d.

6. GSGS 4623 **Throughways of London**
Copied from an undisclosed commercial map original, drawn and photolithographed by the OS in 1947. With War Office Cassini Grid overprinted in purple. Showing main roads, the principal arteries emphasised. Copy BL-d.

---

[263] PRO OS 1/297, minute 5. See Richard Oliver, *A guide to the Ordnance Survey one-inch New Popular Edition*. London: Charles Close Society, 2000, 59.

Compiler's notes to sections 4, 5 and 6

Ireland

The earliest known military mapping of Ireland on the one-inch 205-sheet layout[264] was an outline map with the title *1" provisional edition for <u>military purposes only</u>*, dating from 1915-16. Five sheets only of what may have been full national coverage have so far been recorded (11, 49, 129, 166, 187), so it is impossible to assess its actual extent. It was distinctive for the separate contour plates that were created for it which permitted the contours to be shown in red.[265] Coverage of Northern Ireland at least seems to have been quite extensive, and those plates (though apparently not sheet 11) would later be adapted for use in the coloured sheets which formed part of the GSGS 3917 coverage of Northern Ireland.

Military mapping required after 1922 by the Department of Defence of the newly independent Irish Free State is not listed here. Very little is known about it. There were plans for full coverage of the island at the 1:20,000 scale in 513 sheets each covering an area of 18 by 12 km, overprinted with a metric grid in red. Publication began with four sheets in the Mallow area in 1934-35, then stopped. When it resumed in 1939 the same four sheets were reprinted plus only two more before it stopped for good. Specification changes included woodland, altered from black to green, and the contour interval, adjusted from five metres to twenty feet. The same grid is known to have appeared on maps at the quarter-inch scale used by the Air Corps, but none at the one-inch have been recorded. The move away from the metric went one stage further in 1940 with the issue of a one-inch combined sheet series, covering the island in 55 sheets.[266] The metric grid of the 1930s was replaced by one at 5000 yard intervals, again in red. Each sheet is a combination of four small sheets, covering an area 36 by 24 miles. The same grid was used on maps at the half-inch scale. Both maps were for military use only.

Gridded maps of Ireland made by the War Office in London were definitely in use by 1924, the grid presumably in a form similar to the British System currently in use in Great Britain. In about 1931 this would have necessitated a similar change in design as that which transformed the British System into the Modified British System in Great Britain. No British mapping of Ireland with military grids earlier than 1931 is known to survive, there being an official policy to withdraw and destroy all earlier printings, if only to avoid confusion between grid systems. Reference to the grid itself seems to have been avoided in the standard manuals. As in Great Britain it seems to have had no formal name, and of those recorded "War Office Irish Grid" is preferred here in order to distinguish it from the grid in Great Britain.

The few sheets dating from the 1920s whose existence may be presumed are listed below. In the 1930s Northern Ireland was covered by GSGS 3917. Publication began in 1931, and by 1932 five coloured maps had been produced, in effect as five district maps, with sheet names but without sheet numbers. Their adjoining sheet diagrams only show these coloured sheets. They were in the standard War Office colour scheme of the time, with yellow roads, blue water and red contours. Woodland is uncoloured. All known copies are on Place's waterproof paper. Pivotal to the arrangement of sheet lines was *Belfast*, one of the two published sheets in the Third Edition large sheet series.[267] Owing to its origin, this sheet had a blue tint plate, coastal areas elsewhere being depicted by blue waterlining. It also retained its border – all other sheets in GSGS 3917 were bounded by the neat line only.

After the five coloured sheets publication ceased, followed in November 1932 by the proving of a sheet in black outline, *Ballycastle*. After some delay, publication resumed in 1934. There was apparently a new requirement – the immediate coverage of the whole of Northern Ireland. Evidently the

---

[264] The engraved one-inch map of Ireland covered the entire island in a layout of 205 sheets, each covering an area eighteen by twelve miles. See Roger Hellyer, *Ordnance Survey small-scale maps indexes: 1801-1998*. Kerry: David Archer, 1999, sections 22, 23, 25 for details and indexes.

[265] Contours in red had earlier appeared on the 1912 *Belfast District* map. See Roger Hellyer and Richard Oliver, *A guide to the Ordnance Survey one-inch Third Edition maps, in colour*. London: Charles Close Society, 2004.

[266] An index and further details of this map are given in Roger Hellyer, *Ordnance Survey small-scale maps indexes: 1801-1998*. Kerry: David Archer, 1999, section 29.

[267] Roger Hellyer and Richard Oliver, *A guide to the Ordnance Survey one-inch Third Edition maps, in colour*. London: Charles Close Society, 2004.

reduction in specification to black outline (including contours, waterlining and woodland) was sufficient in order to accomplish this. A standard sheet size of 18 by 24 inches was adopted, but there were several exceptions. The already published coverage of the Armagh and Londonderry areas was covered again. The adjoining sheet diagram on the outline maps shows all sheets in the series.

Two further sheets were produced in 1934, covering areas in the Irish Free State where there were still British naval bases, as GSGS 3943. *Cork*, which as sheet 80 shared essentially the same specification as *Belfast* in the civilian Third Edition large sheet series, was in this version reduced to a black plate only, lacking even the water plate. But at least, like *Belfast*, it retained its border. The other was a large composite map covering the Bantry Bay area.

Standard on all sheets in both these series was the War Office Irish Grid, overprinted in purple. All sheets had titles in black centre top, duplicated top right in purple. Sheet numbers were provided only for the outline sheets, also top right. It was a curious characteristic of *Bantry Bay* in the south and all but two sheets in the north that sheet lines could either fall on those of the traditional small sheet series, or on natural values of the War Office Irish Grid – in several cases a mixture of the two.

Early in 1940 this partial coverage of Ireland was deemed no longer sufficient. Complete coverage was urgently required, and this was to be achieved by means of black outline lithographic copies of the engraved small sheets covering the area still lacking, with an overprint of the grid and other military marginalia in purple. The GSGS number first allocated for "1" Eire" was 3943, soon altered to 3917, perhaps reflecting a subsequent determination also to include coverage of the north. GSOR 5189 *Index to Ireland* was published by the War Office in 1940, showing the half-inch GSGS 4127 in 25 sheets and the one-inch GSGS 3917 in 205. The Ordnance Survey unpublished annual report for 1940-41[268] notes in the section *War work : revision of existing maps* the preparation of 160 small sheet series under GSGS 3917, or about the number required to cover the Irish Free State. There was a further reference to "'2nd Edition' 24 sheets", presumably the republication in an unrevealed format of some of the sheets made to 1934. By June 1940 printing plates seem to have been made of all sheets by the Ordnance Survey as a War Office special service job. One of the job files survives, for sheet 92. The time scale revealed extends from 16 April, with the production of negatives, to proving on 24 June and the preparation of a printing plate the day after. Proof copies appear to have been run off, but it is unlikely that there were any print runs, because within days it had been decided not to proceed with a small sheet series, but instead to prepare a large sheet series covering the whole island, on grid sheet lines covering a standard 50 by 30 km. They were numbered from 301 in order to avoid confusion with the GSGS 3917 small sheets. A new GSGS number, 4136, was allocated on 3 July. Nine days later the first sheets were being printed; by 10 August all 76 sheets were in print.

Very few sheets of this first edition of GSGS 4136 survive. Those recorded have no edition heading, are in black outline with an overprint in red of military information, including grid. A new plate was required for sheet 305 on 14 August, and reprints of sheets 301, 307, 308, 310, 312, 321, 328, 331, 333, 335, 340, 346, 352, 358, 362, 364, 373, 374.[269] A second edition was in progress before the end of the year, with at least twenty sheets issued by December 1940. A green woodland plate was added. The size of the grid figures across the face of the sheet was slightly increased, and a *Diagram of grid reference letters* and main road infill added to the red plate. Early printings had no publication note. The magnetic variation as at the centre of the sheet was given (later transferred to the sheet edges for the Third Edition). The *Second Edition* heading was usually present on the red plate, occasionally it was black. It would seem that some sheets were issued in two or even three different states, as the road specification as originally depicted was revised, first to a military four-part classification,[270] then later to a classification updated to a specific date in 1941. Part way through this process a publication note and OS reproduction note were added, in black. Again the small number of surviving copies makes it impossible to be specific about the number of printings or their variants for any particular sheet.

Layer plates were made for 51 sheets on the east side of the island. There were three bands, 200-400, 400-600, 600-1000 feet. On seven sheets in flat country these were adjusted to 200-300, 300-400, 400-600 or 400-1000 feet. The maps were uncoloured below 200 feet and above the top of the

[268] PRO OS 1/139.

[269] GSGS 4136 series file, at present with DGC.

[270] This version was evidently part way through the process of road classification, and many sheets are overprinted in red *Warning: The road classification for this sheet is incomplete. Some unclassified roads may be suitable for convoy traffic.*

third layer, wherever it lay. The word *(Layered)* was added to the *Second Edition* heading, usually, though not invariably, as part of the orange layer plate. In an earlier description of these maps,[271] I interpreted the evidence available to me at the time to mean that all 51 sheets were printed as layered Second Edition sheets first without the green woods plate, then reprinted with it. A recent examination of at least some of the documents for myself now makes me feel uncomfortable with this conclusion. The British troops were 515 Corps Field Survey Company, R.E., printing maps in Northern Ireland in two double demi trailers. Their layer rulings were laid down from duplicate ruling plates supplied by the Ordnance Survey, and by mid-November 1941 they had completed about half the job. The expectation was that they would be finished by the end of the year, but from print codes on surviving maps it would appear that they were still printing the one thousand copies of each sheet required in February 1942. The likelihood is, therefore, that the survey unit did indeed print all 51 sheets, without the green plate.

However, by November 1941 there was already talk of a third edition of GSGS 4136, and a requirement for massively increased stock levels of each of the sheets in the layered edition area (printings of between 5000 and 13,000 copies, not necessarily layered, were quoted). This was quite beyond the capacity of 515 company to provide. The suggestion was made that the maps needed should be produced from Second Edition plates, with amendments, and printed by the Ordnance Survey as Third Edition in three colours, black, red and green. The sheets required in layered form could then be sent to Northern Ireland for overprinting with layers by the survey unit. The probability is, therefore, that with the Third Edition already in production early in 1942, few layered Second Edition sheets with a green wood plate were in fact issued. The category is thus generally omitted from the list below.

Publication of Third Edition sheets without layers began in February 1942, in not three colours, but five. A blue water plate and an orange contour plate overprinting the black were added to the red, green and black plates mentioned above.[272] Some contours over the 1000 feet level were interpolated. The military four-part road classification added to most second edition sheets was reduced to three, with the least significant roads unclassified. Road classification was revised for all sheets to 1 January 1942. In addition, all 51 sheets for which layer plates existed were issued with layers, in print runs of one thousand. By now the printing was less refined, the linework having spread, and the colour darker. It remained General Staff policy – determined back in November 1941 while the Second Edition was still in production – that layer plates be produced for the remaining 25 sheets. They were made for a further nineteen sheets, and black pulls taken from them, but it seems no more layered sheets were published.

Progress on the preparation of the bog overprint is well documented in the monthly reports of the time.[273] We learn that work was certainly underway by November 1942 on the drawing of bog maps for Northern Ireland, by 515 Corps Field Survey Company, R.E., that in December "arrangements were being made in December for copies of six-inch maps to be sent up from Eire, for the bog information to be abstracted", and that in January 1943 "Northern Ireland is now covered". Work was complete on five counties in the south with another five in hand. "One sheet was printed". Unfortunately it did not reveal which. It also left open to interpretation whether the completion of the work in the north amounted to drawing, or to the printing of sheets, overprinted as far as the border.[274] There is independent evidence that one sheet (304, q.v.) may have been issued in this format, but no copy of such a provisional version has yet been located that will confirm the supposition. The series was produced at a time when an American armoured force was in Northern Ireland.[275]

One thousand copies of each sheet were printed. The production material for the bog areas came from two sources: the six-inch geological field sheets, mostly dating from 1860-1900, loaned either from the Ordnance Survey of Northern Ireland or from the authorities in Dublin via the British Military Mission, and also the one-inch geological maps held by Queen's University, Belfast. The overprint showed known bog areas in solid purple, and suspected area in hatched purple. There was a note at the top of the sheet: *The bog areas on this sheet are shown according to the best available*

---

[271] Roger Hellyer, *Ordnance Survey small-scale maps indexes: 1801-1998.* Kerry: David Archer, 1999, section 28.

[272] Solid blue was referred to in a document dated 24 December 1941, and a specification including stipple blue for larger areas had been agreed by mid-February 1942.

[273] Survey Directorate, British Troops Northern Ireland: monthly reports from 1 July 1942 to 31 May 1943. PRO WO 402/95.

[274] Sheets 303, 304, 307, 311, 317, 318, 319, 325, 326, 327 cover the line of the border.

[275] GSGS 4136 series file, at present with DGC, document dated 28 May 1943.

information. They are likely to vary with the seasons. The information should, wherever possible be confirmed by ground reconnaissance. Sometimes this additional statement followed: *When a Bog Area is bounded by an apparent straight line this indicates that detailed information is not available on the adjoining large scale sheet from which the information was compiled.* The bog map remained current for many years after the war, and was only finally declared obsolete on 16 October 1963.

The record is also somewhat ambiguous about the training area overprint. Seventeen sheets were involved, all with additional headings overprinted in red: *Training Areas Map (2nd Edition) March 1943 (Prepared by T.A.S.C. N.I.)* and *Third Edition with special overprint.* The relevant monthly reports[276] make no mention of more than one edition, and, with no copies of a first edition recorded, the possibility of their existence is omitted from the list below. The February report notes that work was in hand overprinting all seventeen sheets, that plates for three sheets had been prepared, and that printing would be done on completion of all plates. The March report reveals that all seventeen sheets were overprinted, the maps complete and issued. The overprint was in green, yellow and red, sometimes patterned, sometimes screened to suggest other colours. Training area boundaries were marked in solid lining; the areas were numbered, presumably according to lists prepared and published elsewhere.

GSGS 4136 was allocated the NATO Standard Series Designation M721, a number given first by AMS to GSGS 3907, but never used. It would never be used on GSGS 4136 sheets either. The series remained current until M723 became available in Northern Ireland in 1965. Even then only those sheets with coverage entirely within the six counties, 305, 308, 309, 311, 312, 313, 314, 318, 319, 320, 321, were affected, with stocks cancelled in February 1965 and the sheets officially made obsolete in November 1966.[277] In April 1968 there were instructions to reduce the stocks of the unlayered map to 500 copies of each the remaining sheets, the excess to be offered to Ireland. On 8 September 1976 came the instruction: "OS Dublin and OS Belfast are to produce 1:50,000 cover of Ireland. D. Mil. Svy is definitely to take a military version of the cover of Northern Ireland & will probably also take cover of the Republic: the SSD will be M728. If/when there is complete cover in M728 the M721 remaining cover should be made obsolete."[278] In the event it appears that M728 coverage is only of Northern Ireland, with purchase of maps from OSI of coverage in the south as necessary. GSGS 4136 (M721) coverage of the Republic evidently remained available, though presumably little used, until after 1976, though it has not proved possible as yet to pinpoint the date on which it was officially made obsolete.

Sources

Only two sets of GSGS 3917 are known, that in the DGC (ex Military Survey) Superseded Collection, transferred in 2001 from Tolworth to the British Library (BL-d), and another (lacking the 1939 *Belfast*) in the Bodleian Library, Oxford. The Bodleian received the 1931 *Belfast*, at C19:10(4), on 5 July 1949, and the other sheets, at C19:1(73), on 9 September 1981. Both GSGS 3943 sheets are in BL-d, and *Cork* is in the Bodleian at C19:15(65). For GSGS 4136 the BL-d collection is again much the most comprehensive, though it contains only two sheets of the extremely rare first edition – indeed, only five have come to light so far. But it does contain many second, and a virtually complete set of third edition printings, including the layered edition, the bog and the training area overprints. Another fine set of second editions is in the Library of Congress, acquired from the US War Department Map Collection, which is of particular interest for the several layered printings within it. Third edition sets without layers are commonplace, but the other variants will probably now only be found in any quantity in the BL-d collection. There are also several sheets in the layered edition in the National Library of Scotland. Some reproduction materials are in the BL-d collection; others, including the black pulls from the layer plates of an additional nineteen sheets, are in the Map Library, Trinity College, Dublin.

---

[276] Survey Directorate, British Troops Northern Ireland: monthly reports for February and March, 1943, in PRO WO 402/95.

[277] Sheet 304 is also listed in the M723 series file, but not the Product Information Branch card index, both held by DGC. But it probably survived because without it a 5 km band of Donegal would not have been covered.

[278] Information from Product Information Branch card index, held by DGC.

4. GSGS 3917 *Northern Ireland*, later *Ireland*

For a explanation of the detail in each column see pages 86 to 89.

Armagh [Sheet 47]   18 by 12 miles
IG   1932   WO 1000/32   1911   1913   3   3   3   Co   BL-d

Ballycastle. Sheet 8.   18 by 12 miles
IG   1932   no code   1912   1914   3   3   3   O   BL-d
Proof copies are in both the Ob and BL-d sets. With stamp: Zinc Printing Dept O.S.O., Southampton: CR 288 / 30 Nov 1932 / 1st Proof. So far no published copy of this sheet has been located, but its presence on contemporary indexes leaves little doubt that it was issued in 1934 along with the remainder of the outline set.

Ballymoney. Sheets 13 & 19. Part of 7.   18 by c.31 miles
IG   1932   500/34   1912   1914   3   3G   3   O   BL-d
The northern sheet line is at 446 km N.

Belfast [Sheets 16 & 17]   36 by 21 miles
                -       ?1927   ?500/27   3L 3L 3   1
IG   1931   WO 3000/32   1910-2   500/27. 1000/31   3L 3L 3   Co   BL-d 2
IG   1931   WO 1500/39   1910-2   500/27. 1000/31   3L 3L 3   Co   BL-d 2,3
The base map is sheets 16 & 17 in the Third Edition, large sheet series (SSS sheets 36, 37, and parts of 28, 29, 38). Its unique origin provides it with unique features among maps of this series: the blue wash plate, the third edition sheet border. 1. A magnetic variation date of January 1927 on the military overprint plate on the next suggests the possibility of an unrecorded 1927 printing. 2. With civilian prices 1/6,2/-,3/-. See figure 20. 3. With uncoloured contours.

Buncrana. Sheets 11 & 17.   18 by 24 miles
IG   1932   500/34   1910   1924   3   33   3   O   BL-d
An additional imprint line reads *Ordnance Survey Office, Southampton, 1924*. It is more probable that this would have been associated with a 1924 reprint of sheet 17 than a combined sheet. Nineteen Third Edition sheets covering Northern Ireland, including 11 and 17, have so far been recorded with this imprint.

Clogher. Sheets (71. 72.) & 82.   18 by 24 miles
IG   1932   500/34   1910   1912   3   33   3   O   BL-d
The sheet 72 area is covered by an extrusion.

Cookstown. Sheets 27 & 35.   18 by 24 miles
IG   1932   500/34   1912   1914   3   33   3   O   BL-d

County Down S.E. [Sheets 49 & 61. Parts of 48 & 60]   c.28¼ by 24 miles
IG   1931   WO 2000/32   1912   1914   3   3G   3   Co   BL-d
The western sheet line is at 319 km E.

Cushendall. Sheets 14, 20 & 21. Parts of 28 & 29.   c.26¾ by c.27 miles
IG   1932   500/34   1912   1914   3   3G   3   O   BL-d
The eastern sheet line is at 351 km E, the southern at 391 km N, overlapping *Belfast* by about 250 metres.

Donegal. Sheets 24 & 32. Parts of 23 & 31.   c.26 by 24 miles
IG   1932   500/34   1912   1914   3   3G   3   O   BL-d
The western sheet line is at 179 km E.

Dundalk. Sheets 70 & 81.   18 by 24 miles
IG   1932   500/34   1912   191-   3   33   3   O   BL-d

Dungiven. Sheets 12 & 18.   18 by 24 miles
IG   1932   500/34   1912   1914   3   33   3   O   BL-d

Enniskillen. Sheets 45 & 57.   18 by 24 miles
IG   1932   500/34   1910   1924   3 33   3 O   BL-d

An additional imprint line reads *Ordnance Survey Office, Southampton, 1924*. It is more probable that this would have been associated with a 1924 reprint of sheet 57 than a combined sheet. Nineteen Third Edition sheets covering Northern Ireland are recorded with this imprint: so far neither sheet 45 nor 57 is among those recorded.

Londonderry [Sheet 12. Parts of 11, 17 & 18]   28 by 19 miles
            -        1924
IG   1932   WO 1000/32   -   1924   3 -   3 Co BL-d

The publication information reads *Printed at the Ordnance Survey Office, Southampton in 1924*. The sheet lines coincide with a small sheet series sheet line to the east, but nowhere else. This sheet (apart from *Belfast*, q.v.) is unique in that any sheet lines which differ from those of the small sheet series do not fall on natural grid co-ordinates. Just contained within the sheet lines are Dungiven to the south, Buncrana to the west and Magilligan Point to the north. A sheet covering this area was evidently required in 1924, but so far no corroborative evidence has been discovered, in catalogues or on indexes emanating either from the War Office or the Ordnance Survey – its purpose could, presumably, have been either military or civilian.

Lough Swilly [Sheets 1 & 5]   18 by 20½ miles
IG   1932   1000/32   1911   1913   3 3+   3 Co BL-d

Monaghan. Sheets 46 & 58.   18 by 24 miles
IG   1932   500/34   1912   191-   3 33   3 O   BL-d
See figure 21.

Moville. Sheets 2 & 6.   18 by 20½ miles
IG   1932   500/34   1912   1914   3 3+   3 O   BL-d

Newry. Sheets 47 & 59. Parts of 48 & 60.   c.25 by 24 miles
IG   1932   500/34   1912   1914   3 3G   3 O   BL-d
The eastern sheet line is at 319 km E.

Newtown Stewart. Sheets 25 & 33.   18 by 24 miles
IG   1932   500/34   1912   1914   3 33   3 O   BL-d

Six Mile Cross. Sheets 26 & 34.   18 by 24 miles
IG   1932   500/34   1912   1914   3 33   3 O   BL-d

Swanlinbar. Sheets 44 & 56. Part of 43.   18 by 24 miles
IG   1932   500/34   1912   1914   3 3G   3 O   BL-d
The sheet is eighteen miles wide, extended in the north-west corner to 188 km E in sheet 43, in order to cover the Northern Ireland area. This gives a maximum width of some 20¼ miles.

Supplement

The following are lithographed reprints of engraved outline maps, with the War Office Irish Grid overprinted in purple. The only copies recorded have been trimmed close to the printed matter, resulting in the removal of any possible military detail outside the map frame. Thus any GSGS number, print code or publication date is unknown. The grid co-ordinates are displayed unconventionally, in that they appear only at 10 km intervals around the border, and these are enlarged. This may be to avoid confusion with the graticule values displayed at minute intervals, a feature of the border of the one-inch engraved map, were the grid values to appear every kilometre as usual.[279] The 5 km repeater grid values across the face of the sheet remain in place. It may be that these sheets are two surviving proof copies connected with the conversion in 1940 of GSGS 3917 into a map covering the whole of Ireland. The scheme included the publication of 24 "Second Edition" sheets, most of which could only have been in the north. Presumably what was required was the reissue of the 1934 combined sheets in whatever way was possible – it is quite possible that the original reproduction material for them was no longer available. If so, this provides a possible reason why *Ballymoney*, published in 1934 as a combination of sheets 13, 19 and part of 7, had to be reissued as separate sheets. The scheme was abandoned in June 1940 (see page 50).

Sheet 7 *Giant's Causeway*			18 by 12 miles	
IG ? ?	1912		3 3 3 O BFq	

Sheet 19 *Maghera*			18 by 12 miles	
IG ? ?	1913		3 3 3 O BFq	

5. GSGS 3943 *Eire*

For a explanation of the detail in each column see pages 86 to 89.

Bantry Bay. Sheet 199 (Part of) sheets 191, 192, 198, 203, 204.   54.854 km by 43 km
    -        1925   3   3G   3   1
IG   1933   500/34   1908   1925   3   3G   3   O   BL-d   2
1. A note on an index once held by Military Survey that the sheet was "Gridded 1925" would appear to confirm this earlier printing (index in Cu-CCS Archives). 2. Publication information reads *Printed at the Ordnance Survey Office, Southampton, 1925*. The western sheet line is at 50 km E, the south at 17 km N and the north at 60 km N. The eastern sheet line lies on the eastern edge of sheets 192, 199, 204 (at 104.854 km E). With a neat line border, and black waterlining. The lower marginalia is, unusually, within the neat line. The various fortifications in and around Bantry Bay appear on the black plate.

Cork [Sheet 80]   24 by 34 miles
    -        WO 3.25   1908-10   1918   3L 3L   3
IG   1933   WO 3.25. 1400/34   1908-10   1918   3L 3L   3   O   BL-d
The base map is the black outline plate only of sheet 80 in the Third Edition, large sheet series (SSS sheets 187, 195, and parts of 175, 176, 186, 194, 201, 202). The price statement is removed. Evidence for an earlier (pre-GSGS 3943) edition lies in the survival of the print code WO 3.25, also the note on an index once held by Military Survey that the sheet was "Gridded 1924" (index in Cu-CCS Archives). The various fortifications around Cork Harbour and Kinsale appear on the black plate.

---

[279] This had not been an issue with the sheets issued in 1932 and 1934 because all detail of the engraved map outside the neat line had been deleted. Its survival here could be interpreted as a sign of the extreme haste with which this wartime work, if such it be, was carried out. An extract from sheet 19 appears in *Sheetlines* 46 (1996), page 32.

6. GSGS 4136 *Ireland (Large sheet series)*

For a explanation of the detail in each column see pages 86 to 89.

Sheet 301   50 by 30 km

1	2	3	4	6	8	9	13	14	15
1							O		
2	-	-	nc	-	-		C	BL-d	1
2	1940	1941	9000/5/41	OS 1941	m4		C	BL-d	2
3	1940	1942	21,516/4/42 C	-	1.1.42		C	BL-d	
3	1940	1942	21,516/4/42 C	-	1.1.42	1943	CB	BL-d	
3	1940	1942	1500/1/53	-	1.1.42		C	BL-d	

Layer plates were made for this sheet, probably in 1943. A black pull from them is in Dtc. 1. With heading. 2. There is no Second Edition heading.

Sheet 302   50 by 30 km

1	2	3	4	6	8	9	13	14	15
1	-	-	3000/40/C	-	-		O	BL-d	
2	1940	1941	9000/5/41	OS 1941	m4		C	Wc	
3	1940	-	21,516/4/42 C	-	1.1.42		C	BL-d	
3	1940	-	21,516/4/42 C	-	1.1.42	1943	CB	BL-d	
3	1940	1942	1500/12/52	-	1.1.42		C	BL-d	

Layer plates were made for this sheet, probably in 1943. A black pull from them is in Dtc. There was some discussion about a further reprint of this sheet in 1965, but it is unlikely that a printing order was issued.

Sheet 303   30 by 50 km

1	2	3	4	6	8	9	13	14	15
1							O		
2	1940	1941	5000/9/41 LR	OS 1941	m4		C	BL-d	
2	1940	1941	nc	OS 1941	m4		C	BL-d	
2							CLo		
3	1940	1942	31,516/5/42 F	-	1.1.42		C	BL-d	
3	1940	1942	31,516/5/42 F	-	1.1.42		CL	BL-d	
3	1940	1942	31,516/5/42 F	-	1.1.42	nd	CB	BL-d	
3	1940	-	6000/12/42 LR	-	1.1.42		C	BL-d	
3	1940	1942	4000/6/54 SPC,RE	WO 1954	1.1.42		C	BL-d	

Military Survey approved a printing order for this sheet on 17 March 1965, but it is not known whether the job was undertaken.

Sheet 304   50 by 30 km

1	2	3	4	6	8	9	13	14	15
1							O		
2	1940	1941	21,000/5/41	OS 1941	m4		C	BL-d	
2	1940	1941	5000/9/41 LR	OS 1941	m4		C	BL-d	
2							CLo		
3	1940	1942	31,516/5/42 F	-	1.1.42		C	BL-d	
3	1940	1942	31,516/5/42 F	-	1.1.42		CL	BL-d	
3				-			CB		1
3	1940	1942	31,516/5/42 F	-	1.1.42	1943	CB	BL-d	1
3	1940	-	6000/12/42 LR	-	1.1.42		C	BL-d	
3	1940	1942	515/43/213	-	1.1.42		C	IWM	
3	1940	1942	nc	-	1.1.42	3.43	CT	BL-d	
3	1940	1942	1500/12/52	-	1.1.42		C	BL-d	
3	1940	1942	4000/6/54 SPC,RE	WO 1954	1.1.42		C	BL-d	

1. The OS record card suggests two printings with bogs, the first probably with coverage only of Northern Ireland, then the 1943 printing covering also the Irish Free State area.

1	2	3	4	6	8	9	13	14	15

Sheet 305 50 by 30 km

1							O		
2	1940	1941	21,000/3/41	OS 1941	m4		C	BL-d	
2	1940	1941	5000/9/41 LR	OS 1941	m4		C	BL-d	
2							CLo		
3	1940	-	31,516/5/42 F	-	1.1.42		C	BL-d	
3	1940	-	31,516/5/42 F	-	1.1.42		CL	BL-d	
3	1940	-	31,516/5/42 F	-	1.1.42	1942	CB	BL-d	
3	1940	-	7000/12/42 LR	-	1.1.42		C	BL-d	
3	1940	1942	-	-	1.1.42		CT	BL-d torn	
3	1940	1942	4000/6/54 SPC,RE	WO 1954	1.1.42		C	BL-d	

Sheet 306 50 by 30 km

1							O		
2	-	-	nc	-	-		C	BL-d	
2	1940	1941	9000/5/41	OS 1941	m4		C	Wc	
3	1940	1942	21,516/4/42 C	-	1.1.42		C	BL-d	
3	1940	1942	21,516/4/42 C	-	1.1.42	1943	CB	BL-d	
3	1940	1942	1500/12/52	-	1.1.42		C	BL-d	

Layer plates were made for this sheet, probably in 1943. A black pull from them dated 1 February 1943 is in Dtc.

Sheet 307 50 by 30 km

1	-	-	3000/40	-	-		O	BL-d	
2	1940	1941	5000/9/41 LR	OS 1941	m4		C	BL-d	
2							CLo		
3	1940	1942	31,516/5/42 A	-	1.1.42		C	BL-d	
3	1940	1942	31,516/5/42 A	-	1.1.42		CL	BL-d	
3	1940	1942	31,516/5/42 A	-	1.1.42	1943	CB	BL-d	
3	1940	-	6000/12/42 LR	-	1.1.42		C	BL-d	
3	1940	1942	nc	-	1.1.42	3.43	CT	BL-d	
3	1940	1942	4000/6/54 SPC,RE	WO 1954	1.1.42		C	BL-d	

Military Survey approved a printing order for this sheet on 17 March 1965, but it is not known whether the job was undertaken.

Sheet 308 50 by 30 km

1							O		
2	-	-	nc	-	m4		C	BL-d	
2	1940	1941	21,000/3/41	OS 1941	m4		C	NLS	
2	1940	1941	5000/9/41 LR	OS 1941	m4		C	BL-d	
2							CLo		
3	1940	-	31,516/5/42 F	-	1.1.42		C	BL-d	
3	1940	-	31,516/5/42 F	-	1.1.42		CL	BL-d	
3	1940	-	31,516/5/42 F	-	1.1.42	1942	CB	BL-d	
3	1940	-	8000/12/42 LR	-	1.1.42		C	BL-d	
3	1940	1942	nc	-	1.1.42	3.43	CT	BL-d	
3	1940	1942	5000/6/54 SPC,RE	WO 1954	1.1.42		C	BL-d	

Sheet 309 50 by 30 km

1							O		
2	1940	1941	21,000/3/41	OS 1941	m4		C	NLS	
2	1940	1941	2500/8/41	OS 1941	10.7.41		C	BL-d	
2	1940	1941	5000/9/41 LR	OS 1941	m4		C	BL-d	
2							CLo		
3	1940	1942	31,516/5/42 A	-	1.1.42		C	BL-d	
3	1940	1942	31,516/5/42 A	-	1.1.42		CL	BL-d	
3	1940	1942	31,516/5/42 A	-	1.1.42	1942	CB	BL-d	
3	1940	1942	9000/1/43 Wa	-	1.1.42		C	BL-d	
3	1940	1942	nc	-	1.1.42	3.43	CT	BL-d	
3	1940	1942	4000/6/54 SPC,RE	WO 1954	1.1.42		C	BL-d	

1	2	3	4	6	8	9	13	14	15

Sheet 310

1	2	3	4	6	8	9	13	14	15
1							50 by 30 km		
							O		
2	-	-	-	-	-		C	BL-d	
2	1940	1941	9000/4/41	-	m4		C	Wc	
3	1940	1942	nc	-	1.1.42		C	BL-d	1
3	1940	1942	nc	-	1.1.42	1943	CB	BL-d	
3	1940	1942	1500/12/52	-	1.1.42		C	BL-d	

Layer plates were made for this sheet, probably in 1943. A black pull from them is in Dtc. 1. The Causton's printing record copy is in BL Maps 10805(178): WE 6553 – 21673 copies – 1.5.42.

Sheet 311

1	2	3	4	6	8	9	13	14	15
1							50 by 30 km		
							O		
2	1940	1941	5000/9/41 LR	OS 1941	m4		C	BL	
2	1940	1941	nc	OS 1941	m4		C	BL-d	
2							CLo		
3	1940	1942	31,516/5/42 F	-	1.1.42		C	BL-d	
3	1940	1942	31,516/5/42 F	-	1.1.42		CL	BL-d	
3	1940	1942	31,516/5/42 F	-	1.1.42	1943	CB	BL-d	
3	1940	1942	6000/12/42 Wa	-	1.1.42		C	BL-d	
3	1940	1942	nc	-	1.1.42	3.43	CT	BL-d	
3	1940	1942	4000/6/54 SPC,RE	WO 1954	1.1.42		C	BL-d	

Sheet 312

1	2	3	4	6	8	9	13	14	15
1							50 by 30 km		
							O		
2	-	-	nc	-	m4		C	BL-d	
2	1940	1941	21,000/3/41	OS 1941	m4		C	Wc	
2	1940	1941	5000/9/41 LR	OS 1941	m4		C	BL-d	
2	1940	1941	1000/12/41	515(CFS)CRE	1.10.41		CLo	BL-d	
3	1940	1942	31,516/5/42 A	-	1.1.42		C	BL-d	
3	1940	1942	31,516/5/42 A	-	1.1.42		CL	BL-d	
3	1940	1942	31,516/5/42 A	-	1.1.42	1942	CB	BL-d	
3	1940	1942	7000/12/42 Wa	-	1.1.42		C	BL-d	
3	1940	1942	nc	-	1.1.42	3.43	CT	BL-d	
3	1940	1942	4500/5/54 SPC,RE	WO 1954	1.1.42		C	BL-d	

Sheet 313

1	2	3	4	6	8	9	13	14	15
1							50 by 30 km		
							O		
2	-	-	nc	-	m4		C	BL-d	
2	1940	1941	21,000/3/41	OS 1941	m4		C	Wc	
2	1940	1941	3000/8/41	-	10.7.41		C	PC	
2	1940	1941	5000/9/41 LR	OS 1941	m4		C	BL-d	
2							CLo		
2	1940	1941	20,000/5/41	OS 1941	m4		CL	BL-d	
3	1940	1942	31,516/5/42 A	-	1.1.42		C	BL-d	
3	1940	1942	31,516/5/42 A	-	1.1.42		CL	BL-d	
3	1940	1942	31,516/5/42 A	-	1.1.42	1942	CB	BL-d	
3	1940	1942	9000/12/42 Wa	-	1.1.42		C	BL-d	
3	1940	1942	nc	-	1.1.42	3.43	CT	BL-d	
3	1940	1942	1500/12/52	-	1.1.42		C	BL-d	
3	1940	1942	3000/6/54 SPC,RE	WO 1954	1.1.42		C	BL-d	
3	1940	1942	2000/9/62/27/SPC S/STD	SPC RE	1.1.42		CL	BL-d	1

1. The word *Layered* is deleted from the heading. The contours are now on the same plate as the layers.

1	2	3	4	6	8	9	13	14	15

Sheet 314
							50 by 30 km		
1	-	-	3000/40/C	-	-		O	PC	
2	-	-	nc	-	-		C	PC	
2	-	-	nc	-	m4		C	BL-d	
2	1940	1941	21,000/3/41	OS 1941	m4		C	Wc	
2	1940	1941	5000/9/41 LR	OS 1941	m4		C	BL-d	
2							CLo		
3	1940	1942	31,516/5/42/M	-	1.1.42		C	BL-d	
3	1940	1942	31,516/5/42/M	-	1.1.42		CL	PC	
3	1940	1942	31,516/5/42/M	-	1.1.42	1942	CB	BL-d	
3	1940	1942	8000/12/42 Wa	-	1.1.42		C	BL-d	
3	1940	1942	nc	-	1.1.42	3.43	CT	BL-d	
3	1940	1942	1500/1/53	-	1.1.42		C	BL-d	
3	1940	1942	4000/6/54 SPC,RE	WO 1954	1.1.42		C	BL-d	
3	1940	1942	2000/9/62/27/SPC S/STD	SPC RE	1.1.42		CL	BL-d	1

See figures 8 and 9. 1. With no *Layered* heading. The contours are now on the same plate as the layers.

Sheet 315
							50 by 30 km		
1							O		
2	1940	1941	4000/40	OS 1941	m4		C	BL-d	
2	1940	1941	4000/40. 9000/5/41	OS 1941	m4		C	Wc	
3	1940	1942	21,516/4/42 C	-	1.1.42		C	BL-d	
3	1940	1942	21,516/4/42 C	-	1.1.42	1943	CB	BL-d	
3	1940	1942	1000/1/53	-	1.1.42		C	BL-d	

Layer plates were made for this sheet, probably in 1943. A black pull from them is in Dtc.

Sheet 316
							50 by 30 km		
1							O		
2	-	-	nc	-	-		C	BL-d	
2	1940	1941	9000/5/41	OS 1941	m4		C	Wc	
3	1940	1942	21,516/4/42 C	-	1.1.42		C	BL-d	
3	1940	1942	21,516/4/42 C	-	1.1.42	1943	CB	BL-d	
3	1940	1942	1000/1/53	-	1.1.42		C	BL-d	

Layer plates were made for this sheet, probably in 1943. A black pull from them is in Dtc.

Sheet 317
							50 by 30 km		
1							O		
2	1940	1941	21,000/5/41	OS 1941	-		C	Wc	
2	1940	1941	5000/9/41 NI	-	10.7.41		C	BL-d	
2							CLo		
3	1940	-	31,516/5/42 F	-	1.1.42		C	BL-d	
3	1940	-	31,516/5/42 F	-	1.1.42		CL	BL-d	
3	1940	-	31,516/5/42 F	-	1.1.42	1943	CB	BL-d	
3	1940	1942	5000/12/42 Wa	-	1.1.42		C	BL-d	
3	1940	1942	515/43/213	-	1.1.42		C	BL	1
3	1940	1942	nc	-	1.1.42	3.43	CT	BL-d	

Military Survey approved a printing order for this sheet on 17 March 1965, but it is not known whether the job was undertaken. 1. With red, blue, orange and green colour blocks top right.

Sheet 318
							50 by 30 km		
1							O		
2	1940	1941	nc	OS 1941	m4		C	BL-d	
2	1940	1941	21,000/5/41	OS 1941	m4		C	Wc	
2	1940	1941	5000/9/41 LR	OS 1941	m4		C	BL-d	
2							CLo		
3	1940	-	31,516/5/42/M	-	1.1.42		C	BL-d	
3	1940	-	31,516/5/42/M	-	1.1.42		CL	BL-d	
3	1940	-	31,516/5/42/M	-	1.1.42	1943	CB	BL-d	
3	1940	1942	7000/12/42 Wa	-	1.1.42		C	BL-d	
3	1940	-	nc	-	1.1.42	3.43	CT	BL-d	
3	1940	1942	4000/6/54 SPC,RE	WO 1954	1.1.42		C	BL-d	

1	2	3	4	6	8	9	13	14	15
Sheet 319							50 by 30 km		
1							O		
2	1940	1941	21,000/3/41	OS 1941	m4		C	BL-d	
2	1940	1941	5000/9/41 LR	OS 1941	m4		C	BL-d	
2							CLo		
3	1940	1942	31,516/5/42/M	-	1.1.42		C	BL-d	
3	1940	1942	31,516/5/42/M	-	1.1.42		CL	BL-d	
3	1940	1942	31,516/5/42/M	-	1.1.42	1943	CB	BL-d	
3	1940	1942	7000/1/43 Wa	-	1.1.42		C	BL-d	
3	1940	1942	nc	-	1.1.42	3.43	CT	BL-d	
3	1940	1942	4000/6/54 SPC,RE	WO 1954	1.1.42		C	BL-d	
Sheet 320							50 by 30 km		
1							O		
2	1940	1941	21,000/3/41	OS 1941	m4		C	BL-d	
2	1940	1941	5000/9/41 NI	-	10.7.41		C	BL-d	
2	1940	1941	1000/2/42	515(CFS)CRE	1.11.41		CLo	BL-d	
3	1940	1942	31,516/5/42 F	-	1.1.42		C	BL-d	
3	1940	1942	31,516/5/42 F	-	1.1.42		CL	BL-d	
3	1940	1942	31,516/5/42 F	-	1.1.42	1942	CB	BL-d	
3	1940	1942	nc	-	1.1.42	3.43	CT	BL-d	
3	1940	1942	1500/1/53	-	1.1.42		C	BL-d	
3	1940	1942	3000/6/54 SPC,RE	WO 1954	1.1.42		C	BL-d	
Sheet 321							50 by 30 km		
1							O		
2					-		C		
2	1940	1941	21,000/3/41	OS 1941	m4		C	Wc	
2	1940	1941	5000/9/41 NI	-	10.7.41		C	BL-d	
2							CLo		
3	1940	-	31,516/5/42/M	-	1.1.42		C	BL-d	
3	1940	-	31,516/5/42/M	-	1.1.42		CL	BL-d	
3	1940	-	31,516/5/42/M	-	1.1.42	1942	CB	BL-d	
3	1940	1942	8000/12/42 Wa	-	1.1.42		C	PC	
3	1940	-	nc	-	1.1.42	3.43	CT	BL-d	
3	1940	1942	1500/1/53	-	1.1.42		C	BL-d	
3	1940	1942	5000/6/54 SPC,RE	WO 1954	1.1.42		C	BL-d	
Sheet 322							50 by 30 km		
1							O		
2	1940	1941	9000/5/41 C	OS 1941	m4		C	BL-d	
3	1940	1942	21,516/4/42 C	-	1.1.42		C	BL-d	
3	1940	1942	21,516/4/42 C	-	1.1.42	1943	CB	BL-d	
3	1940	1942	3000/5/59/3305/R	1 SPC RE	1.1.42		C	BL-d	
Sheet 323							50 by 30 km		
1							O		
2	-	-	nc	-	-		C	BL-d	
2	1940	1941	9000/5/41	OS 1941	m4		C	Cu	
3	1940	1942	21,516/5/42 C	-	1.1.42		C	BL-d	
3	1940	1942	21,516/5/42 C	-	1.1.42	1943	CB	BL-d	
3	1940	1942	3000/5/59/3305/R	1 SPC RE	1.1.42		C	BL-d	

1	2	3	4	6	8	9	13	14	15
Sheet 324							50 by 30 km		
1							O		
2	-	-	nc	-	-		C	BL-d	
2	1940	1941	9000/5/41	OS 1941	m4		C	Ob	
2							CLo		
3	1940	1942	12,000/3/42 C	-	1.1.42		C	BL-d	
3	1940	1942	12,000/3/42 C	-	1.1.42		CL	BL-d	
3	1940	1942	12,000/3/42 C. 14,516/4/42 C	-	1.1.42		C	BL-d	
3	1940	1942	12,000/3/42 C. 14,516/4/42 C	-	1.1.42	1943	CB	BL-d	
3	1940	1942	3000/6/54 SPC,RE	WO 1954	1.1.42		C	BL-d	
Sheet 325							50 by 30 km		
1							O		
2					-		C		
2	1940	1941	21,000/3/41 C	OS 1941	m4		C	Wc	
2	1940	1941	5000/9/41 NI	-	10.7.41		C	BL-d	
2							CLo		
3	1940	1942	24,000/3/42 C	-	1.1.42		C	BL-d	
3	1940	1942	24,000/3/42 C	-	1.1.42	1943	CB	BL-d	
3	1940	1942	24,000/3/42 C. 7516/4/42 C	-	1.1.42		C	BL-d	
3	1940	1942	24,000/3/42 C. 7516/4/42 C	-	1.1.42		CL	BL-d	
3	1940	1942	7000/1/43 Wa	-	1.1.42		C	BL-d	
3	1940	1942	nc	-	1.1.42	3.43	CT	BL-d	
3	1940	1942	3000/6/54 SPC,RE	WO 1954	1.1.42		C	BL-d	

Military Survey approved a printing order for this sheet on 17 March 1965, but it is not known whether the job was undertaken.

1	2	3	4	6	8	9	13	14	15
Sheet 326							50 by 30 km		
1							O		
2	1940	1941	21,000/3/41	OS 1941	m4		C	Dtc	
2	1940	1941	5000/9/41 NI		10.7.41		C	BL d	
2							CLo		
3	1940	1942	31,516/3/42 LR	-	1.1.42		C	BL-d	
3	1940	1942	31,516/3/42 LR	-	1.1.42		CL	BL-d	
3	1940	1942	31,516/3/42 LR	-	1.1.42	1943	CB	BL-d	
3	1940	1942	12,000/11/42/C	-	1.1.42		C	BL-d	
3	1940	1942	nc	-	1.1.42	3.43	CT	BL-d	
3	1940	1942	3000/6/54 SPC,RE	WO 1954	1.1.42		C	BL-d	

Military Survey approved a printing order for this sheet on 17 March 1965, but it is not known whether the job was undertaken.

1	2	3	4	6	8	9	13	14	15
Sheet 327							50 by 30 km		
1							O		
2	-	-	nc	-	-		C	BL-d	
2	1940	1941	21,000/3/41	OS 1941	m4		C	BL-d	
2	1940	1941	5000/9/41 NI	-	10.7.41		C	BL-d	
2							CLo		
3	1940	1942	21,000/3/42 C	-	1.1.42		C	BL-d	
3	1940	1942	21,000/3/42 C	-	1.1.42		CL	BL-d	
3	1940	1942	21,000/3/42 C	-	1.1.42	1942	CB	BL-d	
3	1940	1942	10,516/5/42 LR	-	1.1.42		C	BL-d	
3	1940	1942	6000/12/42 Wa	-	1.1.42		C	BL-d	
3	1940	1942	nc	-	1.1.42	3.43	CT	BL-d	
3	1940	1942	5000/6/54 SPC,RE	WO 1954	1.1.42		C	BL-d	

Military Survey approved a printing order for this sheet on 17 March 1965, but it is not known whether the job was undertaken.

1	2	3	4	6	8	9	13	14	15
Sheet 328							50 by 30 km		
1							O		
2	-	-	nc	-	-		C	BL-d	
2	1940	1941	9000/5/41 C	OS 1941	m4		C	Wc	
3	1940	1942	21,516/4/42 C	-	1.1.42		C	BL-d	
3	1940	1942	21,516/4/42 C	-	1.1.42	1943	CB	BL-d	
3	1940	1942	3000/5/59/3305/R	1 SPC RE	1.1.42		C	BL-d	
Sheet 329							50 by 30 km		
1							O		
2	1940	1941	9000/5/41 C	OS 1941	m4		C	BL-d	
3	1940	-	21,516/5/42 C	-	1.1.42		C	BL-d	
3	1940	-	21,516/5/42 C	-	1.1.42	1943	CB	BL-d	
3	1940	1942	3000/5/59/3305/R	1 SPC RE	1.1.42		C	BL-d	
Sheet 330							50 by 30 km		
1							O		
2	1940	1941	9000/5/41 C	OS 1941	m4		C	BL-d	
2							CLo		
3	1940	1942	12,000/3/42 C	-	1.1.42		C	BL-d	
3	1940	1942	12,000/3/42 C	-	1.1.42	1943	CB	BL-d	
3	1940	1942	14,516/4/42 LR	-	1.1.42		C	BL-d	
3	1940	1942	14,516/4/42 LR	-	1.1.42		CL	BL-d	
Sheet 331							50 by 30 km		
1							O		
2							C		
2	1940	1941	1000/11/41	515(CFS)CRE	1.10.41		CLo	Wc	
3	1940	1942	13,500/2/42 C	-	1.1.42		C	BL-d	
3	1940	1942	13,500/2/42 C	-	1.1.42		CL	BL-d	
3	1940	1942	13,500/2/42 C	-	1.1.42	1943	CB	BL-d	
3	1940	1942	13,500/2/42 C. 18,016/4/42 C	-	1.1.42		C	BL-d	
Sheet 332							50 by 30 km		
1							O		
2							C		
2	1940	1941	1000/10/41	515(CFS)CRE	1.10.41		CLo	Wc	
3	1940	1942	13,500/2/42 C	-	1.1.42		C	BL-d	1
3	1940	1942	13,500/2/42 C	-	1.1.42		C	EXg	2
3	1940	1942	13,500/2/42 C	-	1.1.42		CL	BL-d	1,3
3	1940	1942	13,500/2/42 C	-	1.1.42		CL	BL-d	1,4
3	1940	1942	13,500/2/42 C	-	1.1.42	1943	CB	BL-d	1
3	1940	1942	18,016/5/42 LR	-	1.1.42		C	BL-d	

1. The print code is present twice on these sheets, in black below the imprint, in blue (faint) above the legend. 2. A classroom teaching set in EXg contains several copies with no sign of the additional print code in blue. 3. The layer bar is misplaced in the bottom margin (clipping the "h" of "Meath"). The colours are yellow in range. 4. The layer bar is bottom side right. The colours are brown in range.

1	2	3	4	6	8	9	13	14	15
Sheet 333							50 by 30 km		
1							O		
2							C		
2	1940	1941	1000/10/41	515(CFS)CRE	1.10.41		CLo	Wc	
3	1940	1942	17,016/4/42 LR	-	1.1.42		C	BL-d	
3	1940	1942	14,503/2/43 C	-	1.1.42		C	BL-d	
3	1940	1942	14,503/2/43 C	-	1.1.42		CL	BL-d	
3	1940	1942	14,503/2/43 C	-	1.1.42	1943	CB	BL-d	
3	1940	1942	3000/5/59/3305/R	1 SPC RE	1.1.42		C	BL-d	

1	2	3	4	6	8	9	13	14	15

Sheet 334

							50 by 30 km		
1							O		
2	1940	1941	9000/5/41 C	OS 1941	m4		C	BL-d	
3	1940	1942	21,516/5/42 C	-	1.1.42		C	BL-d	
3	1940	1942	21,516/5/42 C	-	1.1.42	1943	CB	BL-d	

Layer plates were made for this sheet, probably in 1943. A black pull from them dated 1 February 1943 is in Dtc.

Sheet 335

							50 by 30 km		
1							O		
2	1940	1941	9000/5/41 C	OS 1941	m4		C	BL-d	
3	1940	1942	21,516/5/42 C	-	1.1.42		C	BL-d	
3	1940	1942	21,516/5/42 C	-	1.1.42	1943	CB	BL-d	

Layer plates were made for this sheet, probably in 1943. A black pull from them is in Dtc.

Sheet 336

							50 by 30 km		
1	-	-	3000/40/C	-	-		O	PC	
2	-	-	nc	-	-		C	BL-d	
2							CLo		
3	1940	1942	26,516/3/42 LR	-	1.1.42		C	BL-d	
3	1940	1942	26,516/3/42 LR	-	1.1.42		CL	BL-d	
3	1940	1942	26,516/3/42 LR	-	1.1.42	1943	CB	BL-d	

Sheet 337

							50 by 30 km		
1							O		
2							C		
2	1940	1941	1000/10/41	515(CFS)CRE	1.10.41		CLo	Wc	
3	1940	1942	13,500/2/42 C	-	1.1.42		C	BL-d	
3	1940	1942	13,500/2/42 C	-	1.1.42		CL	BL-d	
3	1940	1942	13,500/2/42 C	-	1.1.42	1943	CB	BL-d	
3	1940	1942	13,500/2/42 C. 18,016/4/42 C	-	1.1.42		C	BL-d	

Sheet 338

							50 by 30 km		
1							O		
2		1941					C		
2	1940	1941	1000/10/41	515(CFS)CRE	1.11.41		CLo	Wc	
3	1940	1942	13,500/2/42 C	-	1.1.42		C	BL-d	
3	1940	1942	13,500/2/42 C	-	1.1.42		CL	BL-d	
3	1940	1942	13,500/2/42 C	-	1.1.42	1943	CB	BL-d	
3	1940	1942	13,500/2/42 C. 18,016/4/42 C	-	1.1.42		C	BL-d	

Sheet 339

							50 by 30 km		
1							O		
2							C		
2	1940	1941	1000/10/41	515(CFS)CRE	1.10.41		CLo	Wc	
3	1940	1942	14,500/2/42 C	-	1.1.42		C	BL-d	
3	1940	1942	14,500/2/42 C	-	1.1.42		CL	BL-d	
3	1940	1942	14,500/2/42 C	-	1.1.42	1943	CB	BL-d	
3	1940	1942	14,500/2/42 C. 17,516/4/42 C	-	1.1.42		C	BL-d	
3	1940	1942	3000/5/59/3305/R	1 SPC RE	1.1.42		C	BL-d	

Sheet 340

							50 by 30 km		
1							O		
2	1940	1941	4000/40	OS 1941	m4		C	BL-d	
2	1940	1941	4000/40. 9000/5/41 C	OS 1941	m4		C	Wc	
3	1940	1942	21,516/5/42 C		1.1.42		C	BL-d	
3	1940	1942	21,516/5/42 C		1.1.42	1943	CB	BL-d	

1	2	3	4	6	8	9	13	14	15

Sheet 341

							50 by 30 km		
1							O		
2	-	-	nc	-	-		C	BL-d	
2	1940	1941	9000/5/41	OS 1941	m4		C	Wc	
3	1940	1942	21,516/5/42 C	-	1.1.42		C	BL-d	
3	1940	1942	21,516/5/42 C	-	1.1.42	1943	CB	BL-d	

Sheet 342

							50 by 30 km		
1							O		
2	-	-	nc	-	-		C	BL-d	
2	1940	1941	9000/5/41	OS 1941	m4		C	Wc	
2							CLo		
3	1940	1942	14,000/3/42 C	-	1.1.42		C	NLS	
3	1940	1942	14,000/3/42 C	-	1.1.42	1943	CB	BL-d	
3	1940	1942	14,000/3/42 C. 12,516/4/42 C	-	1.1.42		C	BL-d	
3	1940	1942	14,000/3/42 C. 12,516/4/42 C	-	1.1.42		CL	BL-d	

Sheet 343

							50 by 30 km		
1							O		
2							C		
2	1940	1941	1000/10/41	515(CFS)CRE	1.10.41		CLo	Wc	
3	1940	1942	14,500/2/42 C	-	1.1.42		C	NLS	
3	1940	1942	14,500/2/42 C	-	1.1.42		CL	BL-d	
3	1940	1942	14,500/2/42 C. 17,016/4/42 C	-	1.1.42		C	BL-d	
3	1940	1942	14,500/2/42 C. 17,016/4/42 C	-	1.1.42	1943	CB	BL-d	

Sheet 344

							50 by 30 km		
1							O		
2							C		
2	1940	1941	1000/10/41	515(CFS)CRE	1.10.41		CLo	Wc	
3	1940	1942	13,500/2/42 C	-	1.1.42		C	BL-d	
3	1940	1942	13,500/2/42 C	-	1.1.42		CL	BL-d	
3	1940	1942	13,500/2/42 C	-	1.1.42	1943	CB	BL-d	
3	1940	1942	13,500/2/42 C. 18,516/4/42 C	-	1.1.42		C	BL-d	

Sheet 345

							50 by 30 km		
1							O		
2	-	-	nc	-	-		C	PC	
2	1940	1941	1000/10/41	515(CFS)CRE	1.11.41		CLo	Wc	1
3	1940	1942	14,500/2/42 C	-	1.1.42		C	BL-d	
3	1940	1942	14,500/2/42 C	-	1.1.42		CL	BL-d	2
3	1940	1942	14,500/2/42 C. 17,016/4/42 C	-	1.1.42		C	BL-d	
3	1940	1942	14,500/2/42 C. 17,016/4/42 C	-	1.1.42	1943	CB	BL-d	
3	1940	1942	3000/5/59/3305/R	1 SPC RE	1.1.42		C	BL-d	

1. Poulaphuca Dam is now shown as under construction, defined by red diagonal lines in the style of the international border. This was not present on the previous state. 2. See figure 10.

Sheet 346

							50 by 30 km		
1							O		
2	-	-	nc	-	-		C	BL-d	
2	1940	1941	9000/5/41	OS 1941	m4		C	Wc	
3	1940	-	21,516/5/42 C	-	1.1.42		C	BL-d	
3	1940	-	21,516/5/42 C	-	1.1.42	1943	CB	BL-d	

1	2	3	4	6	8	9	13	14	15
Sheet 347							50 by 30 km		
1							O		
2	-	-	nc	-	-		C	BL-d	
2	1940	1941	9000/5/41 C	OS 1941	m4		C	Wc	
2							CLo		
3	1940	1942	14,000/3/42 C	-	1.1.42		C	BL-d	
3	1940	1942	14,000/3/42 C	-	1.1.42		CL	BL-d	
3	1940	1942	14,000/3/42 C	-	1.1.42	1943	CB	BL-d	
3	1940	1942	12,516/4/42 LR	-	1.1.42		C	BL-d	
Sheet 348							50 by 30 km		
1							O		
2							C		
2	1940	1941	1000/10/41	515(CFS)CRE	1.10.41		CLo	Wc	
3	1940	1942	17,000/3/42 C	-	1.1.42		C	BL-d	
3	1940	1942	17,000/3/42 C	-	1.1.42		CL	BL-d	
3	1940	1942	17,000/3/42 C	-	1.1.42	1943	CB	BL-d	
3	1940	-	14,516/4/42 LR	-	1.1.42		C	BL-d	
Sheet 349							50 by 30 km		
1							O		
2	1940	1941	13,000/3/41	OS 1941	m4		C	NLS	
2	1940	1941	1000/10/41	515(CFS)CRE	1.10.41		CLo	Wc	
3	1940	1942	16,000/3/42 C	-	1.1.42		C	BL-d	
3	1940	1942	16,000/3/42 C	-	1.1.42		CL	BL-d	
3	1940	1942	16,000/3/42 C	-	1.1.42	1943	CB	BL-d	
3	1940	1942	15,516/4/42 LR	-	1.1.42		C	BL-d	
Sheet 350							50 by 30 km		
1							O		
2							C		
2	1940	1941	1000/11/41	515(CFS)CRE	1.10.41		CLo	Wc	1
3	1940	1942	22,000/3/42 C	-	1.1.42		C	BL-d	
3	1940	1942	22,000/3/42 C	-	1.1.42		CL	BL-d	
3	1940	1942	22,000/3/42 C	-	1.1.42	1943	CB	BL-d	
3	1940	1942	9516/4/42 LR	-	1.1.42		C	BL-d	
3	1940	1942	3000/5/59/3305/R	1 SPC RE	1.1.42		C	BL-d	

1. Poulaphuca Dam is shown as under construction, defined by red diagonal lines in the style of the international border.

1	2	3	4	6	8	9	13	14	15
Sheet 351							50 by 30 km		
1							O		
2	1940	1941	9000/4/41	OS 1941	m4		C	Wc	
3	1940	1942	21,516/5/42 C	-	1.1.42		C	BL-d	
3	1940	1942	21,516/5/42 C	-	1.1.42	1943	CB	BL-d	
3	1940	1942	3000/5/59/3305/R	1 SPC RE	1.1.42		C	BL-d	
Sheet 352							50 by 30 km		
1							O		
2	1940	1941	13,000/4/41	OS 1941	m4		C	Wc	
2							CLo		
3	1940	1942	26,516/4/42 C	-	1.1.42		C	BL-d	
3	1940	1942	26,516/4/42 C	-	1.1.42		CL	BL-d	
3	1940	1942	26,516/4/42 C	-	1.1.42	1943	CB	BL-d	

1	2	3	4	6	8	9	13	14	15
Sheet 353							50 by 30 km		
1							O		
2	1940	1941	13,000/4/41	OS 1941	m4		C	IWM	
2	1940	1941	1000/10/41	515(CFS)CRE	1.11.41		CLo	Wc	
3	1940	1942	15,000/3/42 C	-	1.1.42		C	BL-d	
3	1940	1942	15,000/3/42 C	-	1.1.42	1943	CB	BL-d	
3	1940	1942	15,000/3/42 C. 16,516/4/42 C	-	1.1.42		C	BL-d	
3	1940	1942	15,000/3/42 C. 16,516/4/42 C	-	1.1.42		CL	BL-d	
Sheet 354							50 by 30 km		
1							O		
2	-	-	nc	-	-		C	BL-d	
2	1940	1941	1000/10/41	515(CFS)CRE	1.11.41		CLo	Wc	
3	1940	1942	16,000/3/42 C	-	1.1.42		C	BL-d	
3	1940	1942	16,000/3/42 C	-	1.1.42		CL	BL-d	
3	1940	1942	16,000/3/42 C. 15,516/4/42/C	-	1.1.42		C	BL-d	
3	1940	1942	16,000/3/42 C. 15,516/4/42/C	-	1.1.42	1943	CB	BL-d	
Sheet 355							50 by 30 km		
1							O		
2	-	-	nc	-	-		C	BL-d	
2	1940	1941	1000/11/41	515(CFS)CRE	1.11.41		CLo	Wc	
3	1940	1942	16,000/3/42 C	-	1.1.42		C	BL-d	
3	1940	1942	16,000/3/42 C	-	1.1.42		CL	BL-d	
3	1940	1942	16,000/3/42 C. 15,516/4/42 C	-	1.1.42		C	BL-d	
3	1940	1942	16,000/3/42 C. 15,516/4/42 C	-	1.1.42	1943	CB	BL-d	
3	1940	1942	3000/5/59/3305/R	1 SPC RE	1.1.42		C	BL-d	
Sheet 356							30 by 50 km		
1							O		
2	1940	1941	9000/4/41	OS 1941	m4		C	Wc	
3	1940	1942	21,516/4/42 C	-	1.1.42		C	BL-d	
3	1940	1942	21,516/4/42 C	-	1.1.42	1943	CB	BL-d	

Layer plates were made for this sheet, probably in 1943. A black pull from them is in Dtc.

1	2	3	4	6	8	9	13	14	15
Sheet 357							50 by 30 km		
1							O		
2	1940	1941	9000/4/41	OS 1941	m4		C	Wc	
3	1940	1942	21,516/5/42 C	-	1.1.42		C	BL-d	
3	1940	1942	21,516/5/42 C	-	1.1.42	1943	CB	BL-d	

Layer plates were made for this sheet, probably in 1943. A black pull from them is in Dtc.

1	2	3	4	6	8	9	13	14	15
Sheet 358							50 by 30 km		
1							O		
2							C		
2	1940	1941	1000/11/41	515(CFS)CRE	1.11.41		CLo	Wc	
3	1940	1942	26,516/3/42 LR	-	1.1.42		C	BL-d	
3	1940	1942	26,516/3/42 LR	-	1.1.42		CL	BL-d	
3	1940	1942	26,516/3/42 LR	-	1.1.42	1943	CB	BL-d	
Sheet 359							50 by 30 km		
1							O		
2	1940	1941	13,000/4/41	OS 1941	m4		C	Wc	
2							CLo		
3	1940	1942	12,000/3/42 C	-	1.1.42		C	BL-d	
3	1940	1942	12,000/3/42 C	-	1.1.42		CL	BL-d	
3	1940	1942	12,000/3/42 C	-	1.1.42	1943	CB	BL-d	
3	1940	1942	12,000/3/42 C. 14,516/4/42 C	-	1.1.42		C	BL-d	

1	2	3	4	6	8	9	13	14	15
Sheet 360							50 by 30 km		
1							O		
2							C		
2	1940	1941	1000/11/41	515(CFS)CRE	1.11.41		CLo	Wc	
3	1940	1942	12,000/3/42 C	-	1.1.42		C	BL-d	
3	1940	1942	12,000/3/42 C	-	1.1.42		CL	BL-d	
3	1940	1942	12,000/3/42 C	-	1.1.42	1943	CB	BL-d	
3	1940	1942	12,000/3/42 C. 14,516/4/42 C	-	1.1.42		C	BL-d	
Sheet 361							50 by 30 km		
1							O		
2	-	-	nc	-	-		C	BL-d	
2	1940	1941	1000/11/41	515(CFS)CRE	1.11.41		CLo	Wc	
3	1940	1942	26,516/3/42 LR	-	1.1.42		C	BL-d	
3	1940	1942	26,516/3/42 LR	-	1.1.42		CL	BL-d	
3	1940	1942	26,516/3/42 LR	-	1.1.42	1943	CB	BL-d	
Sheet 362							50 by 30 km		
1							O		
2	1940	1941	13,000/4/41	OS 1941	m4		C	Wc	
3	1940	1942	21,516/5/42 C	-	1.1.42		C	BL-d	
3	1940	1942	21,516/5/42 C	-	1.1.42	1943	CB	BL-d	

Layer plates were made for this sheet, probably in 1943. A black pull from them dated 1 February 1943 is in Dtc.

1	2	3	4	6	8	9	13	14	15
Sheet 363							50 by 30 km		
1							O		
2	-	-	3000/40/C	-	-		C	BL-d	
2	1940	1941	9000/4/41	OS 1941	m4		C	Wc	
3	1940	1942	21,516/5/42 C	-	1.1.42		C	BL-d	
3	1940	1942	21,516/5/42 C	-	1.1.42	1943	CB	BL-d	

Layer plates were made for this sheet, probably in 1943. A black pull from them dated 1 March 1943 is in Dtc.

1	2	3	4	6	8	9	13	14	15
Sheet 364							50 by 30 km		
1							O		
2	1940	1941	13,000/4/41	OS 1941	m4		C	Wc	
2	1940	1941	1000/11/41	515(CFS)CRE	1.11.41		CLo	BL-d	
3	1940	1942	26,516/3/42 LR	-	1.1.42		C	BL-d	
3	1940	1942	?26,516/3/42 LR	-	1.1.42		CL		1
3	1940	1942	26,516/3/42 LR	-	1.1.42	1943	CB	BL-d	

1. The existence of this layered edition has yet to be confirmed, though it is supported by documentary sources.

1	2	3	4	6	8	9	13	14	15
Sheet 365							50 by 30 km		
1							O		
2	1940	1941	13,000/4/41	OS 1941	m4		C	Wc	
2							CLo		
3	1940	1942	26,516/3/42 LR	-	1.1.42		C	BL-d	
3	1940	1942	26,516/3/42 LR	-	1.1.42		CL	BL-d	
3	1940	1942	26,516/3/42 LR	-	1.1.42	1943	CB	BL-d	
Sheet 366							50 by 30 km		
1							O		
2	-	-	nc	-	-		C	BL-d	
2	1940	1941	13,000/4/41	OS 1941	m4		C	Wc	
2							CLo		
3	1940	1942	12,000/3/42 C	-	1.1.42		C	BL-d	
3	1940	1942	12,000/3/42 C	-	1.1.42		CL	BL-d	
3	1940	1942	12,000/3/42 C. 14,516/4/42 C	-	1.1.42		C	BL-d	
3	1940	1942	12,000/3/42 C. 14,516/4/42 C	-	1.1.42	1943	CB	BL-d	

1	2	3	4	6	8	9	13	14	15

Sheet 367

1	2	3	4	6	8	9	13	14	15
1							50 by 30 km		
							O		
2							C		
2	1940	1941	1000/11/41	515(CFS)CRE	1.11.41		CLo	Wc	
3	1940	1942	26,516/4/42 LR	-	1.1.42		C	BL-d	
3	1940	1942	26,516/4/42 LR	-	1.1.42		CL	BL-d	
3	1940	1942	26,516/4/42 LR	-	1.1.42	1943	CB	BL-d	

Sheet 368

1	2	3	4	6	8	9	13	14	15
1							50 by 30 km		
							O		
2	1940	1941	9000/4/41	OS 1941	m4		C	Wc	
3	1940	1942	21,516/5/42 C	-	1.1.42		C	BL-d	
3	1940	1942	21,516/5/42 C	-	1.1.42	1943	CB	BL-d	

Layer plates were made for this sheet, probably in 1943. A black pull from them is in Dtc.

Sheet 369

1	2	3	4	6	8	9	13	14	15
1							50 by 30 km		
							O		
2	-	-	nc	-	-		C	PC	1
2	1940	1941	9000/4/41	OS 1941	m4		C	Wc	2
3	1940	1942	21,516/5/42 C	-	1.1.42		C	BL-d	
3	1940	1942	21,516/5/42 C	-	1.1.42	1943	CB	BL-d	

Layer plates were made for this sheet, probably in 1943. A black pull from them dated 1 February 1943 is in Dtc.
1. The Second Edition heading is black. 2. The Second Edition heading is lacking.

Sheet 370

1	2	3	4	6	8	9	13	14	15
1							50 by 30 km		
							O		
2	1940	1941	13,000/4/41	OS 1941	m4		C	Wc	
2							CLo		
3	1940	1942	26,516/4/42 C	-	1.1.42		C	BL-d	
3	1940	1942	26,516/4/42 C	-	1.1.42		CL	BL-d	
3	1940	1942	26,516/4/42 C	-	1.1.42	1943	CB	BL-d	

Sheet 371

1	2	3	4	6	8	9	13	14	15
1							50 by 30 km		
							O		
2	1940	1941	13,000/4/41	OS 1941	m4		C	Wc	
2							CLo		
3	1940	1942	26,516/4/42 C	-	1.1.42		C	BL-d	
3	1940	1942	26,516/4/42 C	-	1.1.42		CL	BL-d	
3	1940	1942	26,516/4/42 C	-	1.1.42	1943	CB	BL-d	

Sheet 372

1	2	3	4	6	8	9	13	14	15
1	-	-	-	-	-		50 by 30 km		
							O	PC	
2	-	-	nc	-	-		C	BL-d	
2	1940	1941	9000/4/41	OS 1941	m4		C	Wc	
3	1940	1942	21,516/5/42 C	-	1.1.42		C	BL-d	
3	1940	1942	21,516/5/42 C	-	1.1.42	1943	CB	BL-d	

Layer plates were made for this sheet, probably in 1943. A black pull from them dated 1 March 1943 is in Dtc.

Sheet 373

1	2	3	4	6	8	9	13	14	15
1							50 by 30 km		
							O		
2	-	-	nc	-	-		C	BL-d	
2	1940	1941	9000/4/41	OS 1941	m4		C	Wc	
3	1940	1942	21,516/5/42 C	-	1.1.42		C	BL-d	
3	1940	1942	21,516/5/42 C	-	1.1.42	1943	CB	BL-d	

With extrusion for Toe Head etc. Layer plates were made for this sheet, probably in 1943. A black pull from them dated 1 February 1943 is in Dtc.

1	2	3	4	6	8	9	13	14	15

Sheet 374

							50 by 30 km		
1							O		
2	1940	1941	13,000/4/41	OS 1941	m4		C	Wc	
2							CLo		
3	1940	1942	26,516/4/42 C	-		1.1.42	C	BL-d	
3	1940	1942	26,516/4/42 C	-		1.1.42	CL	BL-d	
3	1940	1942	26,516/4/42 C	-		1.1.42	1943	CB	BL-d

Sheet 375

							50 by 30 km		
1							O		
2	1940	1941	9000/4/41	OS 1941	m4		C	Wc	
3	1940	1942	21,516/5/42 C	-		1.1.42	C	BL-d	
3	1940	1942	21,516/5/42 C	-		1.1.42	1943	CB	BL-d

Layer plates were made for this sheet, probably in 1943. A black pull from them is in Dtc.

Sheet 376

							30 by 50 km		
1							O		
2	1940	1941	9000/4/41	OS 1941	m4		C	Wc	
2							CLo		
3	1940	1942	26,516/4/42 C	-		1.1.42	C	BL-d	
3	1940	1942	26,516/4/42 C	-		1.1.42	CL	BL-d	
3	1940	1942	26,516/4/42 C	-		1.1.42	1943	CB	BL-d

National Grid series, 1948-1985

This is a cartobibliography in two parts, the first covering Cassini gridded maps and the second National Grid maps. The two parts have necessarily been organised in fundamentally different ways, but within each a consistency of method has been attempted in the numbering of columns, so that the numbers themselves and their functions may quickly become familiar to the user. No single map requires data in every column, and only the numbers relevant to the current map appear at the top of every page of its listing. The following is a description of the use of all columns that appear in sections 7 to 10 of the book. The layout of the cartobibliography of Cassini gridded series is described beginning on page 86.

Sections 7 to 10.

The headings contain three elements, not always used:

1. Sheet number and name, or, in the case of district maps, sheet title, together with any sheet numbers quoted. Where the title is altered during the life of the map, the alternative forms are noted, with cross reference letters to column 6.

2. Date of revision, as printed on the map. In Great Britain this is in fact reserved for certain district maps in this list. For the revision dates of Popular Edition series sheets, the reader is referred to Hodson (1999) (England and Wales) and Oliver (2000b) (Scotland); for those of the New Popular Edition to Oliver (2000c), for those of the Seventh Series to Oliver (2004). Revision and partial revision dates are provided for M723, the map of Northern Ireland, with letter references in the range "a" to "d". Amendment dates follow, with letter references in the range "e" to "k". These correspond to the suffix letters added to the printing or reproduction dates of the relevant printings in column 4 of the list.

3. Sheet dimensions. The coverage of the sheet is given, width by height. Users may need to compensate for the one mile overlap on the east and south sides of many sheets in the Scotland Popular Edition, which are included in the dimensions given. British National Grid sheets cover an area 40 by 45 km; there was little point in repeatedly entering that information here. Sheet dimensions may be given in kilometres or miles, depending on the base map used. Accuracy seems more valuable than consistency. Where the dimensions of specially made sheets are a product of the grid, details are given in the sheet footnotes in the form (144-176, 244-296) representing in most cases National Grid eastings, then northings, in kilometres.

The lists contain up to sixteen columns:

1. Print code, usually of the civilian source map. On military exercise maps, the GSGS 4620/M722 print code, if known, is entered here, column 11 being reserved for any print code associated with the overprint.

2. M723 only: Crown Copyright date, in the form 1970[so] if an HMSO copyright date on the overprint plate.

3. M723 only: publication date of the OSNI original, usually transferred in M723 to the overprint plate.

4. M723 only: printing or reproduction date of the OSNI original. Supplemented with letter codes which cross refer to dates of [further] revision ("a" to "d") and amendments ("e" to "k"), as listed in the heading. Again, this information is usually transferred in M723 to the overprint plate.

5. First use: all series: price statement (or "np" – no price). The highest of the range of prices of the coloured map is quoted. In some cases the sheet price on military printings does not correspond with that on civilian.

    Second use, M722 only (current October 1971 to August 1972): sheets overprinted in red: *Distribution Restricted. U.K. officials are not to release this map outside the U.K. Government without authority from Directorate of Military Survey,* listed as "DR".

6. Source mapping: New Popular Edition "6", Seventh Series "7", Popular Edition (usually Scotland) "P". For more detailed information see column 14. M723, in all cases derived from OSNI One-inch (Third Series), is not listed. Cross reference letters indicating changes in sheet names appear in this column.

7. Military series number: GSGS 4639, GSGS 4620 (later M722), GSGS 4692 (later M725), M723, and others, as relevant, appearing mainly in the various supplements. The letters "GSGS" and/or "misc." are omitted and implicit. Sheet numbers appear in this column, for training and exercise maps, where relevant.

8. Military edition. The earliest form is *War Office Edition* "WOE", then *First Edition GSGS*, later *Edition 1-GSGS* (the distinction is not drawn here), "1-G", etc.

9. Military publisher: *War Office* "WO", later *D. Survey, War Office and Air Ministry* "DSW", later *D. Survey* [or *Director of Military Survey*], *Ministry of Defence, United Kingdom* "DSM".

10. Publication date of military edition. Surviving civilian publication dates are ignored. The wording in M723 later changes to *Produced under the direction of…….*

11. Military print code, including the abbreviated reference to the printer, if given.

12. Printer, usually the Ordnance Survey. The letter codes are explained in appendix 4.

13. Colour of military overprint: "p"-urple; "b"-lue; "r"-ed. Early New Popular overprints by SPC RE are distinctly mauve rather than purple, but it was decided not to distinguish between them in this list since there was no apparent intention to supply a different overprint colour. Many New Popular military printings and almost all Scottish also have the black rouletted 1 km civilian grid beneath the overprinted one: these are noted "p‡" (NB the 10 km civilian grid was always present). It is naturally also present on ex-civilian stock. In February 1966 the font size of the grid figures was reduced; a full stop is added in the form "r." in these cases.

14. Derivation of printing.
    1. New Popular Edition and Scotland Popular Editions
        a: National Grid with numerical references and eastings printed sideways.
        b: National Grid with letter references and eastings printed upright.
            From 1951. There may or may not be additional marginal changes.
        c: stock of civilian sheets passed over to the military.
            Often with earlier states of the base map than military printings that precede them.
        d: dual civil-military print run.
            There are a few suspected instances among New Popular based maps of this practice which was widespread with the Seventh Series; they have the black grid beneath the purple, and are printed on civilian weight paper.
        t: Overprinted in red: *To be used for training purposes only.*
        T: Overprinted in purple: *This map is for training purposes only since it does not contain revision which has been incorporated in a later edition.*
    2. Seventh Series
        c: stock of civilian sheets passed over to the military.
            Rarely encountered, usually the result of an error in the civilian printing (see "m").
        d: dual civil-military print run.
            As recorded in OS job files, and sometimes DGC Product Information Branch card indexes, where they may be recorded as joint printings. The two sources do not always confirm each other. This was apparently not always a matter of importance for record, and the detail was omitted. There may be many more, unrecorded, instances (see "m" below). Some uncertain cases are included, guarded by a question mark.
        cx, dx: "c" and "d" printings in the civilian ten-colour scheme.
        mt: military printing with tree symbols.
        mo: military printing with no tree symbols.
        m: military printing to the specification of the civilian map.
            It is likely that some of these would be better listed as types "c" or "d", but without documentary record it would be virtually impossible to distinguish between them.
        M723 not relevant.

15. Location of copies. Copies in DGC Superseded now in BL-d are given preference; those still at Feltham are for the most part listed where no copy has been recorded in a public collection. "Card" references give details taken from catalogue cards, once in use by Military Survey, of so far unrecorded printings.

16. Cross reference, usually to footnotes following each sheet list.

Compiler's notes to sections 7 and 8

Great Britain

For information on the transition from pre-war Cassini gridded maps to the post-war National Grid series, and a description of the National Grid (military system), the reader is directed to chapter 8 of Richard Oliver's essay. GSGS 4620 was allocated to a one-inch map of England and Wales on 11 February 1946, and formal printing orders from the War Office for all 115 sheets were placed with the Ordnance Survey on 25 October 1947, well in advance of the January 1950 deadline when the armed forces were to depart from their traditional method of map referencing using the Cassini Grid and change over to the National Grid.[280] The New Popular (or Sixth) Edition[281] was the Ordnance Survey's new National Grid map (on the Transverse Mercator projection, and with sheet lines on natural National Grid values), but since the Ordnance Survey had opted for numerical references for National Grid 100 km values as distinct from the letter references used by the War Office, they had also to prepare overprint plates to provide the army with the reference system it required.

This immense task of printing and overprinting well over three million sheets, in addition to their manifold other commitments, took the Ordnance Survey over two years to fulfil, even though in the case of many sheets the number of copies originally ordered was reduced before printing. However, when early in 1949 it became clear that the Ordnance Survey could not achieve the deadline, the contracts for some sheets were cancelled and placed instead with the Survey Production Centre, Royal Engineers, to whom Kodalines were provided by the Ordnance Survey. The Ordnance Survey's decision not to carry publication of the New Popular Edition into Scotland required that as a temporary expedient the pre-war Popular Edition of Scotland be reprinted, carrying the National Grid. The War Office had no option but to follow suit, and on 7 October 1947 the GSGS number 4639 was allocated, superseding 3908 as the National Grid replaced the Cassini. Sheet 89 was cancelled since its coverage was duplicated by New Popular sheets 75 and 76. All but a handful of sheets in the far north of Scotland were ready by January 1950, and those few were in print by March.

All sheets were issued first in War Office Edition. These were all overprinted on maps carrying the early version of the National Grid with numerical references given to the 100 km squares then in use by civilians. Eastings were printed sideways. Reprints were headed First Edition-GSGS from 1950 onwards. Second Edition-GSGS printings began to appear in 1951. This heading was reserved for base maps carrying the revised from of National Grid reference following the Ordnance Survey's decision to conform with military practice and use letter references for the 100 km squares. Eastings were printed upright. The methodology was altered again in 1954 when new such issues were headed First Edition-GSGS. The style of all these headings altered in about 1954 from First Edition-GSGS to Edition 1-GSGS (etc). Some sheets advanced beyond Edition 2-GSGS to Edition 3 or even Edition 4-GSGS in the case of sheet 187, before being replaced by new editions based on the new Seventh Series map.

In this cartobibliography it would have been desirable to list not only print code and price states of the base map, but also further particulars, such as details of the National Grid marginalia, the imprint, and the magnetic variation date. However space considerations forbade this. Many details of the base maps used for military printings do not necessarily accord with the specification of civilian printings – this is especially so after the first printings. The user must assume that there are likely to be further alterations to the base map than just those listed here. Magnetic variation dates, for example, may be advanced. Changes which are not listed but which seem particularly noteworthy appear in footnotes. Many of the differences may be identified by a comparison between print code and price statements listed here and those in Oliver (2000b), (2000c), and later (2004). However, it is worth bearing in mind

---

[280] Much of the information offered in these introductory remarks, as well as in the notes to the maps that follow, is taken from old printing record cards once in use by Military Survey and Ordnance Survey, and Product Information Branch card indexes held by DGC.

[281] This was nominally an Ordnance Survey map of Great Britain, though in the event only the sheets covering England and Wales were published. It had been determined by 1943 for the time being to confine it to sheets south of the border; hence, no doubt, the allocation by the War Office of the GSGS number 4620 to a map of England and Wales only.

that abnormally late printings with War Office Edition and First Edition-GSGS headings may be found, which usually prove to be superseded ex-civilian stock still carrying the early form of the National Grid, handed over for military use when it would otherwise have been destroyed. Being originally civilian printings, these should accord with the details in Oliver.

Replacement of the New Popular Edition base map with Seventh Series began in 1952, and at last the Ordnance Survey had embarked upon the publication of a one-inch map covering the whole of Great Britain. After a flurry of printings based on the new map, mostly in Wales, for some time Military Survey did not seem too concerned whether they received mapping on the new base or not, and were in many cases content to use up civilian stock of the old New Popular once the new Seventh Series map was made available to the public. Furthermore for several years the only Seventh Series sheets being issued by the Ordnance Survey were within the area already covered in GSGS 4620, and it was not until 14 February 1958 that the new SSD number M722, which gave for the first time military recognition of the map as being of Great Britain, was allocated. Even then it would not be until late 1960 that the first military printings of Scottish sheets were issued. Coverage was complete by the end of 1963, and with it both GSGS 4620 and 4639 were effectively obsolete. But official confirmation of this, and belated confirmation that GSGS 4639[282] had actually been replaced by M722 coverage, was not ratified for another three years, on 30 November 1966. Events moved rather more swiftly in July 1974 when sheets 102 to 204 of the Ordnance Survey's new 1:50,000 map were published. M722 sheets 100 to 190 were immediately declared obsolete, and replaced by the 1:50,000 sheets as M726. In July 1976 all the remaining sheets were superseded in the same way.

Special printings were made in 1961 of the maps of Scotland (GSGS Misc.1941), and of Great Britain (GSGS Misc.1943).[283] Comments on DGC catalogue cards reveal that the maps were known to have been produced but never held in the library. All stock of the Scottish map was to go to HQ Scottish Command, and of the Great Britain map to HQ Eastern Command. It is not known how they differed from the standard topographical map, or why special GSGS numbers were allocated to them.

As with GSGS 3907, GSGS 4620 was much used for military exercises, manoeuvres and examinations. But unlike the derivatives of GSGS 3907 they were, in the main, allocated their own GSGS numbers, initially as part of the GSGS miscellaneous sequence. From 1965 the more significant maps were allocated numbers in the main series. A preliminary attempt has been made here to note those used as training areas, or military exercises. Their treatment is necessarily different from pre-war special maps, in that they are in many cases normal printings of series sheets with a special overprint, and consequently there are two print codes to accommodate. Provisional shortform lists are offered for other more ephemeral mapping.

Sources

The largest collections of both GSGS 4639 and 4620 that I know of have now been transferred from the Superseded Collection of the Defence Geographic Centre, formerly held at Tolworth, to the British Library. For the present the M722 part of the collection remains with DGC, now at Feltham. This is virtually complete, and lacks only five printings known to exist elsewhere. The training area maps are also being retained at present. Outside DGC the largest collections of M722 I have seen are in the Library of Congress, Washington D.C., the British Library, and the Bodleian Library, Oxford. The Bodleian also has in its collection a particularly interesting accumulation of the late printings of GSGS 4620, especially civilian printings overprinted for military use. But many map libraries have substantial collections, and there are comparatively few rare printings. In the following lists copies in the DGC transfer to the British Library [=BL-d] take priority, followed by those in the Bodleian, then in BL Maps 1175(220) [=BL-a] and BL Maps 1175(317) [=BL-b]. The copies retained by DGC are recorded where none have so far been located in public collections. It should be noted that at the time of writing (2004) the GSGS miscellaneous class of maps is still with DGC at Feltham, though arrangements are actively in hand for its transfer to the British Library. This is probably the only substantial collection of these maps in existence.

---

[282] The SSD M724 was allocated in about 1954, though no map carrying this number has ever been recorded.
[283] WOPD 4404/R, dated 24.7.61 for Scotland, and WOPD 4410/R, dated 2.8.61 for Great Britain. In fact, at that date, the map was probably still of England and Wales. Scotland sheet 21 was used for *Exercise Follow On* (q.v.).

7. GSGS 4639 *Scotland*

For a explanation of the detail in each column see pages 196 and 197.

Sheet 1 *Yell & Unst (Shetland Islands)*   18 by 27 miles
2201   5/-   P   4639   WOE   WO   1950   15,000/2/50   OS   p‡ a   BL-d

Sheet 2 *North Mainland (Shetland Islands)*   32 by 21 miles
2202   5/-   P   4639   WOE   WO   1950   15,000/ /50   OS   p‡ a   PC   1
2202   5/-   P   4639   WOE   WO   1950   15,000/3/50   OS   p‡ a   BL-d 1
1. The month element of the print code, lacking at first, was added later.

Sheet 3 *Central Mainland (Shetland Islands)*   27 by 18 miles
2203   5/-   P   4639   WOE   WO   1950   15,000/2/50   OS   p‡ a   BL-d

Sheet 4 *South Mainland (Shetland Islands)*   18 by 27 miles
2204   5/-   P   4639   WOE   WO   1950   15,000/3/50   OS   p‡ a   BL-d

Sheet 5 *Orkney Islands (North)*   27 by 23 miles
2336   5/-   P   4639   WOE   WO   1948   15,000/1/49   OS   p‡ a   BL-d

Sheet 6 *Orkney Islands (Mainland)*   32 by 21 miles
2206   5/-   P   4639   WOE   WO   1950   15,000/3/50   OS   p‡ a   BL-d

Sheet 7 *Orkney Islands (South)*   27 by 18 miles
2207   5/-   P   4639   WOE   WO   1950   15,000/3/50   OS   p‡ a   BL-d

Sheet 8 *Butt of Lewis*   28 by 19 miles
2208   5/-   P   4639   WOE   WO   1950   15,000/1/50   OS   p‡ a   BL-d

Sheet 9 *Cape Wrath*   22 by 28 miles
2209   5/-   P   4639   WOE   WO   1950   15,000/2/50   OS   p‡ a   BL-d

Sheet 10 *Tongue*   28 by 23 miles
2210   5/-   P   4639   WOE   WO   1950   15,000/2/50   OS   p‡ a   BL-d

Sheet 11 *Thurso & Reay*   19 by 28 miles
2211   5/-   P   4639   WOE   WO   1950   15,000/3/50   OS   p‡ a   BL-d

Sheet 12 *Wick*   18 by 28 miles
2212   5/-   P   4639   WOE   WO   1950   15,000/1/50   OS   p‡ a   BL-d

Sheet 13 *Loch Roag & Tarbert*   19 by 27 miles
2213   5/-   P   4639   WOE   WO   1950   15,000/2/50   OS   p‡ a   BL-d

Sheet 14 *Stornoway*   21 by 27 miles
2214   5/-   P   4639   WOE   WO   1950   15,000/2/50   OS   p‡ a   BL-d

Sheet 15 *Lochinver & Loch Assynt*   28 by 19 miles
2215   5/-   P   4639   WOE   WO   1950   15,000/1/50   OS   p‡ a   BL-d

Sheet 16 *Lairg & Loch Shin*   28 by 19 miles
2216   5/-   P   4639   WOE   WO   1950   15,000/1/50   OS   p‡ a   BL-d

Sheet 17 *Helmsdale*   27 by 19 miles
2217   5/-   P   4639   WOE   WO   1949   15,000/12/49   OS   p‡ a   BL-d

1	5	6	7	8	9	10	11	12	13	14	15	16

Sheet 18 *Harris* — 27 by 19 miles
| 2218 | 5/- | P | 4639 | WOE | WO | 1949 | 15,000/12/49 | OS | p‡ | a | BL-d | |

Sheet 19 *Ullapool & Loch Ewe* — 28 by 19 miles
| 2219 | 5/- | P | 4639 | WOE | WO | 1949 | 15,000/12/49 | OS | p‡ | a | BL-d | |

Sheet 20 *Strath Oykell* — 27 by 19 miles
| 2220 | 5/- | P | 4639 | WOE | WO | 1949 | 15,000/12/49 | OS | p‡ | a | BL-d | |

Sheet 21 *Dornoch* — 27 by 19 miles
| 2221 | 5/- | P | 4639 | WOE | WO | 1949 | 15,000/12/49 | OS | p‡ | a | BL-d | |

For further use see Exercise *Follow On* in supplement 4.

Sheet 22 *Sollas* — 27 by 19 miles
| 2222 | 5/- | P | 4639 | WOE | WO | 1949 | 15,000/12/49 | OS | p‡ | a | BL-d | |

Sheet 23 *Benbecula* — 27 by 19 miles
| 2223 | 5/- | P | 4639 | WOE | WO | 1949 | 15,000/12/49 | OS | p‡ | a | BL-d | |

Sheet 24 *Portree & Dunvegan* — 25 by 28 miles
| 2224 | 5/- | P | 4639 | WOE | WO | 1949 | 15,000/12/49 | OS | p‡ | a | BL-d | |

Sheet 25 *Raasay & Applecross* — 23 by 28 miles
| 2225 | 5/- | P | 4639 | WOE | WO | 1949 | 15,000/12/49 | OS | p‡ | a | BL-d | |

Sheet 26 *Loch Maree & Achnasheen* — 28 by 19 miles
| 2226 | 5/- | P | 4639 | WOE | WO | 1949 | 15,000/11/49 | OS | p‡ | a | BL-d | |

Sheet 27 *Strathpeffer & Invergordon* — 28 by 19 miles
| 2227 | 5/- | P | 4639 | WOE | WO | 1949 | 15,000/11/49 | OS | p‡ | a | BL-d | |

Sheet 28 *Nairn & Cromarty* — 28 by 19 miles
| 2228 | 5/- | P | 4639 | WOE | WO | 1949 | 15,000/11/49 | OS | p‡ | a | BL-d | |
| B | 6/6 | P | 4639 | WOE | WO | 1949 | 900/5/60/6228/OS | OS | p | bc | BL-d | 1 |

1. The full National Grid co-ordinates of the south-west corner of the sheet are provided. Published by the War Office, printed for D. Survey (War Office and Air Ministry) by Ordnance Survey, 1957.

Sheet 29 *Elgin & Keith* — 28 by 19 miles
| 2229 | 5/- | P | 4639 | WOE | WO | 1949 | 15,000/11/49 | OS | p‡ | a | Wc | |
| nc | np | P | 4639 | 1-G | DSW | 1957 | 5000/3/58/5511/OS | OS | p‡ | b | BL-d | 1 |

1. The full National Grid co-ordinates of the south-west corner of the sheet are provided.

Sheet 30 *Banff & Fraserburgh* — 27 by 19 miles
| 2230 | 5/- | P | 4639 | WOE | WO | 1949 | 15,000/11/49 | OS | p‡ | a | BL-d | |

Sheet 31 *Peterhead* — 19 by 27 miles
| 2231 | 5/- | P | 4639 | WOE | WO | 1949 | 15,000/ /49 | OS | p‡ | a | BL-d | |

Sheet 32 *Lochboisdale & Eriskay* — 27 by 18 miles
| 2232 | 5/- | P | 4639 | WOE | WO | 1949 | 15,000/6/49 | OS | p‡ | a | BL-d | |

Sheet 33 *Barra & Mingulay* — 27 by 20 miles
| 2233 | 5/- | P | 4639 | WOE | WO | 1949 | 15,000/6/49 | OS | p‡ | a | BL-d | |

Sheet 34 *The Cuillins, Rhum and Canna* — 19 by 28 miles
| 2331 | 5/- | P | 4639 | WOE | WO | 1949 | 15,000/1/49 | OS | p‡ | a | BL-d | |

Sheet 35 *Sound of Sleat* — 23 by 28 miles
| 2337 | 5/- | P | 4639 | WOE | WO | 1949 | 15,000/10/49 | OS | p‡ | a | BL-d | |

Sheet 36 *Lochcarron & Dornie*
28 by 19 miles

| 2236 | 5/- | P | 4639 | WOE | WO | 1949 | 15,000/11/49 | OS | p‡ | a | BL-d |

Sheet 37 *Inverness*
28 by 19 miles

| 2237 | 5/- | P | 4639 | WOE | WO | 1949 | 15,000/11/49 | OS | p‡ | a | BL-d |

Sheet 38 *Grantown-on-Spey & Strath Dearn*
28 by 19 miles

| 2238 | 5/- | P | 4639 | WOE | WO | 1949 | 15,000/11/49 | OS | p‡ | a | BL-d |

Sheet 39 *Dufftown & Huntly*
28 by 19 miles

| 2324 | 5/- | P | 4659 | WOE | WO | 1948 | 15,000/12/48 | OS | p‡ | a | BL-d |

Sheet 40 *Inverurie & Ellon*
27 by 19 miles

| 2310 | 5/- | P | 4639 | WOE | WO | 1948 | 15,000/4/48 | OS | p‡ | a | BL-d |

Sheet 41 *Glen Shiel & Glen Garry*
28 by 19 miles

| 2241 | 5/- | P | 4639 | WOE | WO | 1949 | 15,000/10/49 | OS | p‡ | a | BL-d |

With Levels of parallel roads.

Sheet 42 *Fort Augustus*
28 by 19 miles

| 2242 | 5/- | P | 4639 | WOE | WO | 1949 | 15,000/7/49 | OS | p‡ | a | BL-d |

With Levels of parallel roads.

Sheet 43 *Kingussie*
28 by 19 miles

| 2332 | 5/- | P | 4639 | [WOE] | WO | 1949 | 15,000/1/49 | OS | p‡ | a | BL-d | 1 |

1. The War Office Edition heading is lacking.

Sheet 44 *Ballater & Strathdon*
28 by 19 miles

| 2318 | 5/- | P | 4639 | WOE | WO | 1948 | 15,000/9/48 | OS | p‡ | a | BL-d |

Sheet 45 *Aberdeen*
27 by 19 miles

| 2311 | 5/- | P | 4639 | WOE | WO | 1948 | 15,000/4/48 | OS | p‡ | a | BL-d |

There is an error in the magnetic variation statement: the annual change should be 10', not 10º, east.

Sheet 46 *Ardnamurchan & Loch Shiel*
28 by 20 miles

| 2246 | 5/- | P | 4639 | WOE | WO | 1949 | 15,000/11/49 | OS | p‡ | a | BL-d |

Sheet 47 *Ben Nevis & Fort William*
28 by 20 miles

| 2338 | 5/- | P | 4639 | WOE | WO | 1949 | 15,000/10/49 | OS | p‡ | a | BL-d | |
| | | | | 1-G | | | | | | | card | 1 |

1. A Military Survey catalogue card refers to a print order dated 1 April 1957 for Edition 1-GSGS, to be overprinted on surplus OS stock. Not found.

Sheet 48 *Loch Ericht & Loch Laggan*
28 by 19 miles

| 2248 | 5/- | P | 4639 | WOE | WO | 1949 | 15,000/ /49 | OS | p‡ | a | BL-d |

Sheet 49 *Grampian Mountains & Blair Atholl*
28 by 19 miles

| 2249 | 5/- | P | 4639 | WOE | WO | 1949 | 15,000/7/49 | OS | p‡ | a | BL-d |

Sheet 50 *Glen Clova & Lochnagar*
27 by 19 miles

| 2315 | 5/- | P | 4639 | WOE | WO | 1948 | 15,000/5/48 | OS | p‡ | a | BL-d |

Sheet 51 *Stonehaven & Brechin*
27 by 19 miles

| 2319 | 5/- | P | 4639 | WOE | WO | 1948 | 15,000/11/48 | OS | p‡ | a | BL-d |

Sheet 52 *Coll & Tiree*
28 by 19 miles

| 2333 | 5/- | P | 4639 | WOE | WO | 1949 | 15,000/1/49 | OS | p‡ | a | BL-d |
| 2252 | 5/- | P | 4639 | WOE | WO | 1948 | 2600/2/57 OS | OS | p | ac | BL-d |

1	5	6	7	8	9	10	11	12	13	14	15	16

Sheet 53 *Sound of Mull* — 32 by 19 miles

| 2253 | 5/- | P | 4639 | WOE | WO | 1949 | 15,000/10/49 | OS | p‡ | a | BL-d | |

Sheet 54 *Loch Etive & Glen Coe* — 28 by 19 miles

| 2325 | 5/- | P | 4639 | WOE | WO | 1948 | 15,000/1/49 | OS | p‡ | a | BL-d | |

Sheet 55 *Killin & Loch Rannoch* — 28 by 19 miles

| 2255 | 5/- | P | 4639 | WOE | WO | 1949 | 15,000/ /49 | OS | p‡ | a | BL-d | |

Sheet 56 *Dunkeld & Pitlochry* — 28 by 19 miles

| 2326 | 5/- | P | 4639 | WOE | WO | 1948 | 15,000/1/49 | OS | p‡ | a | BL-d | |

Sheet 57 *Forfar & Dundee* — 27 by 20 miles

| 2327 | 5/- | P | 4639 | WOE | WO | 1948 | 15,000/1/49 | OS | p‡ | a | BL-d | |
| A// | 3/- | P | 4639 | WOE | WO | 1948 | 800/6/60/6228/OS | OS | p | bc | BL-d | 1 |

1. The full National Grid co-ordinates of the south-west corner of the sheet are provided. Published by the War Office, printed for D. Survey (War Office and Air Ministry) by Ordnance Survey.

Sheet 58 *Arbroath & Montrose* — 28 by 20 miles

| 2323 | 5/- | P | 4639 | WOE | WO | 1948 | 15,000/10/48 | OS | p‡ | a | BL-d | |
| C | 6/6 | P | 4639 | WOE | WO | 1948 | 1000/12/60/6228/OS | OS | p | bc | BL-d | 1 |

1. The full National Grid co-ordinates of the south-west corner of the sheet are provided.

Sheet 59 *Iona & Colonsay* — 19 by 31 miles

| 2302 | 5/- | P | 4639 | WOE | WO | 1947 | 15,000/11/47 | OS | p‡ | a | BL-d | |
| 2302 | 5/- | P | 4639 | WOE | WO | 1947 | 5300/2/57 OS | OS | p | ac | BL-d | |

Sheet 60 *North Jura & Firth of Lorne* — 19 by 31 miles

| 2316 | 5/- | P | 4639 | WOE | WO | nd | 15,000/6/48 | OS | p‡ | a | BL-d | |

Sheet 61 *Oban & Loch Awe* — 28 by 19 miles

| 2328 | 5/- | P | 4639 | WOE | WO | 1948 | 15,000/12/48 | OS | p‡ | a | BL-d | |

Sheet 62 *Loch Katrine & Loch Earn* — 28 by 19 miles

| 2293 | 5/- | P | 4639 | WOE | WO | 1949 | 15,000/3/49 | OS | p‡ | a | BL-d | |

Sheet 63 *Perth & Strath Earn* — 27 by 19 miles

| 2320 | 5/- | P | 4639 | WOE | WO | 1948 | 15,000/12/48 | OS | p‡ | a | BL-d | |
| nc | np | P | 4639 | 1-G | WO | 1948 | 15,000/10/55 OS | OS | p‡ | b | BL-d | 1 |

1. The full National Grid co-ordinates of the south-west corner of the sheet are provided.

Sheet 64 *Dundee & St Andrews* — 34 by 21 miles

| 2294 | 5/- | P | 4639 | WOE | WO | 1949 | 15,000/11/49 | OS | p‡ | a | Wc | |
| 2294 | np | P | 4639 | 1-G | WO | 1949 | 15,000/10/55 OS | OS | p‡ | b | BL-d | 1 |

1. The full National Grid co-ordinates of the south-west corner of the sheet are provided.

Sheet 65 *Dunoon & Loch Fyne* — 28 by 18 miles

2308	5/-	P	4639	WOE	WO	1948	15,000/1/48	OS	p‡	a	BL-d	
				1-G							card	1
2308	5/-	P	4639	WOE	WO	1948	1000/5/60/6228/OS	OS	p	ac	BL-d	2

1. A Military Survey catalogue card refers to a print order dated 1 April 1957 for Edition 1-GSGS, to be overprinted on surplus OS stock. Not found. 2. The publisher is still shown as the War Office when it might correctly have been altered to D. Survey (War Office and Air Ministry).

Sheet 66 *Loch Lomond* — 28 by 18 miles

| 2312 | 5/- | P | 4639 | WOE | WO | 1947 | 15,000/4/48 | OS | p‡ | a | BL-d | |
| nc | np | P | 4639 | 1-G | WO | 1947 | 15,000/10/55 OS | OS | p‡ | b | BL-d | 1 |

1. The full National Grid co-ordinates of the south-west corner of the sheet are provided.

Sheet 67 *Stirling & Dunfermline*   27 by 18 miles

2305	5/-	P	4639	WOE	WO	1948	15,000/4/48		OS	p‡	a	BL-d	
2305	np	P	4639	1-G	WO	1948	15,000/10/55 OS		OS	p‡	b	BL-d	1

For further use see supplement 8. 1. The full National Grid co-ordinates of the south-west corner of the sheet are provided.

Sheet 68 *Firth of Forth*   34 by 20 miles

2321	5/-	P	4639	WOE	WO	1948	15,000/1/49		OS	p‡	a	Wc	
nc	np	P	4639	1-G	DSW	1957	10,000/2/58/5511/OS		OS	p‡	b	BL-d	1

1. The full National Grid co-ordinates of the south-west corner of the sheet are provided. Published by the War Office, printed for D. Survey (War Office and Air Ministry) by Ordnance Survey, 1957.

Sheet 69 *Islay*   25 by 30 miles

2329	5/-	P	4639	WOE	WO	1949	15,000/1/49		OS	p‡	a	BL-d

There is a handwritten note a copy in the Bodleian Library: "The S.W. corner (all sea) of this sheet comes within the Irish Grid. (See first copy for actual line)."

Sheet 70 *Sound of Jura*   19 by 30 miles

2317	5/-	P	4639	WOE	WO	1948	15,000/7/48		OS	p‡	a	BL-d

Sheet 71 *Island of Bute*   27 by 23 miles

2299	5/-	P	4639	WOE	WO	1947	15,000/11/47		OS	p‡	a	BL-d

Sheet 72 *Glasgow*   34 by 24 miles

2307	5/-	P	4639	WOE	WO	1947	15,000/11/47		OS	p‡	a	BL-d	
nc	np	P	4639	2-G	DSW	1957	5000/5/57		OS	p	b	BL-d	1
2340	10/6	P	4639	2-G	DSW	1957	4800/5/60/6228/OS		OS	p	ac	BL-d	2

1. The full National Grid co-ordinates of the south-west corner of the sheet are provided. 2. It was incorrect to head this printing Edition 2-GSGS since it is a printing carrying the early form of the National Grid with eastings figured sideways.

Sheet 73 *Falkirk & Motherwell*   28 by 24 miles

2330	5/-	P	4639	WOE	WO	1949	15,000/2/49		OS	p‡	a	BL-d	
nc	np	P	4639	1-G	WO	1949	15,000/10/55 OS		OS	p‡	b	BL-d	1

1. The full National Grid co-ordinates of the south-west corner of the sheet are provided.

Sheet 74 *Edinburgh*   28 by 24 miles

2322	5/-	P	4639	WOE	WO	1948	15,000/10/48		OS	p‡	a	BL-d	
nc	np	P	4639	2-G	WO	1953	5000/10/53 OS		OS	p‡	b	BL-d	1
nc	np	P	4639	2-G	WO	1953	15,000/11/55 OS		OS	p‡	b	BL-d	1

1. The full National Grid co-ordinates of the south-west corner of the sheet are provided.

Sheet 75 *Dunbar & Lammermuir*   27 by 24 miles

nc	5/-	P	4639	WOE	WO	1949	15,000/ /49		OS	p‡	a	BL-d	1
nc	5/-	P	4639	WOE	WO	1949	15,000/11/49		OS	p‡	a	Cu	1
nc	np	P	4639	1-G	WO	1949	15,000/11/55 OS		OS	p‡	b	BL-d	2

1. The month element of the print code, lacking at first, was added later. 2. The full National Grid co-ordinates of the south-west corner of the sheet are provided.

Sheet 76 *Kintyre*   24 by 34 miles

2301	5/-	P	4639	WOE	WO	1947	15,000/3/48		OS	p‡	a	BL-d

Sheet 77 *Island of Arran*   28 by 24 miles

2295	5/-	P	4639	WOE	WO	1949	15,000/10/49		OS	p‡	a	BL-d

Sheet 78 *Kilmarnock & Ayr*   28 by 19 miles

nc	5/-	P	4639	WOE	WO	1949	15,000/7/49		OS	p‡	a	BL-d	
2345	np	P	4639	1-G	WO	1949	15,000/11/55 OS		OS	p‡	b	BL-d	1

1. The full National Grid co-ordinates of the south-west corner of the sheet are provided.

Sheet 79 *Lanark* — 28 by 19 miles

1	5	6	7	8	9	10	11	12	13 14	15	16
2334	5/-	P	4639	WOE	WO	1949	15,000/2/49	OS	p‡ a	Wc	
nc	np	P	4639	1-G	DSW	1958	5000/1/58/5511/OS	OS	p‡ b	BL-d	1

1. The full National Grid co-ordinates of the south-west corner of the sheet are provided.

Sheet 80 *Peebles & Galashiels* — 28 by 19 miles

| 2313 | 5/- | P | 4639 | WOE | WO | 1948 | 15,000/4/48 | OS | p‡ a | BL-d | |
| nc | np | P | 4639 | 2-G | WO | 1953 | 5000/11/53 OS | OS | p‡ b | BL-d | 1 |

For further use see Exercise *Backstop* in supplement 4. 1. The full National Grid co-ordinates of the south-west corner of the sheet are provided.

Sheet 81 *Kelso and the Cheviot* — 27 by 19 miles

| nc | 5/- | P | 4639 | WOE | WO | 1949 | 25,000/7/49 | OS | p‡ a | BL-d | |

For further use see Exercise *Backstop* in supplement 4.

Sheet 82 *Ailsa Craig & Girvan* — 19 by 28 miles

| 2303 | 5/- | P | 4639 | WOE | WO | 1947 | 15,000/3/48 | OS | p‡ a | BL-d | |

Sheet 83 *Loch Doon* — 28 by 19 miles

| 2296 | 5/- | P | 4639 | WOE | WO | 1949 | 15,000/3/49 | OS | p‡ a | BL-d | |

Sheet 84 *Nithsdale & Moffat* — 28 by 19 miles

| 2297 | 5/- | P | 4639 | WOE | WO | 1949 | 15,000/4/49 | OS | p‡ a | BL-d | |

Sheet 85 *Hawick & Eskdale* — 28 by 19 miles

| 2300 | 5/- | P | 4639 | WOE | WO | 1947 | 15,000/3/48 | OS | p‡ a | BL-d | |
| 2300 | np | P | 4639 | 1-G | WO | 1947 | 15,000/9/55 OS | OS | p‡ b | BL-d | 1 |

For further use see Exercise *Backstop* in supplement 4. 1. This issue also has the prewar 1039 M38 R38 print code. The full National Grid co-ordinates of the south-west corner of the sheet are provided.

Sheet 86 *The Cheviot Hills* — 27 by 18 miles

| 2335 | 5/- | P | 4639 | WOE | WO | 1949 | 25,000/2/49 | OS | p‡ a | BL-d | |

For further use see Exercise *Backstop* in supplement 4.

Sheet 87 *Newton Stewart* — 28 by 19 miles

| 2304 | 5/- | P | 4639 | WOE | WO | 1947 | 15,000/2/48 | OS | p‡ a | BL-d | |
| 2304 | 5/- | P | 4639 | WOE | WO | 1947 | 5000/1/57 OS | OS | p ac | BL-d | |

Sheet 88 *Dumfries* — 28 by 18 miles

| 2298 | 5/- | P | 4639 | WOE | WO | 1949 | 15,000/4/49 | OS | p‡ a | BL-d | |
| 2298 | 5/- | P | 4639 | WOE | WO | 1949 | 5400/1/57 OS | OS | p ac | BL-d | |

Sheet 89 was not published.

Sheet 90 *Stranraer* — 20 by 28 miles

| 2309 | 5/- | P | 4639 | WOE | WO | 1947 | 15,000/1/48 | OS | p‡ a | BL-d | |

Sheet 91 *Wigtown* — 27 by 18 miles

| 2314 | 5/- | P | 4639 | WOE | WO | 1948 | 15,000/4/48 | OS | p‡ a | BL-d | |
| 2314 | 5/- | P | 4639 | WOE | WO | 1948 | 2100/5/57 OS | OS | p ac | BL-d | |

Sheet 92 *Castle Douglas & Kirkcudbright* — 32 by 18 miles

| 2306 | 5/- | P | 4639 | WOE | WO | 1947 | 15,000/11/47 | OS | p‡ a | BL-d | |
| 2306 | 5/- | P | 4639 | WOE | WO | 1947 | 4700/1/57 OS | OS | p ac | BL-d | |

Maps of Scotland in supplement 4 are listed following section 8.

8. GSGS 4620 *England and Wales*, later **M722** *Great Britain*

For a explanation of the detail in each column see pages 196 and 197.

Standard sheet coverage 40 by 45 km

Sheet 1 *Shetland Islands (Yell & Unst)*

1	5	6	7	8	9	10	11	12	13	14	15	16
A	3/6	7	M722	1-G	DSW	1963	4000/2/63/6508/OS	OS	r	m	Ob	
A	np	7	M722	1-G	DSW	1963	2000/3/64/6591/OS	OS	r	m	Wc	
A	np	7	M722	1-G	DSM	1967	3500/11/67/6939/OS	OS	r.	m	Wc	
A	np	7	M722	1-G	DSM	1967	4/71/8238/OS	OS	r.	m	DGC	
A/	DR	7	M722	1-G	DSM	1967	6/72/8653/OS	OS	r.	d	Ob	

Sheet 2 *Shetland Islands (North Mainland)*

1	5	6	7	8	9	10	11	12	13	14	15	16
A	4/6	7	M722	1-G	DSW	1963	4000/2/63/6508/OS	OS	r	m	Ob	
A	np	7	M722	1-G	DSW	1963	11,000/12/64/6682/OS	OS	r	m	DGC	
A	np	7	M722	1-G	DSM	1963	1/71/8111/OS	OS	r.	m	Ob	
A/	DR	7	M722	1-G	DSM	1963	4/72/8654/OS	OS	r.	d	BL-b	

Sheet 3 *Shetland Islands (Lerwick)*

1	5	6	7	8	9	10	11	12	13	14	15	16
A	4/6	7	M722	1-G	DSW	1963	4000/2/63/6508/OS	OS	r	m	Ob	
A	np	7	M722	1-G	DSW	1963	11,000/12/64/6682/OS	OS	r	m	DGC	
A/	np	7	M722	1-G	DSM	1963	11/71/8433/OS	OS	r.	d	Ob	

Sheet 4 *Shetland Islands (South Mainland)*

1	5	6	7	8	9	10	11	12	13	14	15	16
A	4/6	7	M722	1-G	DSW	1963	4000/2/63/6508/OS	OS	r	m	Ob	
A	np	7	M722	1-G	DSW	1963	11,000/12/64/6682/OS	OS	r	m	BL-b	
A	np	7	M722	1-G	DSM	1967	3500/ /67/6939/OS	OS	r.	m	BL-b	1
A	np	7	M722	1-G	DSM	1967	3500/11/67/6939/OS	OS	r.	m	DGC	1
A/	np	7	M722	2-G	DSM	1970	12/70/8073/OS	OS	r.	d	Ob	

1. The month element of the print code, lacking at first, was added later.

Sheet 5 *Orkney Islands (North)*

1	5	6	7	8	9	10	11	12	13	14	15	16
A	3/6	7	M722	1-G	DSW	1960	4000/11/60/6229/OS	OS	r	mt	Ob	
A	np	7	M722	1-G	DSW	1960	4000/12/64/6682/OS	OS	r	m	BL-b	
A	np	7	M722	1-G	DSM	1970	1/70/7798/OS	OS	r.	m	Ob	

Sheet 6 *Orkney Islands (Kirkwall)*

1	5	6	7	8	9	10	11	12	13	14	15	16
A	3/6	7	M722	1-G	DSW	1960	4000/11/60/6229/OS	OS	r	mo	Ob	
A	np	7	M722	1-G	DSW	1960	5000/10/64/6644/OS	OS	r	m	Wc	
A/	np	7	M722	1-G	DSM	1960	2500/12/67/7030/OS	OS	r.	d	BL-a	
A/	np	7	M722	1-G	DSM	1960	1/73/8493/OS	OS	r.	d	Ob	

Sheet 7 *Pentland Firth*

1	5	6	7	8	9	10	11	12	13	14	15	16
A	3/6	7	M722	1-G	DSW	1960	4000/10/60/6229/OS	OS	r	mo	Ob	
A	np	7	M722	1-G	DSW	1960	4000/1/65/6682/OS	OS	r	m	DGC	
A/	np	7	M722	1-G	DSM	1960	4/69/7380/OS	OS	r.	d	DGC	
A/	np	7	M722	1-G	DSM	1960	2/71/8104/OS	OS	r.	m	BL-b	
A/	np	7	M722	1-G	DSM	1960	10/74/740050 S	OS	r.	d	DGC	

Sheet 8 *Isle of Lewis*

1	5	6	7	8	9	10	11	12	13	14	15	16
A	3/6	7	M722	1-G	DSW	1961	4000/10/61/6229/OS	OS	r	mt	Ob	
A	np	7	M722	1-G	DSW	1961	6000/1/65/6682/OS	OS	r	m	BL-b	
A/	np	7	M722	1-G	DSM	1961	9/71/8287/OS	OS	r.	m	Ob	

1	5	6	7	8	9	10	11	12	13	14	15	16

Sheet 9 *Cape Wrath*

1	5	6	7	8	9	10	11	12	13	14	15
A/	3/6	7	M722	1-G	DSW	1960	4000/11/60/6229/OS	OS	r	mo	Ob
A/	np	7	M722	1-G	DSW	1960	4000/1/65/6682/OS	OS	r	m	Wc
A//	np	7	M722	2-G	DSM	1967	6500/10/67/6975/OS	OS	r.	d	DGC
A//	np	7	M722	2-G	DSM	1967	9/70/8061/OS	OS	r.	m	BL-b

Sheet 10 *Tongue*

A	3/6	7	M722	1-G	DSW	1961	4000/11/60/6229/OS	OS	r	mo	Ob
A	np	7	M722	1-G	DSW	1964	2000/4/64/6591/OS	OS	r	m	Wc
A/	np	7	M722	1-G	DSM	1967	4000/9/67/6939/OS	OS	r.	d	BL-b
A/	np	7	M722	1-G	DSM	1967	4/70/7941/OS	OS	r.	m	Ob

Sheet 11 *Thurso*

A	3/6	7	M722	1-G	DSW	1960	4000/11/60/6229/OS	OS	r	mo	Ob
A	np	7	M722	1-G	DSW	1960	4000/1/65/6682/OS	OS	r	m	DGC
A	np	7	M722	1-G	DSM	1970	1/70/7806/OS	OS	r.	m	DGC
A/	np	7	M722	1-G	DSM	1970	8/70/7978/OS	OS	r.	d	Ob
A/	np	7	M722	1-G	DSM	1970	1/74/733170 S	OS	r.	d	DGC

Sheet 12 *Isle of Lewis and North Harris*

A	3/6	7	M722	1-G	DSW	1960	4000/11/60/6229/OS	OS	r	mo	Ob
A	np	7	M722	1-G	DSW	1960	4000/1/65/6682/OS	OS	r	m	Wc
A/	np	7	M722	1-G	DSM	1960	7/69/7442/OS	OS	r.	d	Ob
A/	DR	7	M722	1-G	DSM	1960	6/72/8678/OS	OS	r.	d	Ob

Sheet 13 *Loch Inver and Loch Assynt*

A	3/6	7	M722	1-G	DSW	1961	4000/1/61/6229/OS	OS	r	mo	Ob
A/	np	7	M722	1-G	DSW	1961	4000/12/64/6682/OS	OS	r	m	BL-a
A/	np	7	M722	1-G	DSM	1961	4000/1/68/6987/OS	OS	r.	m	BL-b
A/	np	7	M722	1-G	DSM	1961	4/71/8172/OS	OS	r.	m	DGC

Sheet 14 *Lairg*

A	3/6	7	M722	1-G	DSW	1960	4000/9/60/6229/OS	OS	r	mo	Ob
A	np	7	M722	1-G	DSW	1960	4000/1/65/6683/OS	OS	r	m	Wc
A/*	np	7	M722	2-G	DSM	1966	5000/9/66/6861/OS	OS	r.	d	Ob
A/*	np	7	M722	2-G	DSM	1966	1/70/7804/OS	OS	r.	m	Ob

Sheet 15 *Helmsdale*

A	3/6	7	M722	1-G	DSW	1961	4000/1/61/6229/OS	OS	r	mo	Ob
A	np	7	M722	1-G	DSW	1961	4000/2/65/6683/OS	OS	r	m	DGC
A/	np	7	M722	1-G	DSM	1961	11/68/7324/OS	OS	r.	d	Ob
A/	np	7	M722	1-G	DSM	1961	1/70/7803/OS	OS	r.	m	Ob

Sheet 16 *Wick*

A	3/6	7	M722	1-G	DSW	1961	4000/8/61/6229/OS	OS	r	mo	Ob
A	np	7	M722	1-G	DSW	1961	4000/1/65/6683/OS	OS	r	m	Ob
A/	np	7	M722	1-G	DSM	1961	9/69/7522/OS	OS	r.	d	BL-b
A/	np	7	M722	1-G	DSM	1961	10/70/8083/OS	OS	r.	m	Ob

Sheet 17 *North Uist*

A	3/6	7	M722	1-G	DSW	1960	4000/9/60/6229/OS	OS	r	mo	Ob
A	np	7	M722	1-G	DSW	1960	4000/2/65/6683/OS	OS	r	m	Wc
A	np	7	M722	1-G	DSM	1960	1/68/6987/OS	OS	r.	m	BL-a
A/*	np	7	M722	2-G	DSM	1969	7/69/7443/OS	OS	r.	d	Ob
A/*	np	7	M722	2-G	DSM	1969	1/71/8102/OS	OS	r.	m	DGC

Sheet 18 *Harris*

A	4/6	7	M722	1-G	DSW	1961	4000/8/61/6229/OS	OS	r	mt	Ob
A	np	7	M722	1-G	DSW	1961	6000/2/65/6683/OS	OS	r	m	DGC
A/*	np	7	M722	1-G	DSM	1961	11/70/8071/OS	OS	r.	d	Ob

207

1	5	6	7	8	9	10	11	12	13	14	15	16
Sheet 19 *Gairloch*												
A	3/-	7	M722	1-G	DSW	1961	4000/11/60/6007/OS	OS	r	mo	Ob	
A/	4/6	7	M722	2-G	DSW	1964	5000/3/64/6591/OS	OS	r	m	Ob	
A/	np	7	M722	2-G	DSW	1964	7500/12/66/348/OA	BAOR	r	m	BL-a	
A//	np	7	M722	2-G	DSM	1964	2/68/7088/OS	OS	r.	d	DGC	
A//	np	7	M722	2-G	DSM	1964	9/70/8062/OS	OS	r.	m	DGC	
Sheet 20 *Ullapool*												
A	3/6	7	M722	1-G	DSW	1960	4000/11/60/6007/OS	OS	r	mo	Ob	
A/	np	7	M722	2-G	DSM	1964	5000/10/64/6644/OS	OS	r	m	DGC	
A/	np	7	M722	2-G	DSM	1967	8000/11/676939/OS	OS	r.	m	BL-b	
A/	np	7	M722	2-G	DSM	1967	1/70/7844/OS	OS	r.	d	Ob	
A/	np	7	M722	2-G	DSM	1967	10/72/8679/OS	OS	r.	d	Ob	
Sheet 21 *Bonar-Bridge*												
A	3/6	7	M722	1-G	DSW	1961	4000/9/61/6007/OS	OS	r	mo	Ob	1
A	np	7	M722	1-G	DSW	1961	7500/10/64/6644/OS	OS	r	m	DGC	
A/	np	7	M722	1-G	DSM	1961	70/7921/OS	OS	r.	m	Ob	

1. The "9" of the month in the print code has been added in brown; the remainder is in red.

1	5	6	7	8	9	10	11	12	13	14	15	16
Sheet 22 *Dornoch*												
A	3/6	7	M722	1-G	DSW	1960	4000/12/60/6007/OS	OS	r	mo	Ob	
A	np	7	M722	1-G	DSW	1960	5000/9/64/6644/OS	OS	r	m	Ob	
A/	np	7	M722	1-G	DSW	1960	2000/11/65/6774/OS	OS	r	m	DGC	
A/	np	7	M722	1-G	DSM	1960	3/68/7071/OS	OS	r.	m	DGC	
A/	np	7	M722	1-G	DSM	1960	12/70/8079/OS	OS	r.	d	BL-b	
A/	np	7	M722	1-G	DSM	1960	1/74/720035 S	OS	r.	d	DGC	
Sheet 23 *South Uist*												
A	3/6	7	M722	1-G	DSW	1961	4000/1/61/6229/OS	OS	r	m-	Ob	
A	np	7	M722	1-G	DSW	1961	5000/10/64/6644/OS	OS	r	m	DGC	
A	np	7	M722	1-G	DSM	1961	3/68/7072/OS	OS	r.	m	Ob	
A/*	np	7	M722	2-G	DSM	1970	70/7791/OS	OS	r.	m	Ob	
A/*	np	7	M722	2-G	DSM	1970	12/72/8680/OS	OS	r.	d	Ob	
Sheet 24 *North Skye*												
A	3/-	7	M722	1-G	DSW	1960	4000/12/60/6007/OS	OS	r	mo	Ob	
A/	np	7	M722	1-G	DSW	1960	5000/9/64/6644/OS	OS	r	m	NLS	
A/	np	7	M722	1-G	DSM	1967	8500/11/67/6939/OS	OS	r.	m	BL-a	
A//	np	7	M722	1-G	DSM	1967	1/71/8112/OS	OS	r.	m	BL-b	
A///	np	7	M722	1-G	DSM	1967	9/72/721764 S	OS	r.	d	Ob	
Sheet 25 *Portree*												
A	3/-	7	M722	1-G	DSW	1960	4000/11/60/6007/OS	OS	r	mo	Ob	
A/	np	7	M722	1-G	DSW	1960	10,000/7/65/6749/OS	OS	r	m	BL-b	
A//*	DR	7	M722	1-G	DSM	1960	10/71/8225/OS	OS	r.	m	BL-b	
A//*	np	7	M722	1-G	DSM	1960	2/73/721128 S	OS	r.	m	DGC	
Sheet 26 *Lochcarron*												
A	3/-	7	M722	1-G	DSW	1960	4000/11/60/6007/OS	OS	r	mo	Ob	
A/	np	7	M722	1-G	DSW	1960	5000/9/64/6644/OS	OS	r	m	Wc	
A//*	np	7	M722	2-G	DSM	1965	17,000/8/65/6762/OS	OS	r	m	Ob	
A//*	np	7	M722	2-G	DSM	1965	9/69/7586/OS	OS	r.	d	Ob	
A//*/*	np	7	M722	3-G	DSM	1972	11/72/712209 S	OS	r.	d	Ob	
A//*/*	np	7	M722	3-G	DSM	1972	10/74/740977 S	OS	r.	d	DGC	
Sheet 27 *Strathpeffer*												
A	3/-	7	M722	1-G	DSW	1959	4000/10/60/6007/OS	OS	r	mo	Ob	
A/	np	7	M722	2-G	DSM	1964	5000/10/64/6643/OS	OS	r	m	Ob	
A/	np	7	M722	2-G	DSM	1964	8500/9/66/348/OA	BAOR	r	m	DGC	

1	5	6	7	8	9	10	11	12	13	14	15	16
A//*	np	7	M722	3-G	DSM	1969	4/69/7384/OS	OS	r.	d	Ob	
A//*	np	7	M722	3-G	DSM	1969	11/71/8353/OS	OS	r.	m	Ob	
A//*	np	7	M722	3-G	DSM	1969	5/74/730880 S	OS	r.	d	DGC	
A//*	np	7	M722	3-G	DSM	1969	500/8/75/751338 S	OS	r.	m	DGC	

Sheet 28 *Inverness*

1	5	6	7	8	9	10	11	12	13	14	15	16
A	3/6	7	M722	1-G	DSW	1960	4000/10/60/6007/OS	OS	r	mo	Ob	
A/	4/6	7	M722	1-G	DSW	1960	4000/4/64/6591/OS	OS	r	m	DGC	
A/	np	7	M722	1-G	DSW	1960	4000/1/65/6683/OS	OS	r	m	DGC	
A//	np	7	M722	2-G	DSM	1967	15,000/5/67/6924/OS	OS	r.	d	DGC	
A//	np	7	M722	2-G	DSM	1967	2/73/8470/OS	OS	r.	d	Ob	

Sheet 29 *Elgin*

1	5	6	7	8	9	10	11	12	13	14	15	16
A	3/6	7	M722	1-G	DSW	1961	4000/11/61/6007/OS	OS	r	mo	Ob	
A/	4/6	7	M722	1-G	DSW	1964	5000/5/64/6591/OS	OS	r	m	NLS	
A/	np	7	M722	1-G	DSW	1961	10,000/8/66/357/OA	BAOR	r	m	DGC	
A/	np	7	M722	1-G	DSM	1964	12/70/8095/OS	OS	r.	m	BL-b	
A//	np	7	M722	2-G	DSM	1971	12/71/8434/OS	OS	r.	d	BL-a	
A//	np	7	M722	2-G	DSM	1971	10/74/740978 S	OS	r.	d	DGC	

Sheet 30 *Banff*

1	5	6	7	8	9	10	11	12	13	14	15	16
A	3/6	7	M722	1-G	DSW	1961	4000/11/61/6007/OS	OS	r	mo	Ob	
A/	4/6	7	M722	1-G	DSW	1961	14,000/12/63/6581/OS	OS	r	m	BL-a	
A/	np	7	M722	1-G	DSM	1966	5000/6/66/6824/OS	OS	r.	m	Wc	
A/	np	7	M722	1-G	DSM	1966	1/69/7342/OS	OS	r.	m	Ob	
A/	np	7	M722	1-G	DSM	1966	1/70/7845/OS	OS	r.	m	DGC	
A/	np	7	M722	1-G	DSM	1966	8/72/8494/OS	OS	r.	d	Ob	

Sheet 31 *Peterhead*

1	5	6	7	8	9	10	11	12	13	14	15	16
A	3/6	7	M722	1-G	DSW	1961	4000/10/61/6007/OS	OS	r	mo	Ob	
A	np	7	M722	1-G	DSW	1961	5000/9/64/6643/OS	OS	r	m	DGC	
A/	np	7	M722	1-G	DSW	1961	2000/1/65/6689/OS	OS	r	m	DGC	
A/	np	7	M722	1-G	DSM	1961	3/68/7073/OS	OS	r.	m	Ob	
A/	np	7	M722	1-G	DSM	1961	70/7846/OS	OS	r.	d	DGC	
A/	np	7	M722	1-G	DSM	1961	10/72/8681/OS	OS	r.	d	BL-b	

Sheet 32 *Barra*

1	5	6	7	8	9	10	11	12	13	14	15	16
A	3/6	7	M722	1-G	DSW	1961	4000/1/61/6229/OS	OS	r	mt	Ob	
A	np	7	M722	1-G	DSW	1961	5000/1/65/6683/OS	OS	r	m	DGC	
A	np	7	M722	1-G	DSM	1961	12/70/8092/OS	OS	r.	m	BL-b	

Sheet 33 *Rhum and Part of Skye*

1	5	6	7	8	9	10	11	12	13	14	15	16
A	3/-	7	M722	1-G	DSW	1961	4000/4/61/6007/OS	OS	r	mo	Ob	
A/	np	7	M722	1-G	DSW	1964	5000/9/64/6643/OS	OS	r	m	DGC	
A//	np	7	M722	1-G	DSM	1961	5/69/7441/OS	OS	r.	d	Ob	
A//	np	7	M722	1-G	DSM	1961	9/70/8063/OS	OS	r.	m	BL-b	

Sheet 34 *South Skye and Arisaig*

1	5	6	7	8	9	10	11	12	13	14	15	16
A/	4/6	7	M722	1-G	DSW	1962	4000/5/62/6007/OS	OS	r	m	Ob	
A/	np	7	M722	1-G	DSW	1962	5000/9/64/6643/OS	OS	r	m	DGC	
A/	np	7	M722	1-G	DSM	1962	3/68/7074/OS	OS	r.	m	Ob	
A//*	np	7	M722	2-G	DSM	1970	11/69/7654/OS	OS	r.	d	Ob	
A//*	np	7	M722	2-G	DSM	1970	10/70/8080/OS	OS	r.	m	DGC	

Sheet 35 *Loch Arkaig*

1	5	6	7	8	9	10	11	12	13	14	15	16
A	3/-	7	M722	1-G	DSW	1961	4000/61/6007/OS	OS	r	mo	Ob	
A/	4/6	7	M722	2-G	DSW	1964	5000/3/64/6591/OS	OS	r	m	Ob	
A/	np	7	M722	2-G	DSW	1964	8500/10/66/348/OA	BAOR	r	m	DGC	
A//*	np	7	M722	3-G	DSM	1967	4500/5/67/6924/OS	OS	r.	m	DGC	
A//*	np	7	M722	3-G	DSM	1967	1/69/7341/OS	OS	r.	m	Ob	
A//*	np	7	M722	3-G	DSM	1967	3/73/8682/OS	OS	r.	m	BL-b	

Sheet 36 *Fort Augustus*

1	5	6	7	8	9	10	11	12	13	14	15	16
A	3/-	7	M722	1-G	DSW	1961	4000/11/61/6007/OS	OS	r	mo	Ob	
A/*	4/6	7	M722	2-G	DSW	1964	15,000/3/64/6590/OS	OS	r	m	Ob	
A/*	np	7	M722	2-G	DSM	1964	6/70/7976/OS (blue)	OS	r.	m	BL-b	

Sheet 37 *Kingussie*

1	5	6	7	8	9	10	11	12	13	14	15	16
A/	4/6	7	M722	1-G	DSW	1962	4000/4/62/6007/OS	OS	r	m	Ob	
A/	np	7	M722	1-G	DSW	1962	10,000/4/64/6590/OS	OS	r	m	Cu-m	
A/	np	7	M722	1-G	DSW	1962	15,000/10/66/348/OA	BAOR	r	m	DGC	
A/	np	7	M722	1-G	DSM	1962	12/70/8093/OS	OS	r.	m	DGC	
A/	DR	7	M722	1-G	DSM	1962	2/72/8620/OS	OS	r.	d	Ob	

Sheet 38 *Grantown and Cairngorm*

1	5	6	7	8	9	10	11	12	13	14	15	16
A/	4/6	7	M722	1-G	DSW	1962	4000/2/62/6007/OS	OS	r	m	Ob	
A/	4/6	7	M722	1-G	DSW	1962	10,000/1/64/6590/OS	OS	r	m	DGC	
A/	np	7	M722	1-G	DSW	1962	15,000/8/66/357/OA	BAOR	r	m	DGC	
A/	np	7	M722	1-G	DSM	1962	9/70/8064/OS	OS	r.	m	DGC	

Sheet 39 *Strathdon*

1	5	6	7	8	9	10	11	12	13	14	15	16
A	3/6	7	M722	1-G	DSW	1961	4000/11/61/6007/OS	OS	r	mo	Ob	
A	3/6	7	M722	1-G	DSW	1961	5000/4/64/6591/OS	OS	r	m	DGC	
A	np	7	M722	1-G	DSM	1966	13,000/9/66/6823/OS	OS	r.	m	BL-b	
A/	np	7	M722	1-G	DSM	1966	6/73/712378 S	OS	r.	d	DGC	

Sheet 40 *Aberdeen*

1	5	6	7	8	9	10	11	12	13	14	15	16
A/	4/6	7	M722	1-G	DSW	1962	6000/1/62/6007/OS	OS	r	m	Ob	
A/	np	7	M722	1-G	DSW	1962	3000/4/64/6591/OS	OS	r	m	DGC	
A/	np	7	M722	1-G	DSM	1966	10,000/7/66/6823/OS	OS	r.	m	DGC	
B	np	7	M722	2-G	DSM	1969	69/7593/OS	OS	r.	d	DGC	1
B	np	7	M722	2-G	DSM	1969	11/69/7593/OS	OS	r.	d	Ob	1
B	np	7	M722	2-G	DSM	1969	7/70/8034/OS	OS	r.	m	DGC	
B	DR	7	M722	2-G	DSM	1969	4/72/8616/OS	OS	r.	d	Ob	

1. The month element of the print code, lacking at first, was added later.

Sheet 41 *Braemar*

1	5	6	7	8	9	10	11	12	13	14	15	16
A/	4/6	7	M722	1-G	DSW	1961	4000/11/61/6007/OS	OS	r	mo	Ob	
A/	np	7	M722	1-G	DSW	1961	14,000/2/65/6701/OS	OS	r	m	DGC	
A//	np	7	M722	1-G	DSM	1967	12,000/7/67/6938/OS	OS	r.	m	BL-b	
A//	np	7	M722	1-G	DSM	1967	10/70/8081/OS	OS	r.	m	DGC	

Sheet 42 *Ballater*

1	5	6	7	8	9	10	11	12	13	14	15	16
A	3/-	7	M722	1-G	DSW	1961	4000/11/61/6007/OS	OS	r	mo	Ob	
A/	4/6	7	M722	1-G	DSW	1961	12,000/8/63/6555/OS	OS	r	d	Ob	
A/	np	7	M722	1-G	DSM	1961	3/68/7075/OS	OS	r.	m	DGC	
A/	np	7	M722	1-G	DSM	1961	70/7977/OS	OS	r.	m	DGC	

Sheet 43 *Stonehaven*

1	5	6	7	8	9	10	11	12	13	14	15	16
A	3/6	7	M722	1-G	DSW	1961	4000/11/61/6007/OS	OS	r	mo	Ob	
A/	4/6	7	M722	1-G	DSW	1961	14,000/9/63/6571/OS	OS	r	d	NLS	
B	np	7	M722	2-G	DSM	1969	9/69/7552/OS	OS	r.	d	Ob	
B	np	7	M722	2-G	DSM	1969	8/70/8065/OS	OS	r.	m	DGC	

Sheet 44 *Coll and Tiree*

1	5	6	7	8	9	10	11	12	13	14	15	16
A/	3/-	7	M722	1-G	DSW	1961	4000/4/61/6007/OS	OS	r	mo	Ob	1
A/	np	7	M722	1-G	DSW	1961	4000/1/65/6683/OS	OS	r	m	Wc	
A/	np	7	M722	1-G	DSM	1967	2500/10/67/6939/OS	OS	r.	m	DGC	
A/	np	7	M722	1-G	DSM	1967	6/68/7120/OS	OS	r.	m	BL-b	
A/	np	7	M722	1-G	DSM	1967	9/72/8683/OS	OS	r.	d	Ob	

1. This A/ edition is earlier than the civilian, with corrections to 1958.

1	5	6	7	8	9	10	11	12	13	14	15	16

Sheet 45 *Sound of Mull*

1	5	6	7	8	9	10	11	12	13	14	15
A	3/-	7	M722	1-G	DSW	1961	4000/11/61/6007/OS	OS	r	mo	Ob
A/	np	7	M722	1-G	DSW	1961	4000/12/64/6683/OS	OS	r	m	NLS
A/	np	7	M722	1-G	DSW	1961	10,000/10/66/348/OA	BAOR	r	m	DGC
A//*	np	7	M722	2-G	DSM	1971	10/71/8486/OS	OS	r.	d	Ob

Sheet 46 *Loch Linnhe*

A/	3/6	7	M722	1-G	DSW	1961	5000/11/61/6007/OS	OS	r	mo	Ob
A//	4/6	7	M722	1-G	DSW	1961	12,000/8/63/6555/OS	OS	r	m	BL-b
A//	np	7	M722	1-G	DSM	1961	9/70/8066/OS	OS	r.	m	Ob
A///	DR	7	M722	1-G	DSM	1961	5/72/8724/OS	OS	r.	d	BL-b

Sheet 47 *Glencoe*

A/	3/6	7	M722	1-G	DSW	1961	4000/11/61/6007/OS	OS	r	mo	Ob
A/	4/6	7	M722	1-G	DSW	1961	5000/7/64/6591/OS	OS	r	d	DGC
A/	np	7	M722	1-G	DSM	1966	13,000/8/66/6823/OS	OS	r.	m	DGC
A/	np	7	M722	1-G	DSM	1966	3/71/8147/OS	OS	r.	m	BL-b

Sheet 48 *Loch Tay*

nc	3/6	7	M722	1-G	DSW	1961	6000/11/61/6007/OS	OS	r	mo	Ob
A//	np	7	M722	1-G	DSW	1961	5000/8/64/6643/OS	OS	r	m	DGC
A//	np	7	M722	1-G	DSM	1966	15,000/6/66/6824/OS	OS	r.	m	Ob
A//	np	7	M722	1-G	DSM	1966	8/69/7587/OS	OS	r.	d	DGC
A//	np	7	M722	1-G	DSM	1966	6/71/8192/OS	OS	r.	m	BL-b
A//	np	7	M722	1-G	DSM	1966	7/74/740049 S	OS	r	d	DGC

Sheet 49 *Blairgowrie*

A/	4/6	7	M722	1-G	DSW	1962	6000/5/62/6007/OS	OS	r	m	Ob
A/	np	7	M722	1-G	DSW	1962	5000/10/64/6643/OS	OS	r	m	DGC
A//	np	7	M722	1-G	DSM	1966	10,000/6/66/6817/OS	OS	r.	d	DGC
A//	np	7	M722	1-G	DSM	1966	10,000/12/70/8085/OS	OS	r.	m	Ob
A///	DR	7	M722	1-G	DSM	1966	7/72/8722/OS	OS	r.	d	Ob

Sheet 50 *Forfar*

A/	4/6	7	M722	1-G	DSW	1962	6000/4/62/6007/OS	OS	r	m	Ob
A/	np	7	M722	1-G	DSW	1962	5000/8/64/6643/OS	OS	r	m	DGC
A/	np	7	M722	1-G	DSM	1966	18,000/8/66/6823/OS	OS	r.	m	DGC
A//*	np	7	M722	2-G	DSM	1967	10,000/5/67/6924/OS	OS	r.	d	Wc
B	np	7	M722	3-G	DSM	1969	10/69/7553/OS	OS	r.	d	Ob
B	np	7	M722	3-G	DSM	1969	2/71/8105/OS	OS	r.	m	BL-b

Sheet 51 *Iona and Colonsay*

A/	4/6	7	M722	1-G	DSW	1962	4000/7/62/6007/OS	OS	r	m	Ob
A/	np	7	M722	1-G	DSW	1962	5000/4/64/6591/OS	OS	r	m	BL-b
A/	np	7	M722	1-G	DSM	1966	20,000/7/66/6823/OS	OS	r.	m	DGC
A/	np	7	M722	1-G	DSM	1966	5/73/730010 S	OS	r.	m	BL-b

Sheet 52 *Loch Awe*

A//	4/6	7	M722	1-G	DSW	1962	5000/6/62/6007/OS	OS	r	m	Ob
A//	np	7	M722	1-G	DSW	1962	10,000/9/64/6642/OS	OS	r	m	DGC
A//	np	7	M722	1-G	DSM	1962	3/68/7076/OS	OS	r.	m	Ob
A//	np	7	M722	1-G	DSM	1962	12/72/8485/OS	OS	r.	m	Ob
A//	np	7	M722	1-G	DSM	1962	2/74/733171 S	OS	r.	d	DGC

Sheet 53 *Loch Lomond*

A/	4/6	7	M722	1-G	DSW	1962	5000/8/62/6007/OS	OS	r	dx	Ob
A/	np	7	M722	1-G	DSW	1962	10,000/9/64/6642/OS	OS	r	m	DGC
A//*	np	7	M722	2-G	DSM	1966	16,000/8/66/6854/OS	OS	r.	m	Ob
A//*	np	7	M722	2-G	DSM	1966	2/72/8461/OS	OS	r.	m	Ob
A//*	np	7	M722	2-G	DSM	1966	3/75/741096 S	OS	r.	d	DGC

1	5	6	7	8	9	10	11	12	13	14	15	16

Sheet 54 *Stirling*

1	5	6	7	8	9	10	11	12	13	14	15	16
A/	3/6	7	M722	1-G	DSW	1962	6000/6/62/6007/OS	OS	r	m	Ob	1
A/	np	7	M722	1-G	DSW	1962	12,500/8/64/6642/OS	OS	r	d	DGC	
A/	np	7	M722	1-G	DSM	1967	10,000/6/67/6930/OS	OS	r.	d	DGC	
A/	np	7	M722	1-G	DSM	1967	5/70/7957/OS	OS	r.	m	BL-b	
A//*	np	7	M722	2-G	DSM	1971	7/71/8224/OS	OS	r.	d	Ob	
A//*	np	7	M722	2-G	DSM	1971	2/73/721445 S	OS	r.	d	Ob	

1. A civilian printing with a 3/6 price statement has not been recorded.

Sheet 55 *Perth and Alloa*

1	5	6	7	8	9	10	11	12	13	14	15	16
A/	3/6	7	M722	1-G	DSW	1962	6000/6/62/6007/OS	OS	r	m	Ob	
A/	np	7	M722	1-G	DSW	1962	16,000/8/64/6576/OS	OS	r	m	DGC	
A/	np	7	M722	1-G	DSM	1962	2/68/7077/OS	OS	r.	m	BL-a	
B	np	7	M722	2-G	DSM	1969	69/7554/OS	OS	r.	d	Ob	
B/*	np	7	M722	3-G	DSM	1972	12/72/722405 S	OS	r.	d	Ob	

Sheet 56 *St Andrews and Kirkcaldy*

1	5	6	7	8	9	10	11	12	13	14	15	16
A/	4/6	7	M722	1-G	DSW	1962	2000/5/62/6007/OS	OS	r	cx	Ob	
A/	4/6	7	M722	1-G	DSW	1963	5000/2/63/6007/OS	OS	r	d	DGC	1
A/	np	7	M722	1-G	DSW	1963	5000/9/65/6756/OS	OS	r	m	DGC	
A/	np	7	M722	1-G	DSW	1963	10,000/12/65/6795/OS	OS	r	m	DGC	
B	np	7	M722	2-G	DSM	1969	/69/7557/OS	OS	r.	d	Ob	2
B	-	7	M722	2-G	DSM	1969	12/71/8556/OS	OS	r.	m	Ob	3

1. On a copy held by DGC the 6007 in the print code has been altered by hand to 6507. 2. On a copy held by DGC the print code has been altered by hand to 11/69. 3. The *Distribution restricted* notice is lacking.

Sheet 57 *Islay*

1	5	6	7	8	9	10	11	12	13	14	15	16
A/	4/6	7	M722	1-G	DSW	1962	4000/10/62/6007/OS	OS	r	m	Ob	
A/	np	7	M722	1-G	DSW	1962	10,000/9/64/6642/OS	OS	r	m	DGC	
A//	np	7	M722	1-G	DSM	1962	3/68/7078/OS	OS	r.	m	Ob	
A//	np	7	M722	1-G	DSM	1962	7/73/711827 S	OS	r.	d	BL-b	

Sheet 58 *Knapdale*

1	5	6	7	8	9	10	11	12	13	14	15	16
A/	3/-	7	M722	1-G	DSW	1962	4000/8/62/6007/OS	OS	r	m	Ob	
A/	np	7	M722	1-G	DSW	1962	5000/4/64/6592/OS	OS	r	m	DGC	
A/	np	7	M722	1-G	DSM	1966	10,000/8/66/6823/OS	OS	r.	m	Ob	
A//	np	7	M722	1-G	DSM	1966	11/68/7325/OS	OS	r.	d	DGC	1
A//	np	7	M722	2-G	DSM	1968	11/68/7325/OS	OS	r.	d	Ob	2
A//	np	7	M722	2-G	DSM	1968	8/72/8671/OS	OS	r.	m	Ob	
A//	np	7	M722	2-G	DSM	1968	7/74/740048 S	OS	r.	d	DGC	

1. The overprinted detail was erroneous, and replaced by the next. 2. The edition number 1 is blocked out, replaced by 2, and the publication date altered from 1966 to 1968.

Sheet 59 *Firth of Clyde*

1	5	6	7	8	9	10	11	12	13	14	15	16
A/	4/6	7	M722	1-G	DSW	1962	4000/11/62/6007/OS	OS	r	m	Ob	
A/	np	7	M722	1-G	DSW	1962	5000/9/64/6576/OS	OS	r	m	DGC	
B	np	7	M722	2-G	DSM	1965	25,000/11/65/6718/OS	OS	r	d	Ob	
B/	np	7	M722	3-G	DSM	1972	8/72/8655/OS	OS	r.	m	Ob	

Sheet 60 *Glasgow*

1	5	6	7	8	9	10	11	12	13	14	15	16
A/	3/6	7	M722	1-G	DSW	1962	6000/10/62/6007/OS	OS	r	m	Ob	
A//	np	7	M722	1-G	DSW	1962	2500/7/65/6749/OS	OS	r	m	Wc	
B	np	7	M722	2-G	DSM	1965	17,500/10/65/6749/OS	OS	r	d	Ob	
B/*	np	7	M722	3-G	DSM	1968	9/68/7306/OS	OS	r.	d	Ob	
B/*	np	7	M722	3-G	DSM	1968	7/70/8035/OS	OS	r.	m	DGC	
B/*/*	np	7	M722	4-G	DSM	1971	10/71/8435/OS	OS	r.	d	Ob	
B/*/*	np	7	M722	4-G	DSM	1971	2/73/722650 S	OS	r.	m	BL-b	
B/*/*/*	np	7	M722	4-G	DSM	1971	11/73/732009 S	OS	r.	d	DGC	
B/*/*/*	np	7	M722	4-G	DSM	1971	1000/9/75/751350 S	OS	r.	m	DGC	1

1. This is the last known printing of a sheet in Series M722.

1	5	6	7	8	9	10	11	12	13	14	15	16

Sheet 61 *Falkirk and Lanark*

1	5	6	7	8	9	10	11	12	13	14	15	16
A/	4/6	7	M722	1-G	DSW	1962	6000/10/62/6007/OS	OS	r	m	Ob	
A/	np	7	M722	1-G	DSW	1962	3000/8/64/6576/OS	OS	r	m	DGC	
B	np	7	M722	2-G	DSM	1965	15,000/12/65/6747/OS	OS	r	d	Ob	
B/*	np	7	M722	3-G	DSM	1971	9/71/8252/OS	OS	r.	d	Ob	
B/*	np	7	M722	3-G	DSM	1971	8/72/712381 S	OS	r.	d	Ob	
B/*/*	np	7	M722	4-G	DSM	1973	7/73/730625 S	OS	r.	m	DGC	
B/*/*	np	7	M722	4-G	DSM	1973	2500/6/75/751040 S	OS	r.	m	DGC	

Sheet 62 *Edinburgh*

1	5	6	7	8	9	10	11	12	13	14	15	16
A/	3/6	7	M722	1-G	DSW	1962	7000/9/62/6007/OS	OS	r	m	Ob	
A/	np	7	M722	1-G	DSW	1962	2000/9/64/6576/OS	OS	r	m	DGC	
B	np	7	M722	2-G	DSM	1965	25,000/9/65/6715/OS	OS	r	d	Ob	
B/*	np	7	M722	3-G	DSM	1971	5/71/8188/OS	OS	r.	d	Ob	
B/*	np	7	M722	3-G	DSM	1971	7/74/740979 S	OS	r.	d	DGC	

For further use see supplement 8.

Sheet 63 *Dunbar*

1	5	6	7	8	9	10	11	12	13	14	15	16
B	3/6	7	M722	1-G	DSW	1962	5000/11/62/6007/OS	OS	r	m	Ob	
B/	4/6	7	M722	1-G	DSW	1962	4000/4/64/6592/OS	OS	r	m	Wc	
C	np	7	M722	2-G	DSM	1965	12,000/9/65/6756/OS	OS	r	d	Ob	
C	np	7	M722	2-G	DSM	1965	7/71/8108/OS	OS	r.	m	BL-b	
C	np	7	M722	2-G	DSM	1965	1000/8/75/741098 S	OS	r.	d	DGC	

Sheet 64 a *Berwick upon Tweed* b *Berwick-upon-Tweed*

1	5	6	7	8	9	10	11	12	13	14	15	16
1001	5/-	6a	4620	WOE	WO	1948	25,000/4/48	OS	p	a	Wc	
1001	np	6a	4620	1-G	WO	1948	20,000/6/55 OS	OS	p	b	BL-d	
1001	5/-	6a	4620	WOE	WO	1948	7600/12/56 OS	OS	p	ac	BL-d	
A/	3/6	7b	M722	1-G	DSW	1961	4000/1/61/6229/OS	OS	r	mo	Ob	1
A/	4/6	7b	M722	1-G	DSW	1962	10,000/1/62/6387/OS	OS	r	m	BL-b	
B	np	7b	M722	2-G	DSM	1965	15,000/5/65/6718/OS	OS	r	d	Ob	
B	np	7b	M722	2-G	DSM	1965	1/74/720040 S	OS	r.	d	DGC	

1. NB a second Edition 1-GSGS. A civilian printing with a 3/6 price statement has not been recorded.

Sheet 65 *Kintyre*

1	5	6	7	8	9	10	11	12	13	14	15	16
A/	3/6	7	M722	1-G	DSW	1962	4000/10/62/6007/OS	OS	r	m	Ob	1
A/	np	7	M722	1-G	DSW	1962	10,000/10/64/6642/OS	OS	r	m	Ob	
A/	np	7	M722	1-G	DSM	1962	4/68/7079/OS	OS	r.	m	DGC	
A/	np	7	M722	1-G	DSM	1962	2/73/8496/OS	OS	r.	d	Ob	

1. A civilian printing with a 3/6 price statement has not been recorded.

Sheet 66 *Isle of Arran*

1	5	6	7	8	9	10	11	12	13	14	15	16
A/	4/6	7	M722	1-G	DSW	1962	4000/11/62/6007/OS	OS	r	m	Ob	
A/	np	7	M722	1-G	DSW	1962	10,000/8/64/6642/OS	OS	r	m	DGC	
A/	np	7	M722	1-G	DSM	1962	4/68/7080/OS	OS	r.	m	BL-a	
A/	DR	7	M722	1-G	DSM	1962	6/72/8685/OS	OS	r.	m	Ob	

Sheet 67 *Ayr*

1	5	6	7	8	9	10	11	12	13	14	15	16
A/	3/6	7	M722	1-G	DSW	1962	6000/10/62/6007/OS	OS	r	m	Ob	
B	np	7	M722	2-G	DSW	1964	26,000/4/64/6593/OS	OS	r	d	Ob	
B/*	np	7	M722	3-G	DSM	1973	2/73/8661/OS	OS	r.	d	Ob	

Sheet 68 *Biggar, Moffat and Sanquhar*

1	5	6	7	8	9	10	11	12	13	14	15	16
A/	4/6	7	M722	1-G	DSW	1962	8000/1/62/6007/OS	OS	r	m	Ob	
B	np	7	M722	2-G	DSM	1964	20,000/9/64/6652/OS	OS	r	d	Ob	1
B/	np	7	M722	3-G	DSM	1970	/ /7885/OS	OS	r.	m	Ob	
B/	np	7	M722	3-G	DSM	1970	3/74/720043 S	OS	r.	d	DGC	

1. This sheet carries 1965 civilian copyright dates.

1	5	6	7	8	9	10	11	12	13	14	15	16

Sheet 69 *Selkirk*

1	5	6	7	8	9	10	11	12	13	14	15	16
A/	4/6	7	M722	1-G	DSW	1962	5000/11/62/6007/OS	OS	r	m	Ob	
B	np	7	M722	2-G	DSW	1964	30,000/3/64/6593/OS	OS	r	m	Ob	
B	np	7	M722	2-G	DSM	1964	11/71/8467/OS	OS	r.	d	Ob	
B	np	7	M722	2-G	DSM	1964	8/74/740046 S	OS	r.	m	DGC	

Sheet 70 *Jedburgh*

1	5	6	7	8	9	10	11	12	13	14	15	16
A/	3/6	7	M722	1-G	DSW	1961	5000/11/61/6007/OS	OS	r	mo	Ob	
B	np	7	M722	2-G	DSM	1964	31,000/7/64/6576/OS	OS	r	m	Ob	
B/	np	7	M722	3-G	DSM	1970	11/69/7653 OS	OS	r.	m	BL-b	1
B/	np	7	M722	3-G	DSM	1970	/1/70/7653 OS	OS	r.	m	Ob	1
B/	np	7	M722	3-G	DSM	1970	10/72/712211 S	OS	r.	m	Ob	

1. The print order number is the same. The 11/69 printing is not in DGC Superseded.

Sheet 71 *Alnwick*

1	5	6	7	8	9	10	11	12	13	14	15	16
1002	5/-	6	4620	WOE	WO	1948	15,000/4/48	OS	p	a	BL	
nc	10/6	6	4620	2-G	WO	1952	12,000/6/52	OS	p	b	BL-d	
B	10/6	6	4620	2-G	WO	1952	1400/1/57 OS	OS	p	bc	BL-d	
A/	3/6	7	M722	3-G	DSW	1960	5000/7/60/6223/OS	OS	r	mo	Ob	
A/	4/6	7	M722	3-G	DSW	1960	10,000/1/62/6387/OS	OS	r	m	Wc	
B	np	7	M722	4-G	DSW	1965	15,000/8/65/6744/OS	OS	r	m	Ob	
B	np	7	M722	4-G	DSM	1965	6/68/7081/OS	OS	r.	m	Ob	1
B	np	7	M722	4-G	DSM	1965	8/68/7081/OS	OS	r.	m	BL-b	1
B/	np	7	M722	5-G	DSM	1970	70/7936/OS	OS	r.	m	Ob	
B/	np	7	M722	5-G	DSM	1970	1000/8/75/741100 S	OS	r.	d	DGC	

1. The print order number is the same. The 8/68 printing is not in DGC Superseded.

Sheet 72 *Girvan*

1	5	6	7	8	9	10	11	12	13	14	15	16
A/	3/-	7	M722	1-G	DSW	1961	4000/11/61/6007/OS	OS	r	mo	Ob	
A/	3/-	7	M722	1-G	DSW	1961	4000/6/64/6645/OS	OS	r	cx	DGC	
A/	3/6	7	M722	1-G	DSW	1961	4000/6/64/6645/OS	OS	r	cx	PC	
B	np	7	M722	2-G	DSM	1965	14,000/12/64/6645/OS	OS	r	d	Ob	
B	np	7	M722	2-G	DSM	1965	10/71/8351/OS	OS	r.	m	Ob	

Sheet 73 *New Galloway*

1	5	6	7	8	9	10	11	12	13	14	15	16
A/	3/-	7	M722	1-G	DSW	1961	4000/12/61/6007/OS	OS	r	mo	Ob	
B	np	7	M722	2-G	DSM	1965	6000/12/64/6683/OS	OS	r	m	Ob	
B	np	7	M722	2-G	DSM	1966	19,000/8/66/6823/OS	OS	r.	m	BL-b	
B	np	7	M722	2-G	DSM	1966	6/74/740257 S	OS	r.	d	DGC	

Sheet 74 *Dumfries*

1	5	6	7	8	9	10	11	12	13	14	15	16
A/	3/6	7	M722	1-G	DSW	1961	4000/12/61/6007/OS	OS	r	mo	Ob	
B	np	7	M722	2-G	DSM	1965	6000/12/64/6684/OS	OS	r	m	Ob	
B	np	7	M722	2-G	DSM	1965	13,000/6/66/1680/SPC	SPC RE	r	m	BL-b	
B	np	7	M722	2-G	DSM	1965	12/70/8096/OS	OS	r.	d	DGC	
B	np	7	M722	2-G	DSM	1965	2/74/720044 S	OS	r.	d	DGC	

Sheet 75 a. *Dumfries* b. *Dumfries and Gretna*

1	5	6	7	8	9	10	11	12	13	14	15	16
1003	5/-	6a	4620	WOE	WO	1948	25,000/5/48	OS	p	a	BL-d	
nc	np	6a	4620	1-G	WO	1948	20,000/6/55 OS	OS	p	b	BL-d	
A/	3/-	7b	M722	1-G	DSW	1961	4000/1/61/6229/OS	OS	r	mo	DGC	1
A/	3/-	7b	M722	1-G	DSW	1961	10,000/2/62/6387/OS	OS	r	m	Ob	
B	np	7b	M722	2-G	DSM	1964	24,000/9/64/6652/OS	OS	r	d	Ob	2
B/*	np	7b	M722	3-G	DSM	1969	11/69/7641/OS	OS	r.	d	Ob	
B/*	np	7b	M722	3-G	DSM	1969	4/71/8175/OS	OS	r.	m	DGC	
B/*/	np	7b	M722	3-G	DSM	1969	8/72/721095 S	OS	r.	d	Ob	

1. NB a second Edition 1-GSGS. 2. The civilian copyright and publication dates, both 1965, are crossed through.

Sheet 76 *Carlisle*

1	5	6	7	8	9	10	11	12	13	14	15	16
1004	5/-	6	4620	WOE	WO	1948	35,000/5/48	OS	p	a	BL-d	
1004	5/-	6	4620	WOE	WO	1948	10,000/12/56 OS	OS	p	ac	BL-d	

1	5	6	7	8	9	10	11	12	13	14	15	16
A/	3/6	7	M722	2-G	DSW	1962	20,000/8/62/6391/OS	OS	r	m	Ob	
B	4/6	7	M722	4-G	DSW	1963	40,000/9/63/6565/OS	OS	r	d	Ob	
B/*/*	np	7	M722	5-G	DSM	1971	10/71/8295/OS	OS	r.	d	BL-a	
B/*/*	np	7	M722	5-G	DSM	1971	6/74/740045 S	OS	r.	d	DGC	

Edition 3-GSGS was omitted in error. A note against the September 1963 printing in a DGC card catalogue states: "Edn. no. should have been 3-GSGS to supersede previous edn 2-GSGS."

Sheet 77 *Hexham*

1	5	6	7	8	9	10	11	12	13	14	15	16
1005	5/-	6	4620	WOE	WO	1948	15,000/5/48	OS	p	a	BL-d	
1005	5/-	6	4620	WOE	WO	1948	15,000/4/52 SPC RE	SPC RE	p	a	BL-d	1
1005	5/-	6	4620	WOE	WO	1948	1300/1/57 OS	OS	p	ac	BL-d	
A/	3/6	7	M722	2-G	DSW	1961	15,000/8/61/6261/OS	OS	r	mo	Ob	
B	np	7	M722	3-G	DSW	1964	35,000/2/64/6593/OS	OS	r	d	Ob	
B	np	7	M722	3-G	DSM	1964	1/73/8487/OS	OS	r.	d	Ob	

1. OS were requested on 18 February 1952 to forward plates to SPC for this printing.

Sheet 78 *Newcastle upon Tyne*

1	5	6	7	8	9	10	11	12	13	14	15	16
1006	5/-	6	4620	WOE	WO	1948	5000/5/48	OS	p	a	BL-d	1
1006	5/-	6	4620	WOE	WO	1948	5000/3/50	OS	p	a	BL-d	2
1006	5/-	6	4620	WOE	WO	1948	6500/4/52	OS	p	ac	BL-d	3
4022	np	7	4620	2-G	WO	1953	15,000/9/53 OS	OS	r	mo	BL-d	
4022	np	7	4620	2-G	WO	1953	15,000/12/59/6020/OS	OS	r	mo	BL-d	4
B	np	7	M722	3-G	DSM	1964	15,000/10/64/6592/OS	OS	r	m	Ob	
C	np	7	M722	4-G	DSM	1965	25,000/7/65/6718/OS	OS	r	m	Ob	
C/*	np	7	M722	5-G	DSM	1968	68/7113/OS	OS	r.	d	Ob	
C/*	np	7	M722	5-G	DSM	1968	3/71/8148/OS	OS	r.	m	DGC	
D	np	7	M722	6-G	DSM	1971	10/71/8218/OS	OS	r.	d	Ob	
D/*	DR	7	M722	7-G	DSM	1972	6/72/8723/OS	OS	r.	d	Ob	

For further use see supplement 8. 1. A Military Survey catalogue card records the order for 15,000, not 5000 copies, and notes that this order was completed on 23 June 1948. On the other hand 5000 may be the true total printed (albeit an unusually small number) since this figure appears on the OS catalogue card. 2. 1006 appears twice on this printing, in the corner, and on the overprint plate right of the imprint. 3. A 1951 order for a second edition printing on the New Popular base was held back and eventually cancelled on 6 July 1953 pending the arrival of the new Seventh Series map. 6500 civilian copies were overprinted for use in the meantime. 4. Note that GSGS 4620, not M722, is still present on this printing.

Sheet 79 *Stranraer*

1	5	6	7	8	9	10	11	12	13	14	15	16
A/	3/-	7	M722	1-G	DSW	1961	4000/9/61/6007/OS	OS	r	mo	Ob	
B	np	7	M722	2-G	DSM	1964	23,000/7/64/6576/OS	OS	r	m	Ob	
B	np	7	M722	2-G	DSM	1964	1/72/8497/OS	OS	r.	m	Ob	

Sheet 80 *Kirkcudbright*

1	5	6	7	8	9	10	11	12	13	14	15	16
A/	3/-	7	M722	1-G	DSW	1961	4000/11/61/6007/OS	OS	r	mo	Ob	
B	4/6	7	M722	2-G	DSW	1963	33,000/7/63/6546 OS	OS	r	d	Ob	
B/	np	7	M722	3-G	DSM	1970	70/7883/OS	OS	r.	d	Ob	
B/	np	7	M722	3-G	DSM	1970	3/74/720045 S	OS	r.	d	DGC	

Sheet 81 *Dalbeattie*

1	5	6	7	8	9	10	11	12	13	14	15	16
A/	4/6	7	M722	1-G	DSW	1961	5000/11/61/6007/OS	OS	r	mo	Ob	
B	4/6	7	M722	2-G	DSW	1963	33,000/7/63/6546/OS	OS	r	d	Ob	
B	np	7	M722	3-G	DSM	1969	8/69/7588 OS	OS	r.	d	Ob	
B	DR	7	M722	3-G	DSM	1969	6/72/8488/OS	OS	r.	d	Ob	

Sheet 82 *Keswick*

1	5	6	7	8	9	10	11	12	13	14	15	16
1007	5/-	6	4620	WOE	WO	1948	15,000/5/48	OS	p	a	BL-d	
1007	10/6	6	4620	2-G	WO	1952	15,000/7/52	OS	p	b	BL-d	1
1007	5/-	6	4620	WOE	WO	1948	1200/9/55 OS	OS	p	ac	BL-d	
A//	4/6	7	M722	3-G	DSW	1961	15,000/10/61/6261/OS	OS	r	mo	BL-b	
B	np	7	M722	4-G	DSM	1965	35,000/12/64/6593/OS	OS	r	d	Ob	
B/	np	7	M722	4-G	DSM	1965	8/71/8250/OS	OS	r.	d	BL-a	

1. This printing replaced a similar order made and cancelled the year before.

Sheet 83 *Penrith*

1	5	6	7	8	9	10	11	12	13	14	15	16
1008	5/-	6	4620	WOE	WO	1949	25,000/10/49	OS	p	a	BL-d	
1214	5/-	6	4620	WOE	WO	1949	8400/8/55 OS	OS	p	ac	BL-d	
nc	np	7	4620	2-G	WO	1955	12,000/9/55 OS	OS	r	mo	BL-d	
A//	4/6	7	M722	2-G	DSW	1955	25,000/2/63/6387/OS	OS	r	mc	Wc	
B	np	7	M722	3-G	DSM	1964	40,000/9/64/6657/OS	OS	r	d	Ob	
B/*	np	7	M722	4-G	DSM	1970	12/70/8072/OS	OS	r.	d	Ob	

Sheet 84 *Teesdale*

1	5	6	7	8	9	10	11	12	13	14	15	16
1009	5/-	6	4620	WOE	WO	1949	25,000/10/49	OS	p	a	BL-d	
nc	np	6	4620	2-G	WO	1952	15,000/11/52	OS	p	b	BL-d	
1266	10/6	6	4620	2-G	WO	1952	3500/12/56 OS	OS	p	bc	BL-d	
A/	3/-	7	M722	3-G	DSW	1961	20,000/7/61/4344/R	1 SPC RE	r	m	DGC	1
A/	3/-	7	M722	3-G	DSW	1961	20,000/7/61/4344/R	1 SPC RE	r	m	BL-b	2
B	np	7	M722	4-G	DSM	1964	50,000/11/64/6664/OS	OS	r	d	Ob	
B/*	np	7	M722	5-G	DSM	1970	11/69/7644/OS	OS	r.	d	Ob	
B/*	np	7	M722	5-G	DSM	1970	12/71/8463/OS	OS	r.	mc	Ob	

1. Projection and grid data and magnetic information are overprinted in red, the grid data with the erroneous heading *Universal Transverse Mercator*. 2. The grid data heading is corrected to *National Grid*.

Sheet 85 *Durham*

1	5	6	7	8	9	10	11	12	13	14	15	16
nc	5/-	6	4620	WOE	WO	1948	15,000/5/48	OS	p	a	BL-d	
nc	5/-	6	4620	WOE	WO	1948	15,000/4/52 SPC RE	SPC RE	p	a	BL-d	1
nc	6/6	6	4620	1-G	WO	1954	20,000/12/54 OS	OS	p	b	BL-d	2
C	6/6	6	4620	1-G	WO	1954	2400/1/57 OS	OS	p	bc	BL-d	
B	3/6	7	M722	2-G	DSW	1962	20,000/8/62/6391/OS	OS	r	m	BL-b	
B/*	np	7	M722	3-G	DSM	1966	22,000/10/66/348/OA	BAOR	r	m	Ob	
B/*/*	np	7	M722	4-G	DSM	1968	9/68/7237/OS	OS	r.	d	Ob	
B/*/*	np	7	M722	4-G	DSM	1968	8/73/732124 S	OS	r.	d	DGC	
B/*/*/*	np	7	M722	5-G	DSM	1968	12/73/731226 S	OS	r.	d	DGC	3

1. OS were requested on 18 February 1952 to forward plates to SPC RE for this printing. 2. Military Survey wrote to OS on 22 October 1953 regarding surplus stock of 20,000 copies for overprinting, but it would seem none were available. A consequent print order for 20,000 Second Edition copies placed on 26 November 1953 seems to have been remarkably delayed. 3. The imprint date was unaltered: presumably it should have been advanced to 1973.

Sheet 86 *Redcar and Whitby*

1	5	6	7	8	9	10	11	12	13	14	15	16
1011	5/-	6	4620	WOE	WO	1948	15,000/5/48	OS	p	a	BL-d	
1240	10/6	6	4620	2-G	WO	1952	15,000/5/52 SPC RE	SPC RE	p	b	BL-d	1
A/	3/6	7	M722	3-G	DSW	1960	6000/7/60/6223/OS	OS	r	mo	BL-b	
A/	3/6	7	M722	3-G	DSW	1962	10,000/2/62/6387/OS	OS	r	m	BL-b	
A/	4/6	7	M722	3-G	DSW	1962	12,000/10/63/6565/OS	OS	r	m	DGC	
B	np	7	M722	4-G	DSM	1965	30,000/9/65/6715/OS	OS	r	d	Ob	
B/*	np	7	M722	4-G	DSM	1965	7/71/8217/OS	OS	r.	d	BL-a	
B/*	np	7	M722	4-G	DSM	1965	6/74/740044 S	OS	r.	d	DGC	

For further use see Exercises *March Hare, Home Run* in supplement 4. 1. OS were requested on 18 February 1952 to forward plates to SPC RE for this printing.

Sheet 87 *Isle of Man*   24 by 27 miles (Popular Edition), 40 by 45 km (Seventh Series)

1	5	6	7	8	9	10	11	12	13	14	15	16
nc	np	P	4620	WOE	WO	1949	15,000/10/49	OS	p	b	BL-d	1,2
nc	np	P	4620	2-G	WO	1952	10,000/9/52	OS	p	b	BL-d	1,3
nc	np	P	4620	2-G	WO	1952	20,000/8/55 OS	OS	p	b	BL-d	1
B	4/6	7	M722	2-G	DSW	1963	20,000/3/63/6391/OS	OS	r	d	BL-b	4
C	np	7	M722	3-G	DSM	1970	70/7979/OS	OS	r.	d	Ob	5

For further use see supplements 7, 8. 1. Second War Revision sheet 17, on Popular Edition sheet lines is used since New Popular Edition sheet 87 was not published. Elements of the new style marginalia survive, though the black arrow does not. The War Office Cassini Grid is replaced by the National Grid (Military System), overprinted in purple. 2. The sheet is numbered *National Grid sheet 87*. The GSGS 3907 heading *Second War Revision 1940 sheet 17* also survives. 3. The sheet number style is altered to *England & Wales sheet 87*. References to Second War Revision, including the sheet number 17, are deleted. 4. The base map used is now the One-inch Seventh Series; curiously this issue is still designated Edition 2-GSGS. 5. The hill shading added to the civilian version is not present in the military.

Sheet 88 a. *Barrow in Furness* b. *Barrow-in-Furness*

1	5	6	7	8	9	10	11	12	13	14	15	16
1013	5/-	6a	4620	WOE	WO	1948	15,000/5/48	OS	p	a	BL-d	
1013	10/6	6a	4620	2-G	WO	1952	15,000/6/52	OS	p	b	BL-d	1
1013	5/-	6a	4620	WOE	WO	1948	6600/8/55 OS	OS	p	ac	BL-d	
A/	3/-	7b	M722	3-G	DSW	1963	10,000/2/63/6387/OS	OS	r	m	DGC	2
A/	4/6	7b	M722	3-G	DSW	1963	10,000/9/63/6565/OS	OS	r	d	Wc	
B	np	7b	M722	4-G	DSM	1965	10,000/1/65/6657/OS	OS	r	d	Ob	
B	np	7b	M722	4-G	DSM	1967	15,000/10/67/6939/OS	OS	r.	m	DGC	
B	np	7b	M722	4-G	DSM	1967	2/71/8130/OS	OS	r.	m	Ob	

1. This printing order was placed with SPC RE in November 1951, to whom OS were requested to send printing plates. In the event this was cancelled and the work done by OS. 2. A civilian printing with a 3/- price statement has not been recorded.

Sheet 89 *Lancaster and Kendal*

1	5	6	7	8	9	10	11	12	13	14	15	16
1014	5/-	6	4620	WOE	WO	1948	25,000/7/48	OS	p	a	BL-d	
1231	10/6	6	4620	WOE	WO	1948	10,000/6/54 OS	OS	p	ac	BL-d	1
1231	10/6	6	4620	WOE	WO	1948	2800/12/56 OS	OS	p	ac	BL-d	
A//*	4/6	7	M722	2-G	DSW	1962	10,000/12/61/6118/OS	OS	r	m	BL-b	
A//*	4/6	7	M722	2-G	DSW	1962	10,000/10/63/6571/OS	OS	r	m	Wc	
B	np	7	M722	3-G	DSM	1965	15,000/4/65/6715/OS	OS	r	d	Ob	
B	np	7	M722	3-G	DSM	1965	50,000/8/66/357/OA	BAOR	r	m	DGC	
B	np	7	M722	3-G	DSM	1965	3/71/8150/OS	OS	r.	m	DGC	
B/*	DR	7	M722	4-G	DSM	1972	4/72/8656/OS	OS	r.	d	Ob	

1. Military Survey wrote to OS on 22 October 1953 regarding surplus stock of 20,000 copies for overprinting. It would seem that some were available, and an order was placed for 10,000 copies on 26 November.

Sheet 90 a. *Askrigg and Settle* b. *Wensleydale*

1	5	6	7	8	9	10	11	12	13	14	15	16
1199	5/-	6a	4620	WOE	WO	1948	25,000/10/48	OS	p‡	a	BL-d	1
1199	np	6a	4620	2-G	WO	1953	10,000/1/53	OS	p-	b	BL-d	
C	6/6	6a	4620	2-G	WO	1953	3000/3/56 OS	OS	p	bc	Cu-m	2
D	6/6	6a	4620	2-G	WO	1953	3000/3/56 OS	OS	p	bc	Cu-m	2
A/	3/6	7b	M722	3-G	DSW	1960	10,000/7/60/6022/OS	OS	r	mo	BL-b	
B	4/6	7b	M722	4-G	DSW	1962	15,000/11/62/6422/OS	OS	r	m	Cu-m	
B	np	7b	M722	4-G	DSW	1962	5000/7/64/6576/OS	OS	r	m	DGC	
B	np	7b	M722	4-G	DSW	1962	5000/8/66/357/OA	BAOR	r	m	DGC	
B/*	np	7b	M722	4-G	DSM	1967	25,000/6/67/6923/OS	OS	r.	m	BL-b	
B/*	np	7b	M722	4-G	DSM	1967	10/70/8051/OS	OS	r.	m	BL-a	

1. Possibly a dual civilian-military printing: certainly at least some military copies were printed on civilian issue weight paper, and with the civilian grid. 2. An example of the stock of two civilian printings being used for a single military printing.

Sheet 91 *Ripon*

1	5	6	7	8	9	10	11	12	13	14	15	16
1016	5/-	6	4620	WOE	WO	1948	15,000/7/48	OS	p	a	BL-d	
1224	5/-	6	4620	2-G	WO	1951	20,000/11/51	OS	p	b	BL-d	
1224	np	6	4620	2-G	WO	1951	20,000/12/52	OS	p	b	BL-d	
A/	3/6	7	M722	3-G	DSW	1960	5000/9/60/6223/OS	OS	r	mo	Wc	
B	4/6	7	M722	4-G	DSW	1962	25,000/6/62/6387/OS	OS	r	d	BL-b	
B	np	7	M722	4-G	DSM	1966	20,000/6/66/6824/OS	OS	r.	m	DGC	
B/*	np	7	M722	5-G	DSM	1968	5/68/7082/OS	OS	r.	m	Ob	
B/*	np	7	M722	5-G	DSM	1968	1/69/7340/OS	OS	r.	m	Ob	
B/*	np	7	M722	5-G	DSM	1968	10/70/8082/OS	OS	r.	m	Cu-m	
B/*/*	np	7	M722	5-G	DSM	1968	9/72/721765 S	OS	r.	d	Ob	1
B/*/*	np	7	M722	6-G	DSM	1968	3000/6/75/741103 S	OS	r.	m	DGC	1

For further use see Exercises *78 Agra Exercise, Quicksilver* in supplement 4. 1. NB the B/*/* edition was used for both Edition 5-GSGS and 6-GSGS, with the same publication date. This was deemed an error, and the OS were instructed to correct the edition number by overprint. However, with the new map stock already at the depot it was decided to accept the map as Edition 6 after all.

Sheet 92 *Pickering*

1	5	6	7	8	9	10	11	12	13	14	15	16
1198	5/-	6	4620	WOE	WO	1949	15,000/7/49	OS	p	a	BL-d	
nc	10/6	6	4620	2-G	WO	1952	15,000/6/52	OS	p	b	BL-d	1
nc	np	7	4620	3-G	WO	1955	20,000/9/55 OS	OS	r	mo	BL-d	2
1292	10/6	6	4620	2-G	WO	1952	11,400/1/56 OS	OS	p	bc	BL-d	2
B	np	7	M722	4-G	DSM	1965	6000/12/64/6700/OS	OS	r	m	Ob	
B	np	7	M722	4-G	DSM	1966	38,000/6/66/6824/OS	OS	r.	m	DGC	
B/*	np	7	M722	5-G	DSM	1969	12/69/7594/OS	OS	r.	d	Ob	
B/*	np	7	M722	5-G	DSM	1969	4/71/8174/OS	OS	r.	m	DGC	
B/*	np	7	M722	5-G	DSM	1969	7/72/8689/OS	OS	r.	d	Ob	

For further use see Exercises *March Hare, Quicksilver* in supplement 4. 1. This printing order was placed with SPC RE in November 1951, to whom OS were requested to send printing plates. In the event this was cancelled and the work done by OS. 2. NB Seventh Series, Edition 3-GSGS preceding New Popular, Edition 2-GSGS.

Sheet 93 *Scarborough*

1	5	6	7	8	9	10	11	12	13	14	15	16
1018	5/-	6	4620	WOE	WO	1948	15,000/9/48	OS	p	a	BL-d	
1018	5/-	6	4620	2-G	WO	1951	15,000/3/52	OS	p	b	BL-d	
1018	5/-	6	4620	WOE	WO	1948	3100/12/55 OS	OS	p	ac	BL-d	1
B	6/6	6	4620	2-G	WO	1951	3100/12/55 OS	OS	p	bc	BL-d	1
nc	3/6	7	M722	3-G	DSW	1958	15,000/7/59/5753/OS	OS	r	mo	BL-b	
B	np	7	M722	4-G	DSM	1964	10,000/11/64/6680/OS	OS	r	m	Ob	
B	np	7	M722	4-G	DSM	1964	16,000/9/66/348/OA	BAOR	r	m	DGC	
B/*	np	7	M722	4-G	DSM	1964	1/69/7337/OS	OS	r.	m	Ob	
B/*	np	7	M722	4-G	DSM	1964	2/72/8460/OS	OS	r.	d	Ob	

For further use see Exercise *March Hare* in supplement 4. 1. An example of the stock of two civilian print runs being used for a single military printing.

Sheet 94 a. *Preston* b. *Preston and Blackpool*

1	5	6	7	8	9	10	11	12	13	14	15	16
1196	5/-	6b	4620	WOE	WO	1948	21,000/9/48	OS	p	a	BL-d	
1196	5/-	6b	4620	WOE	WO	1948	10,000/9/50	OS	p	a	BL-d	
1019	5/-	6a	4620	WOE	WO	1948	800/10/54 OS	OS	p	ac	BL-d	
B	np	7a	M722	2-G	DSW	1961	10,000/10/61/6022/OS	OS	r	mo	BL-b	
B/*	np	7a	M722	3-G	DSW	1964	28,000/1/64/6581/OS	OS	r	d	Wc	
B/*/*	np	7a	M722	4-G	DSM	1969	3/69/7381/OS	OS	r.	d	Ob	
B/*/*	np	7a	M722	4-G	DSM	1969	10/72/8690/OS	OS	r.	d	Ob	
B/*/*	np	7a	M722	4-G	DSM	1969	10/74/732632 S	OS	r.	m	DGC	

Sheet 95 *Blackburn and Burnley*

1	5	6	7	8	9	10	11	12	13	14	15	16
1020	5/-	6	4620	WOE	WO	1948	21,000/10/48	OS	p	a	BL-d	
1215	10/6	6	4620	2-G	WO	1952	20,000/7/52 SPC RE	SPC RE	p	b	BL-d	
1215	10/6	6	4620	2-G	WO	1952	2500/10/54 OS	OS	p	bc	BL-d	
B	3/6	7	M722	3-G	DSW	1963	15,000/1/63/6388/OS	OS	r	m	DGC	1
B	4/6	7	M722	3-G	DSW	1962	25,000/9/63/6565/OS	OS	r	d	BL-b	
B/*	np	7	M722	4-G	DSM	1967	20,000/5/67/6916/OS	OS	r.	d	DGC	
B/*	np	7	M722	4-G	DSM	1967	9/70/8067/OS	OS	r.	m	BL-a	
B/*	np	7	M722	4-G	DSM	1967	10/74/732640 S	OS	r.	m	DGC	

1. A civilian printing with a 3/6 price statement has not been recorded.

Sheet 96 *Leeds and Bradford*

1	5	6	7	8	9	10	11	12	13	14	15	16
1021	5/-	6	4620	WOE	WO	1948	13,000/9/48	OS	p	a	BL-d	
1216	5/-	6	4620	2-G	WO	1951	15,000/1/52	OS	p	b	BL-d	
nc	np	6	4620	2-G	WO	1951	20,000/11/54 OS	OS	p	b	BL-d	1
1216	5/-	6	4620	2-G	WO	1951	5900/10/55 OS	OS	p	ac	BL-d	
B	4/6	7	M722	3-G	DSM	1962	20,000/8/62/6391/OS	OS	r	m	BL-b	
C	np	7	M722	4-G	DSM	1966	45,000/5/66/6822/OS	OS	r.	d	Ob	
C/*	np	7	M722	5-G	DSM	1969	12/69/7523/OS	OS	r.	d	Ob	
C/*	np	7	M722	5-G	DSM	1969	5/73/722159 S	OS	r.	m	BL-b	
C/*	np	7	M722	5-G	DSM	1969	4/74/733056 S	OS	r.	m	DGC	

For further use see Exercise *Quicksilver* in supplement 4. 1. Military Survey wrote to OS on 22 October 1953 regarding surplus stock of 20,000 copies for overprinting, but it would seem they were not available. The print order for 20,000 Second Edition copies placed on 26 November 1953 seems to have been remarkably delayed.

Sheet 97 *York*

1	5	6	7	8	9	10	11	12	13	14	15	16
1175	5/-	6	4620	WOE	WO	1948	13,000/10/48	OS	p	a	BL-d	
1175	5/-	6	4620	2-G	WO	1951	15,000/1/52	OS	p	b	BL-d	
nc	np	6	4620	2-G	WO	1951	20,000/12/54 OS	OS	p	b	BL-d	
B	3/6	7	M722	3-G	DSW	1962	20,000/9/62/6391/OS	OS	r	m	BL-b	
B	np	7	M722	3-G	DSW	1962	16,000/9/66/348/OA	BAOR	r	m	DGC	
B/*	np	7	M722	4-G	DSM	1972	12/72/8491/OS	OS	r.	m	BL-b	
B/*	np	7	M722	4-G	DSM	1972	10/73/732235 S	OS	r.	m	BL-a	

See figure 13. For further use see Exercises *78 Agra Exercise, Quicksilver* in supplement 4.

Sheet 98 *Market Weighton*

1	5	6	7	8	9	10	11	12	13	14	15	16
1023	5/-	6	4620	WOE	WO	1948	13,000/10/48	OS	p	a	BL-d	
1023	5/-	6	4620	WOE	WO	1948	6000/1/52	OS	p	ac	BL-d	1
1023	np	6	4620	2-G	WO	1953	15,000/1/53	OS	p	b	BL-d	
A/	3/6	7	M722	3-G	DSW	1961	10,000/1/61/6223/OS	OS	r	mo	BL-b	
B	np	7	M722	4-G	DSM	1965	6000/2/65/6684/OS	OS	r	m	BL-b	
B	np	7	M722	4-G	DSM	1966	30,000/5/66/6824/OS	OS	r.	m	BL-b	
B/*	np	7	M722	5-G	DSM	1966	30,000/11/66/6861/OS	OS	r.	d	BL-a	2
B/*	np	7	M722	5-G	DSM	1966	6/73/730881 S	OS	r.	d	BL-b	
B/*	np	7	M722	5-G	DSM	1966	6/74/740043 S	OS	r.	d	DGC	

For further use see Exercises *78 Agra Exercise, Quicksilver,* and Western Command pre Staff College course in supplement 4. 1. A Second Edition printing of 15,000 copies was delayed from 1951 until 1953 when 6000 copies of old civilian stock became available which could be converted to War Office Edition, by overprinting. 2. 6816 in red formed part of the original print code, overprinted in blue by 6861.

Sheet 99 *Hull*

1	5	6	7	8	9	10	11	12	13	14	15	16
1024	5/-	6	4620	WOE	WO	1948	13,000/10/48	OS	p	a	BL-d	
1024	5/-	6	4620	WOE	WO	1948	8000/1/52	OS	p	ac	BL-d	1
1024	np	6	4620	2-G	WO	1953	15,000/1/53	OS	p	b	BL-d	
1024	5/-	6	4620	WOE	WO	1948	1000/8/55 OS	OS	p	ac	BL-d	
A/	3/6	7	M722	3-G	DSW	1961	15,000/2/61/6261/OS	OS	r	mo	BL-b	2
A/	3/6	7	M722	3-G	DSW	1961	15,000/2/61/6261/OS	OS	r	mo	DGC	
B	np	7	M722	4-G	DSM	1966	20,000/6/66/6824/OS	OS	r.	m	DGC	
B/	np	7	M722	5-G	DSM	1968	2/68/7089/OS	OS	r.	d	Ob	
B/	np	7	M722	5-G	DSM	1968	5/73/8691/OS	OS	r.	m	BL-b	

1. A Second Edition printing of 15,000 copies was delayed from 1951 until 1953 when 8000 copies of old civilian stock became available which could be converted to War Office Edition, by overprinting. 2. The month digit of the print code is in blue.

Sheet 100 *Liverpool*

1	5	6	7	8	9	10	11	12	13	14	15	16
1025	5/-	6	4620	WOE	WO	1948	11,000/10/48	OS	p	a	BL-d	
1025	5/-	6	4620	WOE	WO	1948	5000/5/50	OS	p	a	BL-d	
1025	10/6	6	4620	2-G	WO	1952	10,000/5/52	OS	p	b	BL-d	1
1025	10/6	6	4620	2-G	WO	1952	10,000/5/52	OS	rp	bt	BL-d	1
4012	np	7	4620	3-G	WO	1953	10,000/1/53 OS	OS	r	mo	BL-d	
nc	np	7	4620	3-G	WO	1953	20,000/1/55 OS	OS	r	mo	BL-d	
nc	np	7	4620	3-G	WO	1953	no code [1961]	HDA	r	mo	BL-d	
B/*	np	7	M722	4-G	DSM	1965	3000/1/65/6681/OS	OS	r	d	Ob	
C	np	7	M722	5-G	DSM	1965	20,000/12/65/6762/OS	OS	r	d	DGC	
C/*	np	7	M722	6-G	DSM	1969	12/68/7322/OS	OS	r.	d	Ob	
C/*/*	np	7	M722	7-G	DSM	1971	5/71/8189/OS	OS	r.	d	Ob	
C/*/*	DR	7	M722	7-G	DSM	1971	12/71/8464/OS	OS	r.	m	Ob	
C/*/*/*	np	7	M722	7-G	DSM	1971	9/72/721766 S	OS	r.	d	Ob	

1. The unused stock (6640 copies), surplus to requirements after the publication of Edition 3-GSGS, were overprinted for training purposes, completed on 6 June 1953.

Sheet 101 *Manchester*

1	5	6	7	8	9	10	11	12	13	14	15	16
1026	5/-	6	4620	WOE	WO	1948	18,000/12/48	OS	p	a	BL-d	
1241	10/6	6	4620	2-G	WO	1951	15,000/4/52	OS	p	b	BL-d	
1241	10/6	6	4620	WOE	WO	1948	2000/3/54 OS	OS	p	ac	PC	1
nc	np	7	4620	3-G	WO	1954	20,000/1/55/OS	OS	r	mo	BL-d	
nc	np	7	4620	3-G	WO	1954	15,000/1/62/4427/R	1 SPC RE	r	mo	BL-d	2
B	np	7	M722	4-G	DSW	1963	19,000/11/63/6571/OS	OS	r	m	DGC	
B/*	np	7	M722	5-G	DSM	1967	25,000/5/67/6918/OS	OS	r.	m	BL-b	
C	np	7	M722	6-G	DSM	1968	11/68/7226/OS	OS	r.	d	Ob	
C/*	np	7	M722	7-G	DSM	1972	7/72/8712/OS	OS	r.	?d	Ob	

For further use see Exercise *Noahs Ark* in supplement 4. 1. Military Survey wrote to OS on 22 October 1953 regarding surplus stock of 20,000 copies for overprinting, but it would seem none were available. Thus a printing order was placed on 26 November; the appearance of these 2000 copies may have delayed its completion. 2. This is a very late issue still to be listed in GSGS 4620.

Sheet 102 *Huddersfield*

1	5	6	7	8	9	10	11	12	13	14	15	16
1027	5/-	6	4620	WOE	WO	1948	18,000/11/48	OS	p	a	BL-d	
nc	10/6	6	4620	2-G	WO	1952	15,000/6/52	OS	p	b	BL-d	1
1267	10/6	6	4620	2-G	WO	1952	2700/11/54 OS	OS	p	bc	BL-d	
A/	3/6	7	M722	3-G	DSW	1960	10,000/7/60/6236/OS	OS	r	mo	BL-b	
B	np	7	M722	4-G	DSM	1965	7000/1/65/6684/OS	OS	r	m	NLS	
B/*	np	7	M722	5-G	DSM	1966	20,000/4/66/6810/OS	OS	r.	d	Ob	
B/*	np	7	M722	5-G	DSM	1966	4/68/7121/OS	OS	r.	m	BL-b	
B/*/*	np	7	M722	6-G	DSM	1971	6/71/8216/OS	OS	r.	d	Ob	
B/*/*/*	np	7	M722	7-G	DSM	1972	12/72/8676/OS	OS	r.	d	Ob	

1. This printing order was placed with SPC RE in November 1951, to whom OS were requested to send printing plates. In the event this was cancelled and the work done by OS.

Sheet 103 *Doncaster*

1	5	6	7	8	9	10	11	12	13	14	15	16
1028	5/-	6	4620	WOE	WO	1948	13,000/12/48	OS	p	a	BL-d	
1260	5/-	6	4620	2-G	WO	1951	20,000/11/51	OS	p	b	BL-d	
A//	3/6	7	M722	3-G	DSW	1960	10,000/4/60/6223/OS	OS	r	mo	DGC	
B	4/6	7	M722	4-G	DSW	1963	15,000/4/63/6422/OS	OS	r	m	Wc	
B/	np	7	M722	4-G	DSW	1963	13,000/8/66/357/OA	BAOR	r	m	BL-b	
C	np	7	M722	5-G	DSM	1968	3/68/7101/OS	OS	r.	d	Ob	
C/	np	7	M722	6-G	DSM	1971	10/71/8457/OS	OS	r.	d	Ob	
C/	np	7	M722	6-G	DSM	1971	4/73/722366 S	OS	r.	d	BL-b	

Sheet 104 *Gainsborough*

1	5	6	7	8	9	10	11	12	13	14	15	16
1029	5/-	6	4620	WOE	WO	1948	13,000/12/48	OS	p	a	BL-d	
1029	5/-	6	4620	WOE	WO	1948	7500/5/52	OS	p	ac	BL-d	1
1029	np	6	4620	2-G	WO	1952	15,000/10/52	OS	p	b	BL-d	
B	6/6	6	4620	2-G	WO	1952	800/1/57 OS	OS	p	bc	BL-d	
B	4/6	7	M722	3-G	DSW	1962	20,000/6/62/6391/OS	OS	r	d	BL-b	
B	np	7	M722	3-G	DSM	1967	12,000/10/67/6931/OS	OS	r.	m	Ob	
B/*	np	7	M722	3-G	DSM	1967	12/68/7365/OS	OS	r.	d	DGC	
B/*	np	7	M722	3-G	DSM	1967	1/73/8468/OS	OS	r.	d	Ob	

For further use see Western Command pre Staff College course in supplement 4. 1. A printing of 15,000 copies was delayed when 7500 copies of old civilian stock became available which could be converted to military use, by overprinting.

Sheet 105 *Grimsby*

1	5	6	7	8	9	10	11	12	13	14	15	16
nc	5/-	6	4620	WOE	WO	1948	13,000/12/48	OS	p	a	BL-d	
20046	5/-	6	4620	WOE	WO	1948	5500/1/52	OS	p	ac	BL-d	1
nc	np	6	4620	2-G	WO	1953	15,000/1/53	OS	p	b	BL-d	
B	4/6	7	M722	3-G	DSW	1962	3000/11/61/6356/OS	OS	r	d	DGC	
B	4/6	7	M722	3-G	DSW	1962	17,000/1/62/6356/OS	OS	r	m	Ob	2
B/	np	7	M722	3-G	DSM	1962	5/68/7115/OS	OS	r.	d	BL-a	

1. A Second Edition printing of 15,000 copies was delayed from 1951 until 1953 when 5500 copies of old civilian stock became available which could be converted to War Office Edition, by overprinting. 2. Not in DGC Superseded. The printing order number is the same as the previous.

1	5	6	7	8	9	10	11	12	13	14	15	16

Sheet 106 *Anglesey*

1	5	6	7	8	9	10	11	12	13	14	15	16
1031	5/-	6	4620	WOE	WO	1949	15,000/2/49	OS	p	a	BL-d	
1242	10/6	6	4620	WOE	WO	1947	500/8/52	OS	p	ac	BL-d	1
nc	10/6	6	4620	2-G	WO	1951	9500/9/52	OS	p	b	BL-d	1
B	4/6	7	M722	3-G	DSW	1962	20,000/2/62/6387/OS	OS	r	d	Ob	
B/*	np	7	M722	3-G	DSM	1962	1/70/7645/OS	OS	r.	m	Ob	
B/*	np	7	M722	3-G	DSM	1962	3/72/8614/OS	OS	r.	d	Ob	

1. 500 copies of civilian stock were overprinted for military use as a short term measure, the intention being to complete the remainder of the 10,000 copies required on the new Seventh Series base map. Its arrival would seem to have been long enough overdue for the New Popular Edition to have been needed for the main print run as well.

Sheet 107 *Snowdon*

1	5	6	7	8	9	10	11	12	13	14	15	16
1209	5/-	6	4620	WOE	WO	1949	15,000/3/49	OS	p	a	BL-d	
1243	10/6	6	4620	2-G	WO	1952	15,000/5/52	OS	p	b	BL-d	
A/	3/-	7	M722	3-G	DSW	1959	15,000/9/59/6020/OS	OS	r	mo	Cu-m	
A//	np	7	M722	3-G	DSW	1959	no code [1961]	HDA	r	mo	BL-b	
B	4/6	7	M722	4-G	DSW	1962	3000/8/62/6356/OS	OS	r	d	Wc	
B	np	7	M722	4-G	DSW	1962	8000/4/64/6592/OS	OS	r	m	Wc	
B/*	np	7	M722	4-G	DSW	1962	5000/1/66/6756/OS	OS	r	d	DGC	
B/*	np	7	M722	4-G	DSM	1966	25,000/5/66/6823/OS	OS	r.	m	DGC	
B/*/	np	7	M722	5-G	DSM	1969	10/69/7558/OS	OS	r.	d	Ob	
B/*/	DR	7	M722	5-G	DSM	1969	7/72/8692/OS	OS	r.	d	DGC	
B/*/	np	7	M722	5-G	DSM	1969	11/73/732789 S	OS	r.	m	DGC	

For further use see GSGS Misc.2131 in supplement 3 and an unnamed exercise in supplement 4.

Sheet 108 *Denbigh*

1	5	6	7	8	9	10	11	12	13	14	15	16
1211	5/-	6	4620	WOE	WO	1949	15,000/2/49	OS	p‡	a	BL-d	
1284	10/6	6	4620	2-G	WO	1952	15,000/4/52	OS	p	b	BL-d	
nc	np	7	4620	3-G	WO	1955	20,000/4/55 OS	OS	r	mo	BL-d	
nc	np	7	4620	3-G	WO	1955	no code [1961]	HDA	r	mo	BL-d	
B/*	np	7	M722	4-G	DSW	1955	6000/7/65/6741/OS	OS	r	d	Ob	1
B/*	np	7	M722	4-G	DSW	1955	9000/7/65/6741/OS	OS	r	d	DGC	
B/*	np	7	M722	4-G	DSM	1955	9/68/7118/OS	OS	r.	m	Ob	
B/*/	np	7	M722	5-G	DSM	1969	no code [7640/OS ms]	OS	r.	d	Ob	
B/*/	np	7	M722	5-G	DSM	1969	12/72/720051 S	OS	r.	d	DGC	

1. Not in DGC Superseded. The order number is the same as the next. The imprint date was unaltered: presumably it should have been advanced to 1965.

Sheet 109 *Chester*

1	5	6	7	8	9	10	11	12	13	14	15	16
1034	5/-	6	4620	WOE	WO	1949	15,000/1/49	OS	p	a	BL-d	
1269	10/6	6	4620	2-G	WO	1951	20,000/3/52	OS	p	b	BL-d	
4018	np	7	4620	3-G	WO	1952	20,000/7/54 OS	OS	r	mo	BL-d	1
A/	3/-	7	M722	3-G	DSW	1952	20,000/3/60/6118/OS	OS	r	mo	BL-b	
B/*	np	7	M722	4-G	DSM	1966	14,000/6/66/6822/OS	OS	r.	m	Ob	
B/*/*	np	7	M722	5-G	DSM	1968	11/68/7332/OS	OS	r.	d	Ob	
B/*/*	np	7	M722	5-G	DSM	1968	9/72/8498/OS	OS	r.	d	Ob	

For further use see Exercises *Ballista, Noahs Ark* in supplement 4. 1. A curious publication date, yet there is no record of a 1952 printing, other than the one above. A request to OS in October 1953 for 20,000 copies of surplus stock received the reply that none was held. Military Survey thus placed a new printing order on 26 November, and were apparently content to await the 1954 printing on the new base map.

Sheet 110 a. *Stoke on Trent* b. *Stoke-on-Trent*

1	5	6	7	8	9	10	11	12	13	14	15	16
1035	5/-	6a	4620	WOE	WO	1949	11,000/2/49	OS	p	a	BL-d	
1225	5/-	6a	4620	WOE	WO	1948	5000/5/50	OS	p	a	BL-d	
1285	10/6	6a	4620	2-G	WO	1952	6000/7/52	OS	p	b	BL-d	1
		6a	4620				9000		p	c	card	1

1	5	6	7	8	9	10	11	12	13	14	15	16
A/	3/6	7a	M722	3-G	DSW	1958	12,000/12/58/5753/OS	OS	r	mo	DGC	
A/	np	7a	M722	3-G	DSW	1958	no code [1961]	HDA	r	mo	DGC	
B/*	np	7b	M722	4-G	DSM	1964	35,000/7/64/6633/OS	OS	r	d	BL-b	
B/*/*	np	7b	M722	5-G	DSM	1968	4/68/7114/OS	OS	r.	d	Ob	
B/*/*	np	7b	M722	5-G	DSM	1968	2/71/8106/OS	OS	r.	mc	DGC	

For further use see Exercise *Noahs Ark* in supplement 4. 1. The order was for 15,000 copies, the printing of 6000 apparently supplemented by 9000 surplus civilian stock copies. Not found (and not in the OS card catalogue).

Sheet 111 *Buxton and Matlock*

1	5	6	7	8	9	10	11	12	13	14	15	16
1200	5/-	6	4620	WOE	WO	1948	18,000/11/48	OS	p‡	a	BL-d	1
1261	10/6	6	4620	2-G	WO	1952	10,000/8/52 SPC RE	SPC RE	p	b	BL-d	
nc	np	7	4620	3-G	WO	1955	20,000/5/55 OS	OS	r	mo	BL-d	
B	4/6	7	M722	3-G	DSW	1962	20,000/2/62/6388/OS	OS	r	d	BL-b	
B	np	7	M722	3-G	DSM	1966	28,000/7/66/6824/OS	OS	r.	m	DGC	
B/*	np	7	M722	4-G	DSM	1970	9/70/8068/OS	OS	r.	m	Ob	

1. This was possibly a dual civilian-military printing: military copies have been recorded printed on civilian issue weight paper, and with the civilian grid.

Sheet 112 *Nottingham*

1	5	6	7	8	9	10	11	12	13	14	15	16
1037	5/-	6	4620	WOE	WO	1949	11,000/2/49	OS	p	a	BL-d	
1037	5/-	6	4620	WOE	WO	1948	5000/5/50	OS	p	a	BL-d	
1245	10/6	6	4620	2-G	WO	1952	15,000/5/52	OS	p	b	BL-d	
1245	10/6	6	4620	WOE	WO	1948	800/9/55 OS	OS	p	ac	BL-d	
A	3/6	7	M722	3-G	DSW	1958	5000/5/59/5753/OS	OS	r	mo	DGC	
B	3/6	7	M722	4-G	DSW	1958	15,000/7/60/6246/OS	OS	r	mo	Wc	
B	3/6	7	M722	4-G	DSW	1958	10,000/1/62/6388/OS	OS	r	m	BL-b	
B/	4/6	7	M722	4-G	DSW	1958	21,000/7/63/6555/OS	OS	r	d	Cu-m	
C	np	7	M722	5-G	DSM	1967	16,000/12/67/6975/OS	OS	r.	d	BL-a	
C/*	np	7	M722	6-G	DSM	1971	1/71/8136/OS	OS	r.	d	Ob	

For further use see Exercise *Pandora* in supplement 4.

Sheet 113 *Lincoln and Grantham*

1	5	6	7	8	9	10	11	12	13	14	15	16
1038	5/-	6	4620	WOE	WO	1949	13,000/2/49	OS	p	a	BL-d	
1038	10/6	6	4620	2-G	WO	1951	20,000/1/52	OS	p	b	BL-d	
1038	5/-	6	4620	WOE	WO	1948	2000/6/55 OS	OS	p	ac	BL-d	1
A/	4/6	7	M722	2-G	DSW	1961	20,000/4/61/6261/OS	OS	r	mo	BL-b	
B	np	7	M722	3-G	DSM	1966	20,000/2/66/6799/OS	OS	r.	m	BL-b	
B/*	np	7	M722	4-G	DSM	1969	1/69/7328/OS	OS	r.	m	Ob	
B/*	np	7	M722	4-G	DSM	1969	12/72/722074 S	OS	r.	m	DGC	

1. Military Survey placed an order with the OS on 26 November 1953 requesting 2000 copies by overprinting civilian stock, but it would seem they were not available for eighteen months.

Sheet 114 *Boston and Skegness*

1	5	6	7	8	9	10	11	12	13	14	15	16
1039	5/-	6	4620	WOE	WO	1949	13,000/2/49	OS	p	a	BL-d	
1039	5/-	6	4620	WOE	WO	1949	10,000/9/50	OS	p	a	BL-d	
1039	10/6	6	4620	2-G	WO	1952	5000/9/52 SPC RE	SPC RE	p	b	BL-d	
		6	4620	WOE			10,000		p	ac	card	1
1039	5/-	6	4620	2-G	WO	1952	5600/12/56 OS	OS	p	ac	BL-d	2
B	4/6	7	M722	3-G	DSW	1962	20,000/10/62/6391/OS	OS	r	d	DGC	
B/*	np	7	M722	3-G	DSM	1962	6/70/7974/OS	OS	r.	m	Ob	

1. Military Survey wrote to the OS on 7 January 1953 asking them to overprint 10,000 surplus stock copies for military use. The job was completed by 18 February 1953. Not found. 2. This state is headed Second Edition-GSGS, but would probably be better designated War Office Edition, with its early form of the National Grid, with eastings printed sideways.

Sheet 115 *Pwllheli*

1	5	6	7	8	9	10	11	12	13	14	15	16
nc	5/-	6	4620	WOE	WO	1949	15,000/6/49 SPC	SPC RE	p	a	BL-d	1
		6	4620				1800		p	c	card	2
nc	10/6	6	4620	2-G	WO	1952	10,000/6/52	OS	p	b	BL-d	3

1	5	6	7	8	9	10	11	12	13	14	15	16
4021	np	7	4620	3-G	WO	1953	15,000/1/53	OS	r	mo	BL-d	3
C	4/6	7	M722	4-G	DSW	1962	15,000/2/62/6400/OS	OS	r	m	BL-b	
C/*	np	7	M722	4-G	DSM	1962	3/71/8149/OS	OS	r.	m	Ob	
C/*	DR	7	M722	4-G	DSM	1962	5/72/8618/OS	OS	r.	d	Ob	

1. As with all other sheets this printing job was originally the responsibility of the OS, but it was reassigned to SPC RE on 26 January 1949, using Kodalines supplied by the OS. 2. 1800 surplus civilian copies were overprinted for military use, completed 8 May 1952. No record copies were kept. Not found. 3. This order was serviced by 10,000 copies on the New Popular base by June 1952, leaving the remaining 15,000 for printing as soon as the new Seventh Edition base (as it was still called) was available.

Sheet 116 a. *Dolgelley* b. *Dolgellau*

1	5	6	7	8	9	10	11	12	13	14	15	16
nc	5/-	6a	4620	WOE	WO	1949	15,000/6/49 SPC	SPC RE	p	a	BL-d	1
1246	10/6	6a	4620	2-G	WO	1951	15,000/2/52	OS	p	b	BL-d	
nc	np	7a	4620	3-G	WO	1954	20,000/8/54 OS	OS	r	mo	BL-d	2
nc	np	7a	4620	3-G	WO	1954	no code [1961]	HDA	r	mo	BL-d	
B	4/6	7b	M722	4-G	DSW	1962	3000/5/62/6356/OS	OS	r	d	DGC	
B	np	7b	M722	4-G	DSM	1964	4500/6/64/6626/OS	OS	r	m	DGC	
B	np	7b	M722	4-G	DSM	1964	13,000/8/65/6756/OS	OS	r	m	NLS	
B/*	np	7b	M722	5-G	DSM	1966	25,000/10/66/6861/OS	OS	r.	d	NLW	
B/*	DR	7b	M722	5-G	DSM	1966	7/72/8694/OS	OS	r.	d	Ob	
B/*	np	7b	M722	5-G	DSM	1966	6/73/731088 S	OS	r.	mc	BL-a	

For further use see GSGS Misc.2132 in supplement 3; see also supplement 8. 1. As with all other sheets this printing job was originally the responsibility of the OS, but it was reassigned to SPC RE on 26 January 1949, using Kodalines supplied by the OS. 2. Military Survey wrote to the OS on 22 October 1953 regarding surplus stock of 20,000 copies for overprinting, but it would seem none were available. They were apparently content to await the arrival of the Seventh Series map in 1954.

Sheet 117 *Bala and Welshpool*

1	5	6	7	8	9	10	11	12	13	14	15	16
1042	5/-	6	4620	WOE	WO	1948	15,000/3/49	OS	p	a	BL-d	1
1251	10/6	6	4620	2-G	WO	1951	15,000/3/52	OS	p	b	BL-d	
4015	np	7	4620	3-G	WO	1955	20,000/5/55 OS	OS	r	mo	BL-d	
4015	np	7	4620	3-G	WO	1955	no code [1961]	HDA	r	mo	BL-d	
B	np	7	M722	4-G	DSM	1966	15,000/7/66/6824/OS	OS	r.	m	Ob	
B/*	np	7	M722	4-G	DSM	1966	6/68/7117/OS	OS	r.	m	BL-b	

For further use see Exercise *Red Spider* in supplement 4. 1. The civilian printing has *Cambrian Railway* in two places, adjusted here to *GWR (Cambrian Line)*.

Sheet 118 *Shrewsbury*

1	5	6	7	8	9	10	11	12	13	14	15	16
1043	5/-	6	4620	WOE	WO	1949	15,000/3/49	OS	p	a	BL-d	
1277	10/6	6	4620	2-G	WO	1951	15,000/12/51	OS	p	b	BL-d	
nc	np	7	4620	3-G	WO	1954	20,000/7/54 OS	OS	r	mo	BL-d	1
nc	3/6	7	M722	3-G	DSW	1954	20,000/3/61/4344/R	1 SPC RE	r	mo	BL-b	
C	np	7	M722	4-G	DSM	1965	21,000/2/65/6684/OS	OS	r	m	Ob	
C/*	np	7	M722	4-G	DSM	1965	10,000/11/65/6773/OS	OS	r	d	DGC	
C/*	np	7	M722	4-G	DSM	1965	12/70/8097/OS	OS	r.	m	DGC	
C/*	DR	7	M722	4-G	DSM	1965	5/72/8617/OS	OS	r.	d	Ob	

For further use see Exercises *Ballista, Noahs Ark, Red Spider* in supplement 4. 1. Military Survey wrote to the OS on 22 October 1953 regarding surplus stock of 20,000 copies for overprinting, but it would seem none were available. They were apparently content to await the arrival of the Seventh Series map in 1954.

Sheet 119 *Stafford*

1	5	6	7	8	9	10	11	12	13	14	15	16
nc	5/-	6	4620	WOE	WO	1949	11,000/3/49	OS	p‡	a	BL-d	
nc	5/-	6	4620	WOE	WO	1948	5000/5/50	OS	p‡	a	BL-d	
1278	10/6	6	4620	2-G	WO	1952	17,000/6/52	OS	p‡	b	BL-d	1
1278	10/6	6	4620	2-G	WO	1952	3000/7/52	OS	p	bc	PC	1
nc	3/-	7	M722	3-G	DSW	1961	20,000/3/61/6118/OS	OS	r	mo	BL-b	
B/*	np	7	M722	4-G	DSM	1965	20,000/9/65/6741/OS	OS	r	d	Ob	
B/*/*	np	7	M722	5-G	DSM	1969	3/69/7374/OS	OS	r.	m	Ob	
B/*/*	np	7	M722	5-G	DSM	1969	10/72/8695/OS	OS	r.	d	Ob	
B/*/*	np	7	M722	5-G	DSM	1969	8/73/732014 S	OS	r.	m	DGC	

1. A printing order for 20,000 copies, of which 3000 were to be surplus civilian stock overprinted for military use.

1	5	6	7	8	9	10	11	12	13	14	15	16

Sheet 120 a. *Derby and Burton upon Trent* b. *Burton upon Trent* c. *Burton-upon-Trent*

1	5	6	7	8	9	10	11	12	13	14	15	16
1045	5/-	6a	4620	WOE	WO	1949	18,000/6/49	OS	p	a	BL-d	
1045	5/-	6a	4620	1-G	WO	1948	10,000/1/51 SPC RE	SPC RE	p	a	PC	1
1045	5/-	6a	4620	WOE	WO	1948	6000/3/54 OS	OS	p	ac	BL-d	
nc	3/-	7b	M722	2-G	DSW	1959	15,000/11/59/6020/OS	OS	r	mo	BL-b	
A//	np	7b	M722	2-G	DSW	1959	no code [1961]	HDA	r	mo	DGC	
B	4/6	7b	M722	2-G	DSW	1962	3000/12/61/6356/OS	OS	r	m	Wc	
B	np	7b	M722	3-G	DSM	1966	20,000/5/66/6822/OS	OS	r.	d	Ob	
B/*	np	7c	M722	4-G	DSM	1968	10/68/7314/OS	OS	r.	d	Ob	
B/*	DR	7c	M722	4-G	DSM	1968	3/72/8615/OS	OS	r.	d	Ob	
B/*/*	np	7b	M722	4-G	DSM	1968	10/72/720055 S	OS	r.	d	Ob	
B/*/*	np	7b	M722	4-G	DSM	1968	7/73/731836 S	OS	r.	d	DGC	

1. This printing was originally contracted to the OS. It was later cancelled and reassigned to SPC RE. Plates were sent from the OS to SPC RE on 2 January 1951. The magnetic variation date is advanced to 1 June 1951.

Sheet 121 a. *Derby, Nottingham and Leicester* b. *Derby and Leicester*

1	5	6	7	8	9	10	11	12	13	14	15	16
nc	5/-	6a	4620	WOE	WO	1949	11,000/3/49	OS	p‡	a	BL-d	
nc	5/-	6a	4620	WOE	WO	1949	5000/5/50	OS	p‡	a	BL-d	
1238	10/6	6a	4620	1-G	WO	1948	10,000/11/50	OS	p‡	a	BL-d	
1238	10/6	6a	4620	1-G	WO	1948	1200/10/54 OS	OS	p	ac	BL-d	1
nc	np	7b	4620	2-G	WO	1954	20,000/1/55 OS	OS	r	mo	BL-d	
nc	np	7b	4620	2-G	WO	1954	no code [1961]	HDA	r	mo	BL-d	
B	4/6	7b	M722	3-G	DSW	1962	3000/10/62/6356/OS	OS	r	d	DGC	
B	np	7b	M722	3-G	DSW	1962	1000/8/65/6756/OS	OS	r	m	Wc	
B/*	np	7b	M722	4-G	DSM	1966	5000/1/66/6756/OS	OS	r	d	Ob	
B/*	np	7b	M722	4-G	DSM	1966	35,000/9/66/348/OA	BAOR	r	m	BL-b	
B/*/*	np	7b	M722	5-G	DSM	1971	8/71/8215/OS	OS	r.	d	Ob	

1. Military Survey wrote to the OS on 22 October 1953 regarding surplus stock of 20,000 copies for overprinting, but it would seem none were available. A consequent print order for 20,000 copies does not, in its turn, seem to have been fulfilled. 1200 civilian copies which became available late in 1954 seem to have sufficed until the 1955 printing on the new base map.

Sheet 122 *Melton Mowbray*

1	5	6	7	8	9	10	11	12	13	14	15	16
1047	5/-	6	4620	WOE	WO	1949	11,000/3/49	OS	p	a	BL-d	
1047	5/-	6	4620	WOE	WO	1949	5000/7/50	OS	p	a	BL-d	
1047	5/-	6	4620	2-G	WO	1952	20,000/5/52	OS	p	b	BL-d	
1047	5/-	6	4620	WOE	WO	1949	5000/6/55 OS	OS	p	ac	BL-d	
A/	3/6	7	M722	3-G	DSW	1961	10,000/2/61/6236/OS	OS	r	mo	Wc	
B	4/6	7	M722	4-G	DSW	1962	10,000/6/62/6415/OS	OS	r	d	BL-b	
B	np	7	M722	4-G	DSW	1962	15,000/1/65/6684/OS	OS	r	m	NLS	
B/*	np	7	M722	5-G	DSM	1966	20,000/11/66/6866/OS	OS	r.	d	Cu-m	
B/*	np	7	M722	5-G	DSM	1966	70/7975/OS	OS	r.	m	BL-a	

Sheet 123 *Spalding*

1	5	6	7	8	9	10	11	12	13	14	15	16
nc	5/-	6	4620	WOE	WO	1949	21,000/12/49 SPC	SPC RE	p	a	BL-d	1
nc	10/6	6	4620	2-G	WO	1952	5000/8/52	OS	p	b	BL-d	2
nc	np	7	4620	3-G	WO	1954	20,000/8/54 OS	OS	r	mo	BL-d	3
B	np	7	M722	4-G	DSM	1965	24,000/12/65/6794/OS	OS	r	m	BL-b	
B/	np	7	M722	5-G	DSM	1970	70/7882/OS	OS	r.	d	Ob	

1. As with all other sheets this printing job was originally the responsibility of the OS, but it was reassigned to SPC RE on 30 August 1949. 2. A reprint by SPC RE was cancelled in favour of one on the revised base map by the OS. 3. Military Survey wrote to the OS on 22 October 1953 regarding surplus stock of 20,000 copies for overprinting, but it would seem none were available. A consequent print order for 20,000 Second Edition copies in December 1953 does not, in its turn, seem to have been fulfilled, pending the arrival of the Seventh Series map in 1954.

Sheet 124 *King's Lynn*

1	5	6	7	8	9	10	11	12	13	14	15	16
nc	5/-	6	4620	WOE	WO	1948	21,000/10/49 SPC	SPC RE	p‡	a	BL-d	
nc	10/6	6	4620	2-G	WO	1952	20,000/7/52	OS	p‡	b	BL-d	
1301	6/6	6	4620	2-G	WO	1952	1200/2/55 OS	OS	p	bc	BL-d	
A/	3/6	7	M722	3-G	DSW	1958	10,000/9/58/5748/OS	OS	r	mo	BL-b	
B	4/6	7	M722	4-G	DSW	1963	30,000/8/63/6545/OS	OS	r	m	DGC	
B/*	np	7	M722	5-G	DSM	1969	2/69/7375/OS	OS	r.	d	Ob	
B/*	np	7	M722	5-G	DSM	1969	7/71/8116/OS	OS	r.	m	Cu-m	

1. As with all other sheets this printing job was originally the responsibility of the OS, but it was reassigned to SPC RE on 10 May 1949, using Kodalines supplied by the OS.

Sheet 125 *Fakenham*

1	5	6	7	8	9	10	11	12	13	14	15	16
nc	5/-	6	4620	WOE	WO	1949	13,000/4/49	OS	p‡	a	BL-d	
nc	5/-	6	4620	WOE	WO	1949	10,000/6/50	OS	p‡	a	BL-d	
nc	10/6	6	4620	2-G	WO	1952	20,000/7/52	OS	p‡	b	BL-d	1
							1500			bc	card	2
A/	3/6	7	M722	3-G	DSW	1958	12,000/5/58/5753/OS	OS	r	mo	PC	
A/	4/6	7	M722	4-G	DSW	1961	15,000/3/61/6022/OS	OS	r	mo	DGC	3
A//	np	7	M722	5-G	DSM	1964	25,000/9/64/6642/OS	OS	r	m	Wc	
B	np	7	M722	6-G	DSM	1969	10/69/7555/OS	OS	r.	d	Ob	
B	np	7	M722	6-G	DSM	1969	9/71/8288/OS	OS	r.	m	Ob	
B	np	7	M722	6-G	DSM	1969	4/73/722630 S	OS	r.	d	BL-b	

1. A print order for 20,000 copies on the original base map was replaced by this one on the revised base. 2. There was a subsequent printing demand on 26 November 1953 for 1500 copies of overprinted civilian stock, but there is no confirmation that it was fulfilled. 3. A civilian printing with a 4/6 price statement has not been recorded.

Sheet 126 *Norwich*

1	5	6	7	8	9	10	11	12	13	14	15	16
nc	5/-	6	4620	WOE	WO	1949	13,000/5/49	OS	p‡	a	BL-d	
nc	5/-	6	4620	WOE	WO	1949	10,000/6/50	OS	p‡	a	BL-d	
1288	10/6	6	4620	2-G	WO	1952	5000/8/52	OS	p‡	b	BL-d	1
1288	np	6	4620	2-G	WO	1952	20,000/6/55 OS	OS	p‡	b	BL-d	2
A//	4/6	7	M722	3-G	DSW	1961	20,000/3/61/6309/OS	OS	r	mo	BL-b	
A//	np	7	M722	3-G	DSW	1961	16,000/10/66/348/OA	BAOR	r	m	DGC	
B	np	7	M722	4-G	DSM	1969	5/69/7409/OS	OS	r.	d	Ob	
B/	DR	7	M722	4-G	DSM	1969	3/72/8660/OS	OS	r.	d	Ob	

1. A reprint by SPC RE was cancelled in favour of one on the revised base map by the OS. 2. Military Survey wrote to the OS on 22 October 1953 regarding surplus stock of 20,000 copies for overprinting, but it would seem none were available. A consequent print order for 20,000 Second Edition copies placed on 26 November 1953 seems to have been remarkably delayed.

Sheet 127 *Aberystwyth*

1	5	6	7	8	9	10	11	12	13	14	15	16
1052	5/-	6	4620	WOE	WO	1949	15,000/5/49	OS	p	a	BL-d	
1052	5/-	6	4620	WOE	WO	1949	5000/1/52	OS	p	ac	BL-d	1
1052	5/-	6	4620	WOE	WO	1949	5000/1/52	OS	rp	at	BL-d	2
4016	np	7	4620	2-G	WO	1953	15,000/1/53 OS	OS	r	mo	BL-d	
A//	3/6	7	M722	3-G	DSW	1961	15,000/1/61/6223/OS	OS	r	mo	DGC	
A//	np	7	M722	3-G	DSW	1961	12,000/12/64/6684/OS	OS	r	m	NLS	
B	np	7	M722	4-G	DSM	1966	28,000/3/66/6778/OS	OS	r	d	Ob	
B/	np	7	M722	4-G	DSM	1966	7/69/7524/OS	OS	r.	d	Ob	
B/	np	7	M722	4-G	DSM	1966	2/73/722624 S	OS	r.	d	DGC	

For further use see GSGS Misc.2133 in supplement 3. 1. The original demand in July 1951 was for 15,000 copies in Second Edition, but the availability of this surplus civilian stock, overprinted for military use, proved adequate until the 1953 printing on the new base map. 2. The unused stock of 4430 copies, no longer needed after the publication of Edition 2-GSGS, were overprinted a second time for training purposes, completed on 6 June 1953.

1	5	6	7	8	9	10	11	12	13	14	15	16

Sheet 128 *Montgomery and Llandrindod Wells*

1	5	6	7	8	9	10	11	12	13	14	15	16
1053	5/-	6	4620	WOE	WO	1949	15,000/7/49	OS	p	a	BL-d	
1053	5/-	6	4620	WOE	WO	1949	15,000/7/49	OS	rp	at	PC	2
1248	10/6	6	4620	WOE	WO	1949	3700/1/52	OS	p	ac	BL-d	1
1248	10/6	6	4620	WOE	WO	1949	3700/1/52	OS	rp	at	BL-d	2
4017	np	7	4620	2-G	WO	1953	15,000/1/53 OS	OS	r	mo	BL-d	
A/	3/-	7	M722	2-G	DSW	1960	10,000/11/60/6236/OS	OS	r	mo	DGC	
A//	3/6	7	M722	2-G	DSW	1960	10,000/6/62/6388/OS	OS	r	m	BL-b	3
A//	np	7	M722	2-G	DSM	1960	6000/7/66/6824/OS	OS	r.	m	DGC	4
B	np	7	M722	3-G	DSM	1966	19,000/11/66/6849/OS	OS	r.	d	DGC	
B	np	7	M722	3-G	DSM	1966	4/71/8173/OS	OS	r.	m	BL-b	
B/*	np	7	M722	4-G	DSM	1966	9/73/732144 S	OS	r.	d	BL-a	5
B/*	np	7	M722	4-G	DSM	1973	11/73/732735 S	OS	r.	m	DGC	

For further use see Exercise *Red Spider* in supplement 4. 1. The original demand in July 1951 was for 15,000 copies in Second Edition, but the availability of this surplus civilian stock, overprinted for military use, proved adequate until the 1953 printing on the new base map. 2. 5380 unused copies of the combined total of 18,700, surplus to requirements after the publication of the Second Edition, were overprinted for training purposes, completed on 6 June 1953. 3. A civilian printing with a 3/6 price statement has not been recorded. 4. 15,000 in red formed part of the original print code, crossed out and replaced in brown by 6000. 5. The edition number 3 is overprinted 4, though the 1966 publication date was unaltered.

Sheet 129 *Ludlow*

1	5	6	7	8	9	10	11	12	13	14	15	16
1054	5/-	6	4620	WOE	WO	1948	15,000/4/49	OS	p	a	BL-d	
1218	5/-	6	4620	1-G	WO	1948	10,000/ /51	OS	p	a	BL-d	1
1218	5/-	6	4620	1-G	WO	1948	10,000/4/51	OS	p	a	BL-d	1
4013	np	7	4620	2-G	WO	1954	20,000/12/54 OS	OS	r	mo	BL-d	
4013	np	7	4620	2-G	WO	1954	no code [1961]	HDA	r	mo	BL-d	
B//	np	7	M722	3-G	DSM	1966	7000/8/66/6854/OS	OS	r.	m	Ob	
C	np	7	M722	4-G	DSM	1967	20,000/5/67/6900/OS	OS	r.	d	DGC	
C	np	7	M722	4-G	DSM	1967	12/72/8492/OS	OS	r.	?d	BL-b	

For further use see Exercise *Red Spider* in supplement 4. 1. The month element of the print code, lacking at first, was added later. 2. Military Survey wrote to the OS on 22 October 1953 regarding surplus stock of 20,000 copies for overprinting, but it would seem none were available. 20,000 Second Edition copies were ordered on 26 November 1953; with the Seventh Series base already in print it is unclear why the new printing was so delayed.

Sheet 130 *Kidderminster*

1	5	6	7	8	9	10	11	12	13	14	15	16
1055	5/-	6	4620	WOE	WO	1949	11,000/7/49	OS	p	a	BL-d	
1226	5/-	6	4620	WOE	WO	1949	5000/5/50	OS	p	a	BL-d	
1279	10/6	6	4620	2-G	WO	1952	16,000/5/52	OS	p	b	BL-d	1
1279	10/6	6	4620	2-G	WO	1952	4000/7/52	OS	p	bc	PC	1
1279	10/6	6	4620	2-G	WO	1952	2600/10/54 OS	OS	p	bc	BL-d	
A/	3/6	7	M722	3-G	DSW	1961	20,000/5/61/6309/OS	OS	r	mo	BL-b	2
A///*	np	7	M722	3-G	DSM	1966	5000/8/66/6854/OS	OS	r.	m	Wc	
B	np	7	M722	4-G	DSM	1967	17,000/8/67/6900/OS	OS	r.	d	BL-a	
B	np	7	M722	4-G	DSM	1967	12/72/8696/OS	OS	r.	m	DGC	

1. The printing order was for 20,000 copies, of which 4000 were to be surplus civilian stock overprinted for military use. It is probable that the full order was complete by 4 July 1952. 2. A civilian printing with a 3/6 price statement has not been recorded.

Sheet 131 *Birmingham*

1	5	6	7	8	9	10	11	12	13	14	15	16
1056	5/-	6	4620	WOE	WO	1949	18,000/4/49	OS	p	a	BL-d	
1249	10/6	6	4620	2-G	WO	1952	11,000/7/52	OS	p	b	BL-d	1
1249	10/6	6	4620	WOE	WO	1949	9000/7/52	OS	p	ac	Wc	1
A//	3/6	7	M722	3-G	DSW	1960	20,000/3/60/6118/OS	OS	r	mo	BL-b	
B/*	np	7	M722	4-G	DSM	1965	20,000/10/65/6779/OS	OS	r	d	Ob	2
C	np	7	M722	5-G	DSM	1967	16,500/9/676938/OS	OS	r.	d	BL-b	
C	np	7	M722	5-G	DSM	1967	12/71/8600/OS	OS	r.	d	BL-a	
C/*	DR	7	M722	6-G	DSM	1972	4/72/8436/OS	OS	r.	?d	Ob	

For further use see supplement 7. 1. A printing order for 20,000 copies on the original base map from SPC RE (to whom the OS were to provide plates) was replaced by this order, also for 20,000 copies, of which 9000 were to be surplus civilian stock overprinted for military use. 2. Not in DGC Superseded.

1	5	6	7	8	9	10	11	12	13	14	15	16

Sheet 132 *Coventry and Rugby*

1	5	6	7	8	9	10	11	12	13	14	15	16
1220	5/-	6	4620	WOE	WO	1949	18,000/11/49	OS	p‡	a	BL-d	
1271	10/6	6	4620	2-G	WO	1952	20,000/4/52	OS	p‡	b	BL-d	1
1271	10/6	6	4620	2-G	WO	1952	3000/10/54 OS	OS	p	bc	BL-d	
B	np	7	M722	3-G	DSW	1961	20,000/11/61/6309/OS	OS	r	m	BL-b	2
B/*	np	7	M722	4-G	DSM	1964	15,000/11/64/6663/OS	OS	r	m	Ob	
C	np	7	M722	5-G	DSM	1967	12,500/9/67/6938/OS	OS	r.	d	DGC	
C	np	7	M722	5-G	DSM	1967	2/69/7343/OS	OS	r.	m	Ob	

For further use see supplement 7. 1. A copy of a section of this sheet is in BL-d, overprinted for Exercise *Lion*. 2. An unpriced civilian "B" printing has not been recorded.

Sheet 133 *Northampton*

1	5	6	7	8	9	10	11	12	13	14	15	16
nc	5/-	6	4620	WOE	WO	1949	18,000/10/49	OS	p‡	a	BL-d	
nc	5/-	6	4620	WOE	WO	1949	5000/6/50	OS	p‡	a	BL-d	
nc	10/6	6	4620	2-G	WO	1952	20,000/7/52	OS	p‡	b	BL-d	
1268	10/6	6	4620	2-G	WO	1952	1100/10/54 OS	OS	p	bc	PC	
A//*	4/6	7	M722	3-G	DSW	1962	10,000/8/62/6388/OS	OS	r	m	BL-b	
A//*	np	7	M722	3-G	DSM	1966	24,000/5/66/6822/OS	OS	r.	d	Ob	
B	np	7	M722	4-G	DSM	1968	11/68/7321/OS	OS	r.	d	Ob	
B	np	7	M722	4-G	DSM	1968	3/73/8697/OS	OS	r.	d	BL-b	

For further use see supplement 7.

Sheet 134 *Huntingdon and Peterborough*

1	5	6	7	8	9	10	11	12	13	14	15	16
1186	5/-	6	4620	WOE	WO	1947	15,000/10/47	OS	p‡	a	BL-d	
1186	5/-	6	4620	WOE	WO	1947	10,000/6/50	OS	p‡	a	BL	
nc	5/-	6	4620	2-G	WO	1952	15,000/8/52	OS	p‡	b	BL-d	1
20046	5/-	6	4620	WOE	WO	1947	12,000/6/55 OS	OS	p	ac	BL-d	2
1186	5/-	6	4620	WOE	WO	1947	12,000/6/55 OS	OS	p	ac	BL-d	2
A//	4/6	7	M722	2-G	DSW	1963	20,000/3/63/6309/OS	OS	r	m	DGC	3
A///*	np	7	M722	2-G	DSW	1963	25,000/11/64/6665/OS	OS	r	m	DGC	
B	np	7	M722	3-G	DSM	1968	2/69/7227/OS	OS	r.	m	Ob	4
B/	np	7	M722	3-G	DSM	1968	9/71/8251/OS	OS	r.	d	BL-a	

1. A reprint by SPC RE was cancelled in favour of one on the revised base map by the OS. 2. An example of the stock of two civilian print runs being used for a single military printing. 3. NB a second Edition 2-GSGS. 4. On a DGC copy the 7227 in the print code has been altered by hand to 7372.

Sheet 135 *Cambridge and Ely*

1	5	6	7	8	9	10	11	12	13	14	15	16
nc	5/-	6	4620	WOE	WO	1949	13,000/6/49	OS	p‡	a	BL-d	
nc	5/-	6	4620	WOE	WO	1949	10,000/6/50	OS	p‡	a	BL-d	
nc	10/6	6	4620	2-G	WO	1952	20,000/5/52	OS	p‡	b	BL-d	
1286	10/6	6	4620	2-G	WO	1952	8100/2/55 OS	OS	p	bc	BL-d	
A/	3/-	7	M722	3-G	DSW	1959	15,000/11/59/6020/OS	OS	r	mo	BL-b	
A/	np	7	M722	3-G	DSW	1959	20,000/9/62/20/SPC	SPC RE	r	mo	Wc	
B	np	7	M722	4-G	DSM	1966	22,000/10/66/6826/OS	OS	r.	d	DGC	
C	np	7	M722	5-G	DSM	1969	1/69/7344/OS	OS	r.	d	Ob	
C	np	7	M722	5-G	DSM	1969	12/71/8557/OS	OS	r.	?d	Ob	

Sheet 136 *Bury St Edmunds*

1	5	6	7	8	9	10	11	12	13	14	15	16
nc	5/-	6	4620	WOE	WO	1948	13,000/6/49	OS	p‡	a	BL-d	
nc	5/-	6	4620	WOE	WO	1948	10,000/9/50	OS	p‡	a	BL-d	
nc	5/-	6	4620	2-G	WO	1951	20,000/2/52	OS	p‡	b	BL-d	1
nc	np	6	4620	2-G	WO	1951	22,000/4/54 OS	OS	p‡	b	BL-d	1,2
A	6/6	7	4620	3-G	WO	1955	8500/10/55 OS	OS	r	mo	BL-d	3
A/	3/-	7	M722	4-G	DSW	1958	20,000/8/58/5748/OS	OS	r	mo	Wc	
A/	3/-	7	M722	4-G	DSW	1958	20,000/6/62/4512/R	1 SPC RE	r	m	BL-b	
A//	4/6	7	M722	4-G	DSW	1958	24,000/6/63/6546/OS	OS	r	d	DGC	
A//	np	7	M722	4-G	DSM	1967	35,000/12/66/6882/OS	OS	r.	m	DGC	
B	np	7	M722	5-G	DSM	1969	1/69/7329/OS	OS	r.	m	Ob	
B	np	7	M722	5-G	DSM	1969	4/73/711935 S	OS	r.	d	DGC	
B	np	7	M722	5-G	DSM	1969	10/73/732148 S	OS	r.	m	DGC	

For further use see GSGS Misc.1585, GSGS 5025 in supplement 3, Exercise *Hereward* in supplement 4; see also supplement 8. 1. Unusually for a Second Edition GSGS, the original magnetic variation date was left unrevised. 2. Military Survey wrote to the OS on 22 October 1953 regarding surplus stock of 20,000 copies for overprinting, but it would seem none were available. Consequently this print order for 20,000 Second Edition copies was placed on 26 November 1953. 3. A unique instance of this price state surviving on a military printing on a Seventh Series base map.

Sheet 137 *Lowestoft*

nc	5/-	6	4620	WOE	WO	1948	13,000/6/49	OS	p‡	a	BL-d
nc	5/-	6	4620	1-G	WO	1948	10,000/1/51	OS	p‡	a	BL-d
nc	np	6	4620	2-G	WO	1953	15,000/9/53 OS	OS	p‡	b	BL-d 1
B	6/6	6	4620	2-G	WO	1953	1300/9/55 OS	OS	p	bc	BL-d
A/	3/6	7	M722	3-G	DSW	1960	15,000/1/60/6006/OS	OS	r	mo	BL-b
A//	np	7	M722	3-G	DSM	1964	20,000/6/64/6626/OS	OS	r	m	DGC
A//	np	7	M722	3-G	DSM	1967	15,000/8/67/6938/OS	OS	r.	m	BL-b
B	np	7	M722	4-G	DSM	1969	4/69/7376/OS	OS	r.	d	Ob
B	np	7	M722	4-G	DSM	1969	2/71/8114/OS	OS	r.	m	Cu-m
B	DR	7	M722	4-G	DSM	1969	7/72/8619/OS	OS	r.	d	Ob

1. Unusually for a Second Edition GSGS, the original magnetic variation date was left unrevised.

Sheet 138 *Fishguard*

1063	5/-	6	4620	WOE	WO	1949	15,000/6/49	OS	p	a	BL-d
1063	5/-	6	4620	WOE	WO	1949	7800/4/52	OS	p	ac	BL-d
4006	np	7	4620	2-G	WO	1954	20,000/9/54 OS	OS	r	mo	BL-d 1

1. Military Survey wrote to the OS on 22 October 1953 regarding surplus stock of 20,000 copies for overprinting, but it would seem none were available. Consequently a print order for 20,000 Second Edition copies was placed on 26 November 1953; with the Seventh Series base already in print it is unclear why the new printing was so delayed.

Sheet 138/151 *Fishguard and Pembroke*   42 by 48 km

C	np	7	M722	4-G	DSM	1965	20,000/11/65/6747/OS	OS	r	d	Ob
C/	np	7	M722	5-G	DSM	1970	12/70/8074/OS	OS	r.	d	Ob

No Edition 3-GSGS of sheet 138 has been recorded, but there is of sheet 151. With extensions north, south and west, and an inset of Grassholm Island. With the marginalia in a panel in the south-west corner.

Sheet 139 *Cardigan*

nc	5/-	6	4620	WOE	WO	1949	15,000/8/49 SPC	SPC RE	p	a	BL-d 1
1064	5/-	6	4620	WOE	WO	1948	4800/4/52	OS	p	ac	Wc
4007	np	7	4620	2-G	WO	1952	15,000/10/52	OS	r	mo	Wc 2
B/	3/-	7	M722	3-G	DSW	1961	15,000/2/61/6118/OS	OS	r	mo	BL-b 3
C	np	7	M722	4-G	DSM	1966	11,000/10/66/6826/OS	OS	r.	d	DGC
C	np	7	M722	4-G	DSM	1966	2/69/7339/OS	OS	r.	m	Ob
C	np	7	M722	4-G	DSM	1966	12/71/8373/OS	OS	r.	m	Ob

1. As with all other sheets this printing job was originally the responsibility of the OS, but it was reassigned to SPC RE on 10 May 1949, using Kodalines supplied by the OS. 2. A first edition reprint, presumably on the New Popular base map, was cancelled in favour of this, using the new Seventh Series map. 3. A civilian printing with a 3/- price statement has not been recorded.

Sheet 140 *Llandovery*

nc	5/-	6	4620	WOE	WO	1949	15,000/7/49 SPC	SPC RE	p	a	BL-d 1
1065	5/-	6	4620	WOE	WO	1948	11,500/4/52	OS	p	ac	Wc 2
nc	np	7	4620	2-G	WO	1955	25,000/9/55 OS	OS	r	mo	BL-d
B/	4/6	7	M722	2-G	DSW	1964	12,000/1/64/6581/OS	OS	r	m	NLS
C	np	7	M722	3-G	DSM	1966	20,000/10/66/6795/OS	OS	r.	d	DGC
C	np	7	M722	3-G	DSM	1966	1/69/7338/OS	OS	r.	m	Ob
C	DR	7	M722	3-G	DSM	1966	7/72/8462/OS	OS	r.	d	Ob

1. As with all other sheets this printing job was originally the responsibility of the OS, but it was reassigned to SPC RE on 10 May 1949, using Kodalines supplied by the OS. 2. The printing record does not note this as overprinted civilian stock, but the paper quality and print run suggest that it was.

1	5	6	7	8	9	10	11	12	13	14	15	16

Sheet 141 *Brecon*

1	5	6	7	8	9	10	11	12	13	14	15	16
nc	5/-	6	4620	WOE	WO	1949	15,000/8/49 SPC	SPC RE	p	a	BL-d	1
		6	4620	?2-G			1200			?b	card	2
4008	2/6	7	4620	2-G	WO	1952	20,000/5/52	OS	b	mo	BL-d	3
A//	3/6	7	M722	3-G	DSW	1958	20,000/3/59/5753/OS	OS	r	mo	DGC	4
nc	3/6	7	M722	3-G	DSW	1958	25,000/7/61/4385/R	1 SPC RE	r	mo	BL-b	
A///	np	7	M722	4-G	DSM	1964	30,000/8/64/6662/OS	OS	r	d	Ob	
B	np	7	M722	5-G	DSM	1966	64,000/9/66/6826/OS	OS	r.	d	Ob	
B/	np	7	M722	6-G	DSM	1971	10/71/8253/OS	OS	r.	?d	Ob	
B/	np	7	M722	6-G	DSM	1971	11/73/732788 S	OS	r.	d	DGC	

For further use see GSGS Misc.2134 in supplement 3, supplement 5. 1. As with all other sheets this printing job was originally the responsibility of the OS, but it was reassigned to SPC RE on 10 May 1949, using Kodalines supplied by the OS. The top of the unique number 1066 is still visible. 2. This reprint, required by 1 June 1952, was completed by 9 May. Not found. 3. One of the earliest printings to use the Seventh Series base map, completed 23 June 1952. 4. The sheet price is blocked out in blue.

Sheet 142 *Hereford*

1	5	6	7	8	9	10	11	12	13	14	15	16
1067	5/-	6	4620	WOE	WO	1949	10,000/12/49	OS	p	a	BL-d	1
1067	5/-	6	4620	WOE	WO	1949	5000/7/50	OS	p	a	BL-d	
4003	2/6	7	4620	2-G	WO	1952	25,000/7/52	OS	b	mo	BL-d	2
A//	3/6	7	M722	3-G	DSW	1961	20,000/3/61/6022/OS	OS	r	mo	BL-b	
A//	4/6	7	M722	3-G	DSW	1961	25,000/1/64/6590/OS	OS	r	m	Cu-m	
B	np	7	M722	4-G	DSM	1967	30,000/2/67/6882/OS	OS	r.	d	Ob	
B/	np	7	M722	4-G	DSM	1967	9/71/8254/OS	OS	r.	d	Ob	

1. This was the last sheet to be published, completed on 6 January 1950 – and that only after the printing requirement had been reduced from 25,000 to 10,000 as late as 10 November 1949. It was late enough for the magnetic variation date to be advanced to 1 January 1950. 2. A reprint demand for 15,000 sheets was cancelled on 30 April 1951, the same day as the order for this printing was made. Evidently the forthcoming Seventh Series base map was preferred.

Sheet 143 *Gloucester and Malvern*

1	5	6	7	8	9	10	11	12	13	14	15	16
nc	5/-	6	4620	WOE	WO	1949	18,000/9/49 SPC	SPC RE	p‡	a	PC	1
nc	10/6	6	4620	2-G	WO	1951	5000/1/52	OS	p‡	b	BL-d	
nc	10/6	6	4620	2-G	WO	1952	10,000/8/52	OS	p‡	b	BL-d	
nc	np	7	4620	3-G	WO	1955	25,000/4/55 OS	OS	r	mo	BL-d	
A//*/*	4/6	7	M722	3-G	DSW	1955	15,000/10/62/6388/OS	OS	r	d	Wc	
A//*/*	np	7	M722	3-G	DSM	1964	5000/7/64/6576/OS	OS	r	m	Cu-m	
A//*/*	np	7	M722	3-G	DSM	1966	19,000/8/66/6823/OS	OS	r.	m	DGC	
B	np	7	M722	4-G	DSM	1968	4/68/7112/OS	OS	r.	d	Ob	
B/*	np	7	M722	5-G	DSM	1973	2/73/722268 S	OS	r.	d	Ob	

1. As with all other sheets this printing job was originally the responsibility of the OS, but it was reassigned to SPC RE on 10 May 1949, using Kodalines supplied by the OS. An *Outline Edition* black plate was sent; this heading was blocked out and *War Office Edition* overprinted.

Sheet 144 *Cheltenham and Evesham*

1	5	6	7	8	9	10	11	12	13	14	15	16
1210	5/-	6	4620	WOE	WO	1949	29,000/2/49	OS	p‡	a	BL-d	1
nc	10/6	6	4620	2-G	WO	1952	8000/10/52	OS	p‡	b	BL-d	2
										ac	card	2
nc	np	7	4620	3-G	WO	1955	25,000/6/55 OS	OS	r	mo	BL-d	
nc	np	7	4620	3-G	WO	1955	no code [1961]	HDA	r	mo	BL-d	
A//*	np	7	M722	4-G	DSM	1965	15,000/2/65/6684/OS	OS	r	m	NLS	
B	np	7	M722	5-G	DSM	1967	11,000/12/67/6984/OS	OS	r.	d	BL-a	
B	np	7	M722	5-G	DSM	1967	7/70/8033/OS	OS	r.	m	DGC	
B/*	DR	7	M722	6-G	DSM	1972	3/72/8534/OS	OS	r.	d	Ob	

For further use see supplements 1, 7. 1. This printing would appear to combine a regular demand for 27,000 copies, and a special order of 2000 copies for the Staff College. It was completed on 24 February 1949. 2. The printing record notes the completion of an order for 10,000 copies, including 5000 overprinted civilian stock. There may thus be other parts of this printing yet to be identified.

Sheet 145 *Banbury*

1	5	6	7	8	9	10	11	12	13	14	15	16
1187	5/-	6	4620	WOE	WO	1947	35,000/11/47	OS	p‡	a	BL-d	
1187	5/-	6	4620	WOE	WO	1947	5000/3/54 OS	OS	p	ac	BL-d	1
nc	np	7	4620	2-G	WO	1954	20,000/1/55 OS	OS	r	mo	BL-d	2
nc	np	7	4620	2-G	WO	1954	20,000/2/62/4427/R	1 SPC RE	r	mo	BL-d	3
A///*	4/6	7	M722	3-G	DSW	1964	25,000/12/63/6581/OS	OS	r	d	BL-b	
B	np	7	M722	4-G	DSM	1968	1/68/7069/OS	OS	r.	d	BL-a	

For further use see supplements 1, 7. 1. A reprint of 10,000 copies was ordered, then cancelled, in 1950. Military Survey subsequently wrote to the OS on 22 October 1953 regarding surplus stock of 20,000 copies for overprinting, but it would seem that only 5000 were available. A copy in Wc has the month code obliterated on the overprint plate. 2. A further printing order for 20,000 copies was placed in December 1953, but was apparently also not fulfilled, perhaps pending the issue of the new Seventh Series base map. 3. This a very late issue still to be listed in GSGS 4620.

Sheet 146 *Buckingham*

1	5	6	7	8	9	10	11	12	13	14	15	16
1176	5/-	6	4620	WOE	WO	1947	15,000/11/47	OS	p‡	a	BL-d	1
1176	5/-	6	4620	WOE	WO	1947	5000/7/50	OS	p‡	a	BL-d	2
1176	5/-	6	4620	WOE	WO	1947	14,000/1/52	OS	p	ac	BL-d	
nc	np	6	4620	1-G	WO	1954	10,000/1/55 OS	OS	p‡	b	BL-d	3
1307	6/6	6	4620	1-G	WO	1954	1100/9/55 OS	OS	p	bc	BL-d	3
A//*	4/6	7	M722	2-G	DSW	1961	30,000/9/61/6022/OS	OS	r	m	BL-b	
A//*	np	7	M722	2-G	DSW	1961	30,000/8/64/6656/OS	OS	r	m	Wc	
A//*	np	7	M722	2-G	DSW	1961	50,000/9/66/348/OA	BAOR	r	m	DGC	
B	np	7	M722	3-G	DSM	1968	7/68/7090/OS	OS	r.	d	Ob	

For further use see supplements 1, 7. 1. The civilian publication date is 1947. 2. The civilian publication date is 1946. 3. Military Survey wrote to the OS on 22 October 1953 regarding surplus stock of 20,000 copies for overprinting, but it would seem none were available at the time. Further printing orders for 12,000 copies, 2000 of which were to be overprinted civilian stock, were placed on 26 November 1953; these printings may be the result.

Sheet 147 *Bedford and Luton*

1	5	6	7	8	9	10	11	12	13	14	15	16
1188	5/-	6	4620	WOE	WO	1947	15,000/11/47	OS	p‡	a	BL-d	
1188	5/-	6	4620	WOE	WO	1947	5000/5/50	OS	p‡	a	BL-d	
1188	10/6	6	4620	1-G	WO	1947	10,000/3/51	OS	p‡	a	BL-d	
1188	10/6	6	4620	2-G	WO	1952	30,000/8/52	OS	p‡	b	BL-d	1
1188	5/-	6	4620	WOE	WO	1947	1600/9/55 OS	OS	p	ac	BL-d	
A///*	4/6	7	M722	3-G	DSW	1963	20,000/1/63/6391/OS	OS	r	d	Cu-m	
A///*	4/6	7	M722	3-G	DSW	1963	16,000/7/65/6716/OS	OS	r	m	DGC	
A///*	np	7	M722	3-G	DSM	1967	15,000/7/67/6938/OS	OS	r.	m	Wc	
B	np	7	M722	4-G	DSM	1969	12/68/7327/OS	OS	r.	d	Ob	

1. A reprint by SPC RE was cancelled in favour of one on the revised base map by the Ordnance Survey.

Sheet 148 *Saffron Walden*

1	5	6	7	8	9	10	11	12	13	14	15	16
1189	5/-	6	4620	WOE	WO	1947	15,000/1/48	OS	p‡	a	BL-d	
1189	5/-	6	4620	WOE	WO	1947	10,000/ /50	OS	p‡	a	Cu	1
1189	5/-	6	4620	WOE	WO	1947	10,000/10/50	OS	p‡	a	BL-d	1
nc	np	6	4620	2-G	WO	1952	25,000/12/52	OS	p‡	b	BL-d	
16,046/Cr	5/-	6	4620	WOE	WO	1947	6000/2/55 OS	OS	p	ac	BL-d	2
1189	5/-	6	4620	WOE	WO	1947	6000/2/55 OS	OS	p	ac	PC	2
A//	3/6	7	M722	3-G	DSW	1961	15,000/2/61/6236/OS	OS	r	mo	BL-b	
A///*	4/6	7	M722	3-G	DSW	1961	20,000/7/63/6546/OS	OS	r	d	DGC	
B	np	7	M722	4-G	DSM	1968	9/68/7140/OS	OS	r.	d	Ob	
B	np	7	M722	4-G	DSM	1968	12/70/8098/OS	OS	r.	m	BL-b	

1. The month element of the print code, lacking at first, was added later. 2. An example of the stock of two civilian print runs being used for a single military printing. 4000 copies had been ordered on 26 November 1953; this may represent the delayed completion of that order.

1	5	6	7	8	9	10	11	12	13	14	15	16

Sheet 149 *Colchester*

1	5	6	7	8	9	10	11	12	13	14	15	16
20046	5/-	6	4620	WOE	WO	1949	no code	OS	p	aT	BL-d	1
1206	5/-	6	4620	WOE	WO	1949	5750/8/49	OS	p‡	a	BL-d	1
1206	5/-	6	4620	WOE	WO	1949	15,000/6/50	OS	p‡	a	BL-d	
nc	np	6	4620	2-G	WO	1953	15,000/9/53 OS	OS	p‡	b	BL-d	
A	3/-	7	M722	3-G	DSW	1958	20,000/5/58/5753/OS	OS	r	mo	DGC	
nc	3/-	7	M722	3-G	DSW	1958	20,000/7/61/4385/R	1 SPC RE	r	mo	BL-b	
A//*	np	7	M722	4-G	DSM	1966	25,000/7/66/6824/OS	OS	r.	m	Ob	2
B	np	7	M722	5-G	DSM	1969	7/69/7505/OS	OS	r.	d	Ob	
B	np	7	M722	5-G	DSM	1969	7/71/8176/OS	OS	r.	m	DGC	
B	np	7	M722	5-G	DSM	1969	5/73/721685 S	OS	r.	m	BL-b	3

For further use see supplement 8. 1. The Military Survey catalogue card records the order for 15,000 copies, and notes its completion on 26 July 1949. This may have been a mix of copies from the 20046 civilian printing, which did not contain road revision, overprinted for training purposes, and 5750 copies on the new 1206 base map published in 1949, incorporating 1948 road revision; 5700 was the print run number entered on the OS catalogue card. 2. An unpriced civilian "A//*" printing has not been recorded. 3. The "5" for the month appears to have been added by hand.

Sheet 150 *Ipswich*

1	5	6	7	8	9	10	11	12	13	14	15	16
1169	5/-	6	4620	WOE	WO	1949	no code	OS	p	aT	BL-d	1
1207	5/-	6	4620	WOE	WO	1949	6200/8/49	OS	p‡	a	BL-d	1
1207	5/-	6	4620	WOE	WO	1949	15,000/6/50	OS	p-	a	BL-d	2
nc	np	6	4620	1-G	WO	1954	10,000/1/55 OS	OS	p	b	BL-d	3
A/	3/6	7	M722	2-G	DSW	1961	10,000/9/61/6278/OS	OS	r	mo	Wc	
A//	np	7	M722	2-G	DSW	1961	15,000/7/64/6642/OS	OS	r	m	DGC	
A//	np	7	M722	2-G	DSM	1967	11,000/11/67/6984/OS	OS	r.	d	Wc	
B	np	7	M722	3-G	DSM	1969	5/69/7413/OS	OS	r.	d	Ob	
B	np	7	M722	3-G	DSM	1969	9/71/8289/OS	OS	r.	m	Ob	
B	np	7	M722	3-G	DSM	1969	5/73/730057 S	OS	r.	m	BL-b	

1. The Military Survey catalogue card records the order for 15,000 copies, and notes its completion on 29 July 1949. This may have been a mix of copies from the 1169 civilian printing, which did not contain road revision, overprinted for training purposes, and 6200 copies on the new 1207 base map published in 1949, incorporating 1948 road revision; this was the print run entered on the OS catalogue card. 2. The civilian grid is deleted, and the OS publication date is 1946, not 1949. 3. Military Survey wrote to the OS on 22 October 1953 regarding surplus stock of 10,000 copies for overprinting, but it would seem none were available. A consequent print order for 10,000 Second Edition copies was placed on 26 November 1953, which was perhaps completed as this issue.

Sheet 151 *Pembroke*

1	5	6	7	8	9	10	11	12	13	14	15	16
nc	5/-	6	4620	WOE	WO	1949	15,000/7/49	OS	p	a	BL-d	
20046	5/-	6	4620	WOE	WO	1949	2800/1/52	OS	p	ac	BL-d	
4009	2/6	7	4620	2-G	WO	1951	20,000/6/52	OS	b	mo	BL-d	
A//	3/6	7	M722	3-G	DSW	1960	15,000/5/60/6020/OS	OS	r	mo	BL-b	
A//	3/6	7	M722	3-G	DSW	1960	10,000/9/62/6388/OS	OS	r	m	DGC	
A//	4/6	7	M722	3-G	DSW	1960	9000/1/64/6588/OS	OS	r	?d	NLS	1

1. A six colour printing, apparently intended for both military and civilian markets, though in the event the civilian quota was not printed. For the continuation of the sequence see sheet 138/151.

Sheet 152 *Carmarthen and Tenby*

1	5	6	7	8	9	10	11	12	13	14	15	16
nc	5/-	6	4620	WOE	WO	1949	15,000/8/49	OS	p	a	BL-d	
		6	4620	?2-G			1100		p	?b	card	1
nc	2/6	7	4620	2-G	WO	1952	20,000/6/52	OS	b	mo	BL-d	2
B//	3/6	7	M722	3-G	DSW	1961	20,000/9/61/6118/OS	OS	r	mo	BL-b	
C	np	7	M722	4-G	DSM	1966	15,000/6/66/6826/OS	OS	r.	d	DGC	
C	np	7	M722	4-G	DSM	1966	3/71/8151/OS	OS	r.	m	BL-a	

1. This reprint was completed by 9 May 1952. Not found. 2. One of the earliest printings to use the Seventh Series base map, completed 23 June 1952.

1	5	6	7	8	9	10	11	12	13	14	15	16

Sheet 153 *Swansea*

1	5	6	7	8	9	10	11	12	13	14	15	16
1078	5/-	6	4620	WOE	WO	1949	15,000/7/49	OS	p	a	BL-d	
1078	5/-	6	4620	WOE	WO	1949	13,100/4/52	OS	p	ac	PC	1
1250	10/6	6	4620	WOE	WO	1949	13,100/4/52	OS	p	ac	Lu	1
nc	np	7	4620	2-G	WO	1955	25,000/5/55 OS	OS	r	mo	BL-d	
B/*	4/6	7	M722	3-G	DSW	1964	6000/1/64/6588/OS	OS	r	d	DGC	2
B/*	4/6	7	M722	3-G	DSW	1964	6000/1/64/6588/OS	OS	r	d	Ob	
B/*	np	7	M722	3-G	DSW	1964	9000/2/65/6684/OS	OS	r	m	DGC	
C	np	7	M722	4-G	DSM	1966	18,000/2/66/6778/OS	OS	r	m	Ob	
C	np	7	M722	4-G	DSM	1966	1/71/8094/OS	OS	r.	m	DGC	
D	DR	7	M722	5-G	DSM	1972	8/72/8469/OS	OS	r.	m	Ob	

An OS catalogue card has a note of two proofs, with "W O Grid". If made, these may tally with "Three proofs from O.S. of experimental combinations of colours", noted on a Military Survey catalogue card as received on 19 May 1952. 1. An example of the stock of two civilian print runs being used for a single military printing. 2. Lacking the submarine contours note.

Sheet 154 *Cardiff*

1	5	6	7	8	9	10	11	12	13	14	15	16
1079	5/-	6	4620	WOE	WO	1949	15,000/8/49	OS	p	a	BL-d	1
		6	4620				700		p		card	2
nc	2/6	7	4620	2-G	WO	1952	20,000/6/52	OS	b	mo	BL-d	
B/	3/6	7	M722	3-G	DSW	1961	20,000/4/61/6118/OS	OS	r	mo	BL-b	
B/	4/6	7	M722	3-G	DSW	1961	9000/1/64/6588/OS	OS	r	d	DGC	
C	np	7	M722	4-G	DSM	1965	20,000/12/65/6747/OS	OS	r	d	Ob	
C/*	np	7	M722	5-G	DSM	1969	9/69/7444/OS	OS	r.	d	Ob	
D	np	7	M722	6-G	DSM	1972	9/72/8757/OS	OS	r.	d	Ob	

See figure 16. 1. Unusually for a first issue, the magnetic variation date was advanced, to 1 June 1949. 2. This reprint was completed by 8 May 1952. No record copies were kept. Not found.

Sheet 155 *Bristol and Newport*

1	5	6	7	8	9	10	11	12	13	14	15	16
nc	5/-	6	4620	WOE	WO	1949	18,000/9/49	OS	p‡	a	BL-d	
1080	10/6	6	4620	2-G	WO	1951	30,000/7/51	OS	p‡	b	BL-d	1
30046	5/-	6	4620	WOE	WO	1949	4200/4/52	OS	p	ac	Wc	
4020	np	7	4620	3-G	WO	1955	25,000/5/55 OS	OS	r	mo	BL-d	
A//	4/6	7	M722	3-G	DSW	1955	10,000/6/62/6388/OS	OS	r	m	BL-b	
A//	4/6	7	M722	3-G	DSW	1955	25,000/11/63/6581/OS	OS	r	d	Cu-m	
A///*	np	7	M722	4-G	DSM	1966	13,000/7/66/6849/OS	OS	r.	d	Ob	
B	np	7	M722	5-G	DSM	1967	20,000/8/67/6924/OS	OS	r.	d	BL-b	
B	np	7	M722	5-G	DSM	1967	1/70/7589/OS	OS	r.	d	Ob	
C	np	7	M722	6-G	DSM	1972	7/72/8758/OS	OS	r.	d	Ob	

For further use see Exercises *Father Tiber, Surprise Packet* in supplement 4. 1. 15,000 copies were overprinted for use in GSGS Misc.1560 *Exercise Surprise Packet.*

Sheet 156 *Bristol and Stroud*

1	5	6	7	8	9	10	11	12	13	14	15	16
1185	5/-	6	4620	WOE	WO	1947	15,000/10/47	OS	p‡	a	BL-d	
1185	5/-	6	4620	WOE	WO	1947	10,000/8/50	OS	p‡	a	BL-d	
1254	10/6	6	4620	2-G	WO	1951	20,000/6/51	OS	p‡	b	BL-d	1
1254	10/6	6	4620	2-G	WO	1951	20,000/4/52	OS	p‡	b	BL-d	
1254	10/6	6	4620	2-G	WO	1951	1200/10/54 OS	OS	p	bc	BL-d	
nc	np	7	4620	3-G	WO	1955	30,000/11/55 OS	OS	r	mo	BL-d	
nc	np	7	4620	3-G	WO	1955	15,000/2/62/4427/R	1 SPC RE	r	mo	BL-d	
A///	4/6	7	M722	4-G	DSW	1963	20,000/11/63/6581/OS	OS	r	d	Cu-m	
A///	np	7	M722	4-G	DSW	1963	20,000/8/66/357/OA	BAOR	r	m	DGC	
B	np	7	M722	5-G	DSM	1967	32,000/11/67/6938/OS	OS	r.	d	BL-b	
B	np	7	M722	5-G	DSM	1967	7/71/8109/OS	OS	r.	d	DGC	
C	DR	7	M722	6-G	DSM	1972	4/72/8465/OS	OS	r.	d	Ob	

For further use see Exercises *Father Tiber, Surprise Packet* in supplement 4. 1. The printing record is obscure, with the initial demand for 20,000 copies reduced to 15,000, and the instruction that all 15,000 were to be overprinted for use in GSGS Misc.1560 *Exercise Surprise Packet.* However, the evidence of the print codes is that just over 10,000 copies were overprinted.

Sheet 157 *Swindon*

1	5	6	7	8	9	10	11	12	13	14	15	16
1147	5/-	6	4620	WOE	WO	1948	15,000/5/48	OS	p‡	a	BL-d	1
nc	5/-	6	4620	WOE	WO	1948	10,000/8/50	OS	p‡	a	BL-d	
1273	10/6	6	4620	2-G	WO	1951	25,000/8/51	OS	p	b	BL-d	2
1273	10/6	6	4620	2-G	WO	1951	25,000/1/52	OS	p	b	BL-d	3
1273	np	6	4620	2-G	WO	1951	30,000/2/55 OS	OS	p	b	BL-d	
A	3/6	7	M722	3-G	DSW	1961	20,000/2/61/6236/OS	OS	r	mo	BL-b	
A/	np	7	M722	3-G	DSM	1964	20,000/6/64/6626/OS	OS	r	d	BL-b	
A/	np	7	M722	3-G	DSM	1964	30,000/10/66/348/OA	BAOR	r	m	DGC	
B	np	7	M722	4-G	DSM	1968	1/68/7059/OS	OS	r.	d	BL-a	
B/*	DR	7	M722	5-G	DSM	1972	7/72/8751/OS	OS	r.	d	Ob	

For further use see supplement 1, Exercises *Orw...*, *Surprise Packet* in supplement 4, supplement 7. 1. The 1147 printing, published in July 1948, incorporates 1947 road revision. 2. The printing record is obscure, with the initial demand for 20,000 copies reduced to 15,000, and the instruction that all 15,000 were to be overprinted for use in GSGS Misc.1560 *Exercise Surprise Packet*. However, the evidence of the print codes is that 25,000 were actually printed of which 13,000 copies were overprinted. 3. Copies are recorded on civilian weight paper.

Sheet 158 *Oxford and Newbury*

1	5	6	7	8	9	10	11	12	13	14	15	16
1148	5/-	6	4620	WOE	WO	1948	15,000/5/48	OS	p‡	a	PC	1
		6	4620				10,000		p		card	2
1265	10/6	6	4620	2-G	WO	1951	30,000/7/51	OS	p	b	BL-d	3
nc	10/6	6	4620	2-G	WO	1951	20,000/7/52	OS	p	b	BL-d	
nc	np	6	4620	2-G	WO	1948	30,000/11/55 OS (blue)	OS	p	b	BL-d	
A	3/6	7	M722	3-G	DSW	1960	30,000/5/60/6022/OS	OS	r	mo	BL-b	
A/*	4/6	7	M722	4-G	DSW	1964	30,000/1/64/6590/OS	OS	r	m	Ob	
A/*	np	7	M722	4-G	DSM	1966	30,000/6/66/6822/OS	OS	r.	m	Wc	
B	np	7	M722	5-G	DSM	1967	60,000/6/67/6938/OS	OS	r.	d	BL-b	

For further use see supplements 1, Exercise *Surprise Packet* in supplement 4, supplements 7, 8. 1. The 1148 printing, published in July 1948, incorporates 1947 road revision. The neat lines are extended to the outer frame. 2. This reprint was completed by 24 May 1950. Not found. 3. 13,000 copies were overprinted for use in GSGS Misc.1560 *Exercise Surprise Packet*; the printing record notes 15,000 copies.

Sheet 159 *The Chilterns*

1	5	6	7	8	9	10	11	12	13	14	15	16
1202	5/-	6	4620	WOE	WO	1949	1500/1/49	OS	p‡	a	BL-d	1
1159	5/-	6	4620	WOE	WO	1949	27,000/3/49	OS	p‡	a	BL-d	2
nc	10/6	6	4620	2-G	WO	1951	25,000/7/51	OS	p	b	BL-d	3
nc	10/6	6	4620	2-G	WO	1951	25,000/6/52	OS	p	b	BL-d	
nc	np	6	4620	2-G	WO	1951	30,000/1/56 OS	OS	p	b	BL-d	
A/*	4/6	7	M722	3-G	DSW	1962	30,000/2/62/4427/R	1 SPC RE	r	mo	BL-b	4
A/*//*	np	7	M722	4-G	DSM	1964	25,000/11/64/6681/OS	OS	r	d	Ob	
A/*//*	np	7	M722	4-G	DSM	1964	20,000/1/66/6795/OS	OS	r	m	DGC	
B	np	7	M722	5-G	DSM	1969	8/69/7534/OS	OS	r.	m	Ob	
B	np	7	M722	5-G	DSM	1969	11/72/8490/OS	OS	r.	d	Ob	

For further use see supplements 1, Exercise *Surprise Packet* in supplement 4, supplements 7, 8. 1. The standard initial demand for 25,000 copies was not fulfilled. But the immediate requirements of the Staff College were met by a short print run on the unrevised 1202 printing. 2. This issue (on the 1159 printing, published in 1949 incorporating 1947 road revision) combines the standard demand for 25,000 copies, and a special order of 2000 copies, stipulating the revised edition, for the Staff College. It was completed on 8 April 1949. 3. 15,000 copies were overprinted for use in GSGS Misc.1560 *Exercise Surprise Packet*. 4. Projection and grid data and magnetic information are added in red.

Sheet 160 a. *London N.W.* b. *London NW*

1	5	6	7	8	9	10	11	12	13	14	15	16
1160	5/-	6a	4620	WOE	WO	1949	17,000/5/49	OS	p	a	BL-d	1
1160	5/-	6a	4620	WOE	WO	1949	5000/6/50	OS	p	a	BL-d	
1232	10/6	6a	4620	1-G	WO	1949	10,000/1/51	OS	p	a	BL-d	
1232	10/6	6a	4620	2-G	WO	1952	25,000/5/52	OS	p	b	BL-d	
nc	np	6a	4620	2-G	WO	1952	30,000/5/56 OS	OS	p	b	BL-d	

1	5	6	7	8	9	10	11	12	13	14	15	16
A//	3/6	7b	M722	3-G	DSW	1961	30,000/1/62/4368/R	1 SPC RE	r	mo	DGC	2
A//	3/6	7b	M722	3-G	DSW	1961	30,000/1/62/4368/R	1 SPC RE	r	mo	BL-b	3
B	np	7b	M722	4-G	DSM	1965	30,000/1/65/6693/OS	OS		r	m	DGC
B/*	np	7b	M722	5-G	DSM	1967	15,000/10/67/6962/OS	OS		r.	d	Ob
B/*	np	7b	M722	5-G	DSM	1967	6/68/7122/OS	OS		r.	m	BL-b
C	np	7b	M722	6-G	DSM	1970	8/70/7980/OS	OS		r.	d	Ob

For further use see Exercise *Tinder Box* in supplement 4. 1. This issue (on the 1160 printing, published in July 1949 incorporating 1948 road revision) combines the standard demand for 15,000 copies with, in addition, a special order of 2000 copies for the Staff College. It was completed on 16 June 1949. 2. Projection and grid data and magnetic information are overprinted in red, the grid data with the erroneous heading *Universal Transverse Mercator*. 3. The grid data heading is corrected to *National Grid*.

Sheet 161 a. *London, N.E.* b. *London NE*

1	5	6	7	8	9	10	11	12	13	14	15	16
1149	5/-	6a	4620	WOE	WO	1947	15,000/11/47	OS		p‡	a	BL-d	1
1149	5/-	6a	4620	1-G	WO	1947	15,000/11/50	OS		p‡	a	BL-d
1255	np	6a	4620	2-G	WO	1952	30,000/12/52	OS		p‡	b	BL-d
A/	4/6	7b	M722	3-G	DSW	1961	25,000/10/61/6309/OS	OS		r	m	Cu-m
B	np	7b	M722	4-G	DSM	1964	65,000/10/64/6593/OS	OS		r	d	Ob
B/*	np	7b	M722	5-G	DSM	1967	10,000/10/67/6962/OS	OS		r.	d	BL-b
C	np	7b	M722	6-G	DSM	1970	70/3670/OS	OS		r.	d	Ob

For further use see Exercise *Tinder Box* in supplement 4. 1. The 1149 printing, not available to the public until April 1948, incorporates 1946 roads revision.

Sheet 162 a. *Southend-on-Sea* b. *Southend on Sea*

1	5	6	7	8	9	10	11	12	13	14	15	16
note	5/-	6a	4620	WOE	WO	1949	no code	OS		p	aT	BL-d	1
1197	5/-	6a	4620	WOE	WO	1949	12,000/7/49	OS		p‡	a	BL-d	1
1197	5/-	6a	4620	1-G	WO	1949	10,000/4/51	OS		p	ac	BL-d	2
1274	np	6b	4620	2-G	WO	1953	15,000/1/53	OS		p‡	b	BL-d
nc	np	6b	4620	2-G	DSW	1957	10,000/6/57	OS		p‡	b	BL-d
A/	3/6	7a	M722	3-G	DSW	1962	20,000/11/62/6391/OS	OS		r	m	DGC
A//*	np	7a	M722	4-G	DSM	1965	15,000/7/65/6718/OS	OS		r	m	Ob
B	np	7a	M722	5-G	DSM	1969	7/69/7467/OS	OS		r.	d	Ob
B	DR	7a	M722	5-G	DSM	1969	7/72/8700/OS	OS		r.	d	Ob

For further use see Exercise *Tinder Box* in supplement 4. 1. The Military Survey catalogue card records the order for 15,000 copies, and notes its completion on 8 July 1949. This may have been a mix of copies from the 20046/7/46 Wa civilian printing, which did not contain road revision, overprinted for training purposes, and 12,000 copies on the new 1197 base map published in 1949, incorporating the 1948 road revision; however 17,000 was the print run entered on the Ordnance Survey catalogue card. 2. The Military Survey catalogue card records this as Second Edition, but, however, does not record it as overprinted civilian stock, which the quality of the paper used suggests it to be.

Sheet 163 *Barnstaple*

1	5	6	7	8	9	10	11	12	13	14	15
1195	5/-	6	4620	WOE	WO	1947	15,000/3/48	OS		p‡	a	BL-d
1237	10/6	6	4620	1-G	WO	1947	20,000/4/51	OS		p‡	a	BL-d
E/	np	6	M722	2-G	DSW	1957	10,000/7/58/5748/OS	OS		p‡	b	BL-d
A	3/6	7	M722	3-G	DSW	1961	30,000/7/61/6309/OS	OS		r	m	Cu-m
A	4/6	7	M722	3-G	DSW	1961	15,000/9/63/6565/OS	OS		r	d	DGC
B	np	7	M722	4-G	DSM	1967	22,000/3/67/6882/OS	OS		r.	m	BL-b
B	np	7	M722	4-G	DSM	1967	10/71/8352/OS	OS		r.	m	Ob
C	DR	7	M722	4-G	DSM	1967	4/72/8658/OS	OS		r.	d	Ob

Sheet 164 *Minehead*

1	5	6	7	8	9	10	11	12	13	14	15
1190	5/-	6	4620	WOE	WO	1947	15,000/1/48	OS		p‡	a	BL-d
1190	5/-	6	4620	1-G	WO	1947	20,000/4/51	OS		p‡	a	BL-d
1303	np	6	4620	2-G	DSW	1957	10,000/10/57/5510/OS	OS		p‡	b	BL-d
A	3/6	7	M722	3-G	DSW	1961	15,000/3/61/6223/OS	OS		r	mo	BL-b
A	4/6	7	M722	3-G	DSW	1961	27,000/11/63/6571/OS	OS		r	m	Cu-m
B	np	7	M722	4-G	DSM	1966	40,000/10/66/6826/OS	OS		r.	d	BL-b
C	DR	7	M722	5-G	DSM	1972	6/72/8745/OS	OS		r.	d	Ob

For further use see Exercises *Post Haste* in supplement 4.

1	5	6	7	8	9	10	11	12	13	14	15	16

Sheet 165 *Weston-super-Mare*

1	5	6	7	8	9	10	11	12	13	14	15	16
1213	5/-	6	4620	WOE	WO	1949	15,000/8/49	OS	p‡	a	BL-d	
1223	10/6	6	4620	WOE	WO	1949	10,000/10/50	OS	p	a	BL-d	
1223	10/6	6	4620	2-G	WO	1951	20,000/7/51	OS	p	b	BL-d	1
nc	np	6	4620	2-G	WO	1951	20,000/10/54 OS	OS	p	b	BL-d	2
A	3/6	7	M722	3-G	DSW	1960	20,000/7/60/6223/OS	OS	r	mo	BL-b	
A/	np	7	M722	3-G	DSW	1960	10,000/9/64/6642/OS	OS	r	m	Wc	
A//*	np	7	M722	3-G	DSW	1960	15,000/2/65/6642/OS	OS	r	d	Ob	
A//*	np	7	M722	3-G	DSM	1960	4/68/7104/OS	OS	r.	d	Cu-m	
B	np	7	M722	4-G	DSM	1971	7/71/8219/OS	OS	r.	d	Ob	
B	np	7	M722	4-G	DSM	1971	9/72/711936 S	OS	r.	d	Ob	
B	np	7	M722	4-G	DSM	1971	7/73/731227 S	OS	r.	d	DGC	

For further use see Exercises *Father Tiber, Surprise Packet* in supplement 4. 1. The WOPD has been altered, apparently to 25,000 copies. However the OS record card gives the figure 20,000, as does the print code. 15,000 copies were overprinted for use in GSGS Misc.1560 *Exercise Surprise Packet*. 2. Military Survey wrote to the OS on 22 October 1953 regarding surplus stock of 20,000 copies for overprinting, but it would seem none were available. Consequently a print order for 20,000 Second Edition copies was placed on 5 February 1954.

Sheet 166 *Frome*

1	5	6	7	8	9	10	11	12	13	14	15	16
1178	5/-	6	4620	WOE	WO	1947	15,000/10/47	OS	p‡	a	BL-d	
1178	5/-	6	4620	WOE	WO	1947	10,000/6/50	OS	p‡	a	BL-d	
1178	5/-	6	4620	2-G	WO	1951	15,000/7/51	OS	p‡	b	BL-d	1
1178	5/-	6	4620	2-G	WO	1951	20,000/10/51	OS	p‡	b	BL-d	
nc	np	6	4620	2-G	WO	1951	20,000/10/54 OS	OS	p‡	b	BL-d	2
nc	np	6	4620	2-G	DSW	1956	20,000/4/57	OS	p‡	b	BL-d	
A	3/6	7	M722	3-G	DSW	1960	20,000/9/60/6223/OS	OS	r	mo	BL	
A	4/6	7	M722	3-G	DSW	1962	4000/8/62/6388/OS	OS	r	mc	Wc	
A	3/6	7	M722	3-G	DSW	1960	2500/7/63/248/SPC	SPC RE	r	mo	DGC	
A/	4/6	7	M722	3-G	DSW	1962	35,000/7/63/6545/OS	OS	r	d	DGC	
A//*	np	7	M722	4-G	DSM	1966	40,000/12/66/6842/OS	OS	r.	d	BL-b	
A//*	np	7	M722	4-G	DSM	1966	5/71/8191/OS	OS	r.	m	DGC	
B	DR	7	M722	5-G	DSM	1972	1/72/8535/OS	OS	r.	d	Ob	
B	np	7	M722	5-G	DSM	1972	7/73/731829 S	OS	r.	m	BL-a	

For further use see supplements 1, 2, Exercises *Father Tiber, Life Line, Pons Sublicius, Surprise Packet* in supplement 4, supplements 5, 7. 1. All stock copies were overprinted for use in GSGS Misc.1560 *Exercise Surprise Packet*. 2. Military Survey wrote to the OS on 22 October 1953 regarding surplus stock of 20,000 copies for overprinting, but it would seem none were available. Consequently a print order for 20,000 Second Edition copies was placed on 5 February 1954.

Sheet 167 a. *Salisbury Plain* b. *Salisbury*

The title *Salisbury Plain* was adopted for New Popular (or Sixth) Edition issues, wherein mapping was extended west between Warminster and Westbury to allow complete coverage of the War Department lands. The boundary is overprinted in red on Cassini Grid issues. On National Grid issues this feature was transferred to GSGS Misc.433, later GSGS 4974: these maps are listed in supplement 3. Cassini Grid issues have an adjoining sheet diagram showing *Salisbury Plain* set against the Popular Edition sheet lines of GSGS 3907; the diagram on National Grid issues shows the layout of the New Popular Edition centred on an unnumbered sheet entitled *Salisbury Plain*, complete with the extrusion to the west.

With War Office Cassini Grid

1	5	6	7	8	9	10	11	12	13	14	15	16
nc	np	6a	4620	-	WO	1946	12,000/5/46 Wa	OS		br	BL-d	1,2
nc	np	6a	4620	-	WO	1946	6000/7/47	OS		br	BL-d	1,3
nc	np	6a	4620	-	WO	1946	3000/7/49	OS		br	card	1,3

With National Grid

1	5	6	7	8	9	10	11	12	13	14	15	16
nc	np	6a	4620	WOE	WO	1948	15,000/11/48	OS		p a	BL-d	4
nc	np	6a	4620	WOE	WO	1948	10,000/6/50	OS		p a	BL-d	4,5
nc	np	6a	4620	1-G	WO	1948	20,000/2/51	OS		p a	BL-d	6
nc	np	6a	4620	2-G	WO	1951	15,000/7/51	OS		p b	BL-d	7
nc	np	6a	4620	2-G	WO	1951	30,000/10/51	OS		p b	BL-d	
nc	np	6a	4620	2-G	WO	1951	20,000/2/54 OS	OS		p b	BL-d	8
nc	np	6a	4620	2-G	WO	1951	30,000/1/55 OS	OS		p b	BL-d	
nc	np	6a	4620	2-G	DSW	1957	30,000/5/57	OS		p b	BL-d	9

235

1	5	6	7	8	9	10	11	12	13	14	15	16
nc	np	6a	M722	3-G	DSW	1957	30,000/10/58/5748/OS	OS	p	b	Ob	9
A	3/6	7b	M722	4-G	DSW	1960	30,000/9/60/6223/OS	OS	r	mo	DGC	
A	3/6	7b	M722	4-G	DSW	1960	10,000/2/62/6388/OS	OS	r	m	DGC	
A	3/6	7b	M722	4-G	DSW	1960	25,000/4/63/6516/OS	OS	r	m	Wc	
A/*	4/6	7b	M722	4-G	DSW	1960	95,000/11/63/6581/OS	OS	r	d	Cu-m	
A/*	np	7b	M722	4-G	DSM	1960	3/68/7070/OS	OS	r.	m	Ob	
B	np	7b	M722	5-G	DSM	1971	2/71/8133/OS	OS	r.	d	Ob	10
B	np	7b	M722	5-G	DSM	1971	9/71/8459/OS	OS	r.	c	BL-b	11
B/*	np	7b	M722	5-G	DSM	1971	9/71/8458/OS	OS	r.	d	Ob	12

New Popular Edition issues have no legends, and scale bars are placed centrally, perhaps in order to accommodate detail relating to the various overprints that were required of this sheet. For further use see supplements 1, 2, GSGS Misc.433, GSGS 4974, GSGS 5177 in supplement 3, Exercises *Life Line, Pons Sublicius, Surprise Packet* and unnamed in supplement 4, supplements 5, 6, 7, 8; also section 2, supplements 3 and 4. **1**. Without sheet number. **2**. Showing War Department lands, revised to March 1946. **3**. Showing War Department lands, revised to March 1947. See figure 14. **4**. The civilian publication date is 1940, with full revision 1934 and roads revision 1947. The magnetic variation date is 1 January 1949. This revision only became available to the public in the 1150 printing published in July 1949. **5**. 200 copies were to be collected from Crabwood by the School of Artillery on 15 June 1950. **6**. The civilian publication date is altered to 1948. **7**. The magnetic variation date is altered to 1 January 1950. The Military Survey card catalogue includes the note that all copies were to be overprinted for use in GSGS Misc.1560 *Exercise Surprise Packet;* in the event it seems that only 13,000 were. **8**. Military Survey wrote to the OS on 22 October 1953 regarding surplus stock of 20,000 copies for overprinting, but it would seem none were available. Consequently this print order for 20,000 Second Edition copies was placed on 5 February 1954. **9**. Some copies were overprinted in red with GSGS Misc.433 *Salisbury Plain P.T.A.* It was usual for this map to have its own base map printed specially. **10**. A printing intended both for military and civilian use, inadvertently showing public footpaths across live firing ranges. **11**. See note 10. This was the remnant of the civilian stock, hastily withdrawn from public sale and overprinted for military use. It was replaced by edition B/*. **12**. Public footpaths are shown to the edge of the live firing ranges, but not across them.

Sheet 168 *Winchester*

1	5	6	7	8	9	10	11	12	13	14	15	16
note	5/-	6	4620	WOE	WO	1949	1000/1/49	OS	p	ac	BL-d	1
note	5/-	6	4620	WOE	WO	1949	no code	OS	p	aT	PC	2
1162	5/-	6	4620	WOE	WO	1949	17,000/3/49 (blue)	OS	p	a	PC	3,4
1162	5/-	6	4620	WOE	WO	1949	17,000/3/49 (blue)	OS	p	a	BL-d	3,5
1162	5/-	6	4620	WOE	WO	1949	17,000/3/49 (purple)	OS	p	a	BL	3,6
1162	5/-	6	4620	WOE	WO	1949	15,000/6/50	OS	p	a	BL-d	
1162	5/-	6	4620	2-G	WO	1951	15,000/7/51	OS	p	b	BL-d	7
1162	5/-	6	4620	2-G	WO	1951	30,000/10/51	?HDA	p	b	BL-d	8
nc	np	6	4620	2-G	WO	1951	20,000/10/54 OS	OS	p	b	BL-d	
nc	np	6	4620	2-G	WO	1951	30,000/3/56 OS	OS	p	b	BL-d	
A	3/6	7	M722	3-G	DSW	1960	7500/5/60/6022/OS	OS	r	mo	DGC	
A	3/6	7	M722	3-G	DSW	1960	20,000/11/60/4314/R	1 SPC RE	r	mo	Wc	
A	3/6	7	M722	3-G	DSW	1960	25,000/5/62/4492/R	1 SPC RE	r	mo	BL-b	
A/*	4/6	7	M722	3-G	DSW	1963	59,000/7/63/6546/OS	OS	r	d	NLS	
A/*	np	7	M722	3-G	DSW	1963	7/70/8032/OS	OS	r	m	DGC	
B	np	7	M722	4-G	DSM	1971	1/71/8134/OS	OS	r.	d	Ob	
B/*	np	7	M722	5-G	DSM	1971	8/72/8746/OS	OS	r.	d	Ob	
B/*	np	7	M722	5-G	DSM	1971	10/73/732125 S	OS	r.	m	DGC	

For further use see supplements 1, 2, Exercises *Surprise Packet* and unnamed in supplement 4, supplements 6, 8. **1**. The standard initial demand for 15,000 copies was not fulfilled. But the immediate requirements of the Staff College were met, perhaps by overprinting 1000 copies of the unrevised civilian 25,000/6/46 Wa printing. **2**. It is possible that additional civilian stock from the same print run was commandeered for training purposes. **3**. These three issues (on the 1162 printing, published in 1949 incorporating 1947 road revision) are interrelated, and represent the standard requirement of 15,000 copies with, in addition, a special order of 2000 copies, stipulating the revised edition, for the Staff College. It was completed on 8 April 1949. Some copies were run off with print codes reflecting these individual requirements, but were probably not released before being overprinted with the combined total. Thus: **4**. The 17,000/3/49 code is on the blue plate, with 15,000/3/49 on the purple. **5**. The 17,000/3/49 print code is on the blue plate, with 2000/3/49 crossed through. **6**. Additional copies were required bring the total up to 17,000. **7**. All stock copies were overprinted for GSGS Misc.1560 *Exercise Surprise Packet.* **8**. This printing is not present on the OS catalogue card, and the Military Survey catalogue card requested 30,000 copies by 1 November 1951 for 8 FSD from the Hydrographic Department, Admiralty. The rather coarse printing suggests that this may indeed have been the case.

Sheet 169 *Aldershot*

With War Office Cassini Grid

1	5	6	7	8	9	10	11	12	13	14	15	16
nc	np	6	4620	-	WO	1946	10,000/10/46	OS	b		BL-d	1
nc	np	6	4620	-	WO	1946	6000/5/47	OS	b		BL-d	1
nc	np	6	4620	-	WO	1946	300/3/48	OS	-		BL-d	1,2
nc	np	6	4620	-	WO	1946	2000/4/49	OS	b		BL-d	1

With National Grid

1	5	6	7	8	9	10	11	12	13	14	15	16
1125	5/-	6	4620	WOE	WO	1949	650/1/49	OS	p	ac	BL-d	3
1125	5/-	6	4620	WOE	WO	1949	no code	OS	p	aT	BL-d	4
1151	5/-	6	4620	WOE	WO	1949	17,000/3/49	OS	p	a	BL-d	5
1151	5/-	6	4620	WOE	WO	1949	5000/5/50	OS	p	a	BL-d	6
1151	5/-	6	4620	WOE	WO	1949	5000/7/50	OS	p	a	Wc	6
1256	10/6	6	4620	1-G	WO	1949	20,000/4/51	OS	p	a	BL-d	7
nc	10/6	6	4620	1-G	WO	1949	10,000/5/51	OS	p	a	Ob	7,8
1281	np	6	4620	2-G	WO	1951	25,000/4/52	OS	p	b	BL-d	
nc	np	6	4620	2-G	WO	1951	30,000/1/54 OS	OS	p	b	BL-d	
nc	np	6	4620	2-G	WO	1951	30,000/4/55 OS	OS	p	b	BL-d	
nc	np	6	4620	2-G	DSW	1956	30,000/11/56 EP	1 SPC RE	p	b	BL-d	
F/	np	6	4620	2-G	DSW	1951	30,000/7/59/6006/OS	OS	p	b	BL-d	
A	np	7	M722	3-G	DSW	1961	15,000/7/61/6309/OS	OS	r	m	DGC	
A/	4/6	7	M722	3-G	DSW	1961	20,000/4/62/6415/OS	OS	r	d	DGC	
A/	4/6	7	M722	3-G	DSW	1961	40,000/8/63/6545/OS	OS	r	m	BL-b	
A//*	np	7	M722	3-G	DSW	1961	40,000/5/65/6720/OS	OS	r	d	Wc	
A//*	np	7	M722	3 G	DSM	1967	11,000/1/68/6975/OS	OS	r.	m	BL-a	
A//*	np	7	M722	3-G	DSM	1967	8/68/7142/OS	OS	r.	m	Ob	
B	np	7	M722	4-G	DSM	1971	2/71/8135/OS	OS	r.	d	Ob	
B/*	DR	7	M722	5-G	DSM	1972	1/72/8437/OS	OS	r.	d	Ob	
B/*	np	7	M722	5-G	DSM	1972	5/73/730882 S	OS	r.	d	DGC	

For further use see supplement 1, Exercise *Surprise Packet* in supplement 4, supplements 5, 6, 8; also section 2, supplement 4. **1**. Without sheet number. The adjoining sheet diagram shows *Aldershot* set against the Popular Edition sheet lines of GSGS 3907. **2**. Outline edition in grey, retaining the Cassini Grid values (from the blue plate), though not the grid. **3**. The standard initial demand for 15,000 copies was not fulfilled. But the immediate requirements of the Staff College were met, perhaps by overprinting 650 copies of the unrevised civilian 1125 printing. **4**. It is possible that additional civilian stock from the same print run was commandeered for training purposes. **5**. This issue (on the 1151 printing, published in July 1949 incorporating 1947 road revision) combines the standard demand for 15,000 copies with, in addition, a special order of 2000 copies, stipulating the revised edition, for the Staff College. It was completed on 8 April 1949. **6**. The reprint ordered on 16 March 1950 was for 5000 copies, later adjusted to 15,000. 5000 were required by 17 May, the remaining 10,000 in three months, by 17 August. The first lot was completed on 9 June, the second lot, which, judging by the print codes was in the event also only 5000 copies, were completed and awaiting collection by 28 August. There is no mention in the printing record to a third batch to complete the 15,000. **7**. The reprint ordered on 13 December 1950 was for 20,000 copies, later adjusted to 30,000, 5000 of which were to be for overprinting. The order was evidently completed in two batches. **8**. So far only recorded overprinted for use in GSGS Misc.1560 *Exercise Surprise Packet.*

Sheet 170 a. *London S.W.* b. *London SW*

1	5	6	7	8	9	10	11	12	13	14	15	16
1163	5/-	6a	4620	WOE	WO	1949	27,000/5/49	OS	p	a	BL-d	1
1230	10/6	6a	4620	1-G	WO	1949	15,000/11/50	OS	p	a	BL-d	
1287	10/6	6a	4620	2-G	WO	1952	25,000/5/52	OS	p	b	BL-d	
1287	np	6a	4620	2-G	WO	1952	30,000/3/55 OS	OS	p	b	BL-d	
A/	3/6	7b	M722	3-G	DSW	1960	20,000/6/60/6223/OS	OS	r	mo	DGC	
A///*	4/6	7b	M722	3-G	DSW	1960	20,000/4/62/6388/OS	OS	r	d	DGC	
A///*	4/6	7b	M722	3-G	DSW	1960	2000/11/63/6581/OS	OS	r	m	Wc	
A///*	np	7b	M722	3-G	DSW	1960	15,000/1/65/6693/OS	OS	r	m	Cu-m	
B	np	7b	M722	4-G	DSM	1965	25,000/11/65/6747/OS	OS	r	d	Ob	
B/*	np	7b	M722	5-G	DSM	1967	40,000/7/67/6916/OS	OS	r.	d	BL-b	
C	np	7b	M722	6-G	DSM	1970	70/7935/OS	OS	r.	d	Ob	
C	np	7b	M722	6-G	DSM	1970	7/73/731828 S	OS	r.	mc	DGC	

For further use see Exercise *Tinder Box* in supplement 4. **1**. This issue (on the 1163 printing, published in July 1949 incorporating 1948 road revision) combines the standard demand for 25,000 copies with, in addition, a special order of 2000 copies for the Staff College. It was completed on 16 June 1949.

Sheet 171 a. *London, S.E.* b. *London SE*

1	5	6	7	8	9	10	11	12	13	14	15	16
1152	5/-	6a	4620	WOE	WO	1947	15,000/10/47	OS	p‡	a	BL-d	1
1152	5/-	6a	4620	WOE	WO	1947	15,000/6/50	OS	p‡	a	BL-d	
nc	10/6	6a	4620	2-G	WO	1952	25,000/8/52	OS	p‡	b	BL-d	2
nc	np	6a	4620	2-G	WO	1952	30,000/5/55 OS	OS	p‡	b	BL-d	
A//	4/6	7b	M722	3-G	DSW	1962	30,000/7/62/6391/OS	OS	r	mc	DGC	
B	np	7b	M722	4-G	DSM	1964	50,000/11/64/6664/OS	OS	r	mc	Ob	
B/*	np	7b	M722	5-G	DSM	1969	12/68/7336/OS	OS	r.	d	Ob	
C	np	7b	M722	6-G	DSM	1970	70/7679/OS	OS	r.	d	Ob	

For further use see Exercises *Island Fling, Tinder Box* in supplement 4, supplement 5. 1. The 1152 printing, published in February 1948, incorporates 1946 roads revision. 2. This printing order was placed with SPC RE in April 1952, to whom the OS were requested to send printing plates. In the event this was cancelled and the work done by the OS.

Sheet 172 *Chatham and Maidstone*

1	5	6	7	8	9	10	11	12	13	14	15	16
nc	5/-	6	4620	WOE	WO	1948	15,000/2/48	OS	p‡	a	BL-d	1
1208	5/-	6	4620	WOE	WO	1948	5000/6/50	OS	p	a	BL-d	
1208	5/-	6	4620	2-G	WO	1951	20,000/4/52	OS	p	b	BL-d	
nc	np	6	4620	2-G	WO	1951	20,000/12/55 OS	OS	p	b	BL-d	
1293	10/6	6	M722	2-G	DSW	1960	8000/9/60/6247/OS	OS	p	bc	Ob	2
A/*	4/6	7	M722	3-G	DSW	1961	20,000/12/61/OS	OS	r	cx	BL-a	3
A/*//*	np	7	M722	4-G	DSM	1964	40,000/6/64/6633/OS	OS	r	d	Ob	4
B	np	7	M722	5-G	DSM	1970	70/7859/OS	OS	r.	d	Ob	

For further use see Exercises *Island Fling, Tinder Box* in supplement 4, supplement 8. 1. Presumably using the 1153 printing, published in March 1948, which incorporates 1946 road revision. 2. The final printing in this series on a New Popular Edition base map. 3. The A20(M) motorway is shown passing over rather than under the A249, an error that caused this civilian edition to be withdrawn from public sale and replaced by the corrected A/*/ edition. The remnant A/* stock was overprinted for military use, with a note cautioning users about the error: *At MR 777574 the A249 passes over the A20(M)*. 4. The edition number 3 is blocked out and altered to 4.

Sheet 173 *East Kent*

1	5	6	7	8	9	10	11	12	13	14	15	16
1184	5/-	6	4620	WOE	WO	1949	no code	OS	p	aT	BL-d	1
1164	5/-	6	4620	WOE	WO	1949	2500/7/49	OS	p	a	BL-d	1
1164	10/6	6	4620	1-G	WO	1949	10,000/1/51	OS	p	a	BL-d	
1280	10/6	6	4620	2-G	WO	1952	20,000/5/52	OS	p	b	BL-d	
nc	np	6	4620	2-G	WO	1952	30,000/2/55 OS	OS	p	b	BL-d	
A	3/6	7	M722	3-G	DSW	1960	10,000/6/60/6022/OS	OS	r	mo	DGC	
A	3/6	7	M722	3-G	DSW	1960	20,000/8/61/4385/R	1 SPC RE	r	mo	DGC	
A/	np	7	M722	3-G	DSW	1960	10,000/1/65/6693/OS	OS	r	m	DGC	
A//*	np	7	M722	3-G	DSM	1966	25,000/1/66/6787/OS	OS	r	d	BL-b	
B	np	7	M722	4-G	DSM	1969	6/69/7466/OS	OS	r.	d	Ob	
B	np	7	M722	4-G	DSM	1969	no code [SPO 8290/OS ms] OS	OS	r.	?d	Ob	2
B	np	7	M722	4-G	DSM	1969	5/73/722496 S	OS	r.	d	DGC	

For further use see GSGS Misc.1622, GSGS 4959 in supplement 3, Exercises *Island Fling, Tinder Box* in supplement 4, supplements 5, 8. 1. The Military Survey printing record in fact lists neither of these printings, but merely records a requirement of 15,000 sheets which was completed by 25 August 1949. It is probable that this was an unquantified printing on the unrevised 1184 issue, so given over to training, combined with an unusually small print run using the 1164 printing (published in July 1949), which incorporated 1947 road revision. The OS catalogue card endorses the print run of 2500 as printed in July 1949. 2. A copy in DGC has the code SPO 8290/OS added by hand.

Sheet 174 *Bude*

1	5	6	7	8	9	10	11	12	13	14	15	16
1191	5/-	6	4620	WOE	WO	1947	15,000/1/48	OS	p‡	a	BL-d	
1191	5/-	6	4620	1-G	WO	1947	10,000/3/51	OS	p‡	a	BL-d	
nc	np	6	4620	2-G	WO	1952	20,000/10/52	OS	p‡	b	BL-d	
A	3/6	7	M722	3-G	DSW	1962	20,000/12/61/6261/OS	OS	r	mc	BL-b	1
A/*	np	7	M722	3-G	DSM	1966	15,000/5/66/6810/OS	OS	r.	d	BL-b	
A/*	np	7	M722	3-G	DSM	1966	5/71/8190/OS	OS	r.	mc	DGC	
B	np	7	M722	4-G	DSM	1971	11/71/8438/OS	OS	r.	d	Ob	
B	np	7	M722	4-G	DSM	1971	3/73/721426/S	OS	r.	d	DGC	

1. A civilian printing with a 3/6 price statement has not been recorded.

1	5	6	7	8	9	10	11	12	13	14	15	16

Sheet 175 *Okehampton*

1	5	6	7	8	9	10	11	12	13	14	15	16
1212	5/-	6	4620	WOE	WO	1949	15,000/8/49	OS	p‡	a	BL-d	
1212	5/-	6	4620	1-G	WO	1949	10,000/ /51	OS	p‡	a	BL-d	
1270	10/6	6	4620	2-G	WO	1951	15,000/4/52	OS	p‡	b	BL-d	
nc	np	6	4620	2-G	WO	1951	20,000/5/55 OS	OS	p‡	b	BL-d	
A	3/6	7	M722	3-G	DSW	1960	20,000/10/60/6223/OS	OS	r	mo	BL-b	
A	3/6	7	M722	3-G	DSW	1960	10,000/2/62/6388/OS	OS	r	m	Wc	
A	4/6	7	M722	3-G	DSW	1960	25,000/7/63/6555/OS	OS	r	d	Wc	1
A/*	np	7	M722	4-G	DSM	1966	65,000/8/66/6824/OS	OS	r.	m	Ob	1
A/*	np	7	M722	4-G	DSM	1966	9/69/7590/OS	OS	r.	d	Ob	
B	DR	7	M722	5-G	DSM	1971	12/71/8439/OS	OS	r.	m	Ob	
B	np	7	M722	5-G	DSM	1971	5/73/722276 S	OS	r.	m	BL-b	
B	np	7	M722	5-G	DSM	1971	11/73/732787 S	OS	r.	d	DGC	

1. For further use see GSGS Misc.2042 in supplement 3.

Sheet 176 *Exeter*

1	5	6	7	8	9	10	11	12	13	14	15	16
1201	5/-	6	4620	WOE	WO	1947	15,000/11/48	OS	p‡	a	BL-d	
1275	10/6	6	4620	2-G	WO	1951	20,000/12/51	OS	p‡	b	BL-d	
1275	np	6	4620	2-G	WO	1951	20,000/1/55 OS	OS	p‡	b	BL-d	1
A	4/6	7	M722	3-G	DSW	1961	30,000/1/61/6295/OS	OS	r	mo	BL-b	
A	4/6	7	M722	3-G	DSW	1961	40,000/9/63/6565/OS	OS	r	d	Wc	
B	np	7	M722	4-G	DSM	1967	50,000/3/67/6882/OS	OS	r.	d	BL-b	
C	np	7	M722	5-G	DSM	1972	8/72/721767 S	OS	r.	d	Ob	
C	np	7	M722	5-G	DSM	1972	5/73/730008 S	OS	r.	m	DGC	

For further use see Exercise *Post Haste* in supplement 4. 1. Military Survey wrote to the OS on 22 October 1953 regarding surplus stock of 20,000 copies for overprinting, but it would seem none were available. Consequently a print order for 20,000 copies was placed on 5 February 1954.

Sheet 177 *Taunton and Lyme Regis*

1	5	6	7	8	9	10	11	12	13	14	15	16
1205	5/-	6	4620	WOE	WO	1948	15,000/12/48	OS	p‡	a	BL-d	
nc	10/6	6	4620	2-G	WO	1951	10,000/5/51	OS	p‡	b	PC	
1257	10/6	6	4620	2-G	WO	1951	15,000/7/51	OS	p‡	b	BL-d	1
nc	10/6	6	4620	2-G	WO	1951	15,000/8/52	OS	p‡	b	BL-d	
nc	np	6	4620	2-G	DSW	1956	30,000/10/56	OS	p‡	b	BL-d	
A	4/6	7	M722	3-G	DSW	1962	10,000/8/62/6388/OS	OS	r	m	Wc	
A	4/6	7	M722	3-G	DSW	1962	10,000/1/64/6592/OS	OS	r	d	DGC	
A/*	np	7	M722	3-G	DSW	1962	25,000/1/66/6796/OS	OS	r	d	Ob	
A/*	np	7	M722	3-G	DSM	1962	1/68/6975/OS	OS	r.	m	DGC	
B	np	7	M722	4-G	DSM	1970	70/7765/OS	OS	r.	d	Ob	
B	np	7	M722	4-G	DSM	1970	2/73/722442 S	OS	r.	d	Ob	

For further use see Exercises *Life Line, Surprise Packet* in supplement 4. 1. All stock copies were overprinted for GSGS Misc.1560 *Exercise Surprise Packet.*

Sheet 178 *Dorchester*

1	5	6	7	8	9	10	11	12	13	14	15	16
nc	5/-	6	4620	WOE	WO	1949	15,000/8/49	OS	p‡	a	BL-d	
1228	5/-	6	4620	1-G	WO	1949	10,000/1/51	OS	p‡	a	BL-d	
1228	5/-	6	4620	2-G	WO	1951	15,000/7/51	OS	p‡	b	BL-d	1
1228	5/-	6	4620	2-G	WO	1951	25,000/10/51	OS	p‡	b	BL-d	
nc	np	6	4620	2-G	WO	1951	15,000/11/53 OS	OS	p‡	b	BL-d	
nc	np	6	4620	2-G	WO	1951	30,000/12/55 OS	OS	p‡	b	BL-d	
A	3/6	7	M722	3-G	DSW	1960	10,000/2/60/6118/OS	OS	r	mo	DGC	
A	3/6	7	M722	3-G	DSW	1960	30,000/9/61/4385/R	1 SPC RE	r	mo	DGC	

1	5	6	7	8	9	10	11	12	13	14	15	16
A	np	7	M722	3-G	DSW	1960	50,000/6/64/6642/OS	OS	r	m	BL-a	
A/	np	7	M722	3-G	DSM	1960	1/68/6987/OS	OS	r.	m	BL-a	
A/	np	7	M722	3-G	DSM	1960	10/68/7290/OS	OS	r.	m	Ob	
A/	np	7	M722	3-G	DSM	1960	8/70/8037/OS	OS	r.	m	DGC	
B	np	7	M722	4-G	DSM	1970	10/70/8070/OS	OS	r.	d	Ob	
B	np	7	M722	4-G	DSM	1970	11/73/732786 S	OS	r.	m	BL-b	

For further use see supplements 1, 2, Exercise *Surprise Packet* in supplement 4, supplements 5, 8. 1. The printing record has instructions for all 15,000 copies to be overprinted, but according to the print code, only 13,000 copies were overprinted for use in GSGS Misc.1560 *Exercise Surprise Packet*.

Sheet 179 *Bournemouth*

1	5	6	7	8	9	10	11	12	13	14	15	16
1154	5/-	6	4620	WOE	WO	1948	15,000/3/48	OS	p‡	a	BL-d	1
1154	5/-	6	4620	WOE	WO	1948	5000/7/50	OS	p-	a	BL-d	
1236	10/6	6	4620	2-G	WO	1951	20,000/7/51	OS	p	b	BL-d	2
1236	10/6	6	4620	2-G	WO	1951	25,000/10/51	OS	p	b	BL-d	
nc	np	6	4620	2-G	WO	1951	25,000/1/55 OS	OS	p	b	BL-d	
E/	np	6	M722	3-G	DSW	1958	25,000/2/59/5753/OS	OS	p	b	BL-d	
A/	4/6	7	M722	4-G	DSW	1962	20,000/9/62/6388/OS	OS	r	?d	DGC	
A/	np	7	M722	4-G	DSW	1962	25,000/5/64/6592/OS	OS	r	m	Wc	
B	np	7	M722	5-G	DSM	1966	35,000/6/66/6822/OS	OS	r.	d	Ob	
C	np	7	M722	6-G	DSM	1971	4/71/8137/OS	OS	r.	d	DGC	
C	np	7	M722	6-G	DSM	1971	2/73/721684 S	OS	r.	d	Ob	

For further use see supplements 1, 2, Exercise *Surprise Packet* in supplement 4. 1. The 1154 printing, published in March 1948, incorporates 1947 road revision. 2. The printing record has instructions for 15,000 copies to be overprinted, but according to the print code, only 13,000 copies were overprinted for use in GSGS Misc.1560 *Exercise Surprise Packet*.

Sheet 180 *The Solent*

1	5	6	7	8	9	10	11	12	13	14	15	16
1183	5/-	6	4620	WOE	WO	1949	no code	OS	p	aT	BL-d	1,2
1155	5/-	6	4620	WOE	WO	1949	3300/7/49	OS	p	a	PC	1
1233	10/6	6	4620	WOE	WO	1949	5000/7/50	OS	p	a	BL-d	
1233	10/6	6	4620	1-G	WO	1949	10,000/4/51	OS	p	a	BL-d	
1233	10/6	6	4620	2-G	WO	1951	5000/7/51	OS	p	b	BL-d	3,4
1233	10/6	6	4620	2-G	WO	1951	20,000/8/51	OS	p	b	Ob	3,5
nc	10/6	6	4620	2-G	WO	1951	20,000/9/52	OS	p	b	BL-d	
nc	np	6	4620	2-G	WO	1951	30,000/12/55 OS	OS	p	b	BL-d	
A/	4/6	7	M722	3-G	DSW	1962	20,000/6/62/6309/OS	OS	r	m	DGC	
A//	4/6	7	M722	3-G	DSW	1962	30,000/2/64/6590/OS	OS	r	m	Wc	
B	np	7	M722	4-G	DSM	1965	35,000/11/65/6778/OS	OS	r	d	Ob	
B/*	np	7	M722	5-G	DSM	1967	30,000/12/67/7029/OS	OS	r.	d	BL-a	
C	DR	7	M722	6-G	DSM	1971	11/71/8440/OS	OS	r.	d	Ob	
C	np	7	M722	6-G	DSM	1971	5/73/721338 S	OS	r.	m	BL-b	

For further use see supplements 1, 2, Exercise *Surprise Packet* in supplement 4. 1. The Military Survey printing record in fact lists neither of these printings, but merely records a requirement of 15,000 sheets which was completed by 13 November 1949. This would appear to have consisted of this unquantified printing on the unrevised 1183 issue, so given over to training, combined with 3300 copies of the 1155 printing (published in May 1949), which incorporated 1947 road revision. However, the OS catalogue card does not confirm the number printed in 1949. 2. An *Outline Edition* black plate was used for the printing of this sheet. This heading was blocked out and *War Office Edition* overprinted. 3. The Military Survey printing record gives the number of copies required as increased from 10,000 to 25,000. This was apparently achieved in two batches. 4. The OS catalogue card notes this print run as 6000. 5. 15,000 copies were overprinted for use in GSGS Misc.1560 *Exercise Surprise Packet;* so far no copy without overprint has been recorded.

Sheet 181 *Chichester*

1	5	6	7	8	9	10	11	12	13	14	15	16
1194	5/-	6	4620	WOE	WO	1947	25,000/5/48	OS	p‡	a	BL-d	1
1258	10/6	6	4620	2-G	WO	1951	25,000/6/51	OS	p‡	b	BL-d	2
nc	10/6	6	4620	2-G	WO	1951	25,000/7/52	OS	p‡	b	BL-d	
nc	np	6	4620	2-G	DSW	1956	20,000/12/56	OS	p‡	b	BL-d	

1	5	6	7	8	9	10	11	12	13	14	15	16
A	3/6	7	M722	3-G	DSW	1961	30,000/6/61/5261/OS	OS	r	m	DGC	
A/	4/6	7	M722	3-G	DSW	1961	15,000/12/62/6488/OS	OS	r	dx	DGC	
A//*	np	7	M722	3-G	DSW	1961	13,000/9/65/6762/OS	OS	r	d	BL-b	
A//*	np	7	M722	3-G	DSM	1961	1/68/6987/OS	OS	r.	m	DGC	
B	np	7	M722	4-G	DSM	1970	70/7981/OS	OS	r.	d	Ob	

For further use see Exercise *Surprise Packet* in supplement 4. 1. The 1194 printing, published in September 1948, incorporates 1947 road revision. 2. The printing record notes the requirement for two lots of 15,000 copies in March and April 1951. These appear to have been amalgamated in the single though reduced print run of 25,000. This may account for the disregard of the instruction to overprint all 15,000 copies of the second batch, this being reduced to just 10,300 copies overprinted for use in GSGS Misc.1560 *Exercise Surprise Packet*.

Sheet 182 *Brighton and Worthing*

1	5	6	7	8	9	10	11	12	13	14	15	16
nc	5/-	6	4620	WOE	WO	1949	15,000/10/49	OS	p	a	BL-d	1
nc	5/-	6	4620	WOE	WO	1949	10,000/8/50	OS	p	a	BL-d	
nc	10/6	6	4620	2-G	WO	1952	25,000/7/52	OS	p	b	BL-d	2
1235	np	6	4620	2-G	WO	1949	20,000/11/59/6020/OS	OS	p	b	BL-d	3
A	4/6	7	M722	3-G	DSW	1962	4000/7/62/6391/OS	OS	r	cx	BL-b	
A/	4/6	7	M722	3-G	DSW	1962	16,000/5/63/6391/OS	OS	r	d	Cu-m	
A/	np	7	M722	3-G	DSM	1966	18,000/7/66/6824/OS	OS	r.	m	Cu-m	
A//*	np	7	M722	4-G	DSM	1966	22,000/12/66/6861/OS	OS	r.	d	BL-b	
B	np	7	M722	5-G	DSM	1970	10/70/8069/OS	OS	r.	d	Ob	

1. Presumably using the 1156 printing, published in 1947, which incorporates 1947 road revision. 2. This printing order was placed with SPC RE in April 1952. In the event this was cancelled and the work done by the Ordnance Survey. 3. GSGS 4620, not M722, is still present on this printing.

Sheet 183 *Eastbourne*

1	5	6	7	8	9	10	11	12	13	14	15	16
1157	5/-	6	4620	WOE	WO	1949	15,000/10/49	OS	p	a	BL-d	1
1157	10/6	6	4620	1-G	WO	1949	10,000/4/51	OS	p	a	BL-d	
1291	np	6	4620	2-G	WO	1953	10,000/1/53	OS	p	b	BL-d	
1291	np	6	4620	2-G	WO	1953	20,000/6/55 OS	OS	p	b	BL-d	
A	3/6	7	M722	3-G	DSW	1961	20,000/1/61/6246/OS	OS	r	mo	DGC	
A/*	np	7	M722	3-G	DSM	1964	4500/6/64/6626/OS	OS	r	m	Wc	
A/*	np	7	M722	3-G	DSM	1964	5000/1/65/6693/OS	OS	r	m	Wc	
A/*/	np	7	M722	3-G	DSM	1964	20,000/10/65/6773/OS	OS	r	m	BL-b	
B	np	7	M722	4-G	DSM	1969	8/69/7535/OS	OS	r.	d	Ob	
B	np	7	M722	4-G	DSM	1969	2/71/8107/OS	OS	r.	m	BL-b	

1. The 1157 printing, published in July 1947, incorporates 1946 road revision.

Sheet 184 *Hastings*

1	5	6	7	8	9	10	11	12	13	14	15	16
1158	5/-	6	4620	WOE	WO	1947	15,000/10/47	OS	p‡	a	BL-d	1
1180	5/-	6	4620	1-G	WO	1947	10,000/2/51	OS	p	a	BL-d	
1180	5/-	6	4620	2-G	WO	1952	25,000/9/52	OS	p	b	BL-d	
A	3/6	7	M722	3-G	DSW	1961	25,000/4/61/6309/OS	OS	r	m	BL-b	2
A/*	np	7	M722	3-G	DSW	1961	20,000/6/66/1680/SPC	SPC RE	r	m	DGC	
B	np	7	M722	4-G	DSM	1969	69/7556/OS	OS	r.	d	Ob	
B	np	7	M722	4-G	DSM	1969	8/72/8499/OS	OS	r.	d	Ob	

For further use see Exercise *Island Fling* in supplement 4, supplement 8. 1. The 1158 printing, published in November 1947, incorporates 1946 road revision. 2. The first of the Seventh Series sheets to be printed in the six colour scheme that would become standard on the civilian map.

Sheet 185 *Newquay and Padstow*

1	5	6	7	8	9	10	11	12	13	14	15	16
1110	5/-	6	4620	WOE	WO	1949	15,000/10/49	OS	p‡	a	BL-d	
1110	5/-	6	4620	2-G	WO	1951	20,000/3/52	OS	p‡	b	BL-d	
nc	6/6	6	M722	2-G	DSW	1951	20,000/2/60/6020/OS	OS	p‡	b	Ob	
A	4/6	7	M722	3-G	DSW	1962	20,000/6/62/6391/OS	OS	r	m	Wc	
A	4/6	7	M722	3-G	DSW	1962	20,000/9/63/6565/OS	OS	r	d	BL-b	
A/*	np	7	M722	3-G	DSM	1962	7/71/8115/OS	OS	r.	m	Ob	
B	DR	7	M722	4-G	DSM	1972	2/72/8441/OS	OS	r.	d	Ob	
B	np	7	M722	4-G	DSM	1972	5/73/721733 S	OS	r.	d	BL-b	

1	5	6	7	8	9	10	11	12	13	14	15	16

Sheet 186 *Bodmin and Launceston*

1	5	6	7	8	9	10	11	12	13	14	15	16
1192	5/-	6	4620	WOE	WO	1947	15,000/1/48	OS	p‡	a	BL-d	
1192	5/-	6	4620	WOE	WO	1947	15,000/7/50	OS	p‡	a	BL-d	
1192	np	6	4620	2-G	WO	1952	20,000/11/52	OS	p‡	b	BL-d	
nc	3/6	6	M722	2-G	DSW	1952	7500/5/60/6022/OS	OS	p‡	b	PC	
A	4/6	7	M722	3-G	DSW	1962	10,000/5/62/6388/OS	OS	r	m	Wc	
A	np	7	M722	3-G	DSM	1964	25,000/6/64/6576/OS	OS	r	m	Cu-m	
B	np	7	M722	4-G	DSM	1967	25,000/2/67/6882/OS	OS	r.	d	BL-b	
B	np	7	M722	4-G	DSM	1967	1/71/8103/OS	OS	r.	m	DGC	
C	DR	7	M722	4-G	DSM	1967	4/72/8659/OS	OS	r.	d	Ob	

For further use see supplement 8.

Sheet 187 *Plymouth*

1	5	6	7	8	9	10	11	12	13	14	15	16
1179	5/-	6	4620	WOE	WO	1947	15,000/10/47	OS	p‡	a	BL-d	1
1179	5/-	6	4620	WOE	WO	1947	10,000/8/50	OS	p‡	a	BL-d	
1179	np	6	4620	2-G	WO	1952	20,000/12/52	OS	p‡	b	BL-d	
1179	6/6	6	M722	3-G	DSW	1951	20,000/1/59/5753/OS	OS	p‡	b	BL-d	
1179	6/6	6	M722	4-G	DSW	1951	20,000/1/59/5753/OS	OS	p‡	b	BL-d	2
A	4/6	7	M722	5-G	DSW	1962	10,000/4/62/6388/OS	OS	r	mt	DGC	
A	4/6	7	M722	5-G	DSW	1962	25,000/9/62/36/SPC	SPC RE	r	mt	DGC	
A/*	np	7	M722	6-G	DSM	1964	35,000/11/64/6665/OS	OS	r	m	Ob	
B	np	7	M722	6-G	DSM	1967	20,000/8/67/6924/OS	OS	r.	m	DGC	3,5
B	np	7	M722	7-G	DSM	1967	20,000/8/67/6924/OS	OS	r.	m	DGC	4,5
B	np	7	M722	7-G	DSM	1967	6/68/7143/OS	OS	r.	m	Ob	5
B	np	7	M722	7-G	DSM	1967	2/71/8113/OS	OS	r.	m	DGC	5

1. The first sheet to be printed in GSGS 4620, completed on 15 October 1947 (i.e. in advance of the formal order for the sheet). 2. This edition was advanced from 3-GSGS with changes to Grid, Magnetic and True North information. 3. This printing was apparently printed as Edition 6-GSGS in error. 4. The edition number 6 is blocked out and altered to 7. 5. All three military edition B printings were revised to August 1965 within the limits of the *Dartmoor* Tourist Map, and thus differed from the civilian edition B, which was revised to 1971 and published in 1972.

Sheet 188 a. *Torquay* b. *Torbay*

1	5	6	7	8	9	10	11	12	13	14	15	16
1193	5/-	6a	4620	WOE	WO	1947	15,000/1/48	OS	p‡	a	BL-d	
1193	5/-	6a	4620	WOE	WO	1947	15,000/8/50	OS	p‡	a	BL-d	1
nc	6/6	6a	4620	1-G	WO	1947	20,000/4/55 OS	OS	p‡	b	BL-d	
A	4/6	7a	M722	2-G	DSW	1962	10,000/4/62/6388/OS	OS	r	m	BL-b	
A	4/6	7a	M722	2-G	DSW	1962	30,000/10/63/6551/OS	OS	r	m	Ob	
A/	np	7a	M722	2-G	DSW	1962	18,000/11/64/6663/OS	OS	r	m	Cu-m	
B	np	7b	M722	3-G	DSM	1967	20,000/11/67/6971/OS	OS	r.	d	BL-a	
C	np	7b	M722	4-G	DSM	1972	7/72/8657/OS	OS	r.	d	Ob	

1. The civilian magnetic variation dates and values are as before, but the month is altered from *January* to *Jan.*

Sheet 189 *Land's End*

1	5	6	7	8	9	10	11	12	13	14	15	16
nc	5/-	6	4620	WOE	WO	1949	15,000/10/49	OS	p‡	a	BL-d	
nc	5/-	6	4620	2-G	WO	1951	20,000/4/52	OS	p‡	b	BL-d	
A	4/6	7	M722	3-G	DSW	1962	10,000/5/62/6388/OS	OS	r	m	BL-b	
A	4/6	7	M722	3-G	DSW	1962	20,000/2/64/6588/OS	OS	r	m	DGC	
A/	np	7	M722	3-G	DSM	1962	11/68/7288/OS	OS	r.	m	Ob	
B	np	7	M722	4-G	DSM	1971	9/71/8253/OS	OS	r.	d	Ob	
B	np	7	M722	4-G	DSM	1971	2/73/730009 S	OS	r.	d	BL-b	

Sheet 190 *Truro and Falmouth*

1	5	6	7	8	9	10	11	12	13	14	15	16
nc	5/-	6	4620	WOE	WO	1949	15,000/10/49	OS	p‡	a	BL-d	
1229	5/-	6	4620	2-G	WO	1951	20,000/4/52	OS	p‡	b	BL-d	
A	4/6	7	M722	3-G	DSW	1962	14,000/11/62/61/SPC	SPC	r	mo	BL-b	
A	np	7	M722	4-G	DSM	1965	20,000/9/65/6756/OS	OS	r	m	DGC	1
A	np	7	M722	3-G	DSM	1965	20,000/9/65/6756/OS	OS	r	m	DGC	2
A/	np	7	M722	3-G	DSM	1965	11/68/7289/OS	OS	r.	m	Ob	
B	DR	7	M722	4-G	DSM	1972	3/72/8536/OS	OS	r.	d	Ob	

1. The edition number 4 is altered by hand to 3. 2. The edition number 4 is blocked out and overprinted 3.

Supplements to sections 7 and 8

In this section are listed special sheets based on GSGS 4620 (M722) and 4639. Such maps, pre-war, had almost all been members of GSGS 3907. A break from pre-war practice meant that most were allocated their own special GSGS numbers in the miscellaneous sequence. From 1965 the more significant items were given numbers in the standard sequence while those of a more ephemeral nature continued to be allocated miscellaneous numbers.

Supplement 1. *GSGS 4620A England and Wales, layered editions*

Layered editions of GSGS 4620, made for the Staff College. Standard sheet coverage 40 by 45 km

Sheet 144 *Cheltenham and Evesham*

1	5	6	7	8	9	10	11	12	13	14	15	16
1210	5/-	6	4620A	WOE	WO	1949	2000/3/49	OS	p‡	a	BL-d	1
1272	np	6	4620A	2-G	WO	1952	5000/4/53 OS	OS	p‡	b	BL-d	
1272	np	6	4620A	2-G	WO	1952	10,000/10/62/28/SPC	SPC RE	p‡	b	BL-d	

1. Made under PD 4322/OS, the same printing demand as for two composite maps (see the end of this section).

Sheet 145 *Banbury*

1	5	6	7	8	9	10	11	12	13	14	15	16
nc	5/-	6	4620A	WOE	WO	1949	2000/3/49	OS	p‡	a	BL-d	1
nc	5/-	6	4620A	WOE	WO	1949	5000/2/52 SPC RE	SPC RE	p‡	a	BL-d	
nc	np	6	4620A	1-G	WO	1949	5000/11/54 OS	OS	p‡	b	BL-d	
nc	np	6	4620A	1-G	WO	1949	10,000/1/62/4456/R	1 SPC RE	p‡	b	BL-d	

1. Made under PD 4322/OS, the same printing demand as for two composite maps (see the end of this section).

Sheet 146 *Buckingham*

1	5	6	7	8	9	10	11	12	13	14	15	16
1176	5/-	6	4620A	WOE	WO	1947	10,000/11/50	OS	p‡	a	BL-d	
nc	np	6	4620A	1-G	WO	1954	5000/5/54 OS	OS	p‡	b	BL-d	

Sheet 157 *Swindon*

1	5	6	7	8	9	10	11	12	13	14	15	16
1147	5/-	6	4620A	WOE	WO	1948	2000/2/49	OS	p	a	BL-d	1
1147	5/-	6	4620A	WOE	WO	1948	10,000/1/50	OS	p	a	BL-d	2
B//	np	6	4620A	2-G	WO	1951	10,000/10/62/28/SPC	SPC RE	p	b	BL-d	

1. Made under PD 4322/OS, the same printing demand as for two composite maps (see the end of this section). 2. A reprint by SPC was cancelled and reassigned to the Ordnance Survey.

Sheet 158 *Oxford and Newbury*

1	5	6	7	8	9	10	11	12	13	14	15	16
1148	5/-	6	4620A	WOE	WO	1948	2000/3/49	OS	p	a	BL-d	
1148	5/-	6	4620A	WOE	WO	1948	10,000/1/50	OS	p	a	BL-d	1
nc	np	6	4620A	2-G	WO	1951	5000/ /54 OS	OS	p	b	BL-d	
nc	np	6	4620A	2-G	DSW	1956	10,000/11/56	OS	p	b	BL-d	
A	np	7	4620A	3-G	DSW	1962	10,000/3/62/4484/R	1 SPC RE	r	mo	BL-d	2

1. A reprint by SPC was cancelled and reassigned to the Ordnance Survey. 2. The only layered printing recorded on a Seventh Series base map.

Sheet 159 *The Chilterns*

1	5	6	7	8	9	10	11	12	13	14	15	16
1159	5/-	6	4620A	WOE	WO	1949	10,000/11/50	OS	p	a	BL-d	
nc	np	6	4620A	2-G	WO	1951	5000/11/54 OS	OS	p	b	BL-d	
1252	np	6	4620A	2-G	WO	1951	10,000/10/59/6019/OS	OS	p	b	BL-d	

Sheet 166 *Frome*

1	5	6	7	8	9	10	11	12	13	14	15	16
1178	5/-	6	4620A	WOE	WO	1947	2000/6/49	OS	p‡	a	BL-d	
nc	np	6	4620A	2-G	WO	1951	5000/5/54 OS	OS	p‡	b	BL-d	

Sheet 167 *Salisbury Plain*

nc	np	6	4620A	WOE	WO	1948	2000/2/49	OS	p a	BL-d	1
nc	np	6	4620A	WOE	WO	1948	10,000/1/50	OS	p a	BL-d	2
nc	np	6	4620A	WOE	WO	1948	10,000/1/60/6019/OS	OS	p a	BL-d	

See figure 15. For a note on title and extrusions see page 235. 1. Made under PD 4322/OS, the same printing demand as for two composite maps (see the end of this section). 2. A reprint by SPC was cancelled and reassigned to the Ordnance Survey.

Sheet 168 *Winchester*

1162	5/-	6	4620A	WOE	WO	1949	2000/3/49	OS	p a	BL-d	
1162	5/-	6	4620A	WOE	WO	1949	10,000/1/50	OS	p a	BL-d	1
nc	np	6	4620A	2-G	WO	1951	2000/11/52	OS	p b	BL-d	
nc	np	6	4620A	2-G	WO	1951	5000/11/54 OS	OS	p b	BL-d	
nc	np	6	4620A	2-G	WO	1951	10,000/12/59/6091/OS	OS	p b	BL-d	

1. A reprint by SPC was cancelled and reassigned to the Ordnance Survey.

Sheet 169 *Aldershot*

nc	5/-	6	4620A	WOE	WO	1949	10,000/1/50	OS	p a	BL-d	
nc	np	6	4620A	2-G	WO	1951	2000/11/52	OS	p b	BL-d	
nc	np	6	4620A	2-G	WO	1951	5000/5/54 OS	OS	p b	BL-d	
F/	np	6	4620A	2-G	DSW	1951	10,000/3/58/5713/OS	OS	p b	BL-d	
F/	np	6	4620A	2-G	WO	1951	10,000/10/62/28/SPC	SPC RE	p b	BL-d	

Sheet 178 *Dorchester*

nc	5/-	6	4620A	WOE	WO	1949	2000/6/49	OS	p‡ a	BL-d	
1228	5/-	6	4620A	WOE	WO	1949	10,000/2/50	OS	p‡ a	BL-d	1

1. A reprint by SPC was cancelled and reassigned to the Ordnance Survey.

Sheet 179 *Bournemouth*

nc	5/-	6	4620A	WOE	WO	1948	2000/6/49	OS	p a	BL-d	
1154	5/-	6	4620A	WOE	WO	1948	10,000/3/50	OS	p a	BL-d	1

1. A reprint by SPC was cancelled and reassigned to the Ordnance Survey.

Sheet 180 *The Solent*

1155	5/-	6	4620A	WOE	WO	1949	2000/6/49	OS	p a	BL-d	
1155	5/-	6	4620A	WOE	WO	1949	10,000/2/50	OS	p a	BL-d	1

1. A reprint by SPC was cancelled and reassigned to the Ordnance Survey.

Composite maps, with layers

Untitled. Parts of sheets 158, 159, 168 & 169.

-	-	6	4620A	WOE	WO	1949	?2000/6/49	OS			
-	-	6	4620A	WOE	WO	1949	5000/12/49	OS		BL-d	

PD 4322/OS. Covering an area from Sherfield Hill to Wallingford, Newbury to Reading. Military Survey documents refer to a printing of 2000 copies with heading Map A, Map No 1, completed in June 1949. The copy recorded is presumably a reprint of this. The map was to be coloured "with <u>special</u> layering in the same <u>style</u> as GSGS/3907 Composite of 113 & 114 sheets" (see page 157).

Reading-Basingstoke area. Parts of sheets 158, 159, 168 & 169.

-	-	6	4620A	WOE	WO	1949	?2000/5/49	OS			
-	-	6	4620A	WOE	WO	1949	5000/9/54 OS	OS		BL-d	
-	-	6	4620A	WOE	WO	1949	10,000/1/62/4456/R	1 SPC RE		BL-d	

PD 4322/OS. Photolithographed by the Ordnance Survey, 1949. Sheet lines are not square with the grid. Covering an area from Basingstoke to Reading, Cold Ash to Sandhurst. Military Survey documents refer to a printing of 2000 copies with heading Map B, Map No 2, completed in May 1949.

Supplement 2. *M722 mapping at larger and smaller scales*

GSGS Misc.1999: enlargements of M722 sheets to scale 1:50,000   40 by 45 km

1	6	7 and 8	9	10	11	12	15	16
-	7	sheet 166. 1-G	DSW	1963	25/11/63/423/SPC	SPC RE	BL	
-	7	sheet 167. 1-G	DSW	1963	25/11/63/423/SPC	SPC RE	BL	
-	7	sheet 168. 1-G	DSW	1963	nc		BL	
-	7	sheet 178. 1-G	DSW	1963	25/11/63/423/SPC	SPC RE	BL	
20,000/ /62/6388/OS	7	sheet 179. 1-G	DSW	1963	nc		BL	
-	7	sheet 180. 1-G	DSW	1963	nc		BL	

Further copies of these maps are in DGC and the Library of Congress, Washington D.C.

GSGS Misc.2000: reductions of M722 sheets to scale 1:100,000   40 by 45 km

1	6	7 and 8	9	10	11	12	15	16
-	7	sheet 166. 1-G	DSW	1963	25/11/63/423/SPC	SPC RE	BL	
-	7	sheet 167. 1-G	DSW	1963	25/11/63/423/SPC	SPC RE	BL	
-	7	sheet 168. 1-G	DSW	1963	nc		BL	
-	7	sheet 178. 1-G	DSW	1963	25/11/63/423/SPC	SPC RE	BL	
20,000/ /62/6388/OS	7	sheet 179. 1-G	DSW	1963	nc		BL	
-	7	sheet 180. 1-G	DSW	1963	nc		BL	

Further copies of these maps are in DGC and the Library of Congress, Washington D.C.

Supplement 3. *Training area maps*

Catterick area, as the only genuine member of GSGS 4620, is placed first in this sequence. Following that, maps are ordered according to GSGS number, first in the miscellaneous sequence, then from 1965 the GSGS sequence. Mapping of training areas still in use after 1974 was transferred to the 1:50,000 scale as sheets of the new M726 map became available. A few had new individual GSGS numbers allocated, then, from 1977, several were grouped together in GSGS 5295 *1:50,000 UK training areas*.

GSGS 3907 and 4620 **Catterick area**. Parts of New Popular sheets 84, 85, 90, 91   Revised 1920   50 by 38 km

1	6	7 and 8	9	10	11	12	15	16
-	6	3907. 2-E	WO	1948	3000/9/48	OS	BL-d	
-	6	4620. WOE	WO	1948	4000/9/48	OS	BL-d	
-	6	4620. 1-G	WO	1948	10,000/ /51	OS	BL-d	1

First published by the Director General at the Ordnance Survey Office, Chessington, 1948. The need for further stock of a Cassini gridded map was raised by Northern Command on 31 December 1946. But since no reproduction materials existed for reprinting the pre-war map, a new composite mock-up was prepared from New Popular Edition material. Both War Office Cassini and National Grid printings were ordered on 5 July 1948, to be completed by 10 September. They were apparently ready by 4 October. Though constructed on sheet lines which accorded with the new National Grid (391-441, 481-519), the Cassini Grid version was designated the second edition of the pre-war map which had been on War Office Cassini Grid sheet lines (see page 161). It would appear to be an anomaly that GSGS 3907 should have been allocated to this Cassini gridded map, whereas the unnumbered issues of sheets 167 and 169 with Cassini Grid had been designated members of GSGS 4620. The National Grid map was superseded by GSGS Misc.1764 in 1957. 1. Printing of this issue was completed on 12 April 1951. 250 copies were overprinted for use in GSGS Misc.1635 *78 Agra Exercise*. See supplement 4.

GSGS Misc.406 *Redesdale and Otterburn artillery ranges* — 30 by 41 km

1	6	7 and 8	9	10	11	12	15
-	6/P	1-G	WO	1951	8000/7/50	OS	DGC
-	6/P	2-G	WO	1953	1750/7/53 OS	OS	DGC
-	6/P	3-G	WO	1955	2200/6/55 OS	OS	DGC
-	6/P	4-G	DSW	1958	1000/3/58/5728/OS	OS	DGC
-	6/P	4-G	DSW	1958	1500/3/59/5913/OS	OS	DGC

GSGS Misc.406 *Otterburn/Redesdale all arms training area*

1	6	7 and 8	9	10	11	12	15
-	6/P	5-G	DSW	1960	nc	13 FSS RE	DGC
-	6/P	5-G	DSW	1960	1000/4/64/579/SPC	SPC RE	DGC
-	6/P	5-G	DSW	1960	1000/7/64/689/SPC	SPC RE	DGC

On grid sheet lines (370-400, 579-620). For artillery range purposes. The colours of the base map were initially subdued, then much stronger with the change of title in Edition 5-GSGS. The overprint is red, blue and purple. Superseded by GSGS 4954.

GSGS Misc.407 *Ross Links anti-tank range* — 23 by 25 km

1	6	9	10	11	12	15
-	6	WO	1950	5000/3/50	OS	DGC

On grid sheet lines (407-430, 628-653). With an overprint in red.

GSGS Misc.433 *Salisbury Plain – range overprint* — 40 by 45 km

1	6	7 and 8	9	10	11	12	15	16
-	6	sheet 167. 1-G	WO	7.50	20,000/11/51 SPC RE	SPC RE	DGC	1

GSGS Misc.433 *Salisbury Plain P.T.A.*

1	6	7 and 8	9	10	11	12	15	16
-	6	sheet 167. 2-G	WO	1953	5000/4/53 OS	OS	DGC	
-	6	sheet 167. 2-G	WO	1953	13,000/6/53 OS	OS	PC	
-	6	sheet 167. 2-G	WO	1953	10,000/9/55 OS	OS	DGC	
30,000/5/57	6	sheet 167. 2-G	DSW	1953	12,000/2/58/5681/OS	OS	DGC	2
30,000/10/58/5748/OS	6	sheet 167. 3-G	DSW	1959	7000/8/59/4203/R	1 SPC RE	DGC	3
-	6	sheet 167. 3-G	DSW	1959	3000/5/60/4261/R	1 SPC RE	DGC	
-	6	sheet 167. 4-G	DSW	1961	3000/6/61/4378/R	1 SPC RE	DGC	
-	6	sheet 167. 4-G	DSW	1961	1500/10/61/4424/R	1 SPC RE	DGC	
-	6	sheet 167. 4-G	DSW	1961	1000/6/62/4494/R	1 SPC RE	DGC	
-	6	sheet 167. 4-G	DSW	1961	2000/4/63/130/SPC	SPC RE	DGC	
-	6	sheet 167. 4-G	DSW	1961	6000/7/64/632/SPC	SPC RE	DGC	

Earlier versions of the Salisbury Plain map carrying the range overprint were Cassini gridded maps, being first a Popular Edition district map in GSGS 3907, then New Popular sheet 167 (without the sheet number) in GSGS 4620. The overprint first appeared on a National Grid map as GSGS Misc.433; this was superseded by GSGS 4974. With an extrusion between Warminster and Westbury to allow complete coverage of the Imber range area. For Edition 2: Range data drawn & reproduced by Ordnance Survey 1953 from information provided by Southern Command. For Edition 3: Range overprints revised by No 1 SPC, RE 1959 from data provided by Salisbury Plain District. For Edition 4: Amendments carried out from data provided by HQ Salisbury Plain District by No.1 Survey Production Centre, RE April, 1961. 1. The base map is grey, overprinted in red with War Department boundary, aerodromes, rifle ranges and training area boundaries. 2. The base map colour is altered to black. 3. With a more complex overprint, training area, rifle ranges and aerodromes being transferred to a blue plate.

GSGS Misc.1522 *Sennybridge artillery ranges* — 40 by 40 km

1	6	7 and 8	9	10	11	12	15
-	6	1-G	WO	1951	1000/6/52	OS	DGC
-	6	2-G	DSW	1958	1000/3/58/5680/OS	OS	DGC
-	6	2-G	DSW	1958	2000/9/58/5823/OS	OS	DGC
-	6	2-G	DSW	1958	4000/9/59/6076/OS	OS	DGC
-	6	3-G	DSW	1963	2400/5/63/6524/OS	OS	DGC
-	6	3-G	DSW	1963	1000/6/65/1157/SPC	SPC RE	DGC

On grid sheet lines (275-315, 220-260). For artillery range purposes. With an overprint in red, blue and green. The overprint information was supplied by Western Command 1951, with amendments (as applicable) in 1957 and 1963. Superseded by GSGS 4976.

GSGS Misc.1585 _Stanford training and gun areas_ 40 by 45 km

20,000/2/52	6	sheet 136. [1-G]	WO	1952	nc	OS	DGC
22,000/4/54 OS	6	sheet 136. [1-G]	WO	1952	2000/5/54 OS	OS	DGC
8500/10/55 OS	7	sheet 136. 2-G	DSW	1956	4000/11/56	OS	DGC
nc [A/, 3/-]	7	sheet 136. 2-G	DSW	1956	3000/9/59/6087/OS	OS	DGC
20,000/6/62/4512/R	7	sheet 136. 2-G	DSW	1956	4000/6/62/4508/R	1 SPC RE	DGC
24,000/6/63/6546/OS	7	sheet 136. 3-G	DSW	1964	3000/11/64/887/SPC	SPC RE	DGC

Superseded by GSGS 5025.

GSGS Misc.1622 _W.D. land and training areas, home counties_ 40 by 45 km

20,000/5/52	6	sheet 173. [1-G]	WO	1953	nc		DGC
20,000/5/52	6	sheet 173. 2-G	WO	1955	nc		DGC
30,000/2/55 OS	6	sheet 173. 2-G	-	1957	2000/3/57	1 SPC RE	DGC
30,000/2/55 OS	6	sheet 173. 2-G	-	1957	2000/7/57	1 SPC RE	DGC
10,000/6/60/6022/OS	7	sheet 173. 2-G	-	-	4000/4/61/4352/R	1 SPC RE	DGC

Overprinted with War Department properties, also areas where they had training rights, some subject to compensation payments (coloured pink and brown), some not (coloured green). Superseded by GSGS 4959.

GSGS Misc.1764 _Catterick area_ 50 by 38 km

-	7	1-G	DSW	1957	5000/5/57	OS	DGC
-	7	1-G	DSW	1957	2000/7/60/6250/OS	OS	DGC

On grid sheet lines (391-441, 487-525). In adopting sheet lines 6 km north of the GSGS 4620 map of 1948 the training areas in the vicinity of Barnard Castle were more satisfactorily covered. The overprint information was supplied by Northern Command in 1957. Superseded by GSGS 5076.

GSGS Misc.1881 _Dartmoor training areas_ 48 by 48 km

-	6	1-G	DSW	1960	nc	1 SPC RE	DGC
-	6	1-G	DSW	1960	2000/3/61/4358/R	1 SPC RE	DGC
-	6	1-G	DSW	1960	2000/3/63/129/SPC	SPC RE	DGC

On grid sheet lines (242-290, 052-100). An outline map with overprints in red drawn from data provided by Southern Command, 1959. Superseded by GSGS 4987.

GSGS Misc.2042 untitled 40 by 45 km

25,000/7/63/6555/OS	7	sheet 175	150/9/64/784/SPC	SPC RE	DGC
25,000/7/63/6555/OS	7	sheet 175	150/8/65/1219/SPC	SPC RE	DGC
25,000/7/63/6555/OS	7	sheet 175	100/3/66/1531/SPC	SPC RE	DGC
65,000/8/66/6824/OS	7	sheet 175	100/11/66/1842/SPC	SPC RE	DGC

Without legend: with an overprint in black, yellow and red showing undisclosed features of the training area on Dartmoor. Okehampton and Willsworthy Camps are specifically marked.

GSGS Misc.2131 _Area numbers one & two : showing CCF arduous training areas_ 40 by 45 km

5000/7/66/6756/OS	7	sheet 107	50/10/66/1822/SPC	SPC RE	DGC

GSGS Misc.2132 _Area number three : showing CCF arduous training areas_ 40 by 45 km

13,000/8/65/6756/OS	7	sheet 116	50/10/66/1822/SPC	SPC RE	Ob

GSGS Misc.2133 _Plynlimon : showing CCF arduous training areas_ 40 by 45 km

12,000/12/64/6684/OS	7	sheet 127	50/10/66/1822/SPC	SPC RE	Ob

GSGS Misc.2134 _Brecon Beacons : showing CCF arduous training areas_ 40 by 45 km

30,000/8/64/6662/OS	7	sheet 141	50/10/66/1822/SPC	SPC RE	Ob

GSGS Misc.2329 [South Uist firing range]

Part of Seventh Series sheet 23, overprinted by MCE RE from drawing supplied by Ordnance Board, Ministry of Defence. Print code 2/71/998/MCE(RE). Overprinted in red; firing apparently took place from Rubha Ardvule.

GSGS 4954 *Otterburn/Redesdale all arms training area* 30 by 41 km

		6	7 and 8	9	10	11	12	15	16
-			7 1-G	DSM	1965	5000/8/65/6726/OS	OS	DGC	
-			7 1-G	DSM	1965	8/68/613/SPC	SPC RE	DGC	

GSGS 4954 *Otterburn training area*

			7 2-G	DSM	1969	1/69/857/SPC	SPC RE	DGC	
-			7 2-G	DSM	1972	6/72/72127/OR	42 SER	DGC	
-			7 3-G	DSM	1973	9/73/722285 R	42 SER	DGC	

On grid sheet lines (370-400, 579-620), superseding GSGS Misc.406. The range overprints were supplied by Northern Command in 1955, with later amendments. Superseded by GSGS 5259 at 1:50,000.

GSGS 4959 *W.D. land and training areas, home counties* 40 by 45 km

[A/]			7 sheet 173. 1-G			2000/3/65/1018/SPC	SPC RE	DGC	1

GSGS 4959 *M.O.D. land and training areas, home counties*

25,000/1/66/6787/OS	7 sheet 173. 2-G			2000/3/66/1550/SPC	SPC RE	DGC

Superseding GSGS Misc.1622. Overprints were drawn by SPC RE from information supplied by HQ Eastern Command. 1. The base map was an outline printing of sheet 173, 1959, reprinted with minor changes in 1963.

For GSGS 4965 Ten Tors *see supplement 4.*

GSGS 4974 *Salisbury Plain P.T.A.* 40 by 45 km

-			7 sheet 167. 1-G	DSM	1966	10,000/4/66/1612/SPC	SPC RE	DGC	
-			7 sheet 167. 2-G	DSM	1967	10,200/3/67/1943/SPC	SPC RE	DGC	

GSGS 4974 *Salisbury Plain training area*

-			7 sheet 167. 3-G	DSM	1969	9/69/7592/OS	OS	DGC	

GSGS 4974 *Salisbury Plain trg area (1972)*

-			7 [sheet 167]. 4-G	DSM	1972	9/72/720080 M	MCE RE	DGC	
-			7 [sheet 167]. 4-G	DSM	1972	7/73/730071 M	MCE RE	DGC	
-			7 [sheet 167]. 4-G	DSM	1972	8/74/741558 M	MCE RE	DGC	

Superseding GSGS Misc.433. With an extrusion between Warminster and Westbury to allow complete coverage of the Imber range area. The range overprint of the early editions was revised by SPC RE in January 1966 [with later updates] from data provided by HQ Salisbury Plain District. Overprinted in red and purple. By Edition 4 overprint information, now in red, black, blue, purple and green, was supplied by HQ Southern Command. For the air edition see GSGS 5177. Superseded by GSGS 5229 at 1:50,000.

GSGS 4976 *Sennybridge A.A.T.A ranges* 40 by 40 km

-		6	1-G	DSM	1966	7100/4/66/1520/SPC	SPC RE	DGC	

Superseding GSGS Misc.1522. On grid sheet lines (275-315, 220-260). For artillery range purposes, overprinted in red and green. The overprint information was revised by SPC RE from amendments supplied by HQ Western Command, 1965. Superseded by GSGS 5066.

GSGS 4987 *Dartmoor training areas* 50 by 48 km

-			7 1-G	DSM	1966	6000/4/66/1589/SPC	SPC RE	DGC	
-			7 2-G	DSM	1968	11/68/670/SPC	SPC RE	DGC	
-			7 2-G	DSM	1968	5/71/1428/MCE(RE)	MCE RE	DGC	
-			7 2-G	DSM	1972	10/72/721237 M	MCE RE	DGC	
-			7 2-G	DSM	1973	3/74/730494 M	MCE RE	DGC	
-			7 2-G	DSM	1973	2/75/750250 M	MCE RE	DGC	

Superseding GSGS Misc.1881. On grid sheet lines (240-290, 052-100). Overprint prepared from information supplied by HQ Devon and Cornwall subdistrict, 1966, later South West district. With an overprint in red, black, blue and brown. Superseded by GSGS 5246 at 1:50,000.

GSGS 4988 *Glentrool National Forest Park* 44 by 44 km

-			7 1-G	DSM	1966	2000/5/66/1599/SPC	SPC RE	DGC	

GSGS 4988 *Glentrool training area*

-			7 2-G	DSM	1970	5/70/7942/OS	OS	DGC	
-			7 2-G	DSM	1970	8/71/1670/MCE(RE)	MCE RE	DGC	

On grid sheet lines (226-270, 563-607). The base map was produced by SPC RE from M722, parts of sheets 67, 72 and 73. Overprinted in black (Edition 1), then blue (Edition 2), the information supplied by HQ Scottish Command in 1966, then HQ Scotland (Army) in 1970. Superseded by GSGS 5258 at 1:50,000.

GSGS 4989 *Cairngorms training area*   49 by 58 km

[A]		7	1-G	DSM	1966	2000/7/66/6829/OS	OS	DGC	
[A/]		7	2-G	DSM	1971	2000/6/71/1437/MCE(RE)	MCE RE	DGC	

GSGS 4989 *Cairngorms area*

[A/]		7	3-G	DSM	1973	6/73/721449 M	MCE RE	DGC	1

On grid sheet lines (283-332, 770-828). The fully coloured civilian tourist map was employed as the base map, with the standard military grid overprinted in red. 1. With additional grid data overprinted in blue.

GSGS 5025 *Stanford training & gun areas*   40 by 45 km
35,000/12/66/6882/OS   7   sheet 136. 1-G   DSM   1967   5200/6/67/2018/SPC   SPC RE   Ob
Superseding GSGS Misc.1585.

GSGS 5034 *Glen Affric training area*   60 by 41 km

-		7	1-G	DSM	1968	6/68/499/SPC	SPC RE	DGC	1
-		7	1-G	DSM	1968	10/68/739/SPC	SPC RE	DGC	2

On grid sheet lines (190-250, 800-841). Overprint information supplied by HQ Scotland (Army). Superseded by GSGS 5068. 1. Overprinted in black. 2. Overprinted in blue.

GSGS 5065 *Catterick training area : tracked vehicle access and driver training routes*   41 by 59 km

-		7	1-G	DSM	1969	8/69/1251/SPC	SPC RE	DGC
-		7	3-G	DSM	1971	9/71/1731/MCE(RE)	MCE RE	DGC

On grid sheet lines (397-438, 465-524). There is no indication of an Edition 2-GSGS. With an overprint in yellow, magenta, green and orange.

GSGS 5066 *Sennybridge training area*   40 by 35 km

-		7	1-G	DSM	1969	8/69/7537/OS	OS	DGC
-		7	2-G	DSM	1972	1/72/1953/MCE(RE)	MCE RE	DGC
-		7	3-G	DSM	1972	12/72/721543 M	MCE RE	DGC

Superseding GSGS 4976. On grid sheet lines (275-315, 220-255). Edition 1 is *For artillery range purposes*, Editions 2 and 3 list training area information. With an overprint in green, red, blue and purple, the information supplied by HQ Western Command, 1969.

GSGS 5068 *Glen Affric/Strathconnon training area*   56 by 55 km

-		7	1-G	DSM	1969	11/69/503/SPC	SPC RE	DGC
-		7	1-G	DSM	1969	5/71/1396/MCE(RE)	MCE RE	DGC

Superseding GSGS 5034. On grid sheet lines (189-245, 809-864). With an overprint in blue, the overprint information supplied by HQ Scottish Command. The first printing has the excluded areas marked by widely spaced vertical lines which are difficult to see; these were replaced on the second printing by closely spaced diagonal lines.

GSGS 5076 *Catterick and Warcop training centres*   54 by 46 km

-		7	1-G	DSM	1970	4/70/1529/MCE(RE)	MCE RE	DGC
-		7	1-G	DSM	1970	10/71/1816/MCE(RE)	MCE RE	DGC

Superseding GSGS Misc.1764. On grid sheet lines (370-424, 489-535). With an overprint in black, red, yellow and green, from information supplied by HQ Northern Command.

GSGS 5169 *RA range Hebrides*   30 by 72 km

-		7	1-G	DSM	1972	7/72/721270/M	MCE RE	BL

On grid sheet lines (065-095, 810-882). The overprint in black and red drawn from information supplied by RA Range, Hebrides. With an inset of St Kilda. No green plate.

GSGS 5177 *Salisbury Plain trg area (1973) air map*   40 by 45 km

-		7	[sheet 167]. 1-G	DSM	1973	9/73/721092 M	MCE RE	DGC

With an extrusion between Warminster and Westbury to allow complete coverage of the Imber range area. Air information, including the title suffix, was overprinted in blue on GSGS 4974, edition 4 (q.v.). The air overprint was drawn by MCE RE from information supplied by HQ Salisbury Plain Area 1972/3.

Supplement 4. *Military exercise maps*

It is difficult for the outsider, at present without access to the documents that would presumably have accompanied every exercise, to understand how the military authorities organised the maps required. Evidently some exercises were repeated over a period of years. In some cases there was new mapping, sometimes with a new GSGS number, other times not. Sometimes there appears to have been no GSGS number, which may imply the retention of the original one. Often no date appeared on the maps. Some maps were full sheets, some specially prepared, some were sections cut from sheets. Some were overprinted, some had the exercise detail added by hand. Some had printed imprint information, some nothing but a GSGS number added in pencil. Few had formal titles, and some no title at all. In a few cases it is possible that a map listed here was not intended for an exercise at all, but had been prepared for some other purpose. This list is thus a provisional one, which will some time in the future be corrected and amplified once adequate research on the full documentation has become possible. It is arranged alphabetically, with untitled maps at the end. Copies of maps not otherwise cited were recorded in the GSGS miscellaneous collection in DGC Feltham; these maps are destined for transfer to the British Library.

GSGS Misc.1635 *78 Agra Exercise 1953*

10,000/ /51	6	*Catterick area.* 1635/1	250/8/53 OS	OS	BL
20,000/11/51	6	sheet 91. 1635/2	250/8/53 OS	OS	BL
15,000/1/52	6	sheet 97. 1635/3	250/8/53 OS	OS	BL
6000/1/52	6	sheet 98. 1635/4	250/8/53 OS	OS	BL

Copies in BL Maps 1175(201). The overprint in red was drawn and reproduced by Ordnance Survey in 1953.

GSGS Misc.2142 *Exercise April Hare*

Sections of Seventh Series sheets 89 and 90 were used.

GSGS Misc.421 *Exercise Backstop*

15,000/4/48	P	sheet 80	WO	1948	nc	Ob
25,000/7/49	P	sheet 81	WO	1949	nc	Ob
15,000/3/48	P	sheet 85	WO	1947	nc	Ob
25,000/2/49	P	sheet 86	WO	1949	nc	Ob

The mapping used is the Popular Edition map of Scotland.

GSGS Misc.1605 *Exercise Ballista III*

20,000/3/52	6	sheet 109. 1605/1	nc	Ob
15,000/12/51	6	sheet 118. 1605/2	nc	Ob

GSGS Misc.2055 *Exercise Bear Handful II*

Sections of Seventh Series sheets 112 and 113 were used.

GSGS Misc.2107 *Exercise Bear Handful III*

Sections of Seventh Series sheets 112 and 113 were used.

GSGS Misc.2151 *Exercise Druids Drum*

The three sheets for this exercise comprise a quarter-inch map, and two one-inch sheets based on Seventh Series mapping: sheet 2, GSGS Misc.2151/2 *Havant Police Division* (446-482, 096-145); sheet 3, GSGS Misc.2151/3 *Lyndhurst Police Division* (402-53, 091-124). Printed by 42 Survey Engineer Regiment, 200/6/67/385/OA.

GSGS Misc.491 *Exercise Father Tiber*

18,000/9/49	6	sheet 155	350/1/51 SPC RE	SPC RE	Ob
10,000/8/50	6	sheet 156	350/1/51 SPC RE	SPC RE	Ob
15,000/8/49	6	sheet 165	nc		Ob
15,000/8/49	6	sheet 165	500/9/50 SPC RE	SPC RE	DA
10,000/6/50	6	sheet 166	350/1/51 SPC RE	SPC RE	Ob

With an overprint in black and green.

GSGS Misc.1941 *Exercise Follow On*

15,000/12/49	P	sheet 21	120/11/61/4404/R	1 SPC RE	DGC

Using the Popular Edition map of Scotland. GSGS and printer references were added by hand to this copy.

1		6	7 and 8		9	10	11		12	15	16

GSGS Misc.490 *Exercise Hereward*

13,000/6/49	6	sheet 136. 490/2		nc			Ob	

With an overprint in blue and brown. GSGS Misc.490/1 and 490/3 are quarter-inch maps which supply the missing sections of the overprint.

GSGS Misc.1815 *Exercise Island Fling*

25,000/8/52	6	sheet 171. 1815/1	150/2/58 3726/R	1 SPC RE	DGC
20,000/12/55 OS	6	sheet 172. 1815/2	150/2/58 3726/R	1 SPC RE	DGC
25,000/9/52	6	sheet 184. 1815/3	150/2/58 3726/R	1 SPC RE	DGC
30,000/2/55 OS	6	sheet 173. 1815/4	150/2/58 3726/R	1 SPC RE	DGC

Exercise Life Line

40,000/12/66/6842/OS	7	sheet 166	nc	DGC	1
95,000/11/63/6581/OS	7	sheet 167	nc	DGC	
3/68/7070/OS	7	sheet 167	nc	DGC	
70/7765/OS	7	sheet 177	nc	DGC	1

No GSGS number recorded. 1. With two different states of the overprint.

GSGS Misc.2363 *Exercise Life Line*

Sections of three Seventh Series sheets were used: 2363/1 sheet 178, print code 6/71/1488/MCE(RE), 2363/2 sheet 166, print code 6/71/1489/MCE(RE), 2363/3 sheet 167, print code 6/71/1490/MCE(RE).

Exercise Lion

No GSGS number recorded. A section of New Popular Edition sheet 132 (20,000/4/52) was used (copy BL-d).

GSGS Misc.2054 *Exercise March Hare III*

Sections of Seventh Series sheets 86, 92 and 93 were used.

GSGS Misc.2099 *Exercise March Hare IV*

10,000/2/62/6387/OS	7	sheet 86	nc	DGC	
6000/12/64/6700/OS	7	sheet 92	nc	DGC	
10,000/11/64/6680/OS	7	sheet 93	nc	DGC	

With a handwritten WOPD number 1343/SPC. Overdrawn in black.

GSGS Misc.2171 *Exercise March Hare 1968*

30,000/9/65/6715/OS	7	sheet 86	3/68/360/SPC	SPC RE	DGC

Overprinted by SPC RE from material supplied by HQ 44 Para Bde (V) 1968.

GSGS Misc.2206 *Exercise March Hare 1969*

30,000/9/65/6715/OS	7	sheet 86	3/69/1041/SPC	SPC RE	DGC

Overprinted by SPC RE from material supplied by HQ 44 Para Bde (V) 1968.

GSGS Misc.1618 *Exercise Noahs Ark*

15,000/4/52	6	sheet 101. 1618/1	nc	DGC	
20,000/3/52	6	sheet 109. 1618/2	nc	DGC	
6000/7/52	6	sheet 110. 1618/3	nc	Ob	
15,000/12/51	6	sheet 118. 1618/4	nc	Ob	

GSGS Misc.1801 *Exercise Orw…*

25,000/1/52	6	sheet 157. 1801/1	75/8/57	1 SPC RE	DGC

Sheet 158 may also have been required, possibly carrying the remainder of the title.

No GSGS number *Exercise Pandora*

5000/5/50	6	sheet 112	nc	BL-d
15,000/5/52	6	sheet 112	nc	BL-d
5000/5/59/5753/OS	7	sheet 112	nc	BL-d

The dates of the base maps, taken from 1950, 1952 and 1959 stock, suggest an exercise repeated over a number of years. With an overprint in black, brown, red and green.

GSGS Misc.437 *Exercise Pons Sublicius*

| 15,000/10/47 | 6 | sheet 166 | WO | 1950 | 150/9/50 | OS | DGC | |
| 10,000/6/50 | 6 | sheet 167 | WO | 1950 | 150/9/50 | OS | DGC | |

With an overprint in red, green and black.

GSGS Misc.2327 *Exercise Post Haste 1*

| 40,000/10/66/6826/OS | 7 | sheet 164. 2327/2 | | | nc | | DGC | |

The map was printed in March 1971.

GSGS Misc.2330 *Exercise Post Haste 2*

40,000/10/66/6826/OS	7	sheet 164. 2330/1			nc		DGC	
40,000/10/66/6826/OS	7	sheet 164. 2330/2			nc		DGC	
50,000/3/67/6882/OS	7	sheet 176. 2330/3			nc		DGC	
40,000/10/66/6826/OS	7	sheet 164. 2330/5			nc		DGC	
50,000/3/67/6882/OS	7	sheet 176. 2330/6			nc		DGC	

Amended by 42 Survey Engineer Regiment 1971 from data supplied by Junior Division, The Staff College, c/o School of Infantry.

GSGS Misc.2331 *Exercise Post Haste 3*

| 40,000/10/66/6826/OS | 7 | sheet 164. 2331/2 | | | nc | | DGC | |

Amended by 42 Survey Engineer Regiment 1971 from data supplied by Junior Division, The Staff College, c/o School of Infantry.

GSGS Misc.1663 *Exercise Quicksilver*

20,000/12/52	6	sheet 91. 1663/5			nc		Ob	
15,000/6/52	6	sheet 92. 1663/6			nc		Ob	
15,000/1/52	6	sheet 96. 1663/7			nc		Ob	
15,000/1/52	6	sheet 97. 1663/8			nc		Ob	

GSGS Misc.1543 *Exercise Red Spider*

New Popular Edition sheets 117, 118, 128, 129 were employed in this secret exercise, the maps reproduced by the Ordnance Survey in 1951. Maps not found. (Information from DGC catalogue card).

GSGS Misc.2109 *Exercise Sea Horse 5/6 March 1966*   32 by 21 km

A special map *Isle of Purbeck* was used, for intake 39 Waterloo Company RMA Sandhurst. The map comprised a black outline plate only, with no names, and a blue sea plate. On grid sheet lines (374-406, 075-096). Printed by 42 Survey Engineer Regiment, Royal Engineers, print code 1000/3/66/334/OA.

GSGS Misc.1560 *Exercise Surprise Packet*

30,000/7/51	6	sheet 155. 1560/3	WO	1951	15,000/8/51	OS	Ob	
20,000/6/51	6	sheet 156. 1560/4	WO	1951	10,200/8/51	OS	Ob	
25,000/8/51	6	sheet 157. 1560/5	WO	1951	13,000/9/51	OS	Ob	
30,000/7/51	6	sheet 158. 1560/6	WO	1951	13,000/9/51	OS	Ob	
25,000/7/51	6	sheet 159. 1560/7	WO	1951	15,000/8/51	OS	Ob	
20,000/7/51	6	sheet 165. 1560/8	WO	1951	15,000/8/51	OS	Ob	
15,000/7/51	6	sheet 166. 1560/9	WO	1951	15,000/8/51	OS	Ob	
15,000/7/51	6	sheet 167. 1560/10	WO	1951	13,000/9/51	OS	Ob	
15,000/7/51	6	sheet 168. 1560/11	WO	1951	15,000/8/51	OS	Ob	
10,000/5/51	6	sheet 169. 1560/12	WO	1951	13,000/8/51	OS	Ob	1
15,000/7/51	6	sheet 177. 1560/13	WO	1951	15,000/8/51	OS	Ob	
15,000/7/51	6	sheet 178. 1560/1	WO	1951	13,000/9/51	OS	Ob	
20,000/7/51	6	sheet 179. 1560/2	WO	1951	13,000/9/51	OS	Ob	
20,000/8/51	6	sheet 180. 1560/14	WO	1951	15,000/8/51	OS	Ob	
25,000/6/51	6	sheet 181. 1560/15	WO	1951	10,300/8/51	OS	Ob	

Civilian weight paper was used for almost all sheets. 1. 13,000 copies were required, apparently from a print run of 10,000.

GSGS Misc.1957 [Ten Tors]

Comprising a section of Seventh Series sheet 187 (print code 10,000/4/62/6388/OS), headed *Dartmoor*. This is apparently the Ten Tors exercise map, not yet so named.

GSGS Misc.2007 *Ten Tors 1964*

Two sections of Seventh Series sheet 187 numbered 2007/1 and 2007/2 were overprinted for use as an exercise map. Presumably superseded in 1965 by GSGS 4965.

GSGS 4965 *Ten Tors 1965*

Two sections cut from Seventh Series sheet 187 (254-271, 070-099) formed Edition 1-GSGS. All marginalia was trimmed off. With an overprint in black. The print order number (SPO 1075/SPC) dates from April 1965.

GSGS 4965 *Ten Tors 1966*   52 by 48 km

| - | 7 | 2-G | DSM | 1966 | 1000/5/66/1593/SPC | SPC RE | DGC |

A newly designed map on grid sheet lines (240-290, 052-100) superseded edition 1. With an overprint in black, the information supplied in 1966 by Junior Leaders Regiment Newton Abbot.

GSGS 4965 *Ten Tors*   52 by 48 km

-	7	3-G	DSM	1967	1000/4/67/1972/SPC	SPC RE	DGC	1,3
-	7	4-G	DSM	1967	3/68/290/SPC	SPC RE	DGC	1,4
-	7	5-G	DSM	1970	2/70/1875/SPC	SPC RE	DGC	2,4
-	7	5-G	DSM	1970	6/70/8007/OS	OS	DGC	2,4
-	7	5-G	DSM	1970	6/71/1525/MCE(RE)	MCE RE	DGC	2,4
-	7	6-G	DSM	1973	4/73/730188 M	MCE RE	DGC	2,4

Map dimensions were unchanged from edition 2. 1. With an overprint in black. 2. With an overprint in blue. 3. The overprint information was supplied in 1967 by Junior Leaders Regiment Newton Abbot. 4. The overprint information was supplied by Headquarters South West District in 1968 and 1969, with minor revisions in 1973.

GSGS 4965 *Ten Tors*   38 by 50 km

| - | 7 | 7-G | DSM | 1974 | 4/74/732195 R | 42 SER | DGC |

The map area was reduced, though still on grid sheet lines (212 280, 050 100). With an overprint in red, yellow and blue, from information supplied by G. Training HQ UKLF 1973.

GSGS Misc.1726 *Exercise Tinder Box*

25,000/5/52	6	sheet 160. 1726/1	200/4/56 OS	OS	DGC
30,000/12/52	6	sheet 161. 1726/2	200/4/56 OS	OS	DGC
15,000/1/53	6	sheet 162. 1726/3	200/4/56 OS	OS	DGC
30,000/3/55 OS	6	sheet 170. 1726/4	200/4/56 OS	OS	DGC
trimmed	6	sheet 171. 1726/5	200/4/56 OS	OS	DGC
20,000/12/55 OS	6	sheet 172. 1726/6	200/4/56 OS	OS	DGC
30,000/2/55 OS	6	sheet 173. 1726/7	200/4/56 OS	OS	DGC

With an overprint in purple.

GSGS Misc.498 *Western Command pre Staff College course*

| 13,000/10/48 | 6 | sheet 98. 498/1 | WO | 1950 | nc | | DGC |
| 13,000/12/48 | 6 | sheet 104. 498/1 | WO | 1950 | nc | | DGC |

With an overprint in blue and red.

GSGS Misc.1958 [Exercise unnamed]

| [A, 3/6] | 7 | sheet 168 | 450/7/62/4509/R | SPC RE | DGC |

Overprints drawn by Southern Command, 1962.

GSGS Misc.2136 [Exercise unnamed]

Sections of Seventh Series sheets 90 and 91, covering the Catterick camp area. Presumably for some form of exercise, showing the start point and the finish point. Overprinted by SPC RE, print code 1000/10/66/181[?]/SPC.

GSGS Misc.2332 [Exercise unnamed]

| 95,000/11/63/6581/OS | 7 | sheet 167. 2332/2 | nc | | DGC |

The exercise is unnamed, though the heading to the map reads *Comd 1 Div's Marked Map*. Amended by 42 Survey Engineer Regiment 1971 from data supplied by Junior Division, The Staff College, c/o School of Infantry.

GSGS Misc.2368 [Exercise unnamed]

| 10/69/7558/OS | 7 | sheet 107 | 7/71/1545/MCE(RE) | MCE RE | DGC |

MCE 509 *Exercise Home Run 70*

Using photocopies of M722 sheet 86, edition 4-GSGS. Overprinted by MCE, February 1970 (WOPD 27 MCE).

Supplement 5. *Skeleton maps*

GSGS Misc.1850 [sheet 167 *Salisbury Plain*], contours, water. Print code 100/5/59/4128/R
GSGS Misc.2108 [sheet 171 *London SE*], contours, water, woods, red grid. Print code 60/3/66/6816/OS
GSGS Misc.2255 [sheet 167 *Salisbury*], contours, water. Print code 8/70/7983/OS.
GSGS Misc.2256 [sheet 166 *Frome*], contours, water. Print code 8/70/7984/OS.
GSGS Misc.2333 [sheet 178 *Dorchester*], contours, water, woods, black grid. Print code 7/71/1476/MCE(RE).
       Prepared from M722 sheet 178 by 42 Survey Engineer Regiment, 1971.

GSGS 5172 [sheet 141] *Brecon*, contours, water, woods. Print code 5/72/2343/MCE(RE)
GSGS 5172 [sheet 166] *Frome*, contours, water, woods. Print code 4/72/2270/MCE(RE)
GSGS 5172 [sheet 167] *Salisbury*, contours, water, woods. Print code 4/72/2326/MCE(RE)
GSGS 5172 [sheet 169] *Aldershot*, contours, water, woods. Print code 4/72/2320/MCE(RE)
GSGS 5172 [sheet 171] *London SE*, contours, water, woods. Print code 5/72/2325/MCE(RE)
GSGS 5172 [sheet 173] *East Kent*, contours, water, woods. Print code 4/72/2319/MCE(RE)
GSGS 5172 [sheet 178] *Dorchester,* contours, water, woods. Print code 5/72/2324/MCE(RE)

Special maps for R.M.A.S. map reading instruction, using contours, water and grid plates only
       Reproduced from GSGS 4620, later M722 sheet 169.

GSGS Misc.1697 Edition 1-GSGS, no code, reproduced and printed by No 1 SPC RE, 1955
      Another issue, 1500/12/62/63/SPC
      Another issue, 1150/6/65/1266/SPC
GSGS 5067 Edition 1-GSGS, issued June 1969 (print order code WOPD 1293/SPC)

Supplement 6. *Navigation charts*

GSGS Misc.1974 *RAF Decca aeronautical chart*, 1963.
      Three sheets are recorded, based on one-inch Seventh Series:
Sheet 167 *Salisbury – chain 1*. Print code 1000/2/63/6514/OS
Sheet 168 *Winchester – chain 5*. Print code 1000/6/63/6523/OS
Sheet 169 *Aldershot – chain 5*. Print code 1000/5/63/6523/OS

Supplement 7. *Other significant maps*

D.R.A's investigation of graticules
      Experimental versions of New Popular Edition sheet 167 *Salisbury* and 1:25,000 *Larkhill and Westdown* were printed for artillery training with a graticule referencing system in place of a grid. This is based on sectors of 5° of latitude and 5° of longitude, each given a single letter reference (in this case "F"), the 25 1° subdivisions being identified by a second letter. Thus the 51° N, 2° W zone containing Salisbury has the letter reference "FT". There were three trial variants of the one-inch sheet, printed by the Ordnance Survey in November 1945:
      1. With a mesh in 100th of degrees overprinted in purple. See figure 24.
      2. With a mesh in 100th of degrees and partial ladder, overprinted in purple.
      3. With a minute mesh and partial ladder, overprinted in purple.
The published version has a minute mesh in black, and is headed *D.R.A's investigation of graticules* (print code 500/11/45 Cr). Main roads are in orange together with the contours (the trial versions have main roads in red, contours in brown). Copies of all the one-inch sheets are in the DGC Specimen Collection.

GSGS Misc.349/A *Key points Hull area* 28 by 21 km

1	6	7 and 8	9	10	11	12	15	16
-	6		WO	1949	550/3/49 SPC	SPC RE	DGC	

On grid sheet lines (500-528, 420-441). Originally classified *top secret*. The base map is grey, with red, brown and blue plates, but no green plate. Photolithographed by the Ordnance Survey in 1949, the overprint drawn and reproduced by War Office 1949. Fifteen key points are listed, and overprinted in red: Sculcoates generating station; Hull hydraulic power company; pumping stations at Bilton, Dunswell, Cottingham, Springhead; cranes and lock gates of King George Dock, Alexandra Dock, Victoria Dock, Albert Dock, William Wright Dock, St Andrews Dock; Telecommunications Centre (Trunk) (Post Office); British Industrial Solvents Factory; and British Broadcasting Corporation Transmitting Station. There are also some apparently unconnected overprinted locations, suggesting the possible later use of the map for a military exercise: a dropping zone (DZ), in blue, a Royal Observer Corps Post (ROC), in black, and a Sector Operations Centre (SOC), off the mapped area in the south east, in orange.

GSGS Misc.488/11 *Red area map of Isle of Man*

Coverage of the whole of Great Britain was required in this style, and in most cases half-inch administrative maps were used. For Isle of Man coverage, sheet GSGS 3907 Second War Revision sheet 17, renumbered GSGS 4620 War Office Edition sheet 87, 15,000/10/49 printing, was overprinted.

GSGS Misc.1686 *Swindon and Bath* 46 by 36 km

1	6	7 and 8	9	10	11	12	15	16
-	6	1-G	WO	1955	4000/8/55 OS	OS	DGC	

Parts of GSGS 4620 sheets 156, 157, 166 and 167. On grid sheet lines (373-419, 153-189). Apparently a fully developed district map with complete border and marginalia. Without overprint, so its purpose is unclear.

GSGS Misc.2036 *A physiographic map of the Oxford region*

An experimental one-inch map produced in 1965 by reduction of the 1:25,000.

GSGS Misc.2049 [untitled]

1	6	7 and 8	9	11	12	15	16
20,000/3/60/6118/OS	7	sheet 131. 2049/1		12/11/64/892/SPC	SPC RE	DGC	
20,000/11/61/6309/OS	7	sheet 132. 2049/2		12/11/64/892/SPC	SPC RE	DGC	
10,000/8/62/6388/OS	7	sheet 133. 2049/3		12/11/64/892/SPC	SPC RE	DGC	
nc [HDA printing]	7	sheet 144. 2049/4		12/11/64/892/SPC	SPC RE	DGC	
25,000/12/63/6581/OS	7	sheet 145. 2049/5		12/11/64/892/SPC	SPC RE	DGC	
30,000/8/64/6656/OS	7	sheet 146. 2049/6		12/11/64/892/SPC	SPC RE	DGC	
20,000/6/64/6626/OS	7	sheet 157. 2049/7		12/11/64/892/SPC	SPC RE	DGC	
30,000/1/64/6590/OS	7	sheet 158. 2049/8		12/11/64/892/SPC	SPC RE	DGC	
30,000/2/62/4427/R	7	sheet 159. 2049/9		12/11/64/892/SPC	SPC RE	DGC	

According to a DGC catalogue card, these were produced as IDC[?] wall maps. A block of nine sheets, the intention would presumably have been to mount them as a composite map. Printing order reference WOPD 1343/SPC.

GSGS Misc.2324/3

Seventh Series sheet 166, with top and bottom margins trimmed. Showing brigade and battle group boundaries, minefields, killing zones and combat team groupings. Originally classified *secret*. GSGS Misc.2324/1 and 2324/2 comprise several tracings associated with Nuclear Defence TEWT (training exercise without troops).

GSGS 5193 *Power transmission lines*

Tracings were prepared in 1973 as overlays to sheets in M722 showing the routes of these lines. No overprinted maps at the one-inch scale have been recorded; sheets of the new 1:50,000 map M726 were overprinted with similar information in GSGS 5215 *Great Britain power line and obstruction overprint*.

Supplement 8. *Examination papers*

The following is a shortform list of maps overprinted for use as examination and test papers for entrance and promotion by the Staff College, also various command authorities, chiefly Southern Command and Eastern Command. No claim is made that this listing is complete.

Scotland Popular Edition base map

GSGS Misc.1864 sheet 67, 1960, [15,000/10/55 OS]. Print code 5000/11/59/4214/R

New Popular Edition base maps

GSGS Misc.1595 sheet 116, 1952, [15,000/2/52]. Print code 5000/8/53 OS
GSGS Misc.1640/1 sheet 178, 1954, 15,000/11/53 OS
GSGS Misc.1750 sheet 149, 1956, 15,000/9/53 OS
GSGS Misc.1836/4 sheet 186, 1959, 20,000/11/52. Print code 5000/10/58/3983/R
GSGS Misc.1879/2 sheet 169, 1959, 30,000/7/59/6006/OS. Print code 250/10/59/4221/R (added by hand)

Second War Revision sheet 17, renumbered sheet 87 in GSGS 4620

GSGS Misc.1638/1 sheet 87, 1953. Print code 8000/9/53 OS

Seventh Series base maps

GSGS Misc.1662/4 sheet 78, 1955. Print code 5500/11/54 OS
GSGS Misc.1705 sheet 158, 1956, 30,000/11/55 OS. Print code 5500/11/55 OS
GSGS Misc.1802 sheet 167, 1958, 30,000/5/57. Print code 5500/11/57/3644/R
GSGS Misc.2076/4 sheet 168, 1965, [59,000/7/63/6546/OS]. Print code 100/6/65/1163/SPC
GSGS Misc.2011/4 sheet 168, 1964. Printed by SPC RE
GSGS Misc.2115/1 sheet 166, 1966. Print codes blocked out, no new print information. For Southern Command
GSGS Misc.2115/1 sheet 178, 1966. Print codes blocked out, no new print information. For Southern Command
GSGS Misc.2122/1 sheet 62, 1966, 25,000/9/65/6715/OS. Print code 4000/8/66/1732/SPC
GSGS Misc.2123/7 sheet 136, 1966, 24,000/6/63/6546/OS. Print code 120/10/66/1748/SPC
GSGS Misc.2130 sheet 178, 1966, 50,000/6/64/6642/OS. Print code 90/10/66/1816/SPC
GSGS Misc.2159/1 sheet 159, 1967, 20,000/1/66/6795/OS. Print code 120/8/67/2109/SPC
GSGS Misc.2159/8 sheet 172, 1967, 40,000/6/64/6633/OS. Print code 120/9/67/2109/SPC
GSGS Misc.2159/9 sheet 173, 1967, 25,000/1/66/6787/OS. Print code 120/9/67/2109/SPC
GSGS Misc.2159/10 sheet 184, 1967, 20,000/6/66/1680/SPC. Print code 120/9/67/2109/SPC
GSGS Misc.2192/1 sheet 159, 1968, 25,000/11/64/6681/OS. Print code 9/68/614/SPC
GSGS Misc.2224/1 sheet 159, 1969, 20,000/1/66/6795/OS. Print code 9/69/1432/SPC

GSGS Misc.2083, 1965. Special area map (463-503, 110-151). Print code 4000/9/65/1235/SPC
GSGS Misc.2158/1, 1967. Special area map (479-503, 110-160). Print code 1800/8/67/2093/SPC
GSGS Misc.2175, 1968. Special area map (428-468, 160-210). Print code 9/68/488/SPC
GSGS Misc.2213, 1969. Special area map (407-424, 505-537). Print code 9/69/1509/SPC
GSGS Misc.2214, 1969. Special area map (400-432, 486-550). Print code 9/69/1508/SPC
GSGS Misc.2285, 1970. Special area map (328-376, 338-366). Print code 9/70/560/MCE(RE)

Supplement 9. *Map extracts used for examination and other purposes*

Examination extracts

This is a shortform list of map extracts recorded, which were mostly in use in Army Certificate of Education examinations, and carried a variety of subheadings concerned with map reading, geography and expedition skills. No claim is made that this listing is complete – indeed it is certain that some are missing from the Superseded Collection at DGC. Others may be assumed from card catalogues, such as GSGS Misc.1901 *Garstang*, but since these cards often give no scale for a map, it would be dangerous to deduce too much solely from them.

GSGS Misc.389, 1950, 1500/6/50, [Romsey area]. A proof copy without print code is also recorded
GSGS Misc.436, 1950, 3000/1/51, [Auchterarder area]
GSGS Misc.1549, 1951, 12,000/8/51, [Brampton/Haltwhistle area]
GSGS Misc.1577, 1951, 12,000/12/51, The Lleyn Peninsula
GSGS Misc.1592, 1952, 11,500/8/52, Buxton/Matlock area
GSGS Misc.1612, 1953, Swindon area. OS 1954, with unique number 3887 (388-409, 169-184)
GSGS Misc.1612, 1953, 11,000/1/53, Swindon area. GSGS Misc.1613 was printed in error on both these
GSGS Misc.1627, 1953, 12,000/7/53 OS, Cerne Abbas, Dorset area
GSGS Misc.1639, 1953, 1000/10/53 OS, Carmarthen area
GSGS Misc.1645, 1954, 12,000/1/54 OS, Newport-Ryde (Isle of Wight)
GSGS Misc.1654, 1954, 12,200/8/54 OS, Ilfracombe area
GSGS Misc.1666, 1954, 1000/11/54 OS, Lewes area
GSGS Misc.1667, 1955, 13,200/1/55 OS, Winchcombe-Chipping Camden area
GSGS Misc.1676, 1955, 550/3/55 OS, Cockermouth area
GSGS Misc.1684, 1955, 700/4/55 OS, Garstang area
GSGS Misc.1687, 1955, 12,200/7/55 OS, Canterbury-Herne Bay area
GSGS Misc.1704, 1955, 900/10/55 OS, Rye area
GSGS Misc.1713, 1956, 13,200/1/56 OS, Salisbury-Amesbury area
GSGS Misc.1719, 1955, 9200/12/55 OS, [Barham area]
GSGS Misc.1723, 1956, 500/2/56, Minehead area
GSGS Misc.1724, 1956, 900/4/56, Tremadoc Bay area
GSGS Misc.1738, 1956, 550/6/56, Whitchurch area
GSGS Misc.1739, 1956, 13,200/7/56, Marlborough-Chisledon area
GSGS Misc.1755, 1956, 800/10/56, Penrith area
GSGS Misc.1761, 1957, 13,200/1/57, Westbury-Warminster area
GSGS Misc.1762, 1957, 9200/1/57, [Welshpool area]
GSGS Misc.1763, 1957, 1600/1/57, Worthing area
GSGS Misc.1766, 1957, 2000/3/57, Banbury area
GSGS Misc.1789, 1957, 13,200/8/57, Thame-Princes Risborough area
GSGS Misc.1790, 1957, 9200/7/57, [Harlech area]
GSGS Misc.1805, 1957, 1500/9/57/5666/OS, Isle of Man
GSGS Misc.1812, 1958, 19,200/1/58/5695/OS, Axminster
GSGS Misc.1813, 1958, 1400/1/58/5708/OS, Loch Ness
GSGS Misc.1817, 1958, 2000/3/58/5726/OS, Bedford
GSGS Misc.1822, 1960, 11,200/1/60/6210/OS, Dolgelly. Presumably a reprint.
GSGS Misc.1829, 1958, 19,200/8/58/389/OS, Pickering
GSGS Misc.1835, 1958, 2250/10/58/5826/OS, Dunbar
GSGS Misc.1838, 1958, 11,200/1/59/5901/OS, Dunbar-East Linton
GSGS Misc.1839, 1958, 11,200/1/59/5901/OS, Westbury
GSGS Misc.1844, 1959, 2000/5/59/5990/OS, Hemel Hempstead
GSGS Misc.1855, 1959, 11,200/8/59/6017/OS, Wellington, Salop
GSGS Misc.1862, 1959, 3000/10/59/6088/OS, New Abbey
GSGS Misc.1900, 1960, no code recorded, Pickering (copy PC)
GSGS Misc.1906, 1960, 3500/10/60/6269/OS, Cumnock
GSGS Misc.1916, 1961, 3500/2/61/6300/OS, Market Weighton
GSGS Misc.1919, 1961, 8200/6/61/6319/OS, Westbury
GSGS Misc.1921, 1961, 8200/6/61/6319/OS, Neath
GSGS Misc.1924, 1961, 3500/6/61/6326/OS, Keighley
GSGS Misc.1942, 1961, 3000/10/61/6360/OS, Wellington

GSGS Misc.1947, 1962, 3000/2/62/6380/OS, Dunbar
GSGS Misc.1949, 1962, 13,200/4/62/6384/OS, Cumnock
GSGS Misc.1954, 1962, no code, Cumnock
GSGS Misc.1962, 1962, no code, Upton upon Severn
GSGS Misc.1969, 1962, 13,200/12/62/6493/OS, Congleton
GSGS Misc.1971, 1963, 3500/1/63/6502/OS,Westbury
GSGS Misc.1973, 1963, 3500/4/63/6506/OS, Aberdare
GSGS Misc.1980, 1963, 13,200/7/63/6527/OS, Redcar
GSGS Misc.1983, 1963, 3500/9/63/6547/OS, Falkirk
GSGS Misc.1993, 1963, 11,500/11/63/6572/OS, Brierley Hill
GSGS Misc.2004, 1964, 3500/3/64/6604/OS, [Prestatyn]
GSGS Misc.2006, 1964, 11,600/6/64/6613/OS, Dumbarton
GSGS Misc.2010, 1964, 3500/5/64/6624/OS, Loughborough
GSGS Misc.2032, 1964, 3500/10/64/6649/OS, Wellington
GSGS Misc.2044 on 1962 civilian educational extract No 216/88, with ms WOPD 6676/OS, Millom area
GSGS Misc.2050, 1965, 3500/1/65/6688/OS, Blandford
GSGS Misc.2059, 1965, 11,600/8/65/6753/OS, Winscombe
GSGS Misc.2069, 1965, 3500/6/65/6735/OS, Maidenhead
GSGS Misc.2070, 1965, 1500/10/65/6743/OS, Snowdon
GSGS Misc.2071, 1965, 11,600/12/65/6745/OS, Perth
GSGS Misc.2072, 1966, 11,600/3/66/6745/OS, Ivybridge
GSGS Misc.2073, 1966, 11,600/5/66/6745/OS, Ludlow
GSGS Misc.2074, 1966, 11,600/5/66/6745/OS, Melrose and Kelso
GSGS Misc.2093, 1966, 1000/1/66/6781/OS, [Barmouth]
GSGS Misc.2094, 1966, 3500/1/66/6781/OS, Guildford
GSGS Misc.2095, 1966, 3500/4/66/6781/OS, Ennerdale
GSGS Misc.2096, 1966, 1000/4/66/6781/OS, [Keswick]; the base is the Lake District tourist map
GSGS Misc.2097, 1966, 3000/8/66/6781/OS, Stow-on-the-Wold
GSGS Misc.2098, 1966, 500/8/66/6781/OS, Cairngorms
GSGS Misc.2102, 1965, 3500/10/66/6786/OS, Salisbury
GSGS Misc.2117/1, 1967, 3000/10/66/6867/OS, Church Stretton
GSGS Misc.2117/3, 1967, 4250/1/67/6867/OS, Stirling
GSGS Misc.2117/5, 1967, 4250/5/67/6867/OS, Brampton
GSGS Misc.2124/1, 1968, 4000/6/67/6987/OS, Pontypridd. The WOPD should be 6873
GSGS Misc.2124/3, 1968, 4000/11/67/6897/OS, Douglas. The WOPD should be 6873
GSGS Misc.2124/5, 1968, 4000/6/67/6897/OS, Caerphilly. The WOPD should be 6873
GSGS Misc.2137/2, 1968, 4000/7/68/6885/OS, Barnstaple
GSGS Misc.2137/4, 1968,4000/12/68/7367/OS, Brendon Hills
GSGS Misc.2137/6, 1968, 4000/2/69/7386/OS, The Yealm Valley
GSGS Misc.2149/1, 1968, 11,610/9/67/6925/OS, Bacup
GSGS Misc.2161/2, 1970, 3250/8/69/7350/OS, Forfar
GSGS Misc.2161/4, 1970, 3250/11/69/7646/OS, Broadway
GSGS Misc.2161/6, 1970, 3250/2/70/7899/OS, Inverurie
GSGS Misc.2165/1, 1968, 11,600/1/68/6989/OS, Marlborough
GSGS Misc.2173/1, 1968, 11,610/7/68/7154/OS, Folkestone
GSGS Misc.2200, 1969, 11,600/3/69/7352/OS, Llangefni
GSGS Misc.2208, 1969, 1500/6/69/7447/OS, Wells
GSGS Misc.2211, 1970, 11,600/7/69/7450/OS, Upton-upon-Severn
GSGS Misc.2230, 1970, 11,600/2/70/7671/OS, Market Weighton
GSGS Misc.2235, 1970, 350/1/70/7764/OS, Dolgellau
GSGS Misc.2240, 1970, 350/5/70/7926/OS, Truro
GSGS Misc.2241, 1970, 1500/5/70/7937/OS, Barnstaple
GSGS Misc.2245, 1970, 8000/8/70/7954/OS, Coldstream
GSGS Misc.2247, 1968, 250/7/70/7956/OS, Llangollen
GSGS Misc.2303, 1970, 12/70/796/MCE(RE), Calne
GSGS Misc.2304, 1970, 12/70/860/MCE(RE), Upton-upon-Severn
GSGS Misc.2305, 1970, 11/70/790/MCE(RE), extract of *Dartmoor*, without place names
GSGS Misc.2353, 1971, 6/71/8260/OS, Malton
GSGS Misc.2360, 1971, 6/71/8257/OS, Llangollen
GSGS Misc.2366, 1971, 9/71/8307/OS, Bacup
GSGS Misc.2373, 1971, 8/71/8372/OS, Truro area

GSGS Misc.1741, a section of GSGS 4620 mapping used for an exercise for the School of Artillery
GSGS Misc.1928, section of sheet 168, used for examinations
GSGS Misc.1966/1, section of sheet 155, used for examinations
GSGS Misc.2374/1 sections of sheets 178 and 179, used for examinations. Print code 8/71/1652/MCE(RE)
GSGS Misc.2374/2 sections of sheets 178 and 179, used for examinations. Print code 8/71/1653/MCE(RE)

Plates in books

GSGS Misc.1659, *Manual of…… map reading 1955*. London: HMSO, 1956.
GSGS Misc.1688, *Manual of…… map reading 1955*. London: HMSO, 1957.
GSGS Misc.1701/7 JARIC(UK), part of GSGS 4639 sheet 9. Plate VII in *Manual of……air photo reading 1958*.
        London: HMSO, 1958; also reprinted 1962.
GSGS Misc.1809, plates, various scales, for a book, including an extract from a New Popular Edition map.

And finally……

GSGS 5161 *Location map : Directorate of Military Survey and Mapping and Charting Establishment R.E.*
-                    7   1-G   DSM   1972   1/72/2067/MCE(RE)   MCE RE   DGC
Based on M722 part of sheet 170. Offering directions to the Military Survey site at Tolworth, accompanied by
local street plans. Superseded by a map at 1:50,000.

9. GSGS 4692, later M725 *London*

A large map of the London area, made up of parts of sheets in GSGS 4620, was allocated the GSGS number 4692 on 15 September 1949. It appears that the Ordnance Survey prepared the composite base map in 1949, and it is not known why its issue was apparently delayed until 1951. In spite of the small scale of the map, it was later allocated an SSD number in the town plans range, as M924. This may have been perceived as an error, because it was redesignated a special sheet in M722, confirmed by correspondence between Survey 3 and AMS in January and March 1958. This number was apparently assigned only to the New Popular Edition based map. It would never be used. A manuscript note in the GSGS number allocation book dated 16 September 1959 records that because the next edition of the Greater London map was to be made based on Seventh Series mapping, it would take the different SSD M725.[284] The map acquired a third set of sheet lines when the *Greater London* Special Map was adopted as its base, on publication in 1967, so replacing the earlier specially made composite maps. It was declared obsolete on 21 March 1973, it being determined that demands for the area it covered could be met by supplying the relevant four sheets of M722. There was evidently never any intention of producing a similar composite 1:50,000 map in M726.

For a explanation of the detail in each column see pages 196 and 197.

a. *London* b. *Greater London*

-	np	6a	4692	1-G	WO	1951	CBH E7118	HDA	p	BL	1
-	np	7a	M725	2-G	DSW	1960	nc	HDA	r	Ob	2
A	np	7b	M725	3-G	DSM	1967	6700/1/67/6886/OS	OS	r.	DGC	3
A	np	7b	M725	3-G	DSM	1967	1/70/7805/OS	OS	r.	DGC	3
B	np	7b	M725	4-G	DSM	1971	1/71/8027/OS	OS	r.	Ob	4

Printing of the first two issues may have been dealt with by the Admiralty because at the time neither Military Survey nor Ordnance Survey had the facilities to print such large sheets. 1. Printed in Creechbarrow House. On grid sheet lines (492-556, 150-208). *Compiled from parts of New Popular One-Inch Sheets 159, 160, 161, 169, 170 and 171 by Ordnance Survey, 1949,* two years before the date of issue. 2. Sheet limits are 495-556, 150-208; thus 3 km are removed from the sheet in the west, so removing the requirement for coverage from sheets 159 and 169 which were ready in Seventh Series later than the other four. *Compiled from parts of Seventh Series One Inch Sheets 160, 161, 170 and 171 by Ordnance Survey, 1960.* 3. The base map used is the *Greater London* special map (edition A), published in 1967. On grid sheet lines (501-565, 152-207). Building infill is screened black. 4. The second edition of the *Greater London* map (edition B) was published in 1971 with screened red building infill, heralding an element of the specification of the 1:50,000 map three years later.

Administrative and other maps

GSGS Misc.359 London District boundary map, 1949
Not found. Recorded on a DGC catalogue card, but its issue cannot be confirmed. Nothing is known of the base map, nor whether it would have carried Cassini or National Grid.

GSGS Misc.1513 *London District boundaries*   64 by 58 km
CBH E7118 np   6   1-G   WO   1951 nc   HDA   p   DGC
The GSGS 4692 printing with administrative boundaries overprinted in red and purple.

---

[284] This was confirmed retrospectively in the AMS SSD tab. run of 1 May 1962. The initial allocation of the SSD M725 had been to the still hypothetical 1:50,000 map of Ireland; this allocation was cancelled in December 1958.

GSGS Misc.1863 *London District boundaries* 61 by 58 km

| - | np | 7 | - | DSW | 1960 | nc | | OS | r | Ob |

The M725 1960 printing with administrative boundaries. Overprinted in red with the London District boundary, and in purple with sub district boundaries. Overprints plotted and drawn by Ordnance Survey from information supplied by Eastern Command, 1960. After the changes in administrative boundaries following the creation of the Greater London authority in 1965, the map was no longer large enough to cover the area required to show the boundary. A DGC catalogue card suggests nonetheless that a small temporary stock was to be printed to provide cover pending the new map (i.e. GSGS 4968) on the new OS base, which was not ready at that time. This reprint, if made, has not been recorded. The map was declared obsolete in May 1968.

GSGS 4968 *London District boundaries*

An DGC catalogue card gives the allocation date of the GSGS number as 27 May 1965, with the comment that the map will supersede the temporary printing on GSGS Misc.1863, mentioned above. The WOPD is 1239/SPC. Another card gives two details in the comments column, the date 8 November 1966, and "GSGS Misc.1863 superseded". While this seems to suggest the publication of GSGS 4968 late in 1966, no copy has been recorded, and DGC sources cannot confirm that the map was published. It was not necessary to await the *Greater London* map published in 1967, and issued as M725 Edition 3 in January 1967, because an administrative map in grey outline with the same sheet limits had already been made available by Ordnance Survey for civilian use late in 1966 (unique number L1568).

GSGS 5111 *Helicopter routes in the London control zone* 61 by 34 km

| - | np | 7 | | 1-G | DTI,MOD | 1971 | 5/71/8267/OS | OS | - | DGC |

On grid sheet lines (481-542, 159-193), though without the grid; with a graticule at 10' intervals. Published jointly by the Department of Trade and Industry and the Ministry of Defence, made and printed by the Director General of the Ordnance Survey, Southampton, 1971.

GSGS 5111A *Helicopter routes in the London control zone (gridded)* 61 by 34 km

-	DR	7		1-G	DSM	1972	1/72/8631/OS	OS	r.	BL
-	np	7		2-G	DSM	1977	3000/4/77/770495 S	OS	r.	BL
-	np	7		2-G	DSM	1977	5000/4/79/781666 M	MCE RE	r.	DGC

On grid sheet lines (481-542, 159-193), with the National Grid as well as the graticule.

10. M723 *Northern Ireland*

Publication by the Ordnance Survey of Northern Ireland of their One-inch Third Series map began in 1960 and took four years to complete. The map was up to date in its revision, clearly printed, layered, and carried the new Irish Transverse Mercator (or National) Grid. The possibility that Military Survey might adopt it was prompted as early as 1961 by the need to reprint sixteen sheets of the aging GSGS 4136 (apparently Northern Ireland sheets), which still carried the old Cassini Grid, but it was not until 16 March 1965 that the SSD M723 was finally allocated. All sheets were printed in May, but four sheets had already been required for an exercise in April, a need which was fulfilled by an emergency straight printing as GSGS Misc.2057. The base map was kept up to date by OSNI, and Military Survey incorporated the new editions into the reprints they frequently required.

In 1976 came news that the two Irish Ordnance Surveys were jointly to produce a 1:50,000 map of Ireland. D Mil Svy determined immediately to take a military version of the coverage of Northern Ireland, and probably also the Republic. The SSD allocated was M728. But coverage of the Republic proved not to be required, and M728, now a map of Northern Ireland only, began to appear in 1979. It was decided in 1981 (by which time all M728 sheets had been printed, but several only to a provisional specification supplied by enlargement of M723 material) to continue to reprint M723, though not to revise it, maintaining it in concurrent use with M728 until completion of the latter to full specification. This was necessary in order to ensure that series overprinted on M723 would continue to be available at a consistent scale and specification, though at least two new series, GSGS 5309 and GSGS 5309A, were available by August 1981 using 1:50,000 provisional mapping as necessary. M723 was finally declared obsolete in February 1985,[285] and all M728 1:50,000 sheets in final format were in print by August.

Sources

The only remotely complete collection of series M723 that I know of is in the Superseded Collection of DGC at Feltham, and I am most grateful to the authorities there for granting me permission to inspect it and catalogue it. This introduction to the final chapter in the history of the one-inch military map would otherwise have remained unwritten.

For a explanation of the detail in each column see pages 196 and 197.

Sheet 1 *North Coast*   Revised a 1958-59 b 1959; e 1966 f 1972 g 1979   60 by 24 km

4274	1961	1961	1961a	np	2057/1	-	DSM	1965	1000/4/65/1062/SPC	SPC RE	-	Ob	
4274	1961	1961	1965a	9/6	M723	1-G	DSM	1965	10,000/5/65/6717/OS	OS	m	DGC	
4274	1969	1969	1969be	np	M723	2-G	DSM	1969	6/69/7445/OS	OS	m	DGC	
4274	1969	1969	1969be	np	M723	2-G	DSM	1969	8/69/7445/OS	OS	m	DGC	1
4274	1969	1969	1969be	np	M723	2-G	DSM	1969	nc	OS	m	DGC	2
4274	1969	1969	1969be	np	M723	2-G	DSM	1969	8/71/1620/MCE(RE)	MCE RE	m	DGC	
4274	1969	1969	1969be	np	M723	2-G	DSM	1969	5/72/8772/OS	OS	m	DGC	
4274	nd	1969	1969bf	np	M723	3-G	DSM	1973	1/73/722524 S	OS	m	DGC	
4274	nd	1969	1969bf	np	M723	3-G	DSM	1973	2000/1/77/762298 S	OS	m	DGC	
4274	1972	1969	1969bf	np	M723	3-G	DSM	1973	1000/9/78/781183 R	42 SER	m	DGC	3
4274	1972	1969	1969bf	np	M723	3-G	DSM	1973	10,000/3/79/790417 M	MCE RE	m	DGC	
4274	1980so	1961	1980ag	np	M723	4-G	DSM	1980	18,000/3/80/800154 M	MCE RE	r	DGC	
4274	1980so	1961	1980ag	np	M723	4-G	DSM	1980	5000/12/80/801344 M	MCE RE	r	DGC	

On grid sheet lines (265-325, 430-454, with extrusions west and east). 1. This printing incorrectly carried the same SPO number as the previous: 8/69/7624/OS would have been the correct print code. 2. Printed incorrectly with no print code in July 1970. A DGC copy carries the handwritten WOPD 8039/OS. 3. This was apparently a rapid reprint for overprinting as GSGS 5135 and GSGS 5249.

---

[285] GSGS 4136 series file and M723 Product Information Branch card index, both held by DGC.

262

Sheet 2 *Londonderry* Revised a 1958-59; e 1967 f 1976 60 by 40 km

1	2	3	4	5	7	8	9	10	11	12	13	15	16
4275	1962	1962	1965a	9/6	M723	1-G	DSM	1965	10,000/5/65/6717/OS	OS	m	DGC	
4275	1969	1969	1969ae	np	M723	2-G	DSM	1965	7/69/7536/OS	OS	m	DGC	
4275	1969	1969	1969ae	np	M723	2-G	DSM	1965	8/69/7627/OS	OS	m	DGC	
4275	1969	1969	1969ae	np	M723	2-G	DSM	1965	nc	OS	m	DGC	1
4275	1969	1969	1969ae	np	M723	2-G	DSM	1965	5/71/8269/OS	OS	m	DGC	
4275	1969	1969	1969ae	np	M723	2-G	DSM	1965	10/71/8477/OS	OS	m	DGC	
4275	1969	1969	1969ae	np	M723	2-G	DSM	1965	5/72/8762/OS	OS	m	DGC	
4275	nd	1969	1969ae	np	M723	2-G	DSM	1965	1/73/722523 S	OS	m	DGC	
4275	nd	1969	1969ae	np	M723	2-G	DSM	1965	11/73/732737 S	OS	m	DGC	
4275	1976	1969	1969aef	np	M723	3-G	DSM	1976	6000/4/76/760177 S	OS	m	DGC	
4275	nd	1969	1969aef	np	M723	3-G	DSM	1976	7000/1/77/762299 S	OS	m	DGC	
4275	1976	1962	1962af	np	M723	3-G	DSM	1976	10,000/1/80/790486 S	OS	m	DGC	

1. Printed incorrectly with no print code in July 1970. A DGC copy carries the handwritten SPO 8040/OS.

Sheet 3 *Mid-Antrim* Revised a 1957-58 b 1958; e 1965 f 1971 g 1975 60 by 40 km

1	2	3	4	5	7	8	9	10	11	12	13	15	16
4259	1960	1960	1960a	np	2057/2	-	DSM	1965	1000/4/65/1062/SPC	SPC RE	-	Ob	
4259	1960	1960	1965a	6/6	M723	1-G	DSM	1965	10,000/5/65/6717/OS	OS	m	DGC	
4259	1969	1960	1969be	9/6	M723	2-G	DSM	1969	6/69/7446/OS	OS	m	DGC	
4259	1969	1960	1969be	9/6	M723	2-G	DSM	1969	8/69/7628/OS	OS	m	DGC	
4259	1969	1960	1969be	9/6	M723	2-G	DSM	1969	nc	OS	m	DGC	1
4259	1971	1960	1971bef	np	M723	3-G	DSM	1971	3/71/8239/OS	OS	m	DGC	
4259	1971	1960	1971bef	np	M723	3-G	DSM	1971	9/71/8425/OS	OS	m	DGC	
4259	1971	1960	1971bef	np	M723	3-G	DSM	1971	5/72/8764/OS	OS	m	DGC	
4259	nd	1960	1971bef	np	M723	3-G	DSM	1971	1/73/722525 S	OS	m	DGC	
4259	nd	1960	1971bef	np	M723	3-G	DSM	1971	9/73/732023 S	OS	m	DGC	
4259	1975	1960	1975befg	np	M723	4-G	DSM	1975	1/75/742484 S	OS	m	DGC	
4259	nd	1960	1975befg	np	M723	4-G	DSM	1975	5000/1/77/762300 M	MCE RE	m	DGC	
4259	nd	1960	1975befg	np	M723	4-G	DSM	1975	?/9/79/791066 M	MCE RE	m	-	2
4259	nd	1960	1975befg	np	M723	4-G	DSM	1975	18,000/10/79/791247 M	MCE RE	m	DGC	

1. Printed incorrectly with no print code in July 1970. A DGC copy carries the handwritten SPO 8041/OS. 2. The OSNI base map was further revised to 1978, but it was felt that the changes did not warrant a new GSGS edition. A further edition 4-GSGS reprint on the 1975 base was made in September 1979, but in October the printing order was amended so that all stock be set aside for the overprinted versions. No record copy appears to have been kept without overprint.

Sheet 4 *Omagh* Revised a 1959-60; e 1968 f 1978 60 by 40 km

1	2	3	4	5	7	8	9	10	11	12	13	15	16
4349	1963	1963	1965a	9/6	M723	1-G	DSM	1965	10,000/5/65/6717/OS	OS	m	DGC	
4349	1963	1963	1965a	np	M723	2-G	DSM	1965	8/69/7629/OS	OS	m	DGC	1
4349	1963	1963	1965a	np	M723	2-G	DSM	1965	8/69/7629/OS	OS	m	DGC	2
4349	1963	1963	1965a	np	M723	2-G	DSM	1965	nc	OS	m	DGC	3
4349	1963	1963	1965ae	np	M723	2-G	DSM	1965	6/71/8294/OS	OS	m	DGC	
4349	1963	1963	1965ae	np	M723	2-G	DSM	1965	5/72/8766/OS	OS	m	DGC	
4349	nd	1963	1965ae	np	M723	2-G	DSM	1965	1/73/722488 S	OS	m	DGC	
4349	nd	1963	1965ae	np	M723	2-G	DSM	1965	11/73/732738 S	OS	m	DGC	
4349	nd	1963	1965ae	np	M723	2-G	DSM	1965	nc [762301]		m	DGC	4
4349	1978	1963	1965af	np	M723	3-G	DSM	1978	2000/8/78/780359 S	OS	m	DGC	
4349	1978	1963	1965af	np	M723	3-G	DSM	1978	14,000/2/79/790184 M	MCE RE	m	DGC	
4349	1978so	1963	1965af	np	M723	3-G	DSM	1978	15,000/3/80/800145 M	MCE RE	r	DGC	

1. Printed incorrectly with the heading Edition 1-GSGS instead of 2-GSGS. This copy was corrected by hand. 2. Stock copies such as this were corrected by overprint. 3. Printed incorrectly with no print code in July 1970. A DGC copy carries the handwritten SPO 8042/OS. Furthermore the incorrect heading Edition 1-GSGS was still in place; this was corrected by overprint. 4. A reprint reference number 2762301 was assigned on 8 December 1976, but no printing order was ever issued. The matter was investigated in April 1978: "What happened to the r/p on R&R 2762301 – we've received no SPO, no Advance Catch, no copies for Map Lib. though sht. released on CR&R Note 1142 of 8.7.77? Sht. was r/p'ed only for o/p purposes & no imprint no. was put onto stock. It was Catch Released by accident! Surplus stock put in a corner at 8MACD! Control to send a single copy to PIRS." In January 1980 a single copy was annotated and sent to the map library.

1	2	3	4	5	7	8	9	10	11	12	13	15	16

Sheet 5 *East Tyrone*   Revised a 1961-62; e 1967 f 1976   60 by 40 km

1	2	3	4	5	7	8	9	10	11	12	13	15	16
4394	1964	1964	1964a	-	2057/3	-	DSM	1965	1000/4/65/1062/SPC	SPC RE	-	Ob	
4394	1964	1964	1965a	9/6	M723	1-G	DSM	1965	10,000/5/65/6717/OS	OS	m	DGC	
4394	1967	1964	1965a	np	M723	2-G	DSM	1965	8/69/7625/OS	OS	m	DGC	1
4394	1967	1964	1965a	np	M723	2-G	DSM	1965	8/69/7625/OS	OS	m	DGC	2
4394	1967	1964	1965a	np	M723	2-G	DSM	1965	nc	OS	m	DGC	3
4394	1967	1964	1965ae	np	M723	2-G	DSM	1965	5/71/8270/OS	OS	m	DGC	
4394	1967	1964	1965ae	np	M723	2-G	DSM	1965	10/71/8480/OS	OS	m	DGC	
4394	1967	1964	1965ae	np	M723	2-G	DSM	1965	5/72/8768/OS	OS	m	DGC	
4394	nd	1964	1965ae	np	M723	2-G	DSM	1965	1/73/722489 S	OS	m	DGC	
4394	nd	1964	1965ae	np	M723	2-G	DSM	1965	9/73/732024 S	OS	m	DGC	
4394	nd	1964	1965ae	np	M723	2-G	DSM	1965	1000/11/75/751872 M	MCE RE	m	DGC	
4394	nd	1964	1965ae	np	M723	2-G	DSM	1965	6000/3/76/760152 M	MCE RE	m	DGC	
4394	nd	1964	1965af	np	M723	3-G	DSM	1976	5000/12/76/761670 M	MCE RE	m	DGC	
4394	1976[so]	1964	1965af	np	M723	3-G	DSM	1976	6000/8/77/770896 R	42 SER	m	DGC	
4394	1976[so]	1964	1965af	np	M723	3-G	DSM	1976	18,000/2/79/790183 M	MCE RE	m	DGC	
4394	1976[so]	1964	1965af	np	M723	3-G	DSM	1976	13,000/9/80/801268 R	42 SER	r	DGC	
4394	1976[so]	1964	1965af	np	M723	3-G	DSM	1976	1500/4/82/820516 R	42 SER	r	DGC	
4394	1976[so]	1964	1965af	np	M723	3-G	DSM	1976	950/11/84/841545 S	OS	r	DGC	

1. Printed incorrectly with the heading Edition 1-GSGS instead of 2-GSGS. This copy was corrected by hand. 2. Stock copies had the Edition 1-GSGS "refer to" box crossed out, and an Edition 2-GSGS box added alongside. 3. Printed incorrectly with no print code in July 1970. A DGC copy carries the handwritten SPO 8043/OS. Furthermore the incorrect heading Edition 1-GSGS was still in place; this was corrected by overprint.

Sheet 6 *Belfast*   Revised a 1961-62 b 1966-7; e 1971 f 1976   60 by 40 km

1	2	3	4	5	7	8	9	10	11	12	13	15	16
4389	1963	1963	1963a	np	2057/4	-	DSM	1965	1000/4/65/1062/SPC	SPC RE	-	Ob	
4389	1963	1963	1965a	9/6	M723	1-G	DSM	1965	10,000/5/65/6717/OS	OS	m	DGC	
4389	1967	1963	1969b	np	M723	2-G	DSM	1969	3/69/7410/OS	OS	m	DGC	
4389	1967	1963	1969b	np	M723	2-G	DSM	1969	8/69/7630/OS	OS	m	DGC	
4389	1967	1963	1969b	np	M723	2-G	DSM	1969	nc	OS	m	DGC	1
4389	1971	1963	1969be	np	M723	3-G	DSM	1971	7/71/8271/OS	OS	m	DGC	
4389	1971	1963	1969be	np	M723	3-G	DSM	1971	9/71/8426/OS	OS	m	DGC	
4389	1971	1963	1969be	np	M723	3-G	DSM	1971	5/72/2356/MCE(RE)	MCE RE	m	DGC	
4389	nd	1963	1969be	np	M723	3-G	DSM	1971	1/73/722526 S	OS	m	DGC	
4389	nd	1963	1969be	np	M723	3-G	DSM	1971	9/73/732025 S	OS	m	DGC	
4389	nd	1963	1969be	np	M723	3-G	DSM	1971	6/74/740478 S	OS	m	DGC	
4389	nd	1963	1969bf	np	M723	4-G	DSM	1976	11,000/7/76/760145 M	MCE RE	m	DGC	
4389	nd	1963	1969bf	np	M723	4-G	DSM	1976	8000/1/77/762302 M	MCE RE	m	DGC	
4389	1976[so]	1963	1969bf	np	M723	4-G	DSM	1976	20,000/1/80/791134 M	MCE RE	r	DGC	

1. Printed incorrectly with no print code in July 1970. A DGC copy carries the handwritten WOPD 8044/OS.

Sheet 7 *Enniskillen*   Revised a 1960-61; e 1970 f 1978   60 by 40 km

1	2	3	4	5	7	8	9	10	11	12	13	15	16
4366	1963	1963	1965a	9/6	M723	1-G	DSM	1965	10,000/5/65/6717/OS	OS	m	DGC	
4366	1963	1963	1965a	9/6	M723	1-G	DSM	1965	8/69/7631/OS	OS	m	DGC	
4366	1963	1963	1965a	9/6	M723	1-G	DSM	1965	5/70/7973/OS	OS	m	DGC	
4366	1970	1963	1969a	np	M723	2-G	DSM	1969	6/70/7973/OS	OS	m	DGC	1
4366	1970	1963	1969ae	np	M723	2-G	DSM	1969	5/71/8272/OS	OS	m	DGC	
4366	1970	1963	1969ae	np	M723	2-G	DSM	1969	5/72/8770/OS	OS	m	DGC	
4366	nd	1963	1969ae	np	M723	2-G	DSM	1969	1/73/722490 S	OS	m	DGC	
4366	nd	1963	1969ae	np	M723	2-G	DSM	1969	10/73/732739 S	OS	m	DGC	
					M723	2-G			762303 S				2
4366	1978	1963	1963af	np	M723	3-G	DSM	1978	1000/6/78/780003 S	OS	m	DGC	
4366	1978	1963	1963af	np	M723	3-G	DSM	1978	17,000/2/79/790194 M	MCE RE	m	DGC	
4366	1978	1963	1963af	np	M723	3-G	DSM	1978	6000/10/81/810619 R	42 SER	r	DGC	

1. Printed on the same SPO as the previous. The printing record suggests that it had presumably been intended to use the SPO 8003/OS. 2. Not found. Edition 2-GSGS reprint 2762303 was entered into the printing record quite normally (R&R on 8 December 1976 and SPO on 14 January 1977). But the absence of a printing date suggests it was probably not made.

1	2	3	4	5	7	8	9	10	11	12	13	15	16

Sheet 8 *Armagh* — Revised a 1953-57; e 1968 f 1976 — 60 by 40 km

1	2	3	4	5	7	8	9	10	11	12	13	15	16
4273	1962	1962	1965a	9/6	M723	1-G	DSM	1965	10,000/6/65/6717/OS	OS	m	DGC	
4273	1968	1962	1965a	np	M723	2-G	DSM	1965	8/69/7632/OS	OS	m	DGC	1
4273	1968	1962	1965a	np	M723	2-G	DSM	1965	nc	OS	m	DGC	2
4273	1968	1962	1969ae	np	M723	2-G	DSM	1965	5/71/8273/OS	OS	m	DGC	
4273	1968	1962	1969ae	np	M723	2-G	DSM	1965	10/71/8482/OS	OS	m	DGC	
4273	1968	1962	1969ae	np	M723	2-G	DSM	1965	5/72/2358/MCE(RE)	MCE RE	m	DGC	
4273	nd	1962	1969ae	np	M723	2-G	DSM	1965	1/73/722491 S	OS	m	DGC	
4273	nd	1962	1969ae	np	M723	2-G	DSM	1965	9/73/732026 S	OS	m	DGC	
4273	nd	1962	1969ae	np	M723	2-G	DSM	1965	11/74/741874 M	MCE RE	m	DGC	
4273	1976	1962	1969aef	np	M723	3-G	DSM	1976	9000/6/76/760179 S	OS	m	DGC	
4273	nd	1962	1969aef	np	M723	3-G	DSM	1976	8000/1/77/762304 M	MCE RE	m	DGC	
4273	1976[so]	1962	1969aef	np	M723	3-G	DSM	1976	6000/8/79/790355 R	42 SER	m	DGC	
4273	1976[so]	1962	1969aef	np	M723	3-G	DSM	1976	5000/12/80/801338 M	MCE RE	r	DGC	
					M723	3-G			8000/6/81/R				3
4273	1981[so]	1962	1969aef	np	M723	3-G	DSM	1976	2800/2/83/822049 M	MCE RE	r	DGC	

1. Printed incorrectly with the heading Edition 1-GSGS instead of 2-GSGS. This copy was corrected by overprint. 2. Printed incorrectly with no print code in July 1970. A DGC copy carries the handwritten SPO 8045/OS. 3. Not found. A note in the printing record dated 5 June 1981 advises "Stock of this sheet required urgently. Due to industrial action imprint no. had to be devised. It is 8000/6/81/R. Straight reprint". Not in DGC Superseded.

Sheet 9 *South Down* — Revised a 1953-55 b 1953-66 c 1962aphoto; d 1978 e 1973 60 by 40 km

1	2	3	4	5	7	8	9	10	11	12	13	15	16
4405	1964	1964	1965ac	9/6	M723	1-G	DSM	1965	10,000/5/65/6717/OS	OS	m	DGC	
4405	1966	1964	1969bc	np	M723	2-G	DSM	1969	3/69/7411/OS	OS	m	DGC	
4405	1966	1964	1969bc	np	M723	2-G	DSM	1969	8/69/7633/OS	OS	m	DGC	
4405	1966	1964	1969bc	np	M723	2-G	DSM	1969	nc	OS	m	DGC	1
4405	1966	1964	1969bc	np	M723	2-G	DSM	1969	?5/71/8285/OS	OS	m		2
4405	1966	1964	1969bc	np	M723	2-G	DSM	1969	10/71/8479/OS	OS	m	DGC	
4405	nd	1964	1969bc	np	M723	2-G	DSM	1969	5/72/2360/MCE(RE)	MCE RE	m	DGC	
4405	nd	1964	1969bc	np	M723	2-G	DSM	1969	1/73/722492 S	OS	m	DGC	
4405	nd	1964	1973bce	np	M723	2-G	DSM	1969	9/73/732352 S	OS	m	DGC	
4405	nd	1964	1973bce	np	M723	2-G	DSM	1969	1000/12/75/751873 M	MCE RE	m	DGC	
4405	nd	1964	1973bce	np	M723	2-G	DSM	1969	6000/1/77/762135 S	OS	m	DGC	
4405	1969[so]	1964	1973bce	np	M723	2-G	DSM	1969	5000/9/77/771006 R	42 SER	m	DGC	
4405	1980[so]	1964	1978bcde	np	M723	3-G	DSM	1980	18,000/1/80/791106 M	MCE RE	r	DGC	
4405	1980[so]	1964	1978bcde	np	M723	3-G	DSM	1980	8000/10/80/800700 M	MCE RE	r	DGC	
4405	1980[so]	1964	1978bcde	np	M723	3-G	DSM	1980	4200/5/83/830486 R	42 SER	r	DGC	3

1. Printed incorrectly with no print code in July 1970. A DGC copy carries the handwritten WO 8046/OS. 2. Entered into the printing record in the same manner as May 1971 reprints of other sheets. Not in DGC Superseded, and issue not confirmed. 3. This reprint was dropped from the monthly printout by 12 April 1984. On 26 April 42 SER returned a printed copy with the repmat, to which is added the pencilled explanation: "This sheet was reprinted but not catch released. Task was cancelled at last minute. Stock destroyed. Sheet to go to Map Library for superseded collection. 26.4.84"

Dependent issues, 1970-82

GSGS 5102	Royal Ulster Constabulary divisional & subdivisional boundaries
GSGS 5135	Topographic Decca chart Northern Ireland, chain 3
GSGS 5149	Topographic Dectrac chart Northern Ireland, chain 3
GSGS 5249	Helicopter chart Northern Ireland
GSGS 5260	Topographic Dectrac chart Northern Ireland, chain 7
GSGS 5276	Topographic Decca chart Northern Ireland, chain 7
GSGS 5378	Helicopter chart Northern Ireland
GSGS 5383	Topographic Decca chart Northern Ireland, chain 3
GSGS 5385	Topographic Decca chart Northern Ireland, chain 7
GSGS 5387	Topographic Dectrac chart Northern Ireland, chain 3
GSGS 5389	Topographic Dectrac chart Northern Ireland, chain 7

Appendices

Appendix 1. *Current edition lists of GSGS 3908 and 3907*

The information set out below is taken from occasional GSGS 3908 and 3907 sheet lists, issued by General Headquarters Home Forces, and sent to Eastern, Northern, Scottish, Southern and Western Commands, various Corps, and Field Survey Depots, Royal Engineers. Additional copies were sent to GSGS Cheltenham, the Director General OS, the Assistant Director of Intelligence (Maps), and, later, South-Eastern Command, Canadian Corps and Headquarters, Aldershot Area. The intention was to keep recipients informed of the most recent state of each sheet, and further to advise them of which other editions remained current and which therefore they were permitted to keep in stock. The two years from the middle of 1940 witnessed a ceaseless programme of updating Popular Edition mapping to War Revision, and in most cases on to Second War Revision, resulting in a constantly changing situation that required very careful stock control. In some cases a new edition required the immediate disposal of a previous one, in other cases there was virtually no change, and the War Office was evidently very keen to avoid as much waste as possible.

 The first column assumes the *status quo* in 1938, when England sheet 107 was converted from Popular to Fifth Edition mapping. It appears that the run of current edition statements from 31 October 1940 to 31 July 1942 is complete. Whether there are any missing thereafter until that dated 31 May 1944 I have not been able to ascertain. Certainly there was less activity during that time, and only Second War Revision sheet 93 remained to be issued later than May 1944. Thus these statements probably contain the most accurate information we are likely to obtain as to the issue dates of sheets in War Revision and Second War Revision. That said, there are still some details unresolved. Six of the eleven south-west sheets converted to Fifth Edition sheet lines were certainly issued in War Revision much later than is set out in these lists. This may be just a clerical error, which updated nine of the eleven at the same time. But it had no significance because the map was unaltered between Fifth Edition and War Revision states. Secondly, the headings concerning currency printed on the maps is not always fully in accordance with what appears in these tables. Thirdly there are three English War Revision sheets, 116, 117 and 134, that do not appear in these lists. While sheets 116 and 117 may never have been issued in War Revision,[286] copies of sheet 134 do appear to have been circulated. This is in its way frustrating, because it weakens the status of these lists as virtual proof that sheets not listed here as War Revision were never issued in that form. This set of documents is probably significant enough to warrant publication of their full titles.[287]

G.S.G.S. 3907 (E.&W. 1" to 1 mile). Statement for 31st October, 1940, showing current editions.

G.S.G.S. 3907. (England and Wales 1" to 1 mile). Statement for 1st February, 1941. showing current edition.

G.S.G.S. 3907. (England and Wales 1" to 1 mile). Statement for 15th May, 1941, showing current edition.

Current editions of G.S.G.S. 3907 (E.&W.1") Statement for 8th July, 1941
Current editions of G.S.G.S. 3908 (Scot 1") Statement for 8th July 1941 (First list of series to be issued)

Current edition of G.S.G.S. 3907 (E.&W.1") Statement for 31st Oct. 1941
Current editions of G.S.G.S. 3908 (Scot 1") Statement for 31st Oct. 1941 (Second list of series to be issued)

Current edition of G.S.G.S. 3907 (E.&W.1") Statement for 28th Feb. 1942
Current editions of G.S.G.S. 3908 (Scot. 1") Statement for 28th Feb. 1942 (Third list of series to be issued)

Current edition of G.S.G.S. 3907 (E.&W.1") Statement for 31st. July 1942
Current editions of G.S.G.S. 3908 (Scot. 1") Statement for 31st July 1942 (Fourth list of series to be issued)

Current editions. One inch series Great Britain – 31 May 1944. 1. GSGS 3907 (1" E&W)
Current editions. One inch series Great Britain – 31 May 1944. 2. GSGS 3908 (1" Scotland)

---

[286] Copies are in DGC Superseded (now in BL-d), received there as OS file copies.
[287] The Home Forces reference number to the lists to 31 July 1942 is HF/7272/CV. The 31 May 1944 list reference is HF/5715/Svy. Cross references to these documents here are in all cases abbreviated to *GSGS 3907 (or 3908) current edition*, with the relevant date. Copies of the lists to July 1941 are in PRO WO 402/91, and those to July 1942 in PRO WO 402/92. The May 1944 table is in the GSGS 3907 series file, at present with DGC.

Each issue was accompanied by a set of explanatory notes, refined by the last issue to:

> 1. Editions are abbreviated as follows:- Pop = Popular Edition; WR = War Revision Edition; 2WR = Second War Revision.
> 2. Certain sheets in Devon and Cornwall are published on 5th Edition Sheet Lines, with or without the heading *War Revision*; both the 5th and WR editions are the same.
> 3. Editions enclosed in brackets indicate that stocks of this edition are held in reserve for emergency only.
> 4. Where more than one edition is shown against a sheet, these editions may be used concurrently.

Other abbreviations used here: "P" is Popular Edition. England sheets 107 and 114 were converted early to Fifth Edition mapping, and were accounted "Special Popular" editions (here "SP") before conversion to Second War Revision. Sheet 117A was first issued as a numbered sheet in Second War Revision: a Popular Edition district map (here "PD") had been issued on the same sheet lines in 1935. In mid-1940 sheets 118, 119, 127, 128, 136, 137, 138, 143, 144, 145, 146 were converted to Fifth Edition sheet lines and mapping, hence the abbreviation "5".

GSGS 3908 current editions

sheet	1938	31.10.40	1.2.41	15.5.41	8.7.41	31.10.41	28.2.42	31.7.42	31.5.44
1	P	-	-	-	WR/P	WR/P	WR/P	WR/P	WR/P
2	P	-	-	-	WR/P	WR/P	WR/P	WR/P	WR/P
3	P	-	-	-	WR/P	WR/P	WR/P	WR/P	WR/P
4	P	-	-	-	WR/P	WR/P	WR/P	WR/P	WR/P
5	P	-	-	-	WR/P	WR/P	WR/P	WR/P	WR/P
6	P	-	-	-	WR/P	WR/P	WR/P	WR/P	WR/P
7	P	-	-	-	WR/P	WR/P	WR/P	WR/P	WR/P
8	P	-	-	-	WR/P	WR/P	WR/P	WR/P	WR/P
9	P	-	-	-	WR/P	WR/P	WR/P	WR/P	WR/P
10	P	-	-	-	WR/P	WR/P	WR/P	WR/P	WR/P
11	P	-	-	-	WR/P	WR/P	WR/P	WR/P	WR/P
12	P	-	-	-	WR/P	WR/P	WR/P	WR/P	WR/P
13	P	-	-	-	WR/P	WR/P	WR/P	WR/P	WR/P
14	P				WR/P	WR/P	WR/P	WR/P	WR/P
15	P	-	-	-	WR/P	WR/P	WR/P	WR/P	WR/P
16	P	-	-	-	WR/P	WR/P	WR/P	WR/P	WR/P
17	P	-	-	-	WR/P	WR/P	WR/P	WR/P	WR/P
18	P	-	-	-	WR/P	WR/P	WR/P	WR/P	WR/P
19	P	-	-	-	WR/P	WR/P	WR/P	WR/P	WR/P
20	P	-	-	-	WR/P	WR/P	WR/P	WR/P	WR/P
21	P	-	-	-	WR/P	WR/P	WR/P	WR/P	WR/P
22	P	-	-	-	WR/P	WR/P	WR/P	WR/P	WR/P
23	P	-	-	-	WR/P	WR/P	WR/P	WR/P	WR/P
24	P	-	-	-	WR/P	WR/P	WR/P	WR/P	WR/P
25	P	-	-	-	WR/P	WR/P	WR/P	WR/P	WR/P
26	P	-	-	-	WR/P	WR/P	WR/P	WR/P	WR/P
27	P	-	-	-	WR/P	WR/P	WR/P	WR/P	WR/P
28	P	-	-	-	P	WR	WR	WR	WR
29	P	-	-	-	WR/(P)	WR	WR	WR	WR
30	P	-	-	-	WR/P	WR/P	WR/P	WR/P	WR/P
31	P	-	-	-	WR/P	WR/P	WR/P	WR/P	WR/P
32	P	-	-	-	WR/P	WR/P	WR/P	WR/P	WR/P
33	P	-	-	-	WR/P	WR/P	WR/P	WR/P	WR/P
34	P	-	-	-	WR/P	WR/P	WR/P	WR/P	WR/P
35	P	-	-	-	WR/P	WR/P	WR/P	WR/P	WR/P
36	P	-	-	-	WR/P	WR/P	WR/P	WR/P	WR/P
37	P	-	-	-	WR/P	WR/P	WR/P	WR/P	WR/P
38	P	-	-	-	WR/P	WR/P	WR/P	WR/P	WR/P
39	P	-	-	-	WR/P	WR	WR	WR	WR
40	P	-	-	-	WR/P	WR/P	WR/P	WR/P	WR/P
41	P	-	-	-	WR/P	WR/P	WR/P	WR/P	WR/P
42	P	-	-	-	WR/(P)	WR/(P)	WR	WR	WR

sheet	1938	31.10.40	1.2.41	15.5.41	8.7.41	31.10.41	28.2.42	31.7.42	31.5.44	n
43	P	-	-	-	WR/P	WR/P	WR/P	WR/P	WR/P	
44	P	-	-	-	WR/P	WR/P	WR/P	WR/P	WR/P	
45	P	-	-	-	WR	WR	WR	WR	2WR	
46	P	-	-	-	WR/P	WR/P	WR/P	WR/P	WR/P	
47	P	-	-	-	WR/P	WR/P	WR/P	WR/P	WR/P	
48	P	-	-	-	WR/P	WR/P	WR/P	WR/P	WR/P	
49	P	-	-	-	WR/P	WR/P	WR/P	WR/P	WR/P	
50	P	-	-	-	WR/P	WR/P	WR/P	WR/P	WR/P	
51	P	-	-	-	WR/P	WR/P	WR/P	WR/P	WR/P	
52	P	-	-	-	WR/P	WR/P	WR/P	WR/P	WR/P	
53	P	-	-	-	WR/P	WR/P	WR/P	WR/P	WR/P	
54	P	-	-	-	WR/P	WR/P	WR/P	WR/P	WR/P	
55	P	-	-	-	WR/P	WR/P	WR/P	WR/P	WR/P	
56	P	-	-	-	WR/P	WR/P	WR/P	WR/P	WR/P	
57	P	-	-	-	WR/(P)	WR	WR	WR	WR	
58	P	-	-	-	WR	WR	WR	WR	WR	
59	P	-	-	-	WR/P	WR/P	WR/P	WR/P	WR/P	
60	P	-	-	-	WR/P	WR/P	WR/P	WR/P	WR/P	
61	P	-	-	-	WR/(P)	WR	WR	WR	WR	
62	P	-	-	-	WR/P	WR/P	WR/P	WR/P	WR/P	
63	P	-	-	-	WR	WR	WR	WR	WR	
64	P	-	-	-	WR	WR	WR	WR	WR	
65	P	-	-	-	WR/(P)	WR/(P)	WR	WR	WR	
66	P	-	-	-	WR	WR	WR	WR	WR	
67	P	-	-	-	WR	WR	WR	WR	WR	
68	P	-	-	-	WR	WR	WR	WR	WR	
69	P	-	-	-	WR/P	WR/P	WR/P	WR/P	WR/P	
70	P	-	-	-	WR/P	WR/P	WR/P	WR/P	WR/P	
71	P	-	-	-	WR/(P)	WR	WR	WR	WR	
72	P	-	-	-	WR	WR	WR	WR	WR	
73	P	-	-	-	WR	WR	WR	WR	WR	
74	P	-	-	-	WR	WR	WR	WR	WR	
75	P	-	-	-	WR	WR	WR	WR	WR	
76	P	-	-	-	WR/(P)	WR/(P)	WR	WR	WR	
77	P	-	-	-	WR/(P)	WR/(P)	WR	WR	WR	
78	P	-	-	-	WR/(P)	WR/(P)	WR	WR	WR	
79	P	-	-	-	WR/P	WR/P	WR/P	WR/P	WR/P	
80	P	-	-	-	WR/P	WR/P	WR/P	WR/P	WR/P	
81	P	-	-	-	WR/P	WR/P	WR/P	WR/P	WR/P	
82	P	-	-	-	WR/P	WR/P	WR/P	WR/P	WR/P	
83	P	-	-	-	WR/(P)	WR	WR	WR	WR	
84	P	-	-	-	WR/P	WR/P	WR/P	WR/P	WR/P	
85	P	-	-	-	WR/P	WR/P	WR/P	WR/P	WR/P	
86	P	[P	WR/P	WR/P]	WR/P	WR/P	WR/P	2WR	2WR	1
87	P	-	-	-	WR/P	WR/P	WR/P	WR/P	WR/P	
88	P	-	-	-	WR/(P)	WR/(P)	WR	WR	WR	
89	P	[WR	WR/(P)	WR/(P)]	WR/(P)	2WR/WR/P	2WR/WR	2WR/WR	2WR/WR	2
90	P	-	-	-	WR/P	WR/P	WR/P	WR/P	WR/P	
91	P	-	-	-	WR/P	WR/P	WR/P	WR/P	WR/P	
92	P	-	-	-	WR/P	WR/P	WR/P	WR/P	2WR	

Notes

1. On the 31 July 1942 list a difference occurred in the entry for Scotland 86 ("WR/P") and England 3 ("2WR"). This was corrected by *Amendment No 1 to HF/7272/CV dated 31/7/42* on 5 August 1942: "Delete Sheet 86. W.R. or Pop. and Substitute Sheet 86. 2nd W.R." 2. The Popular Edition reference in the 31 October 1941 column should still be in brackets, in accordance with GSGS 3907 sheet 5.

sheet	1938	31.10.40	1.2.41	15.5.41	8.7.41	31.10.41	28.2.42	31.7.42	31.5.44	n

GSGS 3907 current editions

sheet	1938	31.10.40	1.2.41	15.5.41	8.7.41	31.10.41	28.2.42	31.7.42	31.5.44	n
1A	-	-	-	-	-	2WR	2WR	2WR	2WR	
1	P	WR/P	WR/P	WR/P	WR/P	(WR/P)	(WR/P)	(WR/P)	(WR/P)	
2	P	P	P	WR/P	WR/P	WR/P	2WR/WR/P	2WR/WR/P	2WR/WR/P	
3	P	P	WR/P	WR/P	WR/P	WR/P	WR/P	2WR	2WR	4
4	P	P	P	WR/(P)	2WR	2WR	2WR	2WR	2WR	
5	P	WR	WR/(P)	WR/(P)	WR/(P)	2WR/WR/(P)	2WR/WR	2WR/WR	2WR/WR	5
6	P	P	P	2WR	2WR	2WR	2WR	2WR	2WR	1
7	P	WR/(P)	WR/(P)	WR/(P)	WR	WR	2WR	2WR	2WR	
8	P	WR	WR/(P)	WR	WR	WR	WR	2WR	2WR	6
9	P	WR	WR/(P)	2WR	2WR	2WR	2WR	2WR	2WR	
10	P	WR/P	WR/P	WR/P	WR/P	2WR/WR/P	2WR/WR/P	2WR/WR/P	2WR/WR/P	
11	P	P	P	WR/(P)	WR/(P)	WR/(P)	WR/(P)	2WR	2WR	
12	P	WR/P	WR/P	WR/P	WR/P	WR/P	WR/P	WR/P	2WR/WR/P	
13	P	WR/P	WR/P	WR/P	WR/P	WR/P	WR/P	2WR/P	2WR/WR/P	
14	P	P	P	WR/(P)	WR/(P)	WR/(P)	2WR	2WR	2WR	
15	P	WR/(P)	WR/(P)	WR/(P)	WR/(P)	WR/(P)	2WR	2WR	2WR	
16	P	P	WR/(P)	WR/(P)	2WR	2WR	2WR	2WR	2WR	
17	P	WR/P	WR/P	WR/P	WR/P	WR/P	WR/P	WR/P	2WR/WR/P	
18	P	WR/P	WR/P	WR/P	WR/P	WR/P	WR/P	WR/P	2WR/WR/P	
19	P	WR/P	WR/P	2WR/WR/P	2WR/WR/P	2WR/WR/P	2WR/WR/P	2WR/WR/P	2WR/WR/P	
20	P	WR/P	WR/P	WR/P	WR/P	WR/P	WR/P	2WR/WR/P	2WR/WR/P	
21	P	P	2WR	2WR	2WR	2WR	2WR	2WR	2WR	1
22	P	WR/P	2WR/WR/P	2WR/WR/P	2WR/WR/P	2WR/WR/P	2WR/WR/P	2WR/WR/P	2WR/WR/P	
23	P	WR/P	WR/P	WR/(P)	WR	WR	2WR	2WR	2WR	
24	P	WR	WR/(P)	WR	WR	WR	WR	WR	WR	
25	P	WR	WR	WR	WR	WR	2WR/WR	2WR/WR	2WR/WR	
26	P	WR	WR	WR	2WR	2WR	2WR	2WR	2WR	
27	P	WR/(P)	WR/(P)	WR/(P)	WR/(P)	WR	2WR	2WR	2WR	
28	P	P	WR/(P)	WR/(P)	WR	WR	WR	2WR	2WR	
29	P	WR	WR	WR	WR	WR	WR	WR	WR	3
30	P	WR	WR	WR	WR	WR	WR	WR	2WR	
31	P	WR	WR	WR	WR	WR	WR	2WR	2WR	
32	P	WR/(P)	WR	WR	WR	WR	WR	2WR	2WR	
33	P	WR/(P)	WR	WR	2WR	2WR	2WR	2WR	2WR	
34	P	WR/P	WR/P	WR/(P)	2WR	2WR	2WR	2WR	2WR	
35	P	WR	WR	WR	WR	WR	WR	WR	2WR	
36	P	WR	WR	WR	WR	WR	WR	WR	2WR	
37	P	WR	WR	WR	WR	WR	WR	2WR	2WR	
38	P	WR	WR	WR	WR	WR	2WR	2WR	2WR	
39	P	WR/(P)	WR/(P)	2WR	2WR	2WR	2WR	2WR	2WR	
40	P	WR/(P)	WR	2WR	2WR	2WR	2WR	2WR	2WR	
41	P	WR/(P)	WR	WR	WR	WR	WR	WR	WR	3
42	P	WR	WR	WR	WR	WR	WR	WR	WR	3
43	P	WR/(P)	WR/(P)	WR/(P)	WR/(P)	WR/(P)	WR/(P)	2WR	2WR	
44	P	WR/(P)	WR/(P)	WR/(P)	WR/(P)	WR/(P)	WR	WR	WR	
45	P	P	P	P	2WR	2WR	2WR	2WR	2WR	1
46	P	P	WR/(P)	WR/(P)	2WR	2WR	2WR	2WR	2WR	
47	P	WR/(P)	WR/(P)	2WR	2WR	2WR	2WR	2WR	2WR	
48	P	P	2WR/P	2WR	2WR	2WR	2WR	2WR	2WR	1
49	P	WR/P	WR/P	WR/P	WR/P	WR/P	WR/P	WR/P	2WR/WR/P	
50	P	WR/P	WR/P	WR/P	WR/P	WR/P	WR/P	2WR/WR/P	2WR/WR/P	
51	P	WR	WR	WR	WR	WR	WR	WR	WR	
52	P	WR/(P)	WR	WR	WR	WR	WR	WR	WR	3
53	P	P	WR/(P)	WR/(P)	WR/(P)	WR/(P)	WR/(P)	2WR	2WR	7
54	P	WR/(P)	WR	WR	WR	WR	WR	2WR	2WR	
55	P	WR/(P)	WR/(P)	WR/(P)	WR/(P)	2WR	2WR	2WR	2WR	
56	P	WR/(P)	WR/(P)	2WR	2WR	2WR	2WR	2WR	2WR	
57	P	P	P	2WR/P	2WR/P	2WR/P	2WR/P	2WR/P	2WR/P	1
58	P	WR	WR	WR	2WR	2WR	2WR	2WR	2WR	

sheet	1938	31.10.40	1.2.41	15.5.41	8.7.41	31.10.41	28.2.42	31.7.42	31.5.44	n
59	P	WR	WR	WR	WR	WR	WR	WR	2WR/WR	
60	P	WR	WR/(P)	WR	WR	WR	WR	2WR	2WR	
61	P	WR	WR	WR	WR	WR	WR	WR	WR	3
62	P	WR	WR	WR	WR	WR	WR	WR	WR	3
63	P	P	P	P	P	WR/(P)	WR/(P)	2WR	2WR	
64	P	WR/(P)	WR/(P)	WR/(P)	WR	2WR/(WR)	2WR	2WR	2WR	
65	P	WR/(P)	WR	WR	WR	WR	WR	2WR	2WR	
66	P	WR/(P)	WR/(P)	2WR	2WR	2WR	2WR	2WR	2WR	
67	P	WR/(P)	WR/(P)	WR/(P)	WR/(P)	WR/(P)	2WR	2WR	2WR	
68	P	WR/P	WR/P	WR/P	WR/P	WR/P	WR/P	WR/P	2WR/WR/P	
69	P	WR/P	WR/P	WR/P	WR/P	WR/P	WR/P	WR/P	2WR/WR/P	
70	P	WR	WR	WR	WR	WR	WR	2WR/WR/P	2WR/WR/P	
71	P	WR/(P)	WR	WR	WR	WR	WR	WR	2WR	
72	P	WR	WR	WR	WR	WR	WR	2WR	2WR	
73	P	WR	WR	WR	WR	2WR	2WR	2WR	2WR	
74	P	P	P	2WR/WR/(P)	2WR	2WR	2WR	2WR	2WR	
75	P	WR	WR	WR	2WR	2WR	2WR	2WR	2WR	
76	P	WR	WR	WR	WR	WR	2WR/WR	2WR/WR	2WR/WR	
77	P	WR	WR	WR	WR	WR	WR	2WR	2WR	
78	P	WR/P	WR/P	WR/P	WR/P	WR/P	WR/P	WR/P	WR/P	
79	P	WR/P	WR/P	WR/P	WR/P	WR/P	WR/P	WR/P	2WR/WR/P	
80	P	WR/(P)	WR	WR	WR	WR	WR	WR	2WR	
81	P	WR	WR/(P)	WR	WR	WR	WR	WR	WR	3
82	P	WR/(P)	WR	WR	WR	WR	WR	WR	WR	3
83	P	WR/(P)	WR/(P)	WR/(P)	WR/(P)	2WR	2WR	2WR	2WR	
84	P	P	WR/(P)	WR/(P)	2WR	2WR	2WR	2WR	2WR	
85	P	WR/(P)	WR/(P)	WR	WR	2WR	2WR	2WR	2WR	
86	P	P	P	WR/(P)	WR/(P)	2WR	2WR	2WR	2WR	
87	P	WR/(P)	WR/(P)	WR/(P)	WR/(P)	2WR	2WR	2WR	2WR	
88	P	WR/P	WR/P	WR/P	WR/P	WR/P	WR/P	WR/P	WR/P	
89	P	WR	WR/(P)	WR	WR	WR	WR	WR	WR	
90	P	WR/P	WR/P	WR/P	WR/P	WR/P	WR/P	WR/P	2WR/WR/P	
91	P	WR	WR	WR	WR	WR	WR	2WR	2WR	
92	P	WR/(P)	WR/(P)	WR	WR	WR	WR	WR	WR	3
93	P	WR	WR	WR	WR	WR	WR	WR	WR	8
94	P	WR/(P)	WR	WR	WR	2WR	2WR	2WR	2WR	
95	P	P	WR/(P)	WR/(P)	WR/(P)	WR/(P)	2WR	2WR	2WR	
96	P	P	P	WR/(P)	WR/(P)	2WR	2WR	2WR	2WR	
97	P	WR/(P)	WR	WR	WR	2WR	2WR	2WR	2WR	
98	P	WR/(P)	WR/(P)	WR	WR	2WR	2WR	2WR	2WR	
99	P	WR/(P)	WR/(P)	WR/(P)	WR/(P)	WR/(P)	WR	WR	2WR/WR	
100	P	WR/(P)	WR	WR	WR	WR	WR	WR	WR	3
101	P	WR/(P)	WR/(P)	WR/(P)	WR/(P)	WR/(P)	WR/(P)	WR/(P)	2WR/WR(P)	
102	P	WR/(P)	WR/(P)	WR/(P)	WR/(P)	WR/(P)	WR/(P)	2WR	2WR	
103	P	WR/(P)	WR/P	WR/P	WR/P	WR/P	WR/P	2WR	2WR	
104	P	WR/(P)	WR/(P)	WR/(P)	WR/(P)	2WR	2WR	2WR	2WR	
105	P	WR/(P)	WR/(P)	WR	WR	WR	2WR	2WR	2WR	
106	P	P	2WR/(P)	2WR	2WR	2WR	2WR	2WR	2WR	1
107	SP	SP	SP	SP	SP	WR/SP	2WR	2WR	2WR	
108	P	P	P	2WR	2WR	2WR	2WR	2WR	2WR	1
109	P	WR/(P)	WR/(P)	WR/(P)	WR/(P)	WR/(P)	WR/(P)	WR/(P)	WR/(P)	3
110	P	WR	WR	WR	WR	WR	2WR	2WR	2WR	
111	P	WR/(P)	WR/(P)	WR/(P)	WR/(P)	WR/(P)	2WR	2WR	2WR	
112	P	WR	WR	WR	WR	WR	WR	2WR	2WR	
113	P	WR/(P)	WR/(P)	WR	WR	2WR	2WR	2WR	2WR	
114	P	2WR/SP	2WR/SP	2WR/SP	2WR/SP	2WR/SP	2WR	2WR	2WR	1
115	P	P	P	2WR	2WR	2WR	2WR	2WR	2WR	1
116	P	P	P	2WR	2WR	2WR	2WR	2WR	2WR	2
117	P	P	P	-	-	-	-	-	-	2
117A	PD	-	-	2WR	2WR	2WR	2WR	2WR	2WR	
118	P	WR/5	WR/5	WR/5	WR/5	WR/5	WR/5	WR/5	WR/5	

sheet	1938	31.10.40	1.2.41	15.5.41	8.7.41	31.10.41	28.2.42	31.7.42	31.5.44	n
119	P	WR/5	WR/5	WR/5	WR/5	WR/5	WR/5	WR/5	WR/5	
120	P	WR	WR	WR	WR	WR	2WR	2WR	2WR	
121	P	WR/P	WR/P	WR	2WR	2WR	2WR	2WR	2WR	
122	P	WR	WR	WR	WR	WR	WR	2WR	2WR	
123	P	WR	WR	WR	WR	2WR	2WR	2WR	2WR	
124	P	WR/(P)	WR	WR	WR	WR	2WR	2WR	2WR	
125	P	P	P	WR/(P)	WR/(P)	2WR	2WR	2WR	2WR	
126	P	WR/(P)	WR/(P)	2WR	2WR	2WR	2WR	2WR	2WR	
127	P	WR/5	WR/5	WR/5	WR/5	WR/5	WR/5	WR/5	WR/5	
128	P	WR/5	WR/5	WR/5	WR/5	WR/5	WR/5	WR/5	WR/5	
129	P	WR	WR	WR	WR	2WR	2WR	2WR	2WR	
130	P	WR	WR/P	WR	WR	2WR	2WR	2WR	2WR	
131	P	WR	WR	2WR	2WR	2WR	2WR	2WR	2WR	
132	P	WR/(P)	WR	WR	2WR	2WR	2WR	2WR	2WR	9
133	P	P	P	WR/(P)	WR/(P)	2WR	2WR	2WR	2WR	
134	P	P	P	2WR	2WR	2WR	2WR	2WR	2WR	2
135	P	WR	WR	2WR	2WR	2WR	2WR	2WR	2WR	
136	P	WR/5	WR/5	WR/5	WR/5	WR/5	WR/5	WR/5	WR/5	
137	P	WR/5	WR/5	WR/5	WR/5	WR/5	WR/5	WR/5	WR/5	
138	P	WR/5	WR/5	WR/5	WR/5	WR/5	WR/5	WR/5	WR/5	
139	P	WR	WR	WR	WR	2WR	2WR	2WR	2WR	
140	P	WR/(P)	WR/(P)	WR	WR	WR	2WR	2WR	2WR	
141	P	WR	WR/(P)	WR	WR	2WR	2WR	2WR	2WR	
142	P	WR	WR	WR	WR	WR	2WR	2WR	2WR	
143	P	5	5	5	WR/5	WR/5	WR/5	WR/5	WR/5	
144	P	5	5	5	WR/5	WR/5	WR/5	WR/5	WR/5	
145	P	WR/5	WR/5	WR/5	WR/5	WR/5	WR/5	WR/5	WR/5	
146	P	WR/5	WR/5	WR/5	WR/5	WR/5	WR/5	WR/5	WR/5	

Notes

A circular from the Director of Survey, *Location of duplicate plates*,[288] summarises those held at Edinburgh, Bristol and Nottingham before the start of this sequence of lists, as at 8 July 1940. Those at Bristol are "corrected", i.e. presumably War Revision 1940. The sheet numbers (all GSGS 3907) listed are 1, 9, 12, 13, 19, 20, 24, 26, 30, 31, 32, 35, 36, 37, 41, 42, 43, 49, 50, 51, 52, 54, 59, 60, 68, 69, 70, 71, 72, 73, 78, 80, 81, 88, 90, 91, 93, 100, 101, 102, 109, 110, 112, 118, 119, 120, 121, 122, 123, 127, 128, 129, 130, 131, 136, 137, 138, 139, 140, 141, 142, 143, 144, 145, 146. (The "south-west eleven", i.e. 118, 119, 127, 128, 136, 137, 138, 143, 144, 145, 146, would have been converted to Fifth Edition, not War Revision, at this stage). There may have been further "corrected" plates already converted to War Revision (but not yet duplicated) with the War Office or the Ordnance Survey, but this circular does provide an interesting early glimpse at the situation. 1. This sheet was probably not issued in War Revision. 2. The War Revision printing of this sheet was not listed. 3. A Second War Revision outline printing of this sheet was printed, for civilian use. 4. See GSGS 3908 sheet 86 note. 5. See GSGS 3908 sheet 89 note. 6. The 31 October 1940 list notes that Second War Revision sheets 8, 19, 22, 46, 114 would be ready in early November. In some cases there proved to be some delay – by nearly two years for sheet 8. 7. The 31 October 1941 entry for GSGS 3907 sheet has "WR/P"; there is no symbol to suggest an amended entry, so "WR/(P)" is presumably correct, as with the previous and following lists. 8. This sheet was issued in Second War Revision in August 1944. 9. The 31 October 1940 has the obviously erroneous entry "Pop.(or Pop)" for sheet 132. With two War Revision printings in 1940, there is no doubt that the correct entry should read "W.R.(or Pop)".

[288] Circular dated 8 July 1940, ref. CV/2/2, in PRO WO 402/91.

Appendix 2. *Standardisation of editions GSGS 3907*

It seems preferable to allow this most interesting document to speak for itself. I have indulged in a small amount of reordering of detail, expansion of abbreviations, and standardisation of punctuation. Any further editorial detail is in italic or square brackets, otherwise the content is taken directly from the document itself. The earlier version of the table referred to dated 30 March 1941 has not been found. There may be a significance in its date, in that it appears to coincide with when notes as to the currency of editions began to be overprinted in the top margins of the maps themselves. However, for some as yet unexplained reason, these notes appear not to have been added to all the sheets that, according to these tables, would qualify for them.

The copy of the 1 March 1942 table inspected[289] evidently remained in use for some time, and was updated by hand as new editions were published. Its original text is reproduced here. The list also reveals that sheets 24, 44, 51 were ready in Second War Revision, though never issued, even in the outline edition.

HF/7260/CV. From D. Cameron, Major, R.E., for Director of Survey, General Headquarters, Home Forces, sent to all Assistant Directors of Survey, all depots, on 1 March 1942. Copy to the Director General Ordnance Survey.

Attached will be found a Table showing the present and future policy with regard to standardisation of the Editions of GSGS 3907 (E&W 1"). This table replaces that issued with HF/7260/CV dated 30 March 1941. Comparison with the previous table will show the progress made during the past eleven months.

The situation in column 'A' is as at 28 Feb 1942 and corresponds with the new list of current editions.

Column G gives the edition in which Assistant Directors of Survey will print if requested to do so with local resources. It is essential that the sets of duplicate plates should correspond with this list. The Director General, Ordnance Survey has been asked to ensure that this is so, but Assistant Directors of Survey who have the care of sets of plates should make a check to see that they are correct.

GSGS 3907 Table showing proposed standardisation of stocks.

Column headings

Sheet
A. Present situation, *as at 28 February 1942*
B. Intended to standardise on
C. 2WR required
D. 2WR only required when plates of WR break down
E. 2WR to be published with note
F. After publication of 2WR will standardise on
G. Edition for emergency printing only

Sheet	A	B	C	D	E	F	G
1A	2WR	2WR	published	-	-	2WR	2WR
2	2WR/WR/P	NS	published	-	yes	NS	2WR
3	WR/P	2WR	yes	-	-	2WR	WR
4	2WR	2WR	published	-	-	2WR	2WR
5	2WR/WR	NS	published	-	yes	ns	2WR
6	2WR	2WR	published	-	-	2WR	2WR
7	2WR	2WR	published	-	-	2WR	2WR
8	WR	2WR	ready	-	-	2WR	WR
9	2WR	2WR	published	-	-	2WR	2WR
10	2WR/WR/P	NS	published	-	yes	NS	2WR

---

[289] In the GSGS 3907 series file, at present with DGC. Another copy is in PRO WO 402/92.

sheet	A	B	C	D	E	F	G
11	WR/P	2WR	ready	-	-	2WR	2WR
12	WR/P	NS	ready	-	yes	NS	2WR
13	WR WR/P	NS	ready	-	yes	NS	2WR
14	2WR	2WR	published	-	-	2WR	2WR
15	2WR	2WR	published	-	-	2WR	2WR
16	2WR	2WR	published	-	-	2WR	2WR
17	WR/P	NS	no	yes	yes	NS	WR
18	WR/P	NS	ready	-	yes	NS	2WR
19	2WR/WR/P	NS	published	-	yes	NS	2WR
20	WR/P	NS	ready	-	yes	NS	2WR
21	2WR	2WR	published	-	-	2WR	2WR
22	2WR/WR/P	NS	published	-	yes	NS	2WR
23	2WR	2WR	published	-	-	2WR	2WR
24	WR	WR	ready	yes	-	2WR	WR
25	2WR/WR	NS	published	-	yes	NS	2WR
26	2WR	2WR	published	-	-	2WR	2WR
27	2WR	2WR	published	-	-	2WR	2WR
28	WR	2WR	ready	yes	-	2WR	WR
29	WR	2WR	ready	yes	-	2WR	WR
30	WR	WR	no	yes	-	2WR	WR
31	WR	2WR	ready	-	-	2WR	2WR
32	WR	2WR	ready	-	-	2WR	2WR
33	2WR	2WR	published	-	-	2WR	2WR
34	2WR	2WR	published	-	-	2WR	2WR
35	WR	WR	no	yes	-	2WR	WR
36	WR	WR	no	yes	-	WR	WR
37	WR	2WR	ready	-	-	2WR	2WR
38	2WR	2WR	published	-	-	2WR	2WR
39	2WR	2WR	published	-	-	2WR	2WR
40	2WR	2WR	published	-	-	2WR	2WR
41	WR	WR	ready	yes	-	2WR	WR
42	WR	WR	ready	yes	-	2WR	WR
43	WR/(P)	2WR	yes	-	-	2WR	WR
44	WR	WR	ready	yes	-	2WR	WR
45	2WR	2WR	published	-	-	2WR	2WR
46	2WR	2WR	published	-	-	2WR	2WR
47	2WR	2WR	published	-	-	2WR	2WR
48	2WR	2WR	published	-	-	2WR	2WR
49	WR/P	NS	ready	-	yes	NS	2WR
50	WR/P	NS	ready	-	yes	NS	2WR
51	WR	WR	ready	yes	-	2WR	WR
52	WR	WR	no	yes	-	2WR	WR
53	WR/P	2WR	ready	-	-	2WR	2WR
54	WR	2WR	ready	-	-	2WR	2WR
55	2WR	2WR	published	-	-	2WR	2WR
56	2WR	2WR	published	-	-	2WR	2WR
57	2WR/P	NS	published	-	yes	NS	2WR
58	2WR	2WR	published	-	-	2WR	2WR
59	WR	WR	ready	-	yes	NS	WR
60	WR	2WR	ready	-	-	2WR	2WR
61	WR	WR	ready	yes	-	2WR	WR
62	WR	WR	ready	yes	-	2WR	WR
63	WR/(P)	2WR	ready	-	-	2WR	2WR
64	2WR	2WR	published	-	-	2WR	2WR
65	WR	2WR	ready	-	-	2WR	2WR
66	2WR	2WR	published	-	-	2WR	2WR
67	2WR	2WR	published	-	-	2WR	2WR
68	WR/P	NS	no	yes	yes	NS	WR
69	WR/P	NS	ready	-	yes	NS	2WR
70	WR	NS	ready	-	yes	NS	2WR
71	WR	WR	ready	yes	-	2WR	WR

sheet	A	B	C	D	E	F	G
72	WR	WR	yes	-	-	2WR	WR
73	2WR	2WR	published	-	-	2WR	2WR
74	2WR	2WR	published	-	-	2WR	2WR
75	2WR	2WR	published	-	-	2WR	2WR
76	2WR/WR	NS	published	-	yes	NS	2WR
77	WR	2WR	ready	-	-	2WR	2WR
78	WR/P	NS	no	yes	yes	NS	WR
79	WR/P	NS	no	yes	yes	NS	WR
80	WR	WR	ready	yes	-	2WR	WR
81	WR	WR	ready	yes	-	2WR	WR
82	WR	WR	ready	yes	-	2WR	WR
83	2WR	2WR	published	-	-	2WR	2WR
84	2WR	2WR	published	-	-	2WR	2WR
85	2WR	2WR	published	-	-	2WR	2WR
86	2WR	2WR	published	-	-	2WR	2WR
87	2WR	2WR	published	-	-	2WR	2WR
88	WR/P	NS	no	yes	yes	NS	WR
89	WR	WR	no	yes	-	NS	WR
90	WR/P	NS	no	yes	-	NS	WR
91	WR	WR	ready	yes	-	2WR	WR
92	WR	WR	ready	yes	-	2WR	WR
93	WR	WR	no	yes	-	2WR	WR
94	2WR	2WR	published	-	-	2WR	2WR
95	2WR	2WR	published	-	-	2WR	2WR
96	2WR	2WR	published	-	-	2WR	2WR
97	2WR	2WR	published	-	-	2WR	2WR
98	2WR	2WR	published	-	-	2WR	2WR
99	WR	WR	no	yes	-	2WR	WR
100	WR	WR	no	yes	-	2WR	WR
101	WR/(P)	WR	no	yes	-	2WR	WR
102	WR/(P)	2WR	ready	yes	-	2WR	WR
103	WR/P	2WR	ready	-	-	2WR	2WR
104	2WR	2WR	published	-	-	2WR	2WR
105	2WR	2WR	published	-	-	2WR	2WR
106	2WR	2WR	published	-	-	2WR	2WR
107	2WR	2WR	published	-	-	2WR	2WR
108	2WR	2WR	published	-	-	2WR	2WR
109	WR/(P)	WR	no	-	-	2WR	WR
110	2WR	2WR	published	-	-	2WR	2WR
111	2WR	2WR	published	-	-	2WR	2WR
112	WR	WR	yes	-	-	2WR	WR
113	2WR	2WR	published	-	-	2WR	2WR
114	2WR	2WR	published	-	-	2WR	2WR
115	2WR	2WR	published	-	-	2WR	2WR
116	2WR	2WR	published	-	-	2WR	2WR
117A	2WR	2WR	published	-	-	2WR	2WR
118	5/WR	5/WR	no	-	-	-	WR
119	5/WR	5/WR	no	-	-	-	WR
120	2WR	2WR	published	-	-	2WR	2WR
121	2WR	2WR	published	-	-	2WR	2WR
122	WR	2WR	yes	-	-	2WR	WR
123	2WR	2WR	published	-	-	2WR	2WR
124	2WR	2WR	published	-	-	2WR	2WR
125	2WR	2WR	published	-	-	2WR	2WR
126	2WR	2WR	published	-	-	2WR	2WR
127	5/WR	5/WR	no	-	-	-	WR
128	5/WR	5/WR	no	-	-	-	WR
129	2WR	2WR	published	-	-	2WR	2WR
130	2WR	2WR	published	-	-	2WR	2WR
131	2WR	2WR	published	-	-	2WR	2WR
132	2WR	2WR	published	-	-	2WR	2WR

sheet	A	B	C	D	E	F	G
133	2WR	2WR	published	-	-	2WR	2WR
134	2WR	2WR	published	-	-	2WR	2WR
135	2WR	2WR	published	-	-	2WR	2WR
136	5/WR	5/WR	no	-	-	-	WR
137	5/WR	5/WR	no	-	-	-	WR
138	5/WR	5/WR	no	-	-	-	WR
139	2WR	2WR	published	-	-	2WR	2WR
140	2WR	2WR	published	-	-	2WR	2WR
141	2WR	2WR	published	-	-	2WR	2WR
142	2WR	2WR	published	-	-	2WR	2WR
143	5/WR	5/WR	no	-	-	-	WR
144	5/WR	5/WR	no	-	-	-	WR
145	5/WR	5/WR	no	-	-	-	WR
146	5/WR	5/WR	no	-	-	-	WR

Notes

Column A. Brackets ( ) indicate insufficient copies of WR or 2WR to enable Popular Edition to be discarded altogether, although this would be desirable.

Column B. NS (= no standardisation) indicates that two or more editions are considered almost equally good. WR indicates that this edition is considered good enough unless a new printing plate is required.

Column C. Self-explanatory.

Column D. "yes" indicates either that WR is good enough generally speaking or that it is not anticipated that the sheet concerned will be called for urgently in quantity. (see below 2 & 3).

Column E. "yes" means that there will be a note printed on the sheet of the 2WR indicating that it is substantially the same as the WR with slight differences which are noted.

Column F. NS (= no standardisation) in this column is the clearest indication that two or more editions will continue to be current.

2. It should be noted that North of a line running roughly from the Bristol Channel through Nottingham to the Wash 2WR edition is generally less urgent because these areas are not so "hot" operationally. In some areas, however, 2WR is being published for sheets on which there was a good deal of revision for the WR edition.

3. Other things being equal and if the stocks of early editions are exhausted or the plates worn out it should be noted that preference will naturally be given to reprinting in 2WR style as it is simpler technically, and saves one printing.

[4.] Second War Revision [112] awaiting ground revision [?so too sheets 3, 42, 112].

Another series of documents, entitled Out of date stocks to salvage, *were in effect occasional updates to the master list presented above. Issues 1 to 11 have not been found. The three following the March 1942 document are set out below.*[290]

HF/7260/CV. Out of date stocks to salvage (12), 25 March 1942
The following amendments will be made to the table issued with HF/7260/CV dated 1.3.42.

11	2WR	2WR	published	-	-	2WR	2WR
30	WR	WR	ready	-	-	2WR	WR
35	WR	2WR	ready	-	-	2WR	WR
53	2WR	2WR	published	-	-	2WR	2WR
65	2WR	2WR	published	-	-	2WR	2WR
77	2WR	2WR	published	-	-	2WR	2WR
91	WR	2WR	ready	-	-	2WR	WR

The Popular Edition stock of sheets 11 and 53 and the War Revision stock of sheets 11, 53, 65 and 77 were to be turned in to salvage, and struck off stock cards. Second War Revision printings of sheets 8, 13, 20, 31, 32, 37, 43, 54, 60, 63, 70, 91, 103 were on order and were expected to be published within six weeks.

Evidently the February 1942 printing of sheets 11 and 65 had been delayed for some reason.

---

[290] Copies in PRO WO 402/92.

sheet	A	B	C	D	E	F	G

HF/7260/1/CV. Out of date stocks to salvage (13), 11 May 1942
The following amendments will be made to the table issued with HF/7260/CV dated 1.3.42.

sheet	A	B	C	D	E	F	G
3	WR/P	2WR	ready	-	-	2WR	WR
8	2WR	2WR	published	-	-	2WR	2WR
13	2WR/WR/P	NS	published	-	yes	NS	2WR
17	WR/P	NS	ready	-	yes	NS	2WR
20	2WR/WR/P	NS	published	-	yes	NS	2WR
28	WR	2WR	ready	-	-	2WR	WR
31	2WR	2WR	published	-	-	2WR	2WR
32	2WR	2WR	published	-	-	2WR	2WR
37	2WR	2WR	published	-	-	2WR	2WR
42	WR	2WR	ready	-	-	2WR	WR
54	2WR	2WR	published	-	-	2WR	2WR
60	2WR	2WR	published	-	-	2WR	2WR
63	2WR	2WR	published	-	-	2WR	2WR
68	WR/P	NS	ready	-	yes	NS	2WR
70	2WR/WR/P	NS	published	-	yes	NS	2WR
71	WR	2WR	ready	-	-	2WR	WR
103	2WR	2WR	published	-	-	2WR	2WR

Popular Edition stock of sheets 63 and 103 and the War Revision stock of sheets 8, 31, 32, 37, 54, 60, 63 and 103 were to be turned in to salvage, and struck off stock cards. Second War Revision printings of sheets 3, 28, 43, 50, 91 and 102 were on order and were expected to be published within six weeks.

HF/7260/1/CV. Out of date stocks to salvage (14), 10 July 1942
The following amendments will be made to the table issued with HF/7260/CV dated 1.3.42.

sheet	A	B	C	D	E	F	G
3	2WR	2WR	published	-	-	2WR	2WR
28	2WR	2WR	published	-	-	2WR	2WR
36	WR	2WR	ready	-	-	2WR	WR
43	2WR	2WR	published	-	-	2WR	2WR
50	2WR/WR/P	NS	published	-	yes	NS	2WR
72	2WR	2WR	published	-	-	2WR	2WR
91	2WR	2WR	published	-	-	2WR	2WR
102	2WR	2WR	published	-	-	2WR	2WR
112	2WR	2WR	published	-	-	2WR	2WR
122	2WR	2WR	published	-	-	2WR	2WR

Popular Edition stock of sheets 3, 43 and 102 and the War Revision stock of sheets 3, 28, 43, 72, 91, 102, 112 and 122 were to be turned in to salvage, and struck off stock cards.

No further issues known. But they would appear to have been superseded by another sequence of documents conveying the same information:[291]

HF/5715/Svy. Publication of new editions – GSGS 3907 (1" E&W), 4 January 1944

sheet	A	B	C	D	E	F	G
90	2WR/WR/P	NS	published	-	yes	NS	2WR
101	2WR/WR/(P)	NS	published	-	-	NS	2WR

Sheet 101 is not published with note as there is a possibility of standardisation on 2WR at a later printing.

HF/5715/Svy. Publication of new edition – GSGS 3907 (1" E&W), 20 February 1944

sheet	A	B	C	D	E	F	G
99	2WR/WR	NS	published	-	yes	NS	2WR

It is not intended to standardise on this edition at present and the War Revision edition will continue to be issued. As there is a possibility of standardisation on the 2WR at a future date, this sheet is not published with the usual note.

---

[291] Copies of these are in the GSGS 3907 series file, at present with DGC.

Appendix 3. *Sales copies of GSGS 3908 and 3907*

The severe shortage, and shortcomings, of mapping for the use of civilians during the early years of the Second World War,[292] led to agreement on making GSGS 3907 and 3908 mapping available to the public. The initial proposal appears to have come from M.N. MacLeod, Director General of the Ordnance Survey, who on 9 September 1942 wrote to DMO&P (GSGS):[293]

> I have had under consideration recently the question of issuing to the public a civil edition of the one-inch map of Great Britain. The question was dealt with in a letter from the C.-in-C. Home Forces to the War Office in December 1941.
>
> As a consequence of the ruling given in the above letter, no one-inch maps of England and Wales, other than a small number of Outline Editions, have been available to civil departments or to the Government for nearly two years and there seems to be no prospect of the Ordnance Survey being able to print an edition to replace destroyed stocks for some time to come. There have, however, been numerous demands for the map, and amongst other effects, the lack of any maps to sell is having serious financial consequences to the principal O.S. Agents. It seems that the only practicable way of making a one-inch map available for civil use is to place the present military edition on sale. I have been anxious to avoid doing this, in order to prevent the military grid coming into civil use, but in view of the fact that the 1/25,000 map is being used for national planning, this can hardly be prevented by withholding the gridded edition of the one-inch map.
>
> I would accordingly propose that when one-inch sheets are being reprinted for Home Forces, a number of extra copies should be printed for the Ordnance Survey's own use. The extra printing involved is estimated at only about 5 per cent so that no great delay in meeting Service requirements is likely to be caused. Before proceeding further with the suggestion, would you please confirm that there is no military objection. It is not clear from past correspondence whether the War Office objection to the issue of one-inch maps to the public applies only to sheets carrying a different grid from that on the War Office edition.

The idea clearly impressed Colonel Hotine, for GSGS, who on 14 September wrote to MO3:[294]

> 1. Please see 2A [i.e. the DGOS letter above] and discuss with Home Forces.
> 2. Previous G.H.Q. objection was to public issues of maps <u>carrying a different grid</u> owing to danger of confusion in references given by, e.g., Home Guards who had bought copies of civil editions. This objection is met by D.G.O.S's present proposal.
> 3. So far as technical production is concerned, I recommend the proposal. It satisfies a demand (which may well be pressed by another Ministry, since Ordnance Survey is not administered by the War Office) with the least diversion of resources from production of Army and R.A.F. maps. The diversion is not serious and we have sufficient operational control to stop it if this became necessary.
> 4. Sales of maps are controlled by Home Office Order, which would of course, apply to this proposition. It remains, therefore, to consider the differences between the military edition and civil editions of the one-inch map which have been issued to the public during this war.
> 5. The differences are:-
>
>   (a) The military edition is somewhat more up-to-date and (b) It carries the military grid.
>
> All this information appears on 1/25,000 or six-inch maps which have been issued for civil administrative and planning purposes; and there is hardly any doubt that the enemy had it all before the war.
> 6. I recommend agreement with D.G.O.S's proposal.

And so it was agreed. There were four phases to this policy. First, from the start of 1943, Second War Revision mapping, the most up to date available, was put on sale. This mapping perforce included the military grid, which formed an integral part of its black plate. Secondly, some of the sheets still unavailable in Second War Revision were printed in War Revision format. It was possible to offer these to the public without the military grid since it was on a separate purple plate. Printing of these began (as run-on printings of gridded maps required for

---

[292] The background to this matter is set out by Richard Oliver on page 33. See also Roger Hellyer, 'Some notes on civilian use of small scale mapping during the Second World War', *Sheetlines* 48 (1997), 45-57; and 'Some notes on one-inch mapping produced for civilian use during the Second World War', *Sheetlines* 59 (2000), 17-38.

[293] PRO OS 1/219. The GSGS 3907 series file, at present with DGC, dates the correspondence 11 September; perhaps this was the date of receipt.

[294] GSGS 3907 series file, at present with DGC.

military use) in October 1942, and, as with the Second War Revisions, were first announced in Ordnance Survey publication reports (OSPR) at the start of 1943. Thirdly, from late 1943, outline printings with water in blue were offered, (from 1944 with woods in grey as well), mostly in Second War Revision. In some cases these Second War Revision outline issues were made specially and were never in military use.[295] Lastly many War Revision sheets were made available, complete with the overprinted grid, doubtless in order to use up superseded stock which would otherwise have to be turned to salvage. Copies designated for civilian use were usually overprinted in red with a sales copy panel in the bottom right hand corner, though it is often found in the form of a sticker.

OSPR entries have cross references to the lists above where they can be applied to specific printings, as with War Revision printings without grid (†), and outline editions(‡). It is impossible to ascertain the specific printing of gridded War Revision or coloured Second War Revision, and these appear only in tabular form here.

1. *War Revision, coloured sheets without grid*

OSPR 1 January to 31 May 1943
Scotland 1, 7, 8, 12, 13, 14, 17, 18, 25, 28, 29, 30, 33, 34, 37, 38, 44, 48, 50, 52, 55, 62, 68, 70, 71, 72, 74, 75, 76, 78, 80, 84, 87. England and Wales 41, 44, 52, 61, 81, 90, 92, 93, 99, 100, 109, 143, 144, 146 (sheet 82 missing).

OSPR 1 June to 31 July 1943
Scotland 51, 61, 73.

OSPR 1 August to 30 September 1943
Scotland 85.

OSPR October 1943
Scotland 53, 67, 81.

OSPR 1 November 1943 to 31 January 1944
Scotland 49, 79.

2. *Second War Revision, coloured sheets*

OSPR 1 January to 31 May 1943
Scotland sheets 45, 92. England and Wales sheets 1A, 2, 4, 5, 9, 10, 11, 12, 14, 15, 16, 17, 21, 22, 23, 25, 28, 39, 40, 43, 46, 47, 48, 49, 54, 55, 57, 59, 63, 64, 65, 66, 67, 68, 69, 71, 72, 73, 74, 75, 83, 84, 85, 94, 95, 98, 102, 103, 104, 105, 106, 107, 111, 112, 113, 114, 115, 121, 122, 124, 125, 130, 131, 132, 133, 135, 141, 142.

OSPR 1 June to 31 July 1943
England and Wales sheets 6, 18, 30, 96, 116, 126, 134.

OSPR 1 August to 30 September 1943
England and Wales sheets 3 (= Scotland 86), 7, 8, 13, 19, 20, 26, 27, 31, 33, 34, 35, 36, 37, 38, 45, 50, 53, 56, 58, 60, 70, 76, 77, 79, 87, 97, 108, 110, 117A, 120, 129, 140.

OSPR October 1943
Scotland sheet 89 (= England 5). England and Wales sheets 32, 80.

OSPR 1 November 1943 to 31 January 1944
England and Wales sheet 86.

OSPR 1 February to 31 March 1944
England and Wales sheets 91, 123.

OSPR 1 April to 30 June 1944
England and Wales sheet 90.

OSPR 1 July to 30 September 1944
England and Wales sheets 102, 130, 131.

---

[295] There were eleven such sheets: England and Wales 29, 41, 42, 52, 61, 62, 81, 82, 92, 100, 109.

3. *Second War Revision, outline*

OSPR October 1943
England and Wales sheets 7, 25, 29, 62, 71, 111.

OSPR 1 November 1943 to 31 January 1944
England and Wales sheets 4, 20, 26, 30, 35, 36, 42, 45, 49, 52, 54, 60, 61, 81, 85, 92, 93, 94, 100, 105, 112, 113, 116, 120.

OSPR 1 February to 31 March 1944
England and Wales sheets 41, 97.

OSPR 1 July to 30 September 1944
England and Wales sheets 31, 102, 103, 115; 145 (War Revision).

OSPR 1 October to 31 December 1944
England and Wales sheets 11, 19, 37, 72, 83, 84, 91, 95, 106, 107, 109, 110; 118, 119 (War Revision).

OSPR 1 January to 31 March 1945
England and Wales sheets 82, 125; 138 (War Revision).

OSPR 1 April to 30 June 1945
England and Wales sheets 43, 80.

OS annual report 1943-4 (PRO OS 1/173)
England and Wales sheets 4, 7, 20, 25, 26, 29, 30, 35, 36, 41, 42, 45, 49, 52, 54, 60, 61, 62, 71, 81, 85, 92, 93, 94, 97, 100, 105, 111, 112, 113, 116, 120.

OS annual report 1944-5 (PRO OS 1/201)
England and Wales sheets 11, 19, 31, 37, 72, 82, 83, 84, 91, 95, 102, 103, 106, 107, 109, 110, 115, 118, 119, 125, 138, 145.

4. *War Revision, coloured gridded sheets*

OSPR 1 August to 30 September 1943
England and Wales sheets 24, 29, 42, 51, 62, 88, 89, 101, 118, 119, 127, 128, 136, 137, 138, 145.

OSPR October 1943
Scotland sheets 4, 5, 6, 9, 10, 15, 16, 19, 21, 26, 31, 32, 35, 39, 42, 47, 51, 54, 56, 57, 58, 59, 60, 61, 63, 64, 65, 66, 67, 73, 77, 79, 81, 82, 83, 88, 90, 91. England and Wales sheets 78, 79.

OSPR 1 November 1943 to 31 January 1944
Scotland sheets 11, 20, 22, 23, 24, 27, 36, 38, 40, 41, 49, 53, 69.

OSPR 1 February to 31 March 1944
Scotland sheet 3. England and Wales sheets 41, 146.

OSPR 1 April to 30 June 1944
Scotland sheets 2, 7. England and Wales sheets 81, 109.

OSPR 1 July to 30 September 1944
Scotland sheet 68. England and Wales sheets 17, 44, 52, 82, 100, 143, 144.

OSPR 1 October to 31 December 1944
Scotland sheets 62, 72. England and Wales sheets 19, 49, 92, 100, 144, 146.

OSPR 1 January to 31 March 1945
Scotland sheets 14, 28, 29, 34, 45, 48, 52, 75, 78, 79, 80, 84, 85, 87. England and Wales sheets 13, 18, 99.

Appendix 4. *Abbreviations used to identify civilian printing firms and military printing units*

Until 1939, the War Office undertook the majority of its own printing work, the Ordnance Survey dealing with the remainder. The steep rise in the quantities of maps required that accompanied the threat of hostilities necessitated that some printing work be contracted out to civilian companies, and following the Munich crisis in September 1938, five firms were approached in confidence and given trial orders. Causton, Mardon and McCorquodale were employed printing one-inch maps in 1939; Bartholomew, Forman, Johnston and Robinson were recruited in 1940. Each firm was assigned a letter code that concluded the print code added to each printing for which they were responsible, in the form 9000/40 B. This indicates a run of 9000 copies printed by Bartholomew in 1940.

Correspondence between GSGS and OS in October 1941 set out an agreement that a more advanced form of these coded imprints should be used. Henceforth maps were to carry an imprint in the form: 10,000/4/41/A, indicating 10,000 copies printed by Adams & Shardlow in April 1941. The practice of including the month was apparently "recently adopted"; this could hardly have been later than April 1941, the month used in the example quoted in one of the letters. In fact a further seven firms appear to have been recruited in July 1940, all using the system, which would be remarkable were it mere coincidence. Adams & Shardlow apparently took, or were allocated, "AS" in July 1940, which was altered to "A" in August. McCorquodale also adopted codes including a month digit at the same time. The sequential numbers in column 3 below provide the order of tabulation given the Ordnance Survey's letter of 7 October 1941.[296] Later documents reveal the names of more printing firms added to the list of those doing this work,[297] which probably reached its peak with Operation Overlord in June 1944. Negotiations with the OS were conducted on behalf of the companies by the British Federation of Master Printers, who in June 1941 secured an increase in remuneration over that earlier agreed in July 1940.

The first part of this list includes all the firms and military units recorded as having printed military mapping of Great Britain and Ireland during the Second World War. The series and sheet numbers, and associated dates given in columns 4 to 7 offer the first and last known use of each of these firms on military mapping at the one-inch scale. A trail of dots indicates where earlier or later printings by that firm are known in military mapping outside the British Isles, or at other scales. This is followed by a list of mostly military and Admiralty printing units responsible for one-inch military mapping of the British Isles since the war. Punctuation may vary, for instance MCE RE is also found in the forms MCE(RE) and MCE,RE.

Map printers during the Second World War

1	2	3	4	5	6	7
A	Adams Bros & Shardlow, Leicester	9	8.40	3907 36	10.42	3907 86...
AS	? = Adams Bros & Shardlow, Leicester		7.40	3907 129		
	G.W. Bacon & Co, London		not used on one-inch			
B	John Bartholomew, Edinburgh	8	1940	3908 27	8.44	3907 122
BJ	Ben Johnson & Co, York	19	7.40	3907 71	1.43	3907 93
	The British Colour Printing Co, London		not used on one-inch			
	Brown & Bibby, Liverpool		not used on one-inch			
BR	Tom Browne & Co, Nottingham	16	not used on one-inch			
C	Sir Joseph Causton & Sons, Eastleigh	10	1939	3907 12	5.43	3907 32...
C&R / C&R Ltd	Charles & Read, London		9.43	3907 16	12.43	3907 34
CK	Alf Cooke, Leeds	20	7.40	3907 18	1.43	3907 84
CW	? = Chromoworks, London		not used on one-inch			
	Field, Sons & Co, Bradford		not used on one-inch			
	William Finlay & Sons, Belfast		not used on one-inch			
F	Thomas Forman & Sons, Nottingham	7	7.40	3907 60	5.42	4136 303...
FC	? = Fosh & Cross, London		not used on one-inch			
G	Greenslade & Co, Reading	18	not used on one-inch			
H	J. Howitt & Son, Nottingham	12	7.40	3907 13	11.42	3907 13...
HAY	Haycock Press, London		12.43	3907 123	6.44	3907 106...

---

[296] WE 6238, 7 October 1941; this letter and the associated correspondence is not with other relevant documents now in PRO WO 181/309, and its whereabouts are unknown. See Peter K. Clark and Ian Mumford, 'Note on the '1941 style' of coded imprint adopted by the Ordnance Survey and War Office', *Sheetlines* 5 (1982), 9, 12.

[297] PRO OS 1/197: Printing work performed by private firms, general policy, 1940-51. See 'The '1941' style of coded imprint', *Sheetlines* 9 (1984), 18-19. See also Brigadier A.B. Clough, *The Second World War 1939-1945 : Army. Maps and survey.* London: War Office, 1952, 553f.

1	2	3	4	5	6	7
HH	? = Henry Hildesley, London		not used on one-inch			
HOW	? = J Howitt & Son, Nottingham		not used on one-inch			
Hu	Hubners, London		7.43	3907 33…		
H.U.	? = Hubners, London		7.43	3907 13		
J	W. & A.K. Johnston, Edinburgh	6	1940	3908 15	1.43	3908 44…
K	Cook, Hammond & Kell, London	14	not used on one-inch			
L	John Laird & Son, Glasgow	5	7.40	3907 12	11.40	3908 9
M	Mardon, Son & Hall, Bristol	2	1939	3908 7	8.43	3907 75…
Mc	McCorquodale & Co, London	4	1939	3907 45	6.44	3907 126…
McL	McLagan & Cumming, Edinburgh	17	2.42	3908 50	1.43	3908 50
P	George Philip & Son, London	13	not used on one-inch			
R	E.S. & A. Robinson, Bristol	1	1940	3907 8	1.43	3907 92…
S	Edward Stanford, London	15	not used on one-inch			
	S.S. Offset, Birmingham		not used on one-inch			
T	William Thyne, Edinburgh	21	8.40	3907 36		
TL			7.42	3908 49		
W	Waterlow & Sons, London	3	7.40	3907 80	1.43	3907 99
We	? = J. Weiner, London		not used on one-inch			
Ch ?or CH	OSO Chessington		6.43	3907 30	1945	3907 81…
Cr ?or CR	OSO Crabwood		4.41	3907 9	11.43	3907 76
E	OSO Esher (Hinchley Wood)		2.43	3907 102	7.43	3907 23…
LR ?or L/R	OSO London Road [earlier no suffix letters]		3.41	3907 81	3.43	3908 92…
NI	Ordnance Survey of Northern Ireland	11	9.41	4136 317		
Wa ?or WA	OSO Waddon		11.42	3908 45…	5.46	4620 167
WD	War Department		1939	3907 3		
WO	War Office		1.23	[3907] 115	2.42	3907 73
13 CFS CRE	13 (Corps) Field Survey Company, Royal Engineers		10.41	Ripon		
13 S	13 Field Survey Company, Royal Engineers		7.43	3907 123	8.43	3907 133
14 MRS	14 Map Reproduction Section, Royal Engineers		10.43	3907 113	11.43	3907 125
16 MRS	16 Map Reproduction Section, Royal Engineers		1.43	3907 132	1.44	3907 132
515 (CFS) CRE	515 (Corps) Field Survey Company, Royal Engineers		11.41	4136 364	2.42	4136 320
519 RE	519 Field Survey Company, Royal Engineers		12.42	Inveraray		
	660th Engineers US Army		3.43	3907 94		

Map printers after the Second World War

1	2	3	4	5	6	7
CBH	Hydrographic Department, Creechbarrow House, Taunton		1951	4692		
HDA	Hydrographic Department, Admiralty		1961	4620 144		
OS	Ordnance Survey		1.53	4620 127	5.73	4620 99
S	Ordnance Survey		8.72	4620 61	11.84	M723 5…
SPC	Survey Production Centre, Royal Engineers		3.49	Misc.349/A	12.49	4620 123
SPC RE	Survey Production Centre, Royal Engineers		9.50	Misc.491	6.54	4136 308
EP	No.1 Survey Production Centre, Royal Engineers		11.56	4620 169		
no code	No.1 Survey Production Centre, Royal Engineers		3.57	Misc.1622	8.57	Misc.1801
R	No.1 Survey Production Centre, Royal Engineers		2.58	Misc.1815	7.62	Misc.1958
SPC	Survey Production Centre, Royal Engineers		9.62	4620 135	2.70	4965
MCE RE	Mapping and Charting Establishment, Royal Engineers		4.70	5076	5.72	M723 6
M	Mapping and Charting Establishment, Royal Engineers		7.72	5169	2.83	M723 8…
SPC S/STD			9.62	4136 313		
OA	SPC RE (British Army of the Rhine) [BAOR]		8.66	4620 89	12.66	4620 19
OR	42 Survey Engineer Regiment [42 SER]		6.72	4954		
R	42 Survey Engineer Regiment [42 SER]		9.73	4954	5.83	M723 9…
13 FSS RE	13 Field Survey Squadron, Royal Engineers		1960	Misc.406		

Appendix 5. *A concordance of military map serial numbers appearing in this book*

Map scales are only given when not one-inch. Section numbers are in bold, supplement or other additional numbers follow the full stop. Entries quoted as a sheet number are New Popular Edition/Seventh Series unless specified otherwise. Map series referred to in Richard Oliver's essay are listed by chapter number in the form "RO 2" ("RO 2n" if a footnote); those in the compiler's introductory notes "cn", followed by the number of the relevant section. "A" numbers indicate appendices. For layout reasons a few obvious abbreviations have been incorporated, and punctuation has been removed. The word "area" is omitted from examination paper headings.

AMS and NATO SSD numbers

M721	Ireland – RO 7, 14; **4**
M722	Great Britain – RO 8, 9, 10, 11; **8**; A6
M723	Northern Ireland – RO 14, 15; cn **4, 5, 6**; **10**; A6
M724	Scotland – RO 7, 8; **7**; A6
M725	London – RO 9; **9**; A6
M726	1:50,000 Great Britain – RO 11; A6
M728	1:50,000 Northern Ireland – RO 15; cn **4, 5, 6**; **10**; A6
M821	1:25,000 Great Britain – RO 9; A6
M825	1:25,000 Northern Ireland – A6
M924	London – **9**

GSGS series numbers

2748	1:20,000 Great Britain – RO 2, 3, 4, 12; A6
2766	England and Wales trace – RO 2n
3036	1:25,344 East Anglia – RO 2, 3; A6
3786	1:20,000 County of London – **3**; A6
3851	Artillery trace, Popular Edition – cn **1, 2**
3906	1:25,000 Great Britain, Ireland – RO 4, 5, 6, 12, 14n; A6
3907	England and Wales – RO 2, 3, 4, 5, 6, 7, 8, 11, 13, 14; **2**; **2.1**; **2.2**; **2.3**; **2.4**; **2.6**; **2.7**; **2.8**; **2.9**; **8.3**; A1; A2; A3; A6
3908	Scotland – RO 3, 4, 6, 7, 8, 11, 13; **1**; **1.4**; A1; A3; A6
3917	Northern Ireland – RO 3, 13, 14; **4**; A6
3936	1:10,560 Ireland – RO 13n
3942	1:253,440 Northern Ireland – RO 13
3943	Ireland – RO 13; **5**; A6
3950	1:253,440 England and Wales – RO 3
3994	London – **3**
4127	1:126,720 Ireland – cn **4, 5, 6**; A6
4136	Ireland – RO 7, 14, 15; **6**; A6
4159	1:126,720 London – RO 2; A6
4167	1:100,000 Great Britain – RO 2; A6
4620	England and Wales – RO 6, 8, 9, 10, 11; **2.4**; **8**; **8.3**; A6
4620A	England and Wales – RO 8, 9, 14; **8.1**; A6
4623	Throughways of London – **3**
4627	1:25,000 Great Britain – RO 9; A6
4639	Scotland – RO 7, 8, 9, 11; **7**; A6
4692	London – RO 8, 9; **9**; A6

4954	Otterburn/Redesdale all arms TA – **8.3**; A6
4959	WD land and TA, home counties – **8.3**; A6
4965	Ten Tors – **8.4**
4968	London District boundaries – **9**
4974	Salisbury Plain PTA – **8.3**; A6
4976	Sennybridge AATA ranges – **8.3**; A6
4987	Dartmoor training areas – **8.3**; A6
4988	Glentrool National Forest Park – **8.3**; A6
4989	Cairngorms training area – **8.3**; A6
5025	Stanford training & gun areas – **8.3**; A6
5034	Glen Affric training area – **8.3**; A6
5065	Catterick training area – **8.3**; A6
5066	Sennybridge training area – **8.3**; A6
5067	RMAS map reading instruction – **8.5**
5068	Glen Affric/Strathconnon TA – **8.3**; A6
5076	Catterick, Warcop TC – **8.3**; A6
5102	RUC boundaries – **10**; A6
5111	Helicopter routes…London – **9**; A6
5135	Topographic Decca chart NI – **10**
5149	Topographic Dectrac chart NI – **10**
5161	Location map : Mil Svy and MCE RE – **8.9**
5169	RA range Hebrides – **8.3**; A6
5172	Skeleton maps – **8.5**
5177	Salisbury Plain TA air map – **8.3**; A6
5193	Power transmission lines – **8.7**
5215	1:50,000 Great Britain – RO 11; **8.3**
5229	1:50,000 Salisbury Plain – cn **8.3**
5246	1:50,000 Dartmoor – cn **8.3**
5249	Helicopter chart Northern Ireland – **10**
5258	1:50,000 ?Glentrool – cn **8.3**
5259	1:50,000 ?Otterburn/Redesdale – cn **8.3**
5260	Topographic Dectrac chart NI – **10**
5276	Topographic Decca chart NI – **10**
5295	1:50,000 UK training areas – cn **8.3**
5309	1:50,000 Border crossings – cn **10**; A6
5309A	1:50,000 RUC boundaries – cn **10**; A6
5378	Helicopter chart Northern Ireland – **10**
5383	Topographic Decca chart NI – **10**
5385	Topographic Decca chart NI – **10**
5387	Topographic Dectrac chart NI – **10**
5389	Topographic Dectrac chart NI – **10**

1969	Congleton, examination extract – **8**.9	2158	special area map, examination paper – **8**.8
1971	Westbury, examination extract – **8**.9	2159	various sheets, examination papers – **8**.8
1973	Aberdare, examination extract – **8**.9	2161	various areas, examination extracts – **8**.9
1974	RAF Decca aeronautical charts – **8**.6	2165	Marlborough, examination extract – **8**.9
1980	Redcar, examination extract – **8**.9	2171	Exercise March Hare 1968 – **8**.4
1983	Falkirk, examination extract – **8**.9	2173	Folkestone, examination extract – **8**.9
1993	Brierley Hill, examination extract – **8**.9	2175	special area map, examination paper – **8**.8
1999	1:50,000 Great Britain – RO 10; **8**.2	2192	sheet 159, examination paper – **8**.8
2000	1:100,000 Great Britain – RO 10; **8**.2	2200	Llangefni, examination extract – **8**.9
2004	[Prestatyn], examination extract – **8**.9	2206	Exercise March Hare 1969 – **8**.4
2006	Dumbarton, examination extract – **8**.9	2208	Wells, examination extract – **8**.9
2007	Ten Tors 1964 – **8**.4	2211	Upton-upon-Severn, exam extract – **8**.9
2010	Loughborough, examination extract – **8**.9	2213	special area map, examination paper – **8**.8
2011	sheet 168, examination paper – **8**.8	2214	special area map, examination paper – **8**.8
2032	Wellington, examination extract – **8**.9	2224	sheet 159, examination paper – **8**.8
2036	Physiographic map of Oxford region – **8**.7	2230	Market Weighton, exam extract – **8**.9
2042	[Dartmoor] – **8**.3	2235	Dolgellau, examination extract – **8**.9
2044	Millom area, examination extract – **8**.9	2240	Truro, examination extract – **8**.9
2049	[IDC wall maps] – **8**.7	2241	Barnstaple, examination extract – **8**.9
2050	Blandford, examination extract – **8**.9	2245	Coldstream, examination extract – **8**.9
2054	Exercise March Hare III – **8**.4	2247	Llangollen, examination extract – **8**.9
2055	Exercise Bear Handful II – **8**.4	2255	[sheet 167 Salisbury], skeleton map – **8**.5
2057	Northern Ireland – **10**; A6	2256	[sheet 166 Frome], skeleton map – **8**.5
2059	Winscombe, examination extract – **8**.9	2285	special area map, examination paper – **8**.8
2069	Maidenhead, examination extract – **8**.9	2303	Calne, examination extract – **8**.9
2070	Snowdon, examination extract – **8**.9	2304	Upton-upon-Severn, exam extract – **8**.9
2071	Perth, examination extract – **8**.9	2305	Dartmoor, examination extract – **8**.9
2072	Ivybridge, examination extract – **8**.9	2324	[untitled] – **8**.7
2073	Ludlow, examination extract – **8**.9	2327	Exercise Post Haste 1 – **8**.4
2074	Melrose and Kelso, exam extract – **8**.9	2329	[South Uist] firing range – **8**.3; A6
2076	sheet 168, examination paper – **8**.8	2330	Exercise Post Haste 2 – **8**.4
2083	special area map, examination paper – **8**.8	2331	Exercise Post Haste 3 – **8**.4
2093	[Barmouth], examination extract – **8**.9	2332	[Exercise unnamed] – **8**.4
2094	Guildford, examination extract – **8**.9	2333	[sheet 178 Dorchester], skeleton map – **8**.5
2095	Ennerdale, examination extract – **8**.9	2353	Malton, examination extract – **8**.9
2096	[Keswick – Lake District tourist map], examination extract – **8**.9	2360	Llangollen, examination extract – **8**.9
		2363	Exercise Life Line – **8**.4
2097	Stow-on-the-Wold, exam extract – **8**.9	2366	Bacup, examination extract – **8**.9
2098	Cairngorms, examination extract – **8**.9	2368	[Exercise unnamed] – **8**.4
2099	Exercise March Hare IV – **8**.4	2373	Truro area, examination extract – **8**.9
2102	Salisbury, examination extract – **8**.9	2374	sections of sheets 178, 179, for exams – **8**.9
2107	Exercise Bear Handful III – **8**.4		
2108	[sheet 171 London SE], skeleton map – **8**.5		
2109	Exercise Sea Horse – **8**.4		

GSGS Office Reference numbers

2115	various sheets, examination papers – **8**.8
2117	various areas, examination extracts – **8**.9
2122	sheet 62, examination paper – **8**.8
2123	sheet 136, examination paper – **8**.8
2124	various areas, examination extracts – **8**.9
2130	sheet 178, examination paper – **8**.8

1423	Watford area – **2**.9
1426	Warrington area – **2**.9
1527	London – **3**
1826	London – **3**
1839	Wrexham and Oswestry area – **2**.9
1934	Sheet 51 extract – **2**.9
5189	1:1,000,000 Index to Ireland – cn **4**, **5**, **6**

2131	Area numbers one & two – **8**.3; A6
2132	Area number three – **8**.3; A6
2133	Plynlimon – **8**.3; A6
2134	Brecon Beacons – **8**.3; A6
2136	[Exercise unnamed] – **8**.4
2137	various areas, examination extracts – **8**.9

Mapping and Charting Establishment number

2142	Exercise April Hare – **8**.4
2149	Bacup, examination extract – **8**.9
2151	Exercise Druids Drum – **8**.4

509	Exercise Home Run 70 – **8**.4

Appendix 6. *Chronology*

Maps listed are at the one-inch scale unless noted otherwise. Events datable only to the year are listed in advance of those datable to the month. Many dates are taken from print codes, and are thus better described as printing, not publication dates. It is anyway a moot point as to whether most military maps were "published" at all.

1905	Colonel C.F. Close appointed head of MO4 (TSGS)
1908	Topographical Section, General Staff renamed Geographical Section, General Staff
1911	
August	Colonel C.F. Close succeeds Grant as Director General Ordnance Survey
	Colonel W.C. Hedley succeeds Close as head of MO4 (GSGS)
1914	
	Printing of 1:25,344 *Map of East Anglia,* later GSGS 3036, begun
August	Declaration of war against Germany
1915	Publication of *1" provisional edition for military purposes only* map of Ireland begun
1918	
	Printing of GSGS 2748 1:20,000 Provisional Edition with British System (BS) grid begun
November	End of World War I
1919	
June	Publication of one-inch Popular Edition of England and Wales begun
c.1920-1	Printing of GSGS 2748 1:20,000 Great Britain in final format with BS grid begun
c.1921	Half-inch *Salisbury Plain* experimentally overprinted with 1 km BS grid
1921	
	Lt Colonel E.M. Jack succeeds Hedley as head of MI4 (GSGS)
December	Anglo-Irish Treaty empowering the creation of the Irish Free State
1922	
	One-inch scale adopted for military training in place of half-inch
January	Ordnance Survey of Northern Ireland in Belfast created
April	Ordnance Survey of Ireland in Dublin made independent of Ordnance Survey, Southampton
August	Colonel E.M. Jack succeeds Close as Director General Ordnance Survey
	Colonel H.St.J. Winterbotham succeeds Jack as head of MI4 (GSGS)
1923	
January	Earliest known print code on a one-inch map with BS grid – E&W 115
August	*Aldershot Command* plate made
1924	
January	*New Forest* plate made
February	*Blandford* plate made
April-June	Publication of one-inch Popular Edition of Scotland begun
September	Earliest known BS grid with large unfilled rather than small filled letters – E&W 127
1925	
	Printed *Salisbury Plain; Bantry Bay* (with grid)
	First manoeuvre maps with BS grid published
	GSGS 3036 1:25,344 *East Anglia* reprinted with BS grid
March	Printed *Cork* (with grid)
December	*Catterick area* plate made

1926

Printed *Castle Howard training area*
January   Overprinted magnetic variation diagrams added to BS mapping
?March   Printed GSGS 3786 1:20,000 *County of London*, also GSGS 3786A, with a secret overprint
July-Sept   Publication of one-inch Popular Edition of England and Wales completed

1927

?Printed *Belfast* (with grid)
May   War Office exercise at Harrogate using experimental Modified British System (MBS) grid

1928   Printed *London (Tourist Map)* using a variant form of experimental MBS grid

1929   Colonel M.N. MacLeod succeeds Winterbotham as head of MI4 (GSGS)

1930
May   Brigadier H.St.J. Winterbotham succeeds Jack as Director General Ordnance Survey

1931

British military mapping printed without green woodland plate
Replacement of BS by MBS grid on GSGS 3907 and GSGS 3036 1:25,344 begun
GSGS 2748 1:20,000, with BS grid, superseded by GSGS 3906 1:25,000, with MBS grid
Last recorded Scottish sheet published with BS grid – sheet 51
January   GSGS numbers 3907 and 3908 allocated to one-inch maps of England and Wales, and Scotland
October   Publication of one-inch Fifth Edition of England and Wales begun

1932

Last known printing of a one-inch map with BS grid – E&W sheet 31, printing 500/32
Printed GSGS 3917 Northern Ireland coloured sheets (two with 1931 publication dates)
April-June Publication of one-inch Popular Edition of Scotland completed

1933

Printing of GSGS 3907 mapping with MBS completed
Printed GSGS 3908 mapping with MBS grid
Printed *Barden Moor, Netheravon, Tilshead*

1934

Green woodland plate restored to British military mapping
Grid figures at 1 km intervals across face of sheet introduced
Printed *Colchester area, Bordon, Farnborough*
Printing of GSGS 3906 1:25,000 Provisional Edition based on six-inch mapping begun
Printed GSGS 3917 Northern Ireland outline sheets; GSGS 3943 Eire
Publication of OSI 1:20,000 map of Ireland begun
November   "Periodical corrected reprints" added to civilian imprints

1935

Printed *East Kent; Aldershot Command* (Fifth Edition based, with 1934 publication date)
February   Brigadier M.N. MacLeod succeeds Winterbotham as Director General Ordnance Survey
Colonel P.K. Boulnois succeeds MacLeod as head of MI4 (GSGS)

1937   Printed *Dartmoor*

1938

Fifth Edition mapping introduced to GSGS 3907 standard series sheets – sheet 107
Publication of six-inch Special Emergency Edition, with ARP revision, begun

1939

Civilian printing firms start printing GSGS British one-inch mapping
Printed *Builth Wells*
Publication of OSI 1:20,000 map of Ireland resumed, and ceased
September   Declaration of war against Germany
MI4 (GSGS) and MI4 (Air) evacuated to Lypiatt Road, Cheltenham

1940

	Printing of GSGS 3906 1:25,000 regular edition abandoned; emergency 1:25,000 mapping of all of Great Britain and Ireland based on six-inch mapping begun
	Printed *New Forest* (Fifth Edition based), *Llandrindod Wells*
	Printed gridded half-inch map of Ireland, with hill shading, probably for the Air Ministry
	Printed gridded half-inch map of Ireland, coloured edition
	Printed GSGS 4127 half-inch map of Ireland, coloured edition (some sheets in August)
	Printed GSGS 4159 half-inch *Greater London*
	Printed one-inch map in 55 sheets, with 5000 yard grid (Department of Defence, Dublin)
	Printed *Cork,* with 5000 yard grid (Department of Defence, Dublin)
	Printed half-inch map, Modified Edition, with 5000 yard grid (Department of Defence, Dublin)
April	Scheme for SSS military map of the whole of Ireland, first as GSGS 3943, then GSGS 3917
May	Retreat from Dunkirk
June	Printing of War Revision begun (probably June)
	Eleven SW sheets converted to Fifth Edition, mapping and sheet lines (probably June)
	Scheme for GSGS 3917 complete coverage of Ireland abandoned
July	Print codes on military maps dated by month as well as year
	Civilian printing firms involved in printing GSGS mapping increased in number
	GSGS number 4136 allocated to large sheet series map of Ireland
	Printing of GSGS 4136 first edition begun (completed August)
October	Printing of GSGS 3907 Second War Revision begun – sheet 114
November	Bombing of OS headquarters in London Road, Southampton (30 Nov and 1 Dec)
December	Red preferred to sienna for the roads plate on War Revision maps (probable date)
	Printed *Ripon*
	Printing of GSGS 4136 second edition begun

1941

	Printing of GSGS 3906 1:25,000 on six-inch mapping completed
	Printed *Inveraray*
	Layers added to 51 sheets in GSGS 4136 Second Edition (completed 1942)
January	GSGS 3907 2WR 21, 22, 48, 106 apparently printed since November 1940 (without month codes)
	Printing of GSGS 4167 1:100,000 Great Britain training map begins (between Jan and March)
February	GSGS 3907 2WR 10, 19, 115, 131, 134 apparently printed (without month codes)
March	Heading note concerning the currency of different military editions added to rarely revised maps
	Print codes of maps printed at OSO London Road given "LR" suffix.
	Printed GSGS 3907 2WR 9, 47, 108
April	Printed GSGS 3907 2WR 6, 39, 40, 56, 57, 66, 74, 116, 117A, 126, 135
May	Printed GSGS 3907 2WR 4, 16, 34, 45, 58, 121, 132
June	Printed GSGS 3907 2WR 26, 33, 46, 75, 84
July	Printed GSGS 3907 2WR 5, 55, 85, 86, 87, 97, 98, 130, 133, 141
August	Printed GSGS 3907 2WR 94, 104, 113, 123, 125
	Last new GSGS 3907 War Revision printed – sheet 63
	Printed GSGS 4127 half-inch map of Ireland, Second Edition
September	OS detachment moved from Southampton to Forman's printing works at Nottingham
	Printed GSGS 3907 2WR 64, 73, 83, 96, 139
	Printing of GSGS 3908 War Revision completed – sheet 28
	Some GSGS 4136 sheets printed by Ordnance Survey of Northern Ireland
October	Colonel M. Hotine succeeds Boulnois as head of MI4 (GSGS)
	New style margins introduced – Scotland sheets 51, 55 (with September print dates)
	Printed GSGS 3907 2WR 1A, 129
	Publication of civilian two-colour one-inch maps of England and Wales, Scotland begun
November	Printed GSGS 3907 2WR 2, 67, 105, 110, 124, 140, 142
December	Printed GSGS 3907 2WR 7, 38, 120

1942

	United States Army Map Service (AMS) numbers allocated to British military map series
	Printed hill-shaded half-inch map, with 5000 yard grid (Department of Defence, Dublin)
January	522 (Ordnance Survey) Company RE established; assisted with the dispersal from Southampton
February	Final recorded printing of a one-inch map by the War Office
	Final recorded printing using Popular Edition style margins – E&W 2WR 45
	Printed GSGS 3907 2WR 11, 14, 15, 23, 25, 27, 65, 76, 95, 107, 111

	Printing of GSGS 4136 Third Edition begun: 331, 332, 337, 338, 339, 343, 344, 345
March	Printed GSGS 3907 2WR 37, 53, 60, 77, 103
	Printed GSGS 4136 Third Edition 324, 325, 326, 327, 330, 336, 342, 347, 348, 349, 350, 353, 354, 355, 358, 359, 360, 361, 364, 365, 366
April	Printed GSGS 3907 2WR 8, 20, 31, 32, 54, 63, 70
	Printed GSGS 4136 Third Edition 301, 302, 306, 315, 316, 322, 328, 333, 352, 356, 367, 370, 371, 374, 376
May	Printed GSGS 3907 2WR 13, 28, 43, 50, 91, 102
	Completed printing of GSGS 4136 Third Edition: 303, 304, 305, 307, 308, 309, 310, 311, 312, 313, 314, 317, 318, 319, 320, 321, 323, 329, 334, 335, 340, 341, 346, 351, 357, 362, 363, 368, 369, 372, 373, 375
June	Printed GSGS 3907 2WR 72, 112
July	GSGS move from Cheltenham to Eastcote (probably July – by September)
	GSGS move Production Unit and 8th Field Survey Depot, RE from Cheltenham to SPC 'Hygrade'
	OS take over Britannia Works (Purley Way, Waddon, near Croydon) for map printing
	Printed GSGS 3907 2WR 3, 122
August	OSO Esher (Kingston Bypass, Hinchley Wood) occupied by Special Services Drawing Section
	Printed GSGS 3907 2WR 35, 36, 71
	Publication of civilian two-colour one-inch maps of England and Wales, Scotland completed
September	Printed GSGS 3907 2WR 30
November	Printing of one-inch maps at OSO Waddon begun
	Printed GSGS 3907 2WR 12; GSGS 3908 2WR 45
	Printing of WR ungridded sales copies begun (E&W to Jan. 1943, Scotland to Nov. 1943)
	Bog overprint added to GSGS 4136 (completed early 1943)
December	Printed GSGS 3907 2WR 49, 59

1943

	Printed layered half-inch map, with 5000 yard grid (Department of Defence, Dublin)
January	Printed GSGS 3907 2WR 17, 68, 69
	WR ungridded sheets (E&W, Scotland), 2WR coloured sheets go on sale (OSPR Jan-May)
February	Printing of one-inch maps at OSO Esher begun
	Printed GSGS 3907 2WR 80
	Last War Revision reprint in GSGS 3907 – sheet 93
March	Printed *Sennybridge artillery ranges*
	Printed GSGS 3908 2WR 92
	Printed GSGS 4136 with training area overprint
April	Occupation of OSO Chessington (Kingston Road, Chessington) begun
May	GSGS reorganised as the Directorate of Military Survey with Brigadier Hotine as Director
	Printed GSGS 3907 2WR 18
June	Major General G. Cheetham succeeds MacLeod as Director General Ordnance Survey
	Printing of one-inch maps at OSO Chessington begun
August	England and Wales War Revision gridded sheets go on sale (OSPR 1 August to 30 September)
September	Printed GSGS 3907 2WR 79
	Printing of Second War Revision outline sheets begun – 29 (the remainder listed in appendix 3)
October	Second War Revision outline sheets, Scotland War Revision gridded sheets go on sale
December	OSO Chessington occupation completed; becomes Ordnance Survey headquarters until 1969
	Printed GSGS 3907 2WR 90, 101

1944

January	Printed GSGS 3907 2WR 99
	Last War Revision reprints – GSGS 3908 sheets 71, 72
May	OSO London Road, Southampton temporarily relinquished
	Air Force brown comes into use in place of sienna for the roads and contour plate
June	Operation Overlord
August	Printed GSGS 3907 2WR 93 – the last new GSGS 3907 Second War Revision

1945

April-June	Final military printings listed in OSPR
May	End of World War II, in Europe
September	Publication of New Popular Edition and Popular Edition of Scotland (with National Grid) begun
November	Publication of 1:25,000 Provisional Edition of Great Britain begun (40/09 printed in September)

1946

Brigadier R.Ll. Brown succeeds Hotine as Director of Military Survey

Final civilian two-colour one-inch sheets of England and Wales reprinted

January   OSO London Road, Southampton reoccupied

February   GSGS number 4620 allocated to the one-inch map of England and Wales

May   Printed *Salisbury Plain* (New Popular Edition [167]), with Cassini Grid

June   GSGS 4159 half-inch *Greater London* reprinted

October   Printed *Aldershot* (New Popular Edition [169]), with Cassini Grid

1947

January   GSGS number 4627 allocated to the 1:25,000 map of Great Britain (with National Grid)

August   Special printings on Wet Strength Paper of four GSGS 3907 2WR sheets

September   Printing of GSGS 4627 1:25,000 Great Britain sheets begun – 31/75, 31/76

October   Printing order for all 115 GSGS 4620 sheets; first sheet printed – sheet 187

GSGS number 4639 allocated to the one-inch map of Scotland

SPC 'Hillside' relocated to Bushy Park as SPC (Air) (later No.2 SPC)

November   Printing of GSGS 4639 Scotland sheets begun – sheets 59, 71, 72, 92

December   Printed six GSGS 3907 2WR layered sheets, for use in the Staff College

Publication of one-inch New Popular Edition completed

1948

April   Publication of one-inch Popular Edition of Scotland (with National Grid) completed

May   SPC 'Hygrade' relocated to Park Royal as SPC RE (later No.1 SPC RE)

September   Printed *Catterick area* in Cassini Grid and National Grid versions

October   Last series sheet reprinted in GSGS 3907 Second War Revision – sheet 122

1949

February   Printing of GSGS 4620A layered edition (for the Staff College) begun

GSGS number 4692 allocated to the one-inch map of London

March   Printing of one-inch mapping by Survey Production Centre, Royal Engineers begun

Printed GSGS 4627A 1:25,000 layered edition (for the Staff College)

April   Eire declared a republic, later known as the Republic of Ireland

June   Major General R.Ll. Brown succeeds Cheetham as Director General Ordnance Survey

Brigadier J.C.T. Willis succeeds Brown as Director of Military Survey

1950

GSGS 3906, 3907 and 3908 declared obsolete; Northern Ireland sheets in GSGS 3906 now M825

January   National Grid (military system) supersedes War Office Cassini Grid

Printing of GSGS 4620 completed – sheet 142 (with a December 1949 print code)

March   Printing of GSGS 4639 completed – sheets 2, 4, 6, 7, 11;

Printed GSGS Misc.407 *Ross Links anti-tank range*

July   Printed GSGS Misc.406 *Redesdale and Otterburn artillery ranges*

1951

Printed GSGS 4692 First Edition GSGS *London*

April   Reprinted *Catterick area*

May   Printing of GSGS 4620 Edition 2-GSGS begun, with revised form of National Grid – sheet 177

November   Printed GSGS Misc.433 *Salisbury Plain, with range overprint*

1952

Printed GSGS Misc.1585 *Stanford training and gun areas*

May   Seventh Series sheets printed in GSGS 4620 with blue grid (May to July) – sheet 141

June   Printed GSGS Misc.1522 *Sennybridge artillery ranges*

September   Publication of one-inch Seventh Series begun

October   Seventh Series sheets printed in GSGS 4620 with red grid – sheet 139

1953

Printed GSGS Misc.1622 *W.D. land and training areas, home counties*

January   "OS" suffix added into print codes of military maps printed by the Ordnance Survey

July   Major General J.C.T. Willis succeeds Brown as Director General Ordnance Survey

Brigadier L.F. de Vic Carey succeeds Willis as Director of Military Survey

1954	Style of edition designation changed from, e.g., "First Edition-GSGS" to "Edition 1-GSGS"
1955	
February	Application made to Washington for an AMS series number for GSGS 4620; not used until 1958
1956	
October	First GSGS 4620 sheet with "D. Survey, War Office and Air Ministry" imprint – sheet 177
1957	
May	Printed GSGS Misc.1764 *Catterick area*
June	Major General L.F. de Vic Carey succeeds Willis as Director General Ordnance Survey
	Brigadier A.H. Dowson succeeds de Vic Carey as Director of Military Survey
October	First recorded use of the SSD M821 in place of GSGS 4627 on Great Britain 1:25,000
1958	
May	First sheets printed in M722 Great Britain, superseding GSGS 4620 – sheets 125, 149
1960	
	Printed M725 Edition 2-GSGS *London;* GSGS Misc.1881 *Dartmoor training areas*
September	The final printing on a New Popular Edition base map – sheet 172
December	The final reprint of a sheet in GSGS 4639 – sheet 58
1961	
	Major General A.H. Dowson succeeds de Vic Carey as Director General Ordnance Survey
	Brigadier R.C.A. Edge succeeds Dowson as Director of Military Survey
	Some GSGS 4620/M722 sheets printed by the Hydrographic Department, Admiralty
July	Publication of one-inch Seventh Series completed
1962	
February	The last sheet reprinted in GSGS 4620 – sheet 145
April	No.1 and No.2 SPCs combine as SPC RE at Feltham
September	Last known printings of GSGS 4136 – layered editions of sheets 313, 314
October	The final reprints of layered sheets in GSGS 4620A
1963	
January	Final GSGS 4620 New Popular Edition superseded by M722 Seventh Series sheets – 95, 147
February	Final GSGS 4639 Scotland Popular Edition superseded by M722 Seventh Series sheets – 1-4
October	GSGS 4136 with bog overprint declared obsolete
November	Printed six M722 sheets in GSGS Misc.1999 (at 1:50,000), GSGS Misc.2000 (at 1:100,000)
1964	
April	Ministry of Defence formed by amalgamation of War Office, Air Ministry, Admiralty and MOD
June	First M722 sheet with "D. Survey, Ministry of Defence United Kingdom" imprint – sheet 116
1965	
March	The SSD M723 allocated to the map of Northern Ireland based on the One-inch Third Series
	Printed GSGS 4959 *W.D. land and training areas, home counties*
April	Printed GSGS Misc.2057 Northern Ireland – sheets 1, 3, 5, 6
May	Printed M723 Northern Ireland
August	Printed GSGS 4954 *Otterburn/Redesdale all arms training area*
1966	
	Major General R.C.A. Edge succeeds Dowson as Director General Ordnance Survey
	Brigadier B. StG. Irwin succeeds Dowson as Director of Military Survey
February	Grid overprint letters reduced in size – sheet 113
April	Printed GSGS 4974 *Salisbury Plain,* GSGS 4976 *Sennybridge,* GSGS 4987 *Dartmoor*
May	Printed GSGS 4988 *Glentrool National Forest Park*
July	Printed GSGS 4989 *Cairngorms training area*
August	Printing of some M722 sheets by the British Army of the Rhine (August-December)
October	Printed GSGS Misc.2131, 2132, 2133, 2134 maps of CCF arduous training areas
November	GSGS 4620, 4639, and 4136 sheets covering Northern Ireland officially made obsolete

1967
January   Printed M725 Edition 3-GSGS, on *Greater London* base map, edition A
June   Printed GSGS 5025 *Stanford training & gun areas*

1968
January   Print run figure omitted from print codes
April   Stocks of remaining sheets in GSGS 4136 reduced to 500 copies each
June   Printed GSGS 5034 *Glen Affric training area*

1969
May   Ordnance Survey move from Chessington to new headquarters at Maybush, Southampton
August   Printed GSGS 5065 *Catterick training area*; GSGS 5066 *Sennybridge training area*
September Major General B.StG. Irwin succeeds Edge as Director General Ordnance Survey
           Brigadier A. Walmesley White succeeds Irwin as Director of Military Survey
November   Printed GSGS 5068 *Glen Affric/Strathconnon training area*

1970
April   Survey Production Centre RE renamed Mapping and Charting Establishment RE
           Printed GSGS 5076 *Catterick and Warcop training areas*
July   Printing of special series overprinted on M723 base begins with GSGS 5102

1971
January   Printed M725 Edition 4-GSGS, on *Greater London* base map, edition B
February   Printed GSGS Misc.2329, showing the South Uist firing range
May   Printed GSGS 5111 *Helicopter routes in the London control zone*
October   "Distribution restricted" notices appear on M722 mapping

1972
January   Printed GSGS 5111A *Helicopter routes in the London control zone (gridded)*
June   Printing of one-inch maps by 42nd Survey Engineer Regiment begun
July   Introduction of new style print codes in a month/year/six-figure/single letter format
           Printed GSGS 5169 *RA range Hebrides*
August   "Distribution restricted" notices withdrawn from M722 mapping

1973
March   M725 *Greater London* declared obsolete
May   Final recorded use of the "OS" suffix to a print code
September Printed GSGS 5177 *Salisbury Plain training area (1973) air map*

1974
July   Published M726 1:50,000 Great Britain – sheets 102-204; M722 sheets 100-190 declared obsolete

1975
June   Print run figure restored to print codes
September The final printing of a sheet in M722 – sheet 60

1976
June   Published M726 1:50,000 Great Britain – sheets 1-101; M722 sheets 1-99 declared obsolete

1979   Printing of M728 1:50,000 Northern Ireland begun

1981
July   Printing of M728 completed, with provisional mapping
August   Printed GSGS 5309, GSGS 5309A 1:50,000 series, overprinted on M728 provisional mapping

1984
November   Last known printing in M723 – sheet 5

1985
February   M723 declared obsolete
August   Printing of M728 and some overprinted series completed, with final mapping

Bibliography

Published works

Baker, Sir T.D. (chairman), *Report of committee on a military map of the United Kingdom together minutes of evidence and appendices*. London: War Office (A.237), 1892. (Copies RGS, PRO WO 33/52).

Board, C., 'The secret map of the County of London, 1926, and its sequels', *London Topographical Record* 27 (1995), 257-280.

Board, C., 'The three-inch map of London, and its predecessors of 1926', *Sheetlines* 43 (1995), 48-50.

Chasseaud, P., *Artillery's astrologers : a history of British survey & mapping on the Western Front 1914-1918*. Lewes: Mapbooks, 1999.

Clark, P.K. and Mumford, I., 'Note on the '1941 style' of coded imprint adopted by the Ordnance Survey and War Office', *Sheetlines* 5 (1982), 9, 12. With a further note in *Sheetlines* 9 (1984), 18-19.

Clough, Brigadier A.B., *The Second World War 1939-1945 : Army. Maps and survey*. London: War Office, 1952.

Davidson, Viscount, *Final report of the departmental committee on the Ordnance Survey*. London: HMSO, 1938.

Fergusson, T.G., *British military intelligence, 1870-1914 : the development of a modern intelligence organization*. London: Arms and Armour Press, 1984.

Forrest, D., 'GSGS Misc Series 1999 and 2000', *Sheetlines* 52 (1998), 17-20.

Frith, Captain G.R., *The Topographical Section of the General Staff*. Chatham: School of Military Engineering, 1906.

Hellyer, R., 'Sheet lines : some notes on GSGS 3917 and other one-inch large sheet maps of Ireland', *Sheetlines* 43 (1995), 4-24.

Hellyer, R., 'Some further notes on military mapping in Ireland', *Sheetlines* 46 (1996), 29-32.

Hellyer, R., 'Some notes on civilian use of small scale mapping during the Second World War", *Sheetlines* 48 (1997), 45-57.

Hellyer, R., *Ordnance Survey small-scale maps : indexes 1801-1998*. Kerry: David Archer, 1999a.

Hellyer, R., 'Some notes on the origin of the Modified British System of the War Office Cassini Grid', *Sheetlines* 55 (1999b), 3-11.

Hellyer, R., 'Some notes on one-inch mapping produced for civilian use during the Second World War', *Sheetlines* 59 (2000), 17-38.

Hellyer, R., *A guide to the Ordnance Survey 1:25,000 First Series*. London: Charles Close Society, 2003. With an introductory essay by Richard Oliver.

Hellyer, R. and Oliver, R.R., *A guide to the Ordnance Survey one-inch third edition maps, in colour*. London: Charles Close Society, 2004.

Hodson, A.Y., and Gordon, A., *An illustrated history of 250 years of Military Survey*. London: Military Survey Defence Agency, 1997.

Hodson, A.Y., *Popular maps : the Ordnance Survey Popular Edition one-inch map of England and Wales 1919-1926*. London: Charles Close Society, 1999.

Hodson, A.Y., 'MacLeod, MI4 and the Directorate of Military Survey 1919-1943', *Cartographic Journal* 38 (2001), 155-172.

Jewitt, A.C., *Maps for empire : the first 2000 numbered War Office maps 1881-1905*. London: The British Library, 1992.

Nicholson, T.R., 'The Ordnance Survey and smaller scale military maps of Britain 1854-1914', *Cartographic Journal* 25 (1988), 109-127.

Nicholson, T.R., 'One-inch military "specials" 1923-1940', *Sheetlines* 33 (1992), 21-34. With additional information in *Sheetlines* 34 (1992), 39.

Nicholson, T.R., *The birth of the modern Ordnance Survey small-scale map : the Revised New Series colour printed one-inch map of England and Wales 1897-1914*. London: Charles Close Society, 2002.

Oliver, R.R., *Ordnance Survey maps : a concise guide for historians*. Second Edition. London: Charles Close Society, 2004.

Oliver, R.R., 'The evolution of the Ordnance Survey National Grid', *Sheetlines* 43 (1995), 25-46. With amplification and correction in *Sheetlines* 46 (1996), 45-46.

Oliver, R.R., 'The sheet lines and overlaps of the One-inch Fifth and New Popular Editions', *Sheetlines* 44 (1995), 22-44.

Oliver, R.R., *A guide to the Ordnance Survey one-inch Fifth Edition*. Third Edition. London: Charles Close Society, 2000a.

Oliver, R.R., *A guide to the Ordnance Survey one-inch Popular Edition of Scotland*. London: Charles Close Society, 2000b.

Oliver, R.R., *A guide to the Ordnance Survey one-inch New Popular Edition*. London: Charles Close Society, 2000c.

Oliver, R.R., *A guide to the Ordnance Survey one-inch Seventh Series*. Second Edition. London: Charles Close Society, 2004.

Owen, T. and Pilbeam, E., *Ordnance Survey : map makers to Britain since 1791*. Southampton: Ordnance Survey, and London: HMSO, 1992.

Seymour, W.A. (ed.), *A history of the Ordnance Survey*. Folkestone: Dawson, 1980.

Staff College, *Report on the examination for admission to the Staff Colleges at Camberley and Quetta, held in February-March [year]........* London: HMSO, year. From 1927 lacking the words *Report on the....*

Staff College, *Examination of army officers for promotion : papers set in [March/October, year] with remarks by the examiners*. London: HMSO, year.

Military publishers' designations (Map Curators' Group Publication No.2). London: British Cartographic Society, [?1983].

Manual of map reading and field sketching. London: War Office, 1921. With revised editions to 1929, 1940.

Notes on map reading. London: War Office, 1925. With revised editions to 1929, 1940.

Manual of map reading, air photo reading and field sketching: part I: map reading 1955. London: HMSO, 1956; *part II: air photo reading 1958*. London: HMSO, 1958. With various updated editions and reprints.

Map Reading : Training Regulation No.19 (Defence Force Regulations). Dublin: Stationery Office, 1942.

Ordnance Survey publication report. Publications issued: 1 January to 31 May 1943, 1 June to 31 July 1943, 1 August to 30 September 1943, October 1943, 1 November 1943 to 31 January 1944, 1 February to 31 March 1944, 1 April to 30 June 1944, 1 July to 30 September 1944, 1 October to 31 December 1944, 1 January to 31 March 1945, 1 April to 30 June 1945. (Copies in the Bodleian Library, Oxford).

Unpublished and documentary sources

Hall, S., *A history of series GSGS 4136 Ireland 1:63,360 1940-43*. Unpublished typescript for the Ministry of Defence, 1979; copies in Ob and CCS Archives in the Map Department, Cambridge University Library.

Ordnance Survey unpublished annual reports: 1939-40, PRO OS 1/97; 1940-41, PRO OS 1/139; 1941-42, PRO OS 1/140; 1942-43, PRO OS 1/141; 1943-44, PRO OS 1/173; 1944-45, PRO OS 1/201; 1945-46, PRO OS 1/658.

Register of GSGS maps 1-2299, 2300-4795. A photocopy of the original is deposited in the Map Department, PRO. The original is soon to be placed there in class WO 401.

Numerical listing of maps produced by Geographical Section, General Staff and Directorate of Military Survey GSGS 4480 to 5015; 8000 to 8061 in continuation of 'Numerical catalogue of maps, 1944'. Unpublished typed list by Map Research and Library Group, Ministry of Defence, 1987; copies in Ob, CCS Archives in Cu, National Archives & Records Administration, College Park, Maryland, USA.

Report on the work of Home Forces Survey Service during the year 1941. PRO WO 252/1412.

Survey Directorate, GHQ Home Forces, memoranda, 1 January 1940-31 December 1942. PRO WO 402/91, /92.

Survey Directorate, British Troops Northern Ireland, monthly reports, 1 July 1942 – 31 May 1943. PRO WO 402/95.

GSGS 3907, 4136, 4620/M722, M723 series files, at present with DGC, intended for transfer to PRO.

Product Information Branch card indexes, held by DGC.

Sundry other card catalogues, now superseded, originating with Ordnance Survey or Military Survey.

Cross reference lists correlating AMS and GSGS map series numbers, in the National Archives & Records Administration, College Park, Maryland, USA.

Particulars of grids referred to in this book

	true origin	*false origin*
War Office Cassini Grid	Dunnose	500,000 metres west, 100,000 metres south
National Yard Grid	49° N, 2° W	1,000,000 yards west, 1,000,000 yards south
National Grid	49° N, 2° W	400,000 metres west, 100,000 metres south
War Office Irish Grid	53°30' N, 8° W	199,900 metres west, 249,975 metres south
Irish National (or TM) Grid	53°30' N, 8° W	200,000 metres west, 250,000 metres south

Organisational chronology

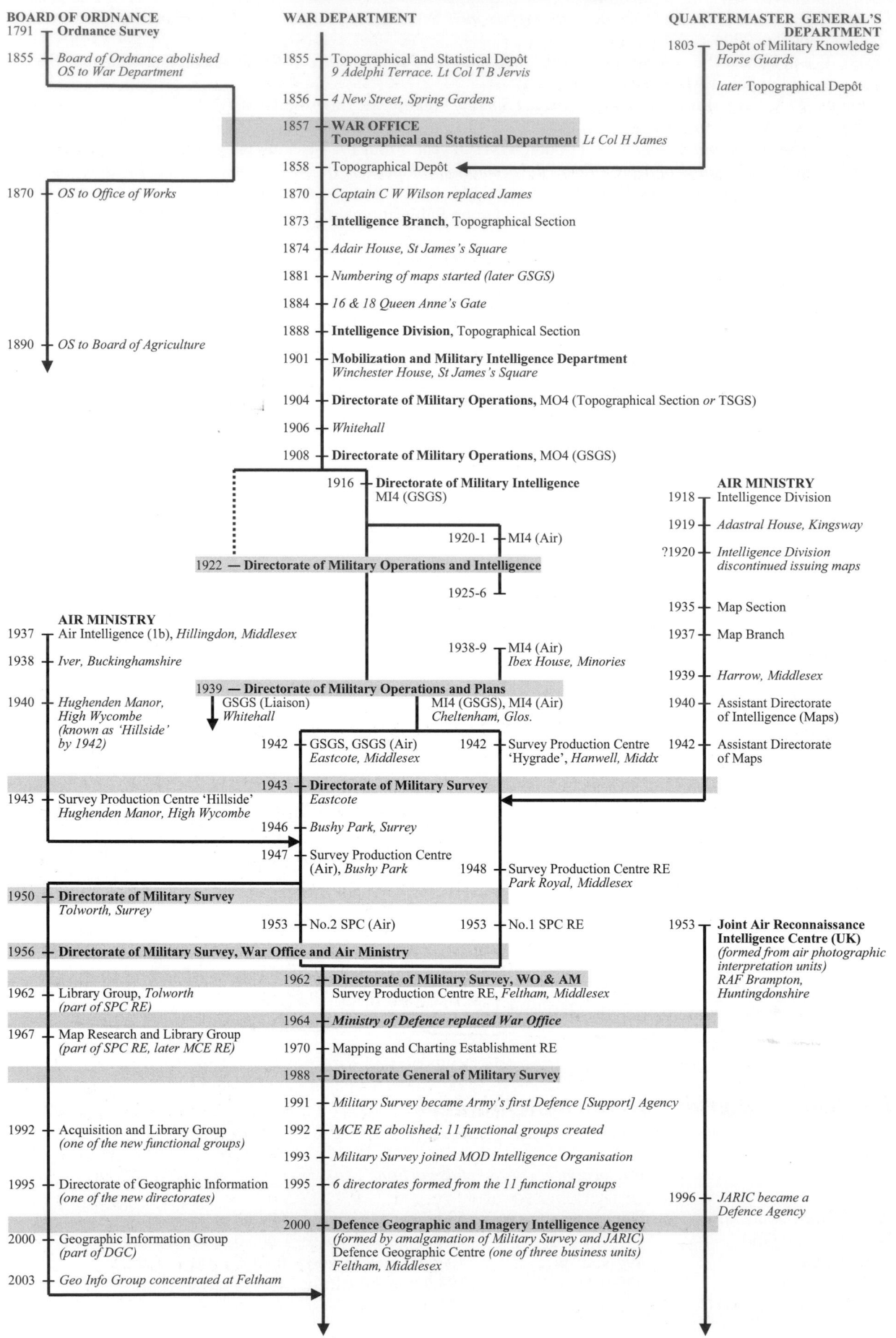

BOARD OF ORDNANCE
1791 — **Ordnance Survey**

1855 — *Board of Ordnance abolished*
       OS to War Department

1870 — *OS to Office of Works*

1890 — *OS to Board of Agriculture*

WAR DEPARTMENT

1855 — Topographical and Statistical Depôt
       9 Adelphi Terrace. Lt Col T B Jervis

1856 — *4 New Street, Spring Gardens*

1857 — **WAR OFFICE**
       Topographical and Statistical Department *Lt Col H James*

1858 — Topographical Depôt

1870 — *Captain C W Wilson replaced James*

1873 — **Intelligence Branch**, Topographical Section

1874 — *Adair House, St James's Square*

1881 — *Numbering of maps started (later GSGS)*

1884 — *16 & 18 Queen Anne's Gate*

1888 — **Intelligence Division**, Topographical Section

1901 — **Mobilization and Military Intelligence Department**
       Winchester House, St James's Square

1904 — **Directorate of Military Operations**, MO4 (Topographical Section *or* TSGS)

1906 — *Whitehall*

1908 — **Directorate of Military Operations**, MO4 (GSGS)

1916 — **Directorate of Military Intelligence**
       MI4 (GSGS)

1920-1 — MI4 (Air)

1922 — **Directorate of Military Operations and Intelligence**

1925-6

1938-9 — MI4 (Air)
         Ibex House, Minories

1939 — **Directorate of Military Operations and Plans**
       GSGS (Liaison)   MI4 (GSGS), MI4 (Air)
       Whitehall   *Cheltenham, Glos.*

1942 — GSGS, GSGS (Air)   1942 — Survey Production Centre
       Eastcote, Middlesex   'Hygrade', Hanwell, Middx

1943 — **Directorate of Military Survey**
       Eastcote

1946 — *Bushy Park, Surrey*

1947 — Survey Production Centre
       (Air), *Bushy Park*   1948 — Survey Production Centre RE
                                        Park Royal, Middlesex

1953 — No.2 SPC (Air)   1953 — No.1 SPC RE

1962 — **Directorate of Military Survey, WO & AM**
       Survey Production Centre RE, *Feltham, Middlesex*

1964 — *Ministry of Defence replaced War Office*

1970 — Mapping and Charting Establishment RE

1988 — **Directorate General of Military Survey**

1991 — *Military Survey became Army's first Defence [Support] Agency*

1992 — *MCE RE abolished; 11 functional groups created*

1993 — *Military Survey joined MOD Intelligence Organisation*

1995 — *6 directorates formed from the 11 functional groups*

2000 — **Defence Geographic and Imagery Intelligence Agency**
       (formed by amalgamation of Military Survey and JARIC)
       Defence Geographic Centre (one of three business units)
       Feltham, Middlesex

**QUARTERMASTER GENERAL'S
DEPARTMENT**
1803 — Depôt of Military Knowledge
       Horse Guards

       later Topographical Depôt

AIR MINISTRY
1918 — Intelligence Division

1919 — *Adastral House, Kingsway*

?1920 — *Intelligence Division
        discontinued issuing maps*

1935 — Map Section

1937 — Map Branch

1939 — *Harrow, Middlesex*

1940 — Assistant Directorate
       of Intelligence (Maps)

1942 — Assistant Directorate
       of Maps

1953 — **Joint Air Reconnaissance
       Intelligence Centre (UK)**
       *(formed from air photographic
       interpretation units)*
       *RAF Brampton,
       Huntingdonshire*

1996 — *JARIC became a
       Defence Agency*

AIR MINISTRY
1937 — Air Intelligence (1b), *Hillingdon, Middlesex*

1938 — *Iver, Buckinghamshire*

1940 — *Hughenden Manor,
       High Wycombe
       (known as 'Hillside'
       by 1942)*

1943 — Survey Production Centre 'Hillside'
       Hughenden Manor, High Wycombe

1950 — **Directorate of Military Survey**
       Tolworth, Surrey

1956 — **Directorate of Military Survey, War Office and Air Ministry**

1962 — Library Group, *Tolworth*
       (part of SPC RE)

1967 — Map Research and Library Group
       (part of SPC RE, later MCE RE)

1992 — Acquisition and Library Group
       (one of the new functional groups)

1995 — Directorate of Geographic Information
       (one of the new directorates)

2000 — Geographic Information Group
       (part of DGC)

2003 — *Geo Info Group concentrated at Feltham*